Check it out at http://www.[...]

Hoover's Online includes:

HOOVER'S GUIDE TO THE TOP TEXAS COMPANIES

The Reference Press
Austin, Texas

R™ **The Reference Press, Inc.**

Copyright © 1995 by The Reference Press, Inc. All rights reserved. No part of this book may be reproduced or transmitted in any form or by any means, electronic or mechanical, including by photocopying, facsimile transmission, recording, or using any information storage and retrieval system, without permission in writing from The Reference Press, Inc., except that brief passages may be quoted by a reviewer in a magazine, newspaper, online, or broadcast review.

10   9   8   7   6   5   4   3   2   1

Publisher Cataloging-In-Publication Data

Hoover's Guide to the Top Texas Companies.

    Includes indexes.
    1. Business enterprises — Directories. 2. Corporations — Directories.
HF3010   338.7

Profiles from *Hoover's Guide to the Top Texas Companies* are also available on America Online, Bloomberg Financial Network, CompuServe, eWorld, Interactive Wall Street Journal, LEXIS/NEXIS, Reuters NewMedia, SandPoint Hoover, and on the Internet at Hoover's Online (http://www.hoovers.com), Farcast (http://www.farcast.com), InfoSeek (http://www.infoseek.com), Pathfinder (http://pathfinder.com), and PAWWS (http://pawws.com). A catalog of Reference Press products is available on the World Wide Web (http://www.hoovers.com).

ISBN 1-878753-93-2 trade paper

This book was produced by The Reference Press on Apple Macintosh computers using Adobe's PageMaker software and fonts from its Clearface and Futura families. Cover design is by Daniel Pelavin. Electronic prepress and printing were done by Custom Printing Company at its Frederick, Maryland, plant. Text paper is Postmark White 60# (manufactured by Union Camp). Cover stock is 10 point, coated one side, film laminated.

US AND WORLD DIRECT SALES
The Reference Press, Inc.
6448 Highway 290 E., Suite E-104
Austin, TX 78723
Phone: 512-454-7778
Fax: 512-454-9401
e-mail: refpress6@aol.com

US WHOLESALER ORDERS
Warner Publisher Services
Book Division
9210 King Palm Drive
Tampa, FL 33619
Phone: 800-873-BOOK
Fax: 813-664-8193

US BOOKSELLERS AND JOBBERS
Little, Brown and Co.
200 West Street
Waltham, MA 02154
Phone: 800-759-0190
Fax: 617-890-0875

THE REFERENCE PRESS

Founder: Gary Hoover
Chairman, President, CEO, and Publisher: Patrick J. Spain

Senior Managing Editor - Editorial: James R. Talbot
Managing Editor - Production: George Sutton
Senior Contributing Editors: Alta M. Campbell, Alan Chai
Senior Editor of Online Publishing: Matt Manning
Editors: Wilson Allen, Chris Barton, Thomas Trotter
Research Manager: Sherri M. Hale
Desktop Publishing Manager: Holly Hans Jackson
Senior Style Editor: Pamela Penick
Researchers: Erin Carson, Chuck Green, Sarah Hallman, Jim Harris, Jenni Maiberger, Brian Pedder
Senior Writers: Joy Aiken, Stuart Hampton, Paul Mitchell, Barbara M. Spain
Writers: Sapna Budev, William Cargill, Rebecca Chastenet, Peter Hines, Terry Hudson, Lesley Kees, Lisa C. Norman, Rebecca Patterson, Jeffrey Twining, Alice Wightman
Financial Editors: Lee Allbritton, Ann Boswell, Sam Gammon, Jenny Hill, Donna Hodges, Dixie Peterson, Suzanne Smith
Style Editors: Calvin Cahan, Jeanne Minnich, Anthony Shuga
Fact Checkers/Proofreaders: Dawn Albright, Hank Bass, Stacey Chambers, Allan Gill, Melanie Hall, Diane Lee, Nancy Nowlin, Carole Sage, John Willis
Database Editors: Tweed Chouinard, J. Kirkland Greer III, Karen Hill
Desktop Publishers: Michelle de Ybarrondo, Kevin Dodds, JoAnn Estrada, Brenda Forsythe, Gregory Gosdin, Louanne Jones
Senior Brand Manager: Leslie A. Wolke
Brand Manager: Richard Finley
Online Production: Sharon Bernard, Kyna Horton, Jeffrey Sandt, Aries Solis, Dennis Sutton
Systems Manager: John Padwick

Senior Vice President, Sales and Marketing: Dana L. Smith
Vice President, Electronic Publishing: Tom Linehan
Treasurer and Controller: Deborah L. Dunlap
Fulfillment Manager: Beth DeVore
Publicity Manager: Jani Spede
Office Manager: Tammy Fisher
Director of Advertising Sales: B.J. Reeves Moore
Customer Service Manager: Rhonda T. Mitchell
Advertising Coordinator: Michelle Swann
Marketing and Publicity Coordinator: Angela Young
Administrative Assistant: Denise Mansfield
Shipping Clerk: Michael Febonio

The Reference Press Mission Statement

1. To produce business information products and services of the highest quality, accuracy, and readability.
2. To make that information available whenever, wherever, and however our customers want it through mass distribution at affordable prices.
3. To continually expand our range of products and services and our markets for those products and services.
4. To reward our employees, suppliers, and shareholders based on their contributions to the success of our enterprise.
5. To hold to the highest ethical business standards, erring on the side of generosity when in doubt.

ABBREVIATIONS

AFL-CIO – American Federation of Labor and Congress of Industrial Organizations

AMA – American Medical Association

AMEX – American Stock Exchange

ARM – adjustable rate mortgage

ASIC – application-specific integrated circuit

ATM – asynchronous transfer mode

CAD/CAM – computer-aided design/computer-aided manufacturing

CASE – computer-aided software engineering

CD-ROM – compact disc – read-only memory

CEO – chief executive officer

CFO – chief financial officer

CISC – complex instruction set computer

CMOS – complimentary metal oxide silicon

COO – chief operating officer

DAT – digital audio tape

DOD – Department of Defense

DOE – Department of Energy

DOS – disk operating system

DOT – Department of Transportation

DRAM – dynamic random-access memory

EPA – Environmental Protection Agency

EPROM – erasable programmable read-only memory

EPS – earnings per share

ESOP – employee stock ownership plan

EU – European Union

EVP – executive vice president

FCC – Federal Communications Commission

FDA – Food and Drug Administration

FDIC – Federal Deposit Insurance Corporation

FPGA – field programmable gate array

FSLIC – Federal Savings and Loan Insurance Corporation

FTC – Federal Trade Commission

FTP – file transfer protocol

GUI – graphical user interface

HMO – health maintenance organization

HR – human resources

HTML – hypertext markup language

IC – integrated circuit

ICC – Interstate Commerce Commission

IPO – initial public offering

IRS – Internal Revenue Service

ISDN – Integrated Services Digital Network

LAN – local-area network

LBO – leveraged buyout

LCD – liquid crystal display

LNG – liquefied natural gas

LP – limited partnership

Ltd. – limited

MIPS – million instructions per second

NAFTA – North American Free Trade Agreement

NASA – National Aeronautics and Space Administration

Nasdaq – National Association of Securities Dealers Automated Quotations

NATO – North Atlantic Treaty Organization

NYSE – New York Stock Exchange

OCR – optical character recognition

OEM – original equipment manufacturer

OPEC – Organization of Petroleum Exporting Countries

OS – operating system

OSHA – Occupational Safety and Health Administration

OTC – over-the-counter

PBX – private branch exchange

PCMCIA – Personal Computer Memory Card International Association

P/E – price-to-earnings ratio

PPO – preferred provider organization

RAM – random-access memory

R&D – research and development

RBOC – Regional Bell Operating Company

RISC – reduced instruction set computer

ROA – return on assets

ROE – return on equity

ROI – return on investment

ROM – read-only memory

S&L – savings and loan

SEC – Securities and Exchange Commission

SEVP – senior executive vice president

SIC – Standard Industrial Classification

SPARC – scalable processor architecture

SVP – senior vice president

VAR – value-added remarketer

VAT – value-added tax

VC – vice chairman

VP – vice president

WAN – wide-area network

www – world wide web

CONTENTS

ABOUT *HOOVER'S GUIDE TO THE TOP TEXAS COMPANIES*

It ain't bragging if you can do it, and Texas companies can do it all. With an economy as refreshingly diverse as its population and topography, the state offers a wealth of corporate resources and a business climate that makes for a fascinating study. The landscape of Texas business stretches from thriving young technology firms in the state's major cities to industry giants in such outposts as Diboll and Pittsburg, while the history of Texas enterprise winds from the ranch Richard King set up in the mid-1800s through the oil fields that shaped the state in the 20th century and into the high-tech Silicon Hills that hold the keys to the next millennium.

This second edition of *Hoover's Guide to the Top Texas Companies* is just one of a series of regional guides produced by The Reference Press. A guide to the top San Francisco companies has already been published, and guides to New York, Chicago, and Southern California companies will follow in the first half of 1996. These books complement our other publications, which include *Hoover's Handbook of American Companies*, *Hoover's Handbook of World Business*, *Hoover's Handbook of Emerging Companies*, *Hoover's Guide to Private Companies*, *Hoover's Guide to Computer Companies*, and *Hoover's MasterList of America's Top 2,500 Employers*, among others. Our company profiles and other information are also available electronically on diskette and CD-ROM and on online services (e.g., America Online and CompuServe) and the Internet (e.g., Hoover's Online at http://www.hoovers.com).

As our longtime readers may remember, the first edition of this book was entitled *The Texas 500: Hoover's Guide to the Top Texas Companies*. The deletion of the phrase "The Texas 500" from the second edition reflects a change in our approach to the book. Although it looked great on the cover (and was very marketable), we found the 500 format to be inherently limiting. First, we found it hard to stick to 500 companies when we had so much more information to include. And although "The Texas 1,000" would have worked just fine, "The Texas 850" would have looked a bit odd on the cover. Second, the nature of such a listing is that you can't skip a company. In other words, if you can't get enough information to include a small private company with annual revenues of $25 million, then you really can't include any smaller companies, no matter how good your data. In light of these drawbacks, we decided to abandon the 500 format and include as many companies as we could.

This book is the product of comprehensive research. Our first step was to consult our extensive database of company information to identify public and private businesses headquartered in Texas. We then turned to other sources to look for companies we may have missed, such as the *Forbes* 500 list of private companies and local newspaper lists. Finally, we contacted all of the companies listed in the book to verify and update our information. Most companies were helpful and cooperative; some were not. (One even attempted to convince us that they had moved from Texas; they hadn't.) For those companies that did not cooperate, we obtained the most reliable information we could find and in some cases made estimates regarding revenue. In all such cases, the revenue figure is marked as an estimate.

Hoover's Guide to the Top Texas Companies profiles all public companies in the state, all private companies with revenues of over $200 million, all private companies with revenues between $50 and $200 million for which we could compile accurate information, and a selection of interesting smaller companies. In addition to traditional for-profit companies, we have also included consortia (e.g., Sematech), cooperatives (e.g., Associated Milk Producers), joint ventures (e.g., Star Petroleum), and universities (e.g., the University of Texas System and the Texas A&M System), among others. We have included these enterprises because we believe they are as important to driving the Texas economy and creating jobs as the for-profit sector.

After determining our universe of Texas businesses, we selected 125 of them for in-depth profiles. These companies range from giant Exxon (1994 revenues of $113.9 billion) to tiny Sterling Information Services (1994 revenues of $3.7 million). We profiled the 50 largest Texas companies in our two-page format, each with up to 10 years of financial data and a separate section on its history. We also included long profiles of a few uniquely Texan enterprises with colorful histories. (e.g., King Ranch and Mary Kay). The remainder of the companies are in our one-page format, with up to 6 years of financial data and a shorter history integrated into the overview of the company. In choosing these companies we have tried to represent the full spectrum of Texas business. All 850 companies in the book have capsule profiles.

This book consists of 5 components:

1. The first section, "Using the Profiles," describes the contents of the profiles and explains the ways in which we gather and compile our data.

2. Next we have included "A List-Lover's Compendium," which contains lists of the largest and fastest-growing companies in the book as well as selected lists from other sources to provide you with different viewpoints.

3. The third section of the book contains the 125 in-depth profiles of Texas businesses. The first 55 profiles are in our long, two-page format. The next 70 are in our medium, one-page format. The profiles are arranged alphabetically within each section.

4. The next section provides capsule profiles of 850 companies. If an in-depth profile also exists for a company, the page number of that profile is included in the entry for easier reference.

5. The book concludes with 3 indexes: (1) the companies organized by industry groupings, (2) the companies organized by headquarters location, and (3) the main index of the book, containing all the names of brands, companies, and people mentioned in the in-depth profiles.

As always, we hope you find our books useful and informative. We invite your comments via phone (512-454-7778), fax (512-454-9401), mail (6448 Hwy. 290 East, Ste. E-104, Austin, TX 78723), or e-mail (comments@hoovers.com).

The Editors
Austin, Texas
October 1995

Using the Profiles

Organization of the Profiles

The 125 company profiles are presented in either a one-page or two-page format. The two-page profiles (of 55 companies) contain extensive historical information, in addition to 10 years of financial data. The one-page profiles (of 70 companies) offer a shorter history and 6 years of financial data. In both formats the profiles are presented in alphabetical order. (Company names that begin with numbers, like 7th Level, Inc., come before the alphabetical listing.) The full legal name of the enterprise appears at the top of the page, unless it is too long to fit, in which case it can be found above the address in the Where section of the profile. All company names used in the profiles appear in the last index in the book.

The annual financial information contained in the Where, What, and How Much sections of the profiles is current through fiscal year-ends occurring as late as April 1995. In the text we have included selected financial data and nonfinan-cial development, such as officer changes, through September 1995.

Overview

In this section we provide a description of the company and what it does. The description usually includes information on the company's strategy, reputation, and ownership. In the one-page profiles we also provide a brief history of the company, including the year of founding and the names of the founders when possible. We recommend that you read this section first.

When

This section, which appears only in the two-page profiles, reflects our belief that every enterprise is the sum of its history and that you have to know where you came from in order to know where you are going. We tried to focus on the people who made the enterprise what it is today. While some companies have very little historical awareness and were unable to give us much information about their pasts, we think the vast majority of the enterprises in the book have colorful backgrounds. These histories are often full of twists and ironies; they can make for some fascinating reading.

Who

Here we list the names of the people who run the company, insofar as space allows. For public companies, we show the ages and pay levels of key officers. We have tried to show current officers, with their pay for the latest year available. The pay shown represents cash compensation, including bonuses, but excludes stock option programs.

While companies are free to structure their management titles any way they please, most modern corporations follow standard practices. The chief officer, the person on whose desk the buck stops, is usually called the chief executive officer (CEO). Often the CEO is also the chairman of the board. As corporate management has become more complex, it is common for the CEO to have a "right-hand person" who oversees the day-to-day operations of the company, permitting the CEO to focus on strategy and long-term issues. This right-hand person is usually designated the chief operating officer (COO) and is often the president of the company. In other cases one person is both chairman and president.

A multitude of other titles exists, including chief financial officer (CFO), senior vice president (SVP), and vice chairman (VC). We always tried to include the CFO and the chief personnel, or human resources, officer. The Who section also includes the name of the company's auditing (accounting) firm. The people named in the profiles are indexed at the back of the book.

Where

Here we provide company street addresses and phone and fax numbers. An index of companies by headquarters location follows the profiles.

We also included as much information on the geographical distribution of the company's business (including sales and profit data) as we could gather and fit on the page. Note that the profit numbers, like those in the What section below, are usually operating profits rather than net profits. Operating profits are generally those before financing costs (interest income and payments) and before taxes, which are considered costs attributable to the whole company rather than to one division or part of the world. For this reason the net incomes (in the How Much section) are usually much lower, since they are after interest and taxes. Pretax profits are after interest but before taxes.

What

This section lists as many of the company's products, services, brand names, divisions, subsidiaries, and joint ventures as we had room for. We tried to include all the major lines and familiar brand names. The nature of this section varies by industry, company, and the amount of information available. If the company publishes sales and profit information by type of business, we included it. The brand, division, and subsidiary names are listed in the last index in the book, with past and present company names.

Key Competitors

In this section we list those companies that compete with the profiled company. This feature is included as a quick way to locate similar companies and compare them. The universe of key competitors includes all public companies and all private companies with annual sales in excess of $500 million. In some instances we have identified smaller private companies as key competitors. All the companies in the book are listed by broad industry groups in the first index at the back of the book.

How Much

Here we present as much data about each enterprise's financial performance as we could compile in the allocated space. Although the information on private companies is somewhat less complete (because they often do not release financial statements), the following information is generally present:

1. A 10-year table (6 years for the one-page profiles), with relevant annualized compound growth rates, covering:
   - Fiscal year sales (year-end assets for most financial institutions)
   - Fiscal year net income (before accounting changes)
   - Net income as a percent of sales (as a percent of assets for most financial firms)
   - Fiscal year earnings per share (EPS, fully diluted)
   - Calendar year stock price high, low, and close

- Calendar year highs and lows divided by fiscal year EPS
- Fiscal year dividends paid per share
- Fiscal year-end book value (common shareholders' equity per share)
- Fiscal year-end or average number of employees

All sales numbers are as reported by the company. We do not modify reported sales by deducting interest income, sales and excise taxes, or similar items. The 10-year information (6 years on the one-page profiles) on the number of employees is intended to aid the reader interested in knowing whether a company has a long-term trend of increasing or decreasing employment. (As far as we know, we are the only company that publishes this information in print.) The year at the top of each column in the How Much section is the year in which the com-pany's fiscal year actually ends. Thus, data for a company whose fiscal year ended on February 28, 1995, are shown in the 1995 column. Stock price information for companies with year-ends between January 1 and April 30 is for the prior calendar year and is so footnoted on the chart.

2. Key fiscal year-end statistics that generally show the financial strength of the enterprise, including:
   - Debt ratio (total debt as a percent of combined total debt and shareholders' equity)
   - Return on average equity (net income divided by the average of beginning and ending common shareholders' equity) for the fiscal year
   - Cash and marketable securities
   - Current ratio (ratio of current assets to current liabilities)

- Total long-term debt (including capital lease obligations)
- Number of shares of common stock out-standing
- Dividend yield (fiscal year dividends per share divided by the calendar year-end closing stock price)
- Dividend payout (fiscal year dividends divided by fiscal year earnings per share)
- Market value (calendar year-end closing stock price multiplied by fiscal year-end number of shares outstanding)
- Research and development as a percent of sales (one-page profiles only)
- Advertising as a percent of sales (one-page profiles only)

For financial institutions and insurance companies we have also included annual sales in this section.

If the company is public, we include its stock ticker symbol and the exchange on which it is traded. We also provide the company's fiscal year-end. Per-share data have been adjusted for stock splits. The data for some public companies have been provided to us by Media General Financial Services. Other public company information was compiled by The Reference Press, which takes full responsibility for the content of this section. For private companies that do not publicly disclose financial information, we made estimates of sales and other statistics gathered from numerous sources.

Texas Economic Outlook

OVERVIEW OF THE TEXAS ECONOMY AND BUSINESS ENVIRONMENT

Reprinted from *Texas Economic Quarterly*, June and September 1995,
published by the office of John Sharp, Comptroller of Public Accounts

Without fanfare the Texas economy in 1995 climbed to its highest performance level since the mid-1980s. During the first quarter, employment growth hit 3.6 percent, second only to the previous quarter for the greatest level of employment growth in over 10 years. Consumer confidence and new business incorporations reached their highest levels since 1984. The number of housing permits reached a post-1986 peak, and there was more help-wanted advertising in Texas newspapers than at any time since the state's Comptroller of Public Accounts began compiling the Texas Help-Wanted Advertising Index in 1981.

Despite a slowing U.S. economy and a weakening by midyear of several economic indicators, Texas's economic outlook through 1997 continued to be upbeat, with most of the state's leading indicators pointing to moderate growth.

Relocations of high-tech companies to the state and a relatively robust construction industry helped Texas avoid the worst effects of a national slowdown in 1995. Texas continued leading all states in the number of new jobs added (see Table 1) and ranked tenth in the rate of employment growth. While national year-over-year employment growth fell by a full percentage point, from 3.1 percent in January 1995 to 2.2 percent in July 1995, Texas job growth slowed from 3.7 percent to just 3.4 percent. Help-wanted advertising, new business incorporations, and new housing permits remained relatively strong. Although new claims for unemployment insurance and the unemployment rate had increased

somewhat, Texas's rate of unemployment remained relatively low at midyear.

Despite a 15 percent increase in rental, property, and investment income, slower wage and salary income growth kept Texas personal income from growing as quickly as might be expected, given the robust employment expansion. For example, while Texas nonfarm job growth in 1994 outpaced national growth by almost a full percentage point, total personal income growth was an insignificant 0.1 percent higher than the nation's growth. The loss of relatively high-wage aerospace and oil/gas jobs, as well as a higher share of workers in lower-wage service-sector jobs, have suppressed Texas income growth.

Table 1
Job Growth in 10 Most Populous States
March 1994 to March 1995

Rank	State	Job Growth	Percentage Change	Rank*
1	Texas	267,400	3.5	15
2	Florida	226,600	4.0	13
3	Michigan	130,800	3.2	19
4	Ohio	122,800	2.4	33
5	Illinois	120,200	2.2	38
6	North Carolina	108,000	3.2	18
7	California	102,800	0.8	47
8	New Jersey	78,200	2.2	37
9	Pennsylvania	71,200	1.4	43
10	New York	32,300	0.4	48
	U. S. Total	3,476,000	3.1	

Note: In order to have comparable data for all states, seasonal adjustments in this table, including those for Texas, were done by the U.S. Bureau of Labor Statistics.

* Rank in percentage job growth among the 50 states.

Source: U. S. Bureau of Labor Statistics.

Interstate 35 MSAs Lead State Job Growth

Of the state's 27 Metropolitan Statistical Areas (MSAs), the strongest employment growth has been along Interstate Highway 35 (Table 2). The Austin-San Marcos MSA enjoyed a 6.2 percent job growth rate from July 1994 to July 1995, owing largely to strong construction activity and the relocation of high-tech firms. Employment in the Killeen-Temple MSA was up 5.9 percent, with increased trade and services spawned largely by the relocation of Third Army Brigade personnel to Fort Hood from Fort Polk, Louisiana. San Antonio MSA employ-

Table 2
Nonfarm Employment Growth for Metropolitan Areas
Ranked by Percent Change: July 1994 to July 1995 (Seasonally Adjusted)

Metropolitan Statistical Area	Total Nonfarm Employment July 1995	July 1994	Annual Change In Percent
Austin-San Marcos	510,400	480,700	6.2
Killeen-Temple	91,200	86,100	5.9
San Antonio	615,200	592,300	3.9
Dallas	1,581,700	1,527,600	3.5
Waco	91,700	88,800	3.3
Fort Worth-Arlington	650,500	630,000	3.3
Bryan-College Station	65,100	63,100	3.2
El Paso	237,800	230,500	3.2
Wichita Falls	55,900	54,200	3.1
Houston	1,750,000	1,699,100	3.0
Amarillo	88,800	86,500	2.7
San Angelo	40,600	39,600	2.5
Odessa-Midland	95,800	93,500	2.5
Tyler	70,500	68,900	2.3
Lubbock	106,100	103,700	2.3
Sherman-Denison	39,800	38,900	2.3
Brownsville-Harlingen-San Benito	92,700	90,800	2.1
Corpus Christi	145,800	143,100	1.9
Galveston-Texas City	84,500	83,200	1.6
Abilene	51,000	50,300	1.4
Beaumont-Port Arthur	149,700	147,700	1.4
Longview-Marshall	82,400	81,300	1.4
McAllen-Edinburg-Mission	119,400	118,100	1.1
Texarkana	48,200	48,000	0.4
Victoria	32,500	32,600	(0.3)
Brazoria	70,800	72,100	(1.8)
Laredo	55,400	56,900	(2.6)

Source: Texas Employment Commission

ment was up 3.9 percent with the continued strength of the local tourism industry. And in the Dallas MSA, employment was up by 3.5 percent, due, as with Austin, to the strength of high-tech industries and construction. Most of Dallas's growth was concentrated in its northern reaches.

Moderate State Economic Growth Expected to Continue

As the national economy slowly recovers from its early 1995 lull, Texas should continue to experience moderate economic growth through 1997 (Table 3). Gross state product is forecast to increase at an annual rate of around 3.5 percent over the next 3 years. After increasing by approximately 2.5 percent in 1995, statewide nonfarm employment will increase about 2 percent annually in both 1996 and 1997, while the unemployment rate will average just under 6 percent. Personal income will grow by 6 to 6.5 percent annually, with inflation holding at about 3 percent. Because of strong net in-migration of roughly 100,000 new residents per year, the state's population will increase by 1.5 percent annually, reaching a total of 19.3 million residents in 1997.

Table 3
Texas Economic History and Outlook
For Calendar Years 1992 to 1997

	1992	1993	1994	1995*	1996*	1997*
TEXAS FORECASTS						
Gross State Product (bil. 1987$)	349.8	361.3	376.6	390.7	404.2	418.1
Annual % Change	3.1	3.3	4.2	3.7	3.5	3.4
Personal Income (bil. $)	326.2	345.0	367.4	390.3	415.4	442.1
Annual % Change	7.8	5.8	6.5	6.2	6.4	6.4
Nonfarm Employment (thou.)	7,268.0	7,481.3	7,740.4	7,939.3	8,106.9	8,282.8
Annual % Change	1.3	2.9	3.5	2.6	2.1	2.2
Resident Population (thou.)	17,712.7	18,065.9	18,421.5	18,756.9	19,055.2	19,340.9
Annual % Change	11.9	2.0	2.0	1.8	1.6	1.5
Unemployment Rate (%)	7.0	6.5	5.8	5.8	5.9	5.9
Oil Price ($ per Barrel)	18.40	16.28	15.16	16.48	16.94	17.58
Natural Gas Price ($ per MCF)	1.58	1.82	1.64	1.54	1.58	1.63
Oil/Gas Drilling Rig Count	250	262	275	288	284	287
U. S. ECONOMY						
Gross Domestic Product (bil. 1987$)	4,979.3	5,134.5	5,342.3	5,503.6	5,634.1	5,758.1
Annual % Change	2.3	3.1	4.0	3.0	2.4	2.2
Consumer Price Index (1982-84=100)	140.4	144.6	148.3	152.5	157.2	161.9
Annual % Change	3.0	3.0	2.6	2.8	3.1	3.0
Prime Interest Rate (%)	6.3	6.0	7.1	9.4	9.4	8.6

* Projected
Sources: John Sharp, Texas Comptroller of Public Accounts (Spring 1995 Forecast) and the WEFA Group

OUTLOOK BY INDUSTRY

Service Sectors Serve Up Most Jobs

The service-producing sector — which includes wholesale and retail trade; finance, insurance, and real estate; transportation, communications, and public utilities; business, health, and other services; and government — is expected to account for 94 percent of the new jobs in Texas through 1997. Over four of every five Texas nonfarm jobs are in this broad sector. Although some of these jobs in sectors such as financial and business services are relatively high-paying, most are not. For example, the average salary of workers in goods-producing sectors is 28 percent higher than for service-producing sector workers. As noted earlier, this is the predominant factor behind rather slow personal income growth in the face of fairly rapid job growth.

Wholesale and Retail Trade. As of July 1995, trade jobs were up 4 percent over the past year, the highest growth rate since the mid-1980s. Wholesale employment grew by 18,000, with retail up by 58,000. Although personal income growth is somewhat weak, business and consumer expenditures for building materials, appliances, furniture, and other housing-related items remain relatively vigorous because of continuing strength in residential construction activity. Apparel sales remain sluggish, while overall retail spending along the Mexican border has been hurt by the weak peso and Mexico's recession. Although employment growth in trade will moderate through 1997, as hiring to meet the needs of expanded sales volume slows, the sector still is expected to grow about 2 percent annually,

adding 34,000 jobs in 1996 and another 36,000 in 1997.

Finance, Insurance, and Real Estate. Although abundant housing starts helped finance, insurance, and real estate employment increase by a strong 3 percent in 1994, the outlook for the next 3 years is less positive. So far this year, employment is up by almost one percent. As higher gains from long-term investments replace short-term business investments (including checking/savings accounts and bank CDs), the banking sector will be hard-pressed to maintain positive job growth, especially in light of continuing consolidations. Banking will lose an additional 3,600 jobs through 1997, an annual loss of about 1.5 percent. Insurance had its best year in 1994 since 1983, with 3.4 percent employment growth. But the outlook is for more moderate gains of 1.2 percent in 1996 and 1.8 percent in 1997, as recent growth in insurable goods purchases return to normal. On the other hand, due to ongoing net migration into the state and relatively attractive mortgage rates spurring new housing construction, jobs in the real estate industry are expected to increase by a strong 3.3 percent in 1996 and 4.6 percent in 1997.

Transportation, Communications, and Public Utilities. The outlook here is a mixed bag. All segments of the transportation industry (rail, air, and trucking) have added jobs over the past year, with the strongest gains in trucking (4.8 percent). Reduced operation costs, abundant fuel at good prices, corporate reaction to trucking deregulation, and growing international trade all coalesced to spur employment growth. For 1996 and 1997, transportation employment is expected to increase by about 3 percent annually. In communications, Internet providers and cellular equipment are a part of a changing world of technology. With Texas companies participating in this communications revolution, sector employment was up 7.7 percent over the past year. Communications is expected to continue growing, but at a less hectic 2 percent annually in 1996 and 1997. Finally, losses in the public utilities industry due to cost-containment pressures, which are expected to mitigate somewhat, will allow utilities to see job growth of about one percent annually in 1996 and 1997.

Services. All parts of the services sector are growing. Business and engineering services added 54,000 jobs, a phenomenal 9 percent, over the past year because of outsourcing from manufacturers and the strength of the manufacturing sector. Although health services employment growth has moderated through efforts to curtail spiraling health care costs, the number of jobs was still up by almost 5 percent. Finally, employment in other personal services such as hotels, theaters, personal care, and social and recreational services was up by nearly 3 percent. Over the next 3 years, business and engineering services will gain jobs at about 3 percent a year, moderating the recent blistering rates as manufacturing and construction slow. Health services will grow 3 to 4 percent a year, driven by an expanding elderly population but restrained by the continued need for cost containment. Other personal services will follow the current growth path, aided by continuing migration to the state, with nearly 4 percent employment growth per year.

Government. Federal government employment continues shrinking, while jobs at the state and local level are increasing. Federal civilian employment is now in its fifth straight year of decline and is expected to continue falling in 1996 and 1997. Likewise, the number of military personnel at bases across the state has been declining since 1985 and will likely fall another 4 percent by 1997. Jobs in state and local government, on the other hand, increased about 3 percent over the past year and are expected to grow about 2 percent annually in 1996 and 1997. State employment is increasing mainly because of increasing staffing needs associated with the massive prison construction program. At the local level, most job increases are in school districts, as the school-age population continues to increase.

Energy Industry Will Continue to Shrink

Texas's energy industry will continue to shrink for the next 3 years. Although much of the oil price volatility has subsided, natural gas prices and overall domestic drilling activity remain weak. As of July 1995 statewide oil and gas employment had declined by 7,300 over the past year. The industry is expected to lose an additional 1,500 jobs in 1996 and 1,200 jobs in 1997.

Construction—Only a Lull in the Activity

Although an increase in mortgage rates in the latter part of 1994 caused some downturn in statewide residential construction activity in early 1995, that lull should be short-lived. The expectation of continued low inflation, with the resulting strength in the bond market, has pushed fixed mortgage rates down, from over 9 percent in late 1994 to under 8 percent by midyear. In response, existing home sales have picked up. Renewed consumer demand has pushed up residential building permits, from a low of 75,000 units (annualized rate) in April 1995 to almost 100,000 units by the beginning of summer.

Nonresidential and nonbuilding construction also are experiencing strong activity. With nearly 88 million square feet of space added in 1994, nonresidential building construction reached its most active level since 1986. The overbuilt real estate of the early 1980s has gradually been absorbed, prompting new space to be built. The demand for industrial and distribution space is being intensified by continuing relocations and expansions, particularly in the state's electronics industry. Significant new retail space is being added as "megastores" such as Home Depot, Office Depot, and Sam's Club rapidly expand in the state's major metropolitan areas. The value of nonbuilding construction — roads, bridges, and other infrastructure — reached over $4 billion in 1994 for the first time in 6 years. Much of this new construction activity is being fueled by state highway construction programs in the Dallas–Fort Worth and Houston areas.

As of July 1995 total construction employment in Texas was up by more than 7 percent, or 27,000 jobs, over the past year. Residential and nonresidential construction activity will remain strong through 1997, with 90,000 to 95,000 new homes and over 90 million square feet in nonresidential space added annually. Job growth, however, will moderate as employers adjust to the higher level of construction activity of recent years. Overall, statewide construction employment is expected to increase by almost 6 percent in 1995, another 2 percent in 1996, and one percent in 1997.

Manufacturing Outlook — Some Up, Some Down

Statewide manufacturing employment grew by 15,900 jobs, or 1.6 percent, over the past year (July 1994–1995). Jobs in the durable goods sector increased by 17,000, or more than 3 percent, because of hiring by computer, electronics, and other high-technology firms. Aerospace employment, however, continued its decline as national defense expenditures fall. Over the past year nondurables employment declined slightly, mainly due to layoffs in the apparel industry and consolidations in petroleum refining and chemicals.

After a 1.5 percent increase in 1995, total manufacturing employment will increase by between one-half and one percent annually in 1996 and 1997. This seemingly modest employment growth masks the health of Texas manufacturing, since employment changes alone do not reflect the industry's strength. Technological advancements, for example, allow more productivity from each manufacturing worker. Thus, the gross state product in manufacturing will rise much faster than the absolute number of jobs: a 2.5 percent annual rate from 1995 through 1997. Also, because of growing markets and relatively low housing and business costs, Texas is adding new manufacturing jobs in the face of losses in other industrial states.

The fastest-growing Texas manufacturing industries through 1997 will be electronics and building materials. Electronics and computers are expected to add over 13,000 jobs by 1997. Building materials employment will increase by nearly 6,000. As in the recent past, however, employment in petroleum refining, apparel, and aerospace transportation will continue to decline.

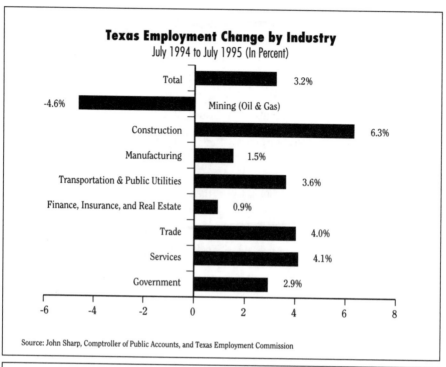

Texas Employment Change by Industry

July 1994 to July 1995 (In Percent)

Industry	Percent
Total	3.2%
Mining (Oil & Gas)	-4.6%
Construction	6.3%
Manufacturing	1.5%
Transportation & Public Utilities	3.6%
Finance, Insurance, and Real Estate	0.9%
Trade	4.0%
Services	4.1%
Government	2.9%

Source: John Sharp, Comptroller of Public Accounts, and Texas Employment Commission

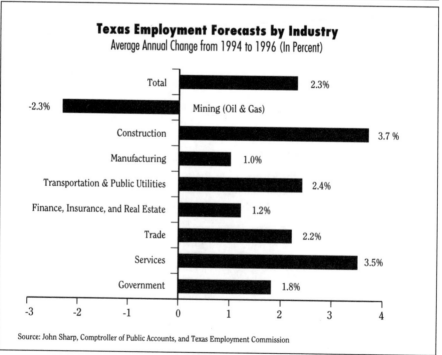

Texas Employment Forecasts by Industry

Average Annual Change from 1994 to 1996 (In Percent)

Industry	Percent
Total	2.3%
Mining (Oil & Gas)	-2.3%
Construction	3.7 %
Manufacturing	1.0%
Transportation & Public Utilities	2.4%
Finance, Insurance, and Real Estate	1.2%
Trade	2.2%
Services	3.5%
Government	1.8%

Source: John Sharp, Comptroller of Public Accounts, and Texas Employment Commission

Texas — Bigger than Russia?

Texas's gross state product exceeds that of Russia, the world's geographically largest nation, by nearly $100 billion (U.S.). As compiled by the latest release of gross national product data by the World Bank, the Texas economy would rank eleventh in the world if the state were a nation (again). In terms of gross national product per capita, Texas also would rank as one of the world's richest nations. The state would rank eighth among all nations in GNP per person, being exceeded by Switzerland, Luxembourg, Japan, Denmark, Norway, and (just barely) Sweden and the U.S.

Gross National Product (GNP) Estimates: 1993

Rank	Nation	Total GNP (Billion U.S. $)	Rank	Nation	Per Capita GNP (U.S. $)
1	United States*	$6,387.69	1	Switzerland	$36,410
2	Japan	3,926.67	2	Luxembourg	35,850
3	Germany	1,903.00	3	Japan	31,450
4	France	1,289.24	4	Denmark	26,510
5	Italy	1,134.98	5	Norway	26,340
6	United Kingdom	1,042.70	6	Sweden	24,830
7	China	581.11	7	United States*	24,750
8	Canada	574.88	8	TEXAS**	24,540
9	Spain	533.99	9	Iceland	23,620
10	Brazil	471.98	10	Germany	23,560
11	TEXAS**	443.28	11	Kuwait	23,350
12	Russia	348.41	12	Austria	23,120
13	Korea	338.06	13	United Arab Emirates	22,470
14	Mexico	324.95	14	France	22,360
15	Netherlands	316.40	15	Belgium	21,210
16	Australia	309.97	16	Netherlands	20,710
17	India	262.81	17	Canada	20,670
18	Switzerland	254.07	18	Italy	19,620
19	Argentina	244.01	19	Singapore	19,310
20	Sweden	216.29	20	Finland	18,970

* Includes Texas
** If Texas were a sovereign nation

Source: The World Bank Atlas, 1995 (for GNP of nations). U.S. Bureau of Economic Analysis and John Sharp, Texas Comptroller of Public Accounts (for Texas gross state product). These gross product numbers are based on market exchange rates and do not account for purchasing power, which varies greatly from nation to nation.

Texas Stock Index

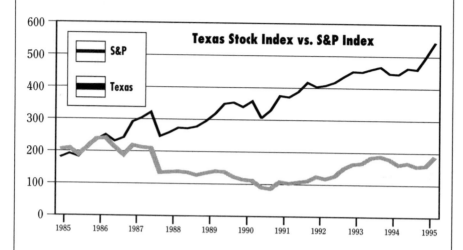

Texas Stock Index vs. S&P Index

- S&P
- Texas

Texas Stock Index Companies, August 1995*

*Sector composition may change each month due to mergers, acquisitions and other occurrences.

FINANCE, INSURANCE AND REAL ESTATE SECTOR STOCKS
1. American General Corporation
2. American National Insurance Company
3. Centex Corporation
4. Cullen/Frost Bankers Inc.
5. Lomas Financial Corporation
6. Victoria Bankshares Inc.
7. Weingarten Realty Inc.

ENERGY SECTOR STOCKS
1. Coastal Corporation
2. Dresser Industries Inc.
3. ENSERCH Corporation
4. Halliburton Company
5. Mesa Inc.
6. Mitchell Energy and Development Corp.
7. Tenneco Inc.
8. Valero Energy Corporation

TECHNOLOGY SECTOR STOCKS
1. Carrington Labs Inc.
2. Compaq Computer Corporation
3. Datapoint Corporation
4. Dell Computer Corporation
5. DSC Communication Corporation
6. Recognition International Inc.
7. Tandy Corporation
8. Tech Sym Corporation
9. Texas Instruments Inc.

GENERAL SECTOR STOCKS
1. Brinker International
2. Browning-Ferris Industries Inc.
3. Central & South West Corporation
4. Commercial Metals Company
5. Continental Airlines
6. Daniel Industries
7. Elcor Corporation
8. Ennis Business Forms Inc.
9. Farah Inc.
10. GNI Group
11. Houston Industries Inc.
12. Justin Industries Inc.
13. Kimberly-Clark Corporation
14. La Quinta Motor Inns Inc.
15. Luby's Cafeterias Inc.
16. NCH Corporation
17. Oshmans Sporting Goods Inc.
18. Pancho's Mexican Buffet Inc.
19. Pier 1 Imports
20. Proler International Corporation
21. Quanex Corporation
22. Republic Gypsum Company
23. Southdown Inc.
24. Southern Union Gas Company
25. Southwest Airlines
26. Stewart and Stevenson Services Inc.
27. Sysco Corporation
28. Temple Inland Inc.
29. Texas Industries Inc.
30. Texas Utilities Company
31. Valhi Inc.

Source: John Sharp, Comptroller of Public Accounts

TEXAS

A List-Lover's Compendium

The 50 Largest Companies by Sales in Texas

Rank	Company	City	Sales ($ mil.)
1	Exxon Corporation	Irving	113,904
2	Shell Oil Company	Houston	21,581
3	J. C. Penney Company, Inc.	Plano	20,380
4	AMR Corporation	Fort Worth	16,137
5	Caltex Petroleum Corporation	Irving	14,751
6	Tenneco Inc.	Houston	12,174
7	SYSCO Corporation	Houston	12,118
8	SBC Communications Inc.	San Antonio	11,619
9	Compaq Computer Corporation	Houston	10,866
10	Texas Instruments Incorporated	Dallas	10,315
11	The Coastal Corporation	Houston	10,215
12	Electronic Data Systems Corporation	Plano	10,052
13	Enron Corp.	Houston	8,984
14	Kimberly-Clark Corporation	Dallas	7,364
15	Army & Air Force Exchange Service	Dallas	7,100
16	The Southland Corporation	Dallas	6,760
17	USAA	San Antonio	6,181
18	Star Enterprise	Houston	6,086
19	EOTT Energy Partners, L.P.	Houston	5,921
20	Halliburton Company	Dallas	5,741
21	Continental Airlines, Inc.	Houston	5,670
22	Texas Utilities Company	Dallas	5,664
23	Dresser Industries, Inc.	Dallas	5,331
24	FoxMeyer Health Corporation	Carrollton	5,177
25	Burlington Northern Santa Fe Corporation	Fort Worth	4,995
26	Tandy Corporation	Fort Worth	4,944
27	H. E. Butt Grocery Company	San Antonio	4,850
28	American General Corporation	Houston	4,841
29	Cooper Industries, Inc.	Houston	4,588
30	Panhandle Eastern Corporation	Houston	4,585
31	Browning-Ferris Industries, Inc.	Houston	4,315
32	The University of Texas System	Austin	4,030
33	Houston Industries Incorporated	Houston	4,002
34	Lyondell Petrochemical Company	Houston	3,857
35	Central and South West Corporation	Dallas	3,623
36	Dell Computer Corporation	Austin	3,475
37	FINA, Inc.	Dallas	3,421
38	Centex Corporation	Dallas	3,278
39	NGC Corporation	Houston	3,238
40	Temple-Inland Inc.	Diboll	2,938
41	CompUSA Inc.	Dallas	2,813
42	NorAm Energy Corp.	Houston	2,801
43	Associated Milk Producers, Inc.	San Antonio	2,629
44	Diamond Shamrock, Inc.	San Antonio	2,606
45	Southwest Airlines Co.	Dallas	2,592
46	Pennzoil Company	Houston	2,563
47	Baker Hughes Incorporated	Houston	2,505
48	Randall's Food Markets, Inc.	Houston	2,400
49	Trinity Industries, Inc.	Dallas	2,315
50	MAXXAM Inc.	Houston	2,116

The 50 Largest Employers in Texas

Rank	Company	City	Sales ($ mil.)
1	J. C. Penney Company, Inc.	Plano	202,000
2	AMR Corporation	Fort Worth	109,800
3	Exxon Corporation	Irving	86,000
4	Electronic Data Systems Corporation	Plano	70,000
5	The University of Texas System	Austin	68,996
6	Army & Air Force Exchange Service	Dallas	60,000
7	SBC Communications Inc.	San Antonio	58,750
8	Halliburton Company	Dallas	57,200
9	Texas Instruments Incorporated	Dallas	56,333
10	Tenneco Inc.	Houston	55,000
11	Tandy Corporation	Fort Worth	45,800
12	Kimberly-Clark Corporation	Dallas	42,707
13	Cooper Industries, Inc.	Houston	40,800
14	Brinker International, Inc.	Dallas	38,000
15	Continental Airlines, Inc.	Houston	37,800
16	Browning-Ferris Industries, Inc.	Houston	37,000
17	Burlington Northern Santa Fe Corporation	Fort Worth	30,711
18	The Southland Corporation	Dallas	30,417
19	Dresser Industries, Inc.	Dallas	29,200
20	SYSCO Corporation	Houston	26,200
21	H. E. Butt Grocery Company	San Antonio	25,000
22	Heritage Media Corporation	Dallas	24,500
23	Shell Oil Company	Houston	21,496
24	Randall's Food Markets, Inc.	Houston	21,000
25	Club Corporation International	Dallas	19,200
26	Sisters of Charity of the Incarnate Word Health Care System	Houston	19,000
27	The Texas A&M University System	College Station	19,000
28	Service Corporation International	Houston	18,756
29	Living Centers of America, Inc.	Houston	17,800
30	Michaels Stores, Inc.	Irving	17,440
31	Southwest Airlines Co.	Dallas	16,818
32	Trinity Industries, Inc.	Dallas	16,500
33	The Coastal Corporation	Houston	16,300
34	Administaff Inc.	Kingwood	16,000
35	USAA	San Antonio	15,233
36	Temple-Inland Inc.	Diboll	15,000
37	Baker Hughes Incorporated	Houston	14,700
38	Contran Corporation	Dallas	14,500
39	Compaq Computer Corporation	Houston	14,372
40	MAXXAM Inc.	Houston	13,860
41	ShowBiz Pizza Time, Inc.	Irving	13,500
42	American General Corporation	Houston	12,900
43	Valhi, Inc.	Dallas	11,500
44	Houston Industries Incorporated	Houston	11,498
45	Lennox International Inc.	Richardson	11,000
46	Texas Utilities Company	Dallas	10,798
47	NCH Corporation	Irving	10,569
48	Pennzoil Company	Houston	10,501
49	Pilgrim's Pride Corporation	Pittsburg	10,300
50	Greyhound Lines, Inc.	Dallas	10,100
50	Luby's Cafeterias, Inc.	San Antonio	10,100

The 50 Fastest-Growing Companies by Sales in Texas

Rank	Company	City	Annual % Change	Sales ($ mil.)
1	HighwayMaster Communications, Inc.	Dallas	694	14
2	Spinnaker Industries, Inc.	Dallas	425	34
3	id Software, Inc.	Mesquite	333	13
4	Polyphase Corporation	Dallas	242	25
5	SA Holdings, Inc.	Richardson	238	10
6	Smith International, Inc.	Houston	196	654
7	American Oncology Resources, Inc.	Houston	183	20
8	Columbus Realty Trust	Dallas	161	31
9	Positron Corporation	Houston	154	6
10	Burlington Resources Coal Seam Gas Royalty Trust	Dallas	149	17
11	Healthcare America, Inc.	Austin	148	150
12	Security Capital Pacific Trust	El Paso	137	186
13	Falcon Drilling Company, Inc.	Houston	135	138
14	WRT Energy Corporation	The Woodlands	134	11
15	STB Systems, Inc.	Richardson	129	90
16	TGC Industries, Inc.	Plano	129	23
17	Equity Corporation International	Lufkin	121	49
18	American Realty Trust, Inc.	Dallas	118	21
19	Panhandle Eastern Corporation	Houston	116	4,585
20	Tivoli Systems Inc.	Austin	112	27
21	NRP Inc.	Dallas	109	38
22	MaxServ Inc.	Austin	109	16
23	Search Capital Group Inc.	Dallas	107	14
24	D.R. Horton, Inc.	Arlington	107	393
25	Canmax Inc.	Irving	106	10
26	U.S. Physical Therapy, Inc.	Houston	105	17
27	NeoStar Retail Group, Inc.	Dallas	104	504
28	Teletouch Communications, Inc.	Tyler	100	7
29	HarCor Energy, Inc.	Houston	97	13
30	Cyrix Corporation	Richardson	97	246
31	TSX Corporation	El Paso	92	72
32	EqualNet Holding Corp.	Houston	92	68
33	CellStar Corporation	Carrollton	88	518
34	USA Waste Services, Inc.	Dallas	88	176
35	Arch Petroleum Inc.	Fort Worth	88	83
36	ProNet Inc.	Plano	86	40
37	Enterra Corporation	Houston	83	302
38	Landry's Seafood Restaurants, Inc.	Houston	83	63
39	Lomak Petroleum, Inc.	Fort Worth	82	35
40	Noble Drilling Corporation	Houston	81	352
41	Bellwether Exploration Company	Houston	80	19
42	Coda Energy, Inc.	Dallas	79	72
43	South West Property Trust Inc.	Dallas	78	59
44	Medical Innovations, Inc.	Houston	76	59
45	Smith Environmental Technologies Corporation	Dallas	76	105
46	PC Service Source, Inc.	Carrollton	76	42
47	CableMaxx, Inc.	Austin	75	14
48	VTEL Corporation	Austin	72	54
49	Tracor, Inc.	Austin	70	694
50	Seitel, Inc.	Houston	70	74

Note: To be included on this list, companies must have sales greater than $5 million. These rates may have resulted from acquisitions or internal growth.

The 50 Fastest-Growing Employers in Texas

Rank	Company	City	Annual % Change	Employees
1	Smith Environmental Technologies Corporation	Dallas	481	1,260
2	MedicalControl, Inc.	Dallas	234	244
3	Merit Studios, Inc.	Dallas	206	55
4	PC Service Source, Inc.	Carrollton	189	260
5	Enterra Corporation	Houston	180	3,500
6	Seitel, Inc.	Houston	165	90
7	Heartland Wireless Communications, Inc.	Richardson	164	370
8	Physician Reliance Network, Inc.	Dallas	158	394
9	WRT Energy Corporation	The Woodlands	140	60
10	Bristol Hotel Company	Dallas	135	4,000
11	The UniMark Group, Inc.	Argyle	130	1,347
12	Smith International, Inc.	Houston	128	4,100
13	Randall's Food Markets, Inc.	Houston	119	21,000
14	Input/Output, Inc.	Stafford	114	449
15	Coda Energy, Inc.	Dallas	108	150
16	NeoStar Retail Group, Inc.	Dallas	108	6,150
17	SA Holdings, Inc.	Richardson	107	58
18	Kitty Hawk, Inc.	Dallas	106	204
19	DocuCon, Incorporated	San Antonio	97	375
20	CableMaxx, Inc.	Austin	95	189
21	King Ranch, Inc.	The Woodlands	94	700
22	Sun Coast Resources Inc.	Houston	94	66
23	Energy BioSystems Corporation	The Woodlands	91	61
24	Landry's Seafood Restaurants, Inc.	Houston	89	2,500
25	ProNet Inc.	Plano	89	321
26	Texas Biotechnology Corporation	Houston	87	97
27	Lomak Petroleum, Inc.	Fort Worth	85	220
28	USA Waste Services, Inc.	Dallas	85	1,200
29	Search Capital Group Inc.	Dallas	84	118
30	Columbus Realty Trust	Dallas	80	180
31	U.S. Delivery Systems, Inc.	Houston	79	3,732
32	CompUSA Inc.	Dallas	78	7,819
33	Celebrity, Inc.	Tyler	77	489
34	CellStar Corporation	Carrollton	77	1,250
35	Palm Harbor Homes, Inc.	Dallas	70	2,887
36	Drypers Corporation	Houston	69	762
37	Polyphase Corporation	Dallas	67	179
38	Citizens, Inc.	Austin	65	71
39	Foxworth-Galbraith Lumber Company	Dallas	64	1,800
40	Hernandez Engineering Inc.	Houston	63	564
41	The Leather Factory, Inc.	Fort Worth	63	325
42	RailTex, Inc.	San Antonio	62	652
43	Cash America International, Inc.	Fort Worth	62	2,475
44	Pratt Hotel Corporation	Dallas	61	5,150
45	Taco Cabana, Inc.	San Antonio	60	4,650
46	FoxMeyer Health Corporation	Carrollton	60	4,804
47	Cameron Ashley Inc.	Dallas	59	1,151
48	RF Monolithics, Inc.	Dallas	58	377
49	Golf Enterprises, Inc.	Dallas	58	1,735
50	Stevens International, Inc.	Fort Worth	56	820

Note: To be included on this list, companies must have 50 or more employees. These rates may have resulted from acquisitions or internal growth.

The 50 Largest Job Creators in Texas

Rank	Company	City	Jobs Added	Employees
1	Randall's Food Markets, Inc.	Houston	11,400	21,000
2	J. C. Penney Company, Inc.	Plano	9,000	202,000
3	Brinker International, Inc.	Dallas	9,000	38,000
4	Heritage Media Corporation	Dallas	8,200	24,500
5	Club Corporation International	Dallas	6,200	19,200
6	Service Corporation International	Houston	6,040	18,756
7	Browning-Ferris Industries, Inc.	Houston	5,400	37,000
8	H. E. Butt Grocery Company	San Antonio	5,228	25,000
9	Administaff Inc.	Kingwood	4,000	16,000
10	Compaq Computer Corporation	Houston	3,831	14,372
11	Tandy Corporation	Fort Worth	3,800	45,800
12	CompUSA Inc.	Dallas	3,417	7,819
13	Dresser Industries, Inc.	Dallas	3,274	29,200
14	NeoStar Retail Group, Inc.	Dallas	3,197	6,150
15	Lennox International Inc.	Richardson	3,000	11,000
16	Smith International, Inc.	Houston	2,300	4,100
17	Bristol Hotel Company	Dallas	2,300	4,000
18	Enterra Corporation	Houston	2,250	3,500
19	SYSCO Corporation	Houston	2,000	26,200
20	H. B. Zachry Company	San Antonio	2,000	10,000
21	Pratt Hotel Corporation	Dallas	1,950	5,150
22	FoxMeyer Health Corporation	Carrollton	1,804	4,804
23	Trinity Industries, Inc.	Dallas	1,800	16,500
24	Taco Cabana, Inc.	San Antonio	1,750	4,650
25	U.S. Delivery Systems, Inc.	Houston	1,647	3,732
26	Southwest Airlines Co.	Dallas	1,643	16,818
27	Hollywood Casino Corporation	Dallas	1,575	6,275
28	ShowBiz Pizza Time, Inc.	Irving	1,500	13,500
29	Stewart & Stevenson Services, Inc.	Houston	1,450	4,300
30	INDRESCO Inc.	Dallas	1,405	4,508
31	American General Corporation	Houston	1,400	12,900
32	DSC Communications Corporation	Plano	1,373	5,414
33	Palm Harbor Homes, Inc.	Dallas	1,187	2,887
34	Landry's Seafood Restaurants, Inc.	Houston	1,177	2,500
35	Whole Foods Market, Inc.	Austin	1,150	5,300
36	Pillowtex Corporation	Dallas	1,134	3,770
37	Healthcare America, Inc.	Austin	1,122	3,371
38	Tandycrafts, Inc.	Fort Worth	1,100	3,700
39	Smith Environmental Technologies Corporation	Dallas	1,043	1,260
40	Wyndham Hotel Company Ltd.	Dallas	1,000	7,000
41	Cash America International, Inc.	Fort Worth	945	2,475
42	Rowan Companies, Inc.	Houston	924	3,484
43	The University of Texas System	Austin	912	68,996
44	Pride Petroleum Services, Inc.	Houston	850	3,850
45	Paging Network, Inc.	Plano	847	3,997
46	DF&R Restaurants, Inc.	Bedford	808	3,223
47	Tracor, Inc.	Austin	800	9,700
48	First USA, Inc.	Dallas	800	2,600
49	The UniMark Group, Inc.	Argyle	762	1,347
50	Farah Incorporated	El Paso	700	6,000
50	National Convenience Stores Incorporated	Houston	700	5,300
50	Hastings Books, Music & Video, Inc.	Amarillo	700	3,500
50	Foxworth-Galbraith Lumber Company	Dallas	700	1,800

Note: To be included on this list, companies must have 50 or more employees. These rates may have resulted from acquisitions or internal growth.

The Texas 500: Largest Companies by Sales
in *Hoover's Guide to the Top Texas Companies*

Rank	Company	Sales ($ mil.)
1	Exxon Corporation	113,904
2	Shell Oil Company	21,581
3	J. C. Penney Company, Inc.	20,380
4	AMR Corporation	16,137
5	Caltex Petroleum Corporation	14,751
6	Tenneco Inc.	12,174
7	SYSCO Corporation	12,118
8	SBC Communications Inc.	11,619
9	Compaq Computer Corporation	10,866
10	Texas Instruments Incorporated	10,315
11	The Coastal Corporation	10,215
12	EDS	10,052
13	Enron Corp.	8,984
14	Kimberly-Clark Corporation	7,364
15	Army & Air Force Exchange Service	7,100
16	The Southland Corporation	6,760
17	USAA	6,181
18	Star Enterprise	6,086
19	EOTT Energy Partners, L.P.	5,921
20	Halliburton Company	5,741
21	Continental Airlines, Inc.	5,670
22	Texas Utilities Company	5,664
23	Dresser Industries, Inc.	5,331
24	FoxMeyer Health Corporation	5,177
25	Burlington Northern Santa Fe Corporation	4,995
26	Tandy Corporation	4,944
27	H. E. Butt Grocery Company	4,850
28	American General Corporation	4,841
29	Cooper Industries, Inc.	4,588
30	Panhandle Eastern Corporation	4,585
31	Browning-Ferris Industries, Inc.	4,315
32	The University of Texas System	4,030
33	Houston Industries Incorporated	4,002
34	Lyondell Petrochemical Company	3,857
35	Central and South West Corporation	3,623
36	Dell Computer Corporation	3,475
37	FINA, Inc.	3,421
38	Centex Corporation	3,278
39	NGC Corporation	3,238
40	Temple-Inland Inc.	2,938
41	CompUSA Inc.	2,813
42	NorAm Energy Corp.	2,801
43	Associated Milk Producers, Inc.	2,629
44	Diamond Shamrock, Inc.	2,606
45	Southwest Airlines Co.	2,592
46	Pennzoil Company	2,563
47	Baker Hughes Incorporated	2,505
48	Randall's Food Markets, Inc.	2,400
49	Trinity Industries, Inc.	2,315
50	MAXXAM Inc.	2,116
51	Sisters of Charity of the Incarnate Word Health Care System	2,027
52	ENSERCH Corporation	1,857
53	Valero Energy Corporation	1,837
54	Kaiser Aluminum Corporation	1,782
55	Gulf States Toyota, Inc.	1,743
56	Commercial Metals Company	1,666
57	Blue Cross and Blue Shield of Texas Inc.	1,505
58	Grocers Supply Co. Inc.	1,450
59	American National Insurance Co.	1,395
60	Sammons Enterprises, Inc.	1,300
61	The Texas A&M University System	1,287
62	CompuCom Systems, Inc.	1,256
63	Contran Corporation	1,213
64	Stewart & Stevenson Services, Inc.	1,138
65	Service Corporation International	1,117
66	Cooper Cameron Corporation	1,110
67	First USA, Inc.	1,082
68	Oryx Energy Company	1,082
69	Burlington Resources Inc.	1,055
70	Brinker International, Inc.	1,042
71	Zale Corporation	1,036
72	Tejas Gas Corporation	1,032
73	Plains Cotton Cooperative Assn.	1,014
74	DSC Communications Corp.	1,003
75	Hunt Consolidated Inc.	1,000
76	Lennox International Inc.	1,000
77	U.S. Home Corporation	995
78	Michaels Stores, Inc.	995
79	Pilgrim's Pride Corporation	923
80	Memorex Telex N.V.	910
81	NL Industries, Inc.	908
82	Mitchell Energy & Development Corp.	895
83	National Convenience Stores	881
84	Tesoro Petroleum Corporation	877
85	Baylor Health Care System	875
86	AmeriServ Food Co.	875
87	El Paso Natural Gas Company	870
88	Aviall Inc.	863
89	Mary Kay Cosmetics Inc.	850
90	Tauber Oil Company	846
91	Southwestern Public Service Co.	843
92	Valhi, Inc.	842
93	Texas Industries, Inc.	831
94	Vastar Resources, Inc.	817
95	Brookshire Grocery Company	811
96	Minyard Food Stores Inc.	810
97	Wingate Partners LP	800
98	Lincoln Property Company	790
99	GSC Enterprises, Inc.	789
100	Club Corporation International	773

The Texas 500: Largest Companies by Sales
in *Hoover's Guide to the Top Texas Companies* (continued)

Rank	Company	Sales ($ mil.)	Rank	Company	Sales ($ mil.)
101	Union Texas Petroleum Holdings	770	151	Glazer's Wholesale Drug	520
102	Dr Pepper/Seven-Up Companies	769	152	CellStar Corporation	518
103	H. B. Zachry Company	750	153	Harte-Hanks Communications	514
104	NCH Corporation	735	154	Ben E. Keith Co.	513
105	Destec Energy, Inc.	727	155	Charlie Thomas Auto World	510
106	Pier 1 Imports, Inc.	712	156	Dal-Tile International, Inc.	506
107	Quanex Corporation	704	157	NeoStar Retail Group, Inc.	504
108	Sterling Chemicals, Inc.	701	158	Atmos Energy Corporation	500
109	Aectra Refining & Marketing Inc.	700	159	Living Centers of America, Inc.	499
110	Tracor, Inc.	694	160	Haggar Corporation	491
111	Harris Methodist Health System	681	161	Paging Network, Inc.	490
112	Color Tile Inc.	675	162	Justin Industries, Inc.	483
113	Fiesta Mart Inc.	675	163	Anadarko Petroleum Corporation	483
114	Virginia Indonesia Co.	665	164	Southern Union Company	480
115	Smith International, Inc.	654	165	Parker & Parsley Petroleum Co.	480
116	Brookshire Brothers Incorporated		166	TNP Enterprises, Inc.	478
117	Adams Resources & Energy, Inc.	650	167	Sterling Software, Inc.	473
118	Enterprise Products Company	635	168	Memorial Healthcare System	471
119	A. H. Belo Corporation	630	169	The Methodist Hospital System	470
120	Greyhound Lines, Inc.	628	170	Coca-Cola Bottling Group-Southwest	470
		616			
121	Western National Corporation	616	171	Hollywood Casino Corporation	464
122	Holly Corporation	615	172	Williamson-Dickie Manufacturing	450
123	Bank United of Texas FSB	614	173	Howell Corporation	449
124	Austin Industries Inc.	613	174	INDRESCO Inc.	441
125	Capstead Mortgage Corporation	604	175	Rowan Companies, Inc.	438
126	Hines Interests L.P.	600	176	BJ Services Company	435
127	Camco International Inc.	590	177	Kirby Corporation	433
128	Pride Companies, L.P.	590	178	PM Realty Group	430
129	County Seat Stores Inc.	588	179	Riviana Foods Inc.	427
130	Imperial Holly Corporation	587	180	Goodman Manufacturing Corp.	425
131	Enron Oil & Gas Co.	572	181	Nabors Industries, Inc.	423
132	Administaff Inc.	564	182	University of Houston	414
133	E-Z Serve Corporation	563	183	Triangle Pacific Corp.	410
134	National-Oilwell	562	184	Seagull Energy Corporation	408
135	Southdown, Inc.	562	185	Eljer Industries, Inc.	406
136	Redman Industries, Inc.	558	186	Whole Foods Market, Inc.	402
137	Specialty Retailers Inc.	557	187	Chief Auto Parts Incorporated	400
138	Apache Corporation	546	188	McCoy Corporation	400
139	Rexene Corporation	538	189	Petro Inc.	400
140	El Paso Electric Company	537	190	Wyndham Hotel Company Ltd.	400
141	Keystone International, Inc.	535	191	Southern Foods Groups Inc.	395
142	Home Interiors & Gifts, Inc.	534	192	D.R. Horton, Inc.	393
143	Chaparral Steel Company	532	193	Santa Fe Energy Resources, Inc.	391
144	Dr Pepper Bottling Company of Texas	532	194	Luby's Cafeterias, Inc.	391
145	Affiliated Foods Incorporated	530	195	P and P Equity Company Ltd.	390
146	Southwestern Life Corporation	530	196	Aramco Services Co.	380
147	United Insurance Companies, Inc.	529	197	Texas Olefins Co.	375
148	East Texas Distributing Inc.	525	198	American Rice, Inc.	373
149	Overhead Door Corporation	524	199	Weatherford International Inc.	372
150	APS Holding Corporation	524	200	Curtis C. Gunn, Inc.	365

The Texas 500: Largest Companies by Sales
in *Hoover's Guide to the Top Texas Companies* (continued)

Rank	Company	Sales ($ mil.)	Rank	Company	Sales ($ mil.)
201	Keystone Consolidated Industries	365	251	AMRE, Inc.	286
202	La Quinta Inns, Inc.	362	252	Cactus Feeders Inc.	285
203	Weekley Homes Inc.	360	253	Pro Group Holdings, Inc.	285
204	Global Marine, Inc.	359	254	Cinemark USA Inc.	283
205	Tyler Corporation	358	255	Cullen/Frost Bankers, Inc.	282
206	Lone Star Technologies, Inc.	357	256	TIC United Corporation	275
207	FFP Partners, L.P.	356	257	Baptist Memorial Hospital System	275
208	Darling International Inc.	354	258	Frozen Food Express Industries	275
209	Wainoco Oil Corporation	354	259	Lomas Financial Corporation	271
210	Daisytek International Corporation	353	260	Transport Holdings Inc.	271
211	Associated Materials Incorporated	353	261	Kinetic Concepts, Inc.	270
212	Software Spectrum, Inc.	352	262	Academy Corporation	268
213	Noble Drilling Corporation	352	263	ShowBiz Pizza Time, Inc.	268
214	Pillowtex Corporation	352	264	Snyder Oil Corporation	262
215	Allwaste, Inc.	351	265	Texas Tech University	262
216	Foxworth-Galbraith Lumber Co.	350	266	Cash America International, Inc.	262
217	United Supermarkets Incorporated	350	267	Ensco International, Inc.	262
218	Wilson Industries Incorporated	350	268	Ancira Enterprises Inc.	261
219	BMC Software, Inc.	345	269	Plains Resources Inc.	257
220	Space Industries International Inc.	340	270	Tandycrafts, Inc.	257
221	TransTexas Gas Corporation	336	271	Kent Electronics Corporation	254
222	Palm Harbor Homes, Inc.	331	272	E.R. Fant, Inc.	252
223	Crinco Investments Inc.	330	273	Darr Equipment Company	250
224	Harris County Hospital District	330	274	King Ranch, Inc.	250
225	Aquila Gas Pipeline Corporation	329	275	Quintana Petroleum Corporation	250
226	The Continuum Company, Inc.	324	276	Rayco Ltd.	250
227	Presbyterian Healthcare System	321	277	Energy Ventures, Inc.	249
228	Owen Healthcare, Inc.	320	278	Cyrix Corporation	246
229	Crown Sterling Suites	320	279	Sonat Offshore Drilling Inc.	243
230	Gillman Companies	320	280	Farah Incorporated	243
231	Integrated Floor Sources Inc.	320	281	Sterling Electronics Corporation	242
232	Perot Systems Corporation	320	282	The Bombay Company, Inc.	242
233	Heritage Media Corporation	318	283	Zapata Corporation	241
234	The Men's Wearhouse, Inc.	317	284	Whataburger Systems Inc.	240
235	National Western Life Insurance	317	285	Oceaneering International, Inc.	240
236	Affiliated Computer Services, Inc.	313	286	Cabot Oil & Gas Corporation	237
237	Oshman's Sporting Goods, Inc.	311	287	HCB Contractors	236
238	Diamond Offshore Drilling	308	288	Hi-Lo Automotive, Inc.	235
239	Enterra Corporation	302	289	Pool Energy Services Co.	234
240	Stewart Information Services Corp.	302	290	Mrs. Baird's Bakeries Inc.	230
241	American General Hospitality Inc.	300	291	Southwest Research Institute Inc.	230
242	Dallas Auto Auction Inc.	300	292	Battle Mountain Gold Company	230
243	E Z Mart Stores Incorporated	300	293	MESA Inc.	229
244	Vanguard Energy Corporation	300	294	Fulbright & Jaworski L.L.P.	226
245	Weiner's Stores, Inc.	300	295	Furr's/Bishop's, Incorporated	225
246	BancTec, Inc.	298	296	TRISM, Inc.	225
247	Cameron Ashley Inc.	296	297	Stanley Stores Inc.	225
248	Pratt Hotel Corporation	295	298	Recognition International Inc.	219
249	Tejas Power Corporation	295	299	Alan Young Buick-GMC Truck, Inc.	218
250	MorningStar Group, Inc.	292	300	Lufkin Industries, Inc.	217

Rank	Company	Sales ($ mil.)
301	Brazos Electric Power Cooperative Inc.	217
302	Hastings Books, Music & Video, Inc.	217
303	Santa Rosa Health Care Corp.	215
304	Northern Border Partners, L.P.	212
305	Vinson & Elkins L.L.P.	211
306	Richards Group Inc.	210
307	Rip Griffin Truck/Travel Centers	210
308	Kaneb Services, Inc.	209
309	Daniel Industries, Inc.	204
310	Vallen Corporation	203
311	50-OFF Stores, Inc.	202
312	East Texas Medical Center Regional Healthcare Sysem	201
313	Tri-State Wholesale Associated Grocers Inc.	201
314	Blue Bell Creameries L.P.	200
315	Dunlap Co.	200
316	Dupey Management Corp.	200
317	Gerland's Food Fair Inc.	200
318	JaGee Corp	200
319	Mundy Cos.	200
320	New Process Steel Corp.	200
321	Sun Coast Resources Inc.	200
322	Tarrant Distributors Inc.	200
323	W. O. Bankston Enterprises Inc.	200
324	University of North Texas	199
325	Unimar Company	198
326	Tech-Sym Corporation	198
327	Teppco Partners, L.P.	197
328	Centex Construction Products, Inc.	194
329	Nu-Kote Holding, Inc.	194
330	RSR Corporation	193
331	Tuboscope Vetco International	192
332	MAXXIM Medical, Inc.	191
333	Tuesday Morning Corporation	190
334	Martin Gas Corporation	190
335	Southwest Texas State University	190
336	Suiza Foods Corporation	189
337	American Homestar Corporation	188
338	Security Capital Pacific Trust	186
339	Frank Parra Autoplex	186
340	Pride Petroleum Services, Inc.	182
341	International Bancshares Corp.	182
342	U.S. Long Distance Corporation	182
343	Dallas Semiconductor Corporation	181
344	Serv-Tech, Inc.	181
345	Pioneer Chlor Alkali Investments	180
346	Southern Methodist University	178
347	USA Waste Services, Inc.	176
348	Enserch Exploration, Inc.	175
349	Baker & Botts L.L.P.	175
350	Bass Enterprises Production Co.	175

Rank	Company	Sales ($ mil.)
351	Friona Industries LP	175
352	Mustang Tractor and Equipment Co.	175
353	Southwest Toyota, Inc.	175
354	Trammell Crow Company	175
355	TTI Inc.	175
356	Drypers Corporation	174
357	Pogo Producing Company	174
358	Clear Channel Communications	173
359	Supertravel	173
360	Datapoint Corporation	173
361	Sanifill, Inc.	173
362	Landmark Graphics Corporation	171
363	Pearce Industries Inc.	170
364	Reading & Bates Corporation	169
365	Chemical Lime Company	168
366	EZCORP, Inc.	168
367	NCI Building Systems, Inc.	168
368	Rice University	168
369	TCA Cable TV, Inc.	162
370	Fossil, Inc.	162
371	Express One International, Inc.	161
372	Allright Corporation	160
373	Elcor Corporation	159
374	Life Insurance Company of the Southwest	159
375	AMRESCO, Inc.	157
376	U.S. Delivery Systems, Inc.	156
377	Champion Healthcare Corporation	154
378	Hat Brands Inc.	154
379	Powell Industries, Inc.	152
380	Greiner Engineering, Inc.	152
381	Fish Engineering & Construction Partners Ltd.	150
382	Friendly Chevrolet	150
383	Lawrence Marshall Chevrolet-Olds	150
384	MMI Products Inc.	150
385	Plantation Foods Inc.	150
386	Rice Food Markets Inc.	150
387	UETA Inc.	150
388	Walsh-Lumpkin Drug Co.	150
389	Healthcare America, Inc.	150
390	Baylor University	149
391	Business Records Corporation Holding Company	144
392	Convex Computer Corporation	144
393	SpectraVision, Inc.	144
394	Ennis Business Forms, Inc.	140
395	Solo Serve Corporation	139
396	Sunbelt Nursery Group, Inc.	139
397	Falcon Drilling Company, Inc.	138
398	Helen of Troy Limited	138
399	Coastal Bancorp, Inc.	138
400	Input/Output, Inc.	135

The Texas 500: Largest Companies by Sales
in *Hoover's Guide to the Top Texas Companies* (continued)

Rank	Company	Sales ($ mil.)
401	Anderson Grain Corporation	134
402	Gundle SLT Environmental, Inc.	133
403	Stevens Transport Inc.	131
404	The C.D. Hartnett Company	130
405	L&H Packing Company Inc.	130
406	U.S. Contractors Inc.	130
407	U.S. Gas Transportation, Inc.	130
408	Strafco, Inc.	128
409	Pedernales Electric Cooperative	128
410	Victoria Bankshares, Inc.	128
411	Taco Cabana, Inc.	127
412	Block Distributing Company Inc.	127
413	National Instruments Corporation	127
414	Evergreen Media Corporation	126
415	Akin, Gump, Strauss, Hauer & Feld	125
416	Brenham Wholesale Grocery Co.	125
417	Hollywood Marine Inc.	125
418	Igloo Holdings Inc.	125
419	R Corporation	125
420	Reliable Chevrolet Inc.	125
421	Sunbelt Corporation	125
422	Warren Electric Co.	125
423	Encore Wire Corporation	123
424	Tecnol Medical Products, Inc.	121
425	Weingarten Realty Investors	121
426	Triton Energy Corporation	120
427	CompuAdd Computer Corporation	120
428	Locke Purnell Rain Harrell	120
429	Thompson and Knight PC	120
430	Alamo Group, Inc.	120
431	Nuevo Energy Company	119
432	Texas Christian University	119
433	Celebrity, Inc.	119
434	EmCare Holdings Inc.	118
435	Digicon, Inc.	118
436	Old America Stores, Inc.	118
437	Fresh America Corp.	116
438	Park Place Motor Cars	115
439	Intercontinental Life Corp.	115
440	Lamar University	115
441	Southwest Securities Group, Inc.	114
442	CJC Holdings Inc.	110
443	Fojtasek Companies Inc.	110
444	Hydril Co.	110
445	K.S.A. Industries Inc.	110
446	Linbeck Construction Corporation	110
447	Maverick Markets Inc.	110
448	Pay 'N Save Inc.	110
449	Voluntary Hospitals of America Inc.	110
450	Wholesale Electric Supply Company of Houston, Inc.	110

Rank	Company	Sales ($ mil.)
451	The York Group Inc.	110
452	Evans Systems, Inc.	110
453	PageMart, Inc.	109
454	Computer Language Research, Inc.	109
455	Kitty Hawk, Inc.	108
456	National Realty, L.P.	108
457	The Hallwood Group Incorporated	107
458	Southwestern Irrigated Cotton Growers Association	107
459	Stevens International, Inc.	107
460	Westbridge Capital Corp.	107
461	Cornerstone Natural Gas, Inc.	106
462	Smith Environmental Technologies	105
463	Dual Drilling Company	104
464	Stephen F. Austin State University	104
465	IMCO Recycling Inc.	101
466	Astraea Aviation Services, Inc.	100
467	AZTX Cattle Co.	100
468	Barrett-Crofoot, LLP	100
469	Bracewell and Patterson L.L.P.	100
470	Davis Food City Inc.	100
471	Garden Ridge Corporation	100
472	Gold Line Refining Ltd.	100
473	Houston McLane Company, Inc.	100
474	Hunt Building Corporation	100
475	Independent Grocers Inc.	100
476	Jackson and Walker LLP	100
477	Merichem Co.	100
478	Periodical Management Group Inc.	100
479	Tetco Inc.	100
480	United Meridian Corporation	99
481	Benchmark Electronics, Inc.	98
482	Dallas Cowboys Football Club, Ltd.	98
483	Friedman Industries, Incorporated	98
484	El Chico Restaurants, Inc.	98
485	Titan Holdings, Inc.	98
486	Cross Timbers Oil Company	96
487	U.S. Intec, Inc.	96
488	GAINSCO, Inc.	94
489	Hogan Systems, Inc.	93
490	DF&R Restaurants, Inc.	92
491	Paragon Group, Inc.	92
492	Kinsel Motors Inc.	90
493	Wyatt Cafeterias Inc.	90
494	STB Systems, Inc.	90
495	Westcott Communications, Inc.	90
496	Lucky Lady Oil Company	89
497	Sport Supply Group, Inc.	89
498	TETRA Technologies, Inc.	89
499	American Eagle Group, Inc.	88
500	Texas Southern University	87

The Texas 500: Largest Companies by Employees
in *Hoover's Guide to the Top Texas Companies*

Rank	Company	Employees	Rank	Company	Employees
1	J. C. Penney Company, Inc.	202,000	51	Luby's Cafeterias, Inc.	10,100
2	AMR Corporation	109,800	52	Texas Tech University	10,066
3	Exxon Corporation	86,000	53	H. B. Zachry Company	10,000
4	Electronic Data Systems	70,000	54	Kaiser Aluminum Corporation	9,744
5	The University of Texas System	68,996	55	Tracor, Inc.	9,700
6	Army & Air Force Exchange Service	60,000	56	Zale Corporation	9,500
7	SBC Communications Inc.	58,750	57	Pier 1 Imports, Inc.	8,671
8	Halliburton Company	57,200	58	Whataburger Systems Inc.	8,500
9	Texas Instruments Incorporated	56,333	59	Central and South West Corporation	8,055
10	Tenneco Inc.	55,000	60	Brookshire Grocery Company	8,000
11	Tandy Corporation	45,800	61	Caltex Petroleum Corporation	8,000
12	Kimberly-Clark Corporation	42,707	62	Cooper Cameron Corporation	8,000
13	Cooper Industries, Inc.	40,800	63	Specialty Retailers Inc.	8,000
14	Brinker International, Inc.	38,000	64	CompUSA Inc.	7,819
15	Continental Airlines, Inc.	37,800	65	County Seat Stores Inc.	7,600
16	Browning-Ferris Industries, Inc.	37,000	66	Furr's/Bishop's, Incorporated	7,300
17	Burlington Northern Santa Fe	30,711	67	University of Houston	7,197
18	The Southland Corporation	30,417	68	Baylor Health Care System	7,000
19	Dresser Industries, Inc.	29,200	69	Wyndham Hotel Company Ltd.	7,000
20	SYSCO Corporation	26,200	70	Enron Corp.	6,978
21	H. E. Butt Grocery Company	25,000	71	NorAm Energy Corp.	6,840
22	Heritage Media Corporation	24,500	72	The Methodist Hospital System	6,700
23	Shell Oil Company	21,496	73	Fiesta Mart Inc.	6,500
24	Randall's Food Markets, Inc.	21,000	74	Minyard Food Stores Inc.	6,500
25	Club Corporation International	19,200	75	Memorial Healthcare System	6,428
26	Sisters of Charity of the Incarnate Word Health Care System	19,000	76	Dell Computer Corporation	6,400
27	The Texas A&M University System	19,000	77	Diamond Shamrock, Inc.	6,400
28	Service Corporation International	18,756	78	Haggar Corporation	6,400
29	Living Centers of America, Inc.	17,800	79	Centex Corporation	6,395
30	Michaels Stores, Inc.	17,440	80	Dal-Tile International, Inc.	6,300
31	Southwest Airlines Co.	16,818	81	Wingate Partners LP	6,300
32	Trinity Industries, Inc.	16,500	82	Hollywood Casino Corporation	6,275
33	The Coastal Corporation	16,300	83	Harte-Hanks Communications	6,225
34	Administaff Inc.	16,000	84	NeoStar Retail Group, Inc.	6,150
35	USAA	15,233	85	Crown Sterling Suites	6,000
36	Temple-Inland Inc.	15,000	86	Farah Incorporated	6,000
37	Baker Hughes Incorporated	14,700	87	Williamson-Dickie Manufacturing	6,000
38	Contran Corporation	14,500	88	La Quinta Inns, Inc.	5,800
39	Compaq Computer Corporation	14,372	89	American General Hospitality Inc.	5,600
40	MAXXAM Inc.	13,860	90	Baptist Memorial Hospital System	5,500
41	ShowBiz Pizza Time, Inc.	13,500	91	Chief Auto Parts Incorporated	5,500
42	American General Corporation	12,900	92	Cinemark USA Inc.	5,500
43	Valhi, Inc.	11,500	93	Panhandle Eastern Corporation	5,500
44	Houston Industries Incorporated	11,498	94	University of North Texas	5,500
45	Lennox International Inc.	11,000	95	DSC Communications Corp.	5,414
46	Texas Utilities Company	10,798	96	National Convenience Stores Inc.	5,300
47	NCH Corporation	10,569	97	Whole Foods Market, Inc.	5,300
48	Pennzoil Company	10,501	98	Pratt Hotel Corporation	5,150
49	Pilgrim's Pride Corporation	10,300	99	Justin Industries, Inc.	5,007
50	Greyhound Lines, Inc.	10,100	100	Austin Industries Inc.	5,000

The Texas 500: Largest Companies by Employees
in *Hoover's Guide to the Top Texas Companies* (continued)

Rank	Company	Employees	Rank	Company	Employees
101	Brookshire Brothers Incorporated	5,000	151	Healthcare America, Inc.	3,371
102	Harris County Hospital District	5,000	152	Oshman's Sporting Goods, Inc.	3,300
103	Harris Methodist Health System	5,000	153	Sammons Enterprises, Inc.	3,300
104	Presbyterian Healthcare System	5,000	154	Santa Rosa Health Care Corp.	3,300
105	Nabors Industries, Inc.	4,833	155	Hi-Lo Automotive, Inc.	3,246
106	FoxMeyer Health Corporation	4,804	156	DF&R Restaurants, Inc.	3,223
107	Taco Cabana, Inc.	4,650	157	The Men's Wearhouse, Inc.	3,190
108	INDRESCO Inc.	4,508	158	Weatherford International	
109	Associated Milk Producers, Inc.	4,500		Incorporated	3,158
110	Blue Cross and Blue Shield of		159	NL Industries, Inc.	3,100
	Texas Inc.	4,500	160	Nu-Kote Holding, Inc.	3,100
111	Memorex Telex N.V.	4,500	161	Allright Corporation	3,000
112	Mundy Cos.	4,500	162	The Continuum Company, Inc.	3,000
113	Pool Energy Services Co.	4,449	163	Crinco Investments Inc.	3,000
114	Commercial Metals Company	4,314	164	Mrs. Baird's Bakeries Inc.	3,000
115	Stewart & Stevenson Services, Inc.	4,300	165	National-Oilwell	3,000
116	ENSERCH Corporation	4,282	166	Owen Healthcare, Inc.	3,000
117	Camco International Inc.	4,264	167	PM Realty Group	3,000
118	Overhead Door Corporation	4,250	168	Sterling Software, Inc.	3,000
119	APS Holding Corporation	4,200	169	E-Z Serve Corporation	2,940
120	Eljer Industries, Inc.	4,200	170	Bank United of Texas FSB	2,936
121	Keystone International, Inc.	4,200	171	Aviall Inc.	2,900
122	Lincoln Property Company	4,200	172	Mitchell Energy & Development	2,900
123	Dupey Management Corp.	4,100	173	U.S. Contractors Inc.	2,900
124	El Chico Restaurants, Inc.	4,100	174	Palm Harbor Homes, Inc.	2,887
125	Smith International, Inc.	4,100	175	Virginia Indonesia Co.	2,850
126	Allwaste, Inc.	4,037	176	Texas Industries, Inc.	2,800
127	The Bombay Company, Inc.	4,000	177	BJ Services Company	2,780
128	Bristol Hotel Company	4,000	178	FINA, Inc.	2,770
129	Star Enterprise	4,000	179	Diamond Offshore Drilling	2,750
130	Triangle Pacific Corp.	4,000	180	50-OFF Stores, Inc.	2,742
131	Tyler Corporation	4,000	181	Noble Drilling Corporation	2,673
132	Weiner's Stores, Inc.	4,000	182	Quanex Corporation	2,652
133	Paging Network, Inc.	3,997	183	Riviana Foods Inc.	2,645
134	Pancho's Mexican Buffet, Inc.	3,967	184	First USA, Inc.	2,600
135	Redman Industries, Inc.	3,967	185	Hunt Consolidated Inc.	2,600
136	Color Tile Inc.	3,900	186	Southdown, Inc.	2,600
137	Pride Petroleum Services, Inc.	3,850	187	Southwest Research Institute Inc.	2,600
138	Southern Methodist University	3,800	188	United Supermarkets Incorporated	2,600
139	Pillowtex Corporation	3,770	189	E Z Mart Stores Incorporated	2,500
140	U.S. Delivery Systems, Inc.	3,732	190	Landry's Seafood Restaurants, Inc.	2,500
141	Tandycrafts, Inc.	3,700	191	Old America Stores, Inc.	2,500
142	Dunlap Co.	3,500	192	Petro Inc.	2,500
143	Enterra Corporation	3,500	193	Space Industries International Inc.	2,500
144	Hastings Books, Music & Video	3,500	194	Trammell Crow Company	2,500
145	Rowan Companies, Inc.	3,484	195	Wyatt Cafeterias Inc.	2,500
146	Stewart Information Services	3,470	196	Cash America International, Inc.	2,475
147	A. H. Belo Corporation	3,469	197	TRISM, Inc.	2,442
148	Stephen F. Austin State University	3,450	198	El Paso Natural Gas Company	2,403
149	Tuesday Morning Corporation	3,450	199	Mary Kay Cosmetics Inc.	2,400
150	AMRE, Inc.	3,385	200	Associated Materials Incorporated	2,310

The Texas 500: Largest Companies by Employees
in *Hoover's Guide to the Top Texas Companies* (continued)

Rank	Company	Employees	Rank	Company	Employees
201	Energy Ventures, Inc.	2,300	251	Blue Bell Creameries L.P.	1,600
202	Ensco International, Inc.	2,300	252	GSC Enterprises, Inc.	1,600
203	Frozen Food Express Industries	2,300	253	McCoy Corporation	1,600
204	Kirby Corporation	2,300	254	Pay 'N Save Inc.	1,600
205	Perot Systems Corporation	2,300	255	Solo Serve Corporation	1,600
206	Southwest Texas State University	2,300	256	Zapata Corporation	1,600
207	BancTec, Inc.	2,274	257	Lone Star Technologies, Inc.	1,592
208	Lyondell Petrochemical Company	2,263	258	EZCORP, Inc.	1,572
209	Texas Southern University	2,212	259	Greiner Engineering, Inc.	1,550
210	Affiliated Computer Services, Inc.	2,200	260	Tetco Inc.	1,550
211	Lomas Financial Corporation	2,146	261	Vinson & Elkins L.L.P.	1,550
212	Kaneb Services, Inc.	2,134	262	Clear Channel Communications	1,549
213	Unimar Company	2,130	263	Darling International Inc.	1,531
214	Hat Brands Inc.	2,100	264	Fulbright & Jaworski L.L.P.	1,527
215	Sonat Offshore Drilling Inc.	2,100	265	Recognition International Inc.	1,525
216	Gerland's Food Fair Inc.	2,003	266	Falcon Drilling Company, Inc.	1,509
217	East Texas Medical Center Regional Healthcare System	2,000	267	Champion Healthcare Corp.	1,500
			268	Gulf States Toyota, Inc.	1,500
218	Hydril Co.	2,000	269	Imperial Holly Corporation	1,500
219	Keystone Consolidated Industries	2,000	270	Reading & Bates Corporation	1,500
220	Plantation Foods Inc.	2,000	271	Daniel Industries, Inc.	1,450
221	Rice University	2,000	272	Ben E. Keith Co.	1,446
222	Southwestern Public Service Co.	2,000	273	Datapoint Corporation	1,444
223	TIC United Corporation	2,000	274	Battle Mountain Gold Company	1,407
224	Tech-Sym Corporation	1,988	275	Dr Pepper Bottling Company of Texas	1,400
225	Tuboscope Vetco International Corporation	1,954	276	Home Interiors & Gifts, Inc.	1,400
226	Lufkin Industries, Inc.	1,950	277	MorningStar Group, Inc.	1,400
227	Oceaneering International, Inc.	1,950	278	OccuSystems Inc.	1,400
228	TransTexas Gas Corporation	1,950	279	PageMart, Inc.	1,400
229	Kinetic Concepts, Inc.	1,938	280	Stanley Stores Inc.	1,400
230	Southern Foods Groups Inc.	1,900	281	Gadzooks, Inc.	1,388
231	Cullen/Frost Bankers, Inc.	1,862	282	Serv-Tech, Inc.	1,383
232	Burlington Resources Inc.	1,850	283	Digicon, Inc.	1,362
233	Southern Union Company	1,811	284	U.S. Home Corporation	1,353
234	CompuCom Systems, Inc.	1,800	285	The UniMark Group, Inc.	1,347
235	Foxworth-Galbraith Lumber Company	1,800	286	Ennis Business Forms, Inc.	1,340
			287	Watermarc Food Management	1,320
236	Gal-Tex Hotel Corporation	1,800	288	Rexene Corporation	1,310
237	Sam Houston State University	1,760	289	Spaghetti Warehouse, Inc.	1,310
238	Suiza Foods Corporation	1,740	290	American National Insurance Company	1,300
239	Golf Enterprises, Inc.	1,735	291	Hines Interests L.P.	1,300
240	Sunbelt Nursery Group, Inc.	1,720	292	Houston McLane Company, Inc.	1,300
241	Atmos Energy Corporation	1,709	293	Pro Group Holdings, Inc.	1,300
242	Academy Corporation	1,700	294	Sanifill, Inc.	1,300
243	Global Marine, Inc.	1,700	295	Texas Christian University	1,300
244	Goodman Manufacturing Corporation	1,700	296	Business Records Corporation Holding Company	1,275
245	Tecnol Medical Products, Inc.	1,700	297	FFP Partners, L.P.	1,274
246	Grant Geophysical, Inc.	1,679	298	Smith Environmental Technologies Corporation	1,260
247	NRP Inc.	1,663			
248	Valero Energy Corporation	1,658	299	AmeriServ Food Co.	1,250
249	MAXXIM Medical, Inc.	1,626	300	CellStar Corporation	1,250
250	Baylor University	1,600			

Rank	Company	Employees
301	Charlie Thomas Auto World	1,250
302	Dave & Buster's, Inc.	1,250
303	Integrated Floor Sources Inc.	1,250
304	Garden Ridge Corporation	1,240
305	Rip Griffin Truck/Travel Centers	1,240
306	Akin, Gump, Strauss, Hauer & Feld	1,235
307	NCI Building Systems, Inc.	1,224
308	American Homestar Corporation	1,212
309	Sterling Chemicals, Inc.	1,210
310	Baker & Botts L.L.P.	1,200
311	CJC Holdings Inc.	1,200
312	Fojtasek Companies Inc.	1,200
313	Grocers Supply Co. Inc.	1,200
314	Igloo Holdings Inc.	1,200
315	Oryx Energy Company	1,200
316	Paragon Group, Inc.	1,200
317	Rice Food Markets Inc.	1,200
318	USA Waste Services, Inc.	1,200
319	BMC Software, Inc.	1,185
320	Apache Corporation	1,182
321	Strafco, Inc.	1,176
322	Lancer Corporation	1,172
323	Amber's Stores, Inc.	1,153
324	The Hallwood Group Inc.	1,152
325	Cameron Ashley Inc.	1,151
326	American Rice, Inc.	1,146
327	El Paso Electric Company	1,100
328	Stevens Transport Inc.	1,100
329	The York Group Inc.	1,100
330	Anadarko Petroleum Corporation	1,085
331	NGC Corporation	1,070
332	Norwood Promotional Products	1,066
333	Lamar University	1,050
334	Marcus Cable Company L.P.	1,035
335	Victoria Bankshares, Inc.	1,034
336	U.S. Long Distance Corporation	1,023
337	Alamo Group, Inc.	1,012
338	The M/A/R/C Group	1,010
339	Parker & Parsley Petroleum	1,004
340	Coca-Cola Bottling Group-Southwest	1,000
341	Darr Equipment Company	1,000
342	Glazer's Wholesale Drug	1,000
343	ICO, Inc.	1,000
344	MMI Products Inc.	1,000
345	Southwestern Life Corporation	1,000
346	Sunbelt Corporation	1,000
347	Union Texas Petroleum Holdings	1,000
348	TCA Cable TV, Inc.	991
349	Centex Construction Products	990
350	Vastar Resources, Inc.	964
351	Kent Electronics Corporation	957
352	Dr Pepper/Seven-Up Companies	952
353	Enterprise Products Company	950
354	Voluntary Hospitals of America	950
355	Wilson Industries Incorporated	950
356	Chaparral Steel Company	943
357	Computer Language Research	937
358	Astraea Aviation Services, Inc.	900
359	DI Industries, Inc.	900
360	Dual Drilling Company	900
361	EOTT Energy Partners, L.P.	900
362	Landmark Graphics Corporation	900
363	TNP Enterprises, Inc.	893
364	National Instruments Corporation	892
365	Angelo State University	870
366	Ace Cash Express, Inc.	867
367	Convex Computer Corporation	857
368	Powell Industries, Inc.	857
369	Tesoro Petroleum Corporation	857
370	Affiliated Foods Incorporated	850
371	International Bancshares Corporation	850
372	TSX Corporation	850
373	SEMATECH, Inc.	841
374	Chemical Lime Company	826
375	Team, Inc.	823
376	Dallas Semiconductor Corp.	821
377	Stevens International, Inc.	820
378	Express One International, Inc.	810
379	Curtis C. Gunn, Inc.	800
380	East Texas Distributing Inc.	800
381	Hart Graphics, Inc.	800
382	Plains Cotton Cooperative Association	800
383	United Insurance Companies, Inc.	770
384	Seagull Energy Corporation	764
385	Drypers Corporation	762
386	Gillman Companies	750
387	Pearce Industries Inc.	750
388	Rayco Ltd.	750
389	Galveston-Houston Company	742
390	Enron Oil & Gas Co.	740
391	IMCO Recycling Inc.	740
392	Fresh America Corp.	732
393	Vallen Corporation	729
394	Hogan Systems, Inc.	721
395	Equity Corporation International	715
396	P and P Equity Company Ltd.	715
397	TTI Inc.	709
398	Consolidated Graphics, Inc.	702
399	AMRESCO, Inc.	700
400	Aramco Services Co.	700

The Texas 500: Largest Companies by Employees
in *Hoover's Guide to the Top Texas Companies* (continued)

Rank	Company	Employees	Rank	Company	Employees
401	Bass Enterprises Production Co.	700	451	Bracewell and Patterson L.L.P.	500
402	The Container Store	700	452	HCB Contractors	500
403	King Ranch, Inc.	700	453	Hornbeck Offshore Services, Inc.	500
404	Mustang Tractor and		454	L&H Packing Company Inc.	500
	Equipment Co.	700	455	Periodical Management Group	500
405	Trinity University	700	456	Thompson and Knight PC	500
406	RSR Corporation	690	457	Vertex Communications	
407	Renters Choice, Inc.	688		Corporation	500
408	STB Systems, Inc.	675	458	Teppco Partners, L.P.	499
409	Marine Drilling Companies, Inc.	670	459	Cabot Oil & Gas Corporation	495
410	Medical Innovations, Inc.	670	460	SEACOR Holdings, Inc.	492
411	Software Spectrum, Inc.	667	461	American Ecology Corporation	491
412	MaxServ Inc.	660	462	Celebrity, Inc.	489
413	RailTex, Inc.	652	463	Sport Supply Group, Inc.	489
414	Atwood Oceanics, Inc.	650	464	BeautiControl Cosmetics, Inc.	477
415	Davis Food City Inc.	650	465	Cliffs Drilling Company	477
416	Hollywood Marine Inc.	650	466	DSI Industries, Inc.	475
417	WellTech Inc.	650	467	D.R. Horton, Inc.	461
418	Santa Fe Energy Resources, Inc.	647	468	Snyder Oil Corporation	460
419	InterVoice, Inc.	634	469	Input/Output, Inc.	449
420	TGC Industries, Inc.	634	470	Bollinger Industries Inc.	440
421	Nuevo Energy Company	630	471	Benchmark Electronics, Inc.	439
422	Sun Coast Industries, Inc.	624	472	Ancira Enterprises Inc.	434
423	Elcor Corporation	623	473	TETRA Technologies, Inc.	433
424	Westcott Communications, Inc.	616	474	Pittencrieff Communications, Inc.	420
425	American Oncology Resources	613	475	Patterson Energy, Inc.	417
426	Physicians Resource Group, Inc.	605	476	Pedernales Electric Cooperative	417
427	Destec Energy, Inc.	603	477	Bettis Corporation	414
428	Andrews & Kurth L.L.P.	600	478	Production Operators Corp	414
429	Martin Gas Corporation	600	479	Walden Residential Properties	411
430	Maverick Markets Inc.	600	480	Evans Systems, Inc.	402
431	Pioneer Chlor Alkali Investments	600	481	Friona Industries LP	400
432	Weekley Homes Inc.	600	482	Jackson and Walker LLP	400
433	W. O. Bankston Enterprises Inc.	600	483	Locke Purnell Rain Harrell	400
434	Evergreen Media Corporation	585	484	Transport Holdings Inc.	400
435	Temtex Industries, Inc.	576	485	Wainoco Oil Corporation	400
436	Electric & Gas Technology, Inc.	573	486	MESA Inc.	399
437	Camden Property Trust	564	487	Physician Reliance Network, Inc.	394
438	Hernandez Engineering Inc.	564	488	Spinnaker Industries, Inc.	389
439	Horizon Mental Health		489	Proler International Corp.	387
	Management, Inc.	556	490	Tejas Gas Corporation	387
440	Fossil, Inc.	555	491	Adams Resources & Energy, Inc.	377
441	Sterling Electronics Corporation	554	492	RF Monolithics, Inc.	377
442	Southwest Securities Group, Inc.	550	493	Reliability Inc.	376
443	Tandy Brands, Inc.	550	494	DocuCon, Incorporated	375
444	Pride Companies, L.P.	545	495	Aztec Manufacturing Co., Inc.	374
445	Fitz and Floyd, Silvestri		496	Enserch Exploration, Inc.	373
	Corporation	535	497	Heartland Wireless	
446	Gundle SLT Environmental, Inc.	534		Communications, Inc.	370
447	Holly Corporation	531	498	Tarrant Distributors Inc.	370
448	Charter Bancshares, Inc.	517	499	Frank Parra Autoplex	365
449	First Financial Bankshares, Inc.	515	500	South West Property Trust Inc.	360
450	Whitehall Corporation	512	500	UETA Inc.	360

Texas Companies on the *FORTUNE* 500 List of Largest U.S. Corporations

Rank	Company	City	1994 Sales ($ mil.)	Employees
3	Exxon	Irving	101,459	86,000
32	J.C. Penney	Plano	21,082	202,000
49	AMR	Fort Worth	16,137	109,800
68	Tenneco	Houston	13,222	55,000
89	SBC Communications	San Antonio	11,619	59,400
99	SYSCO	Houston	10,943	26,000
100	Compaq Computer	Houston	10,866	14,372
106	Texas Instruments	Dallas	10,315	56,333
110	Coastal	Houston	10,013	16,300
129	Enron	Houston	8,984	6,978
160	Kimberly-Clark	Dallas	7,364	42,707
186	Cooper Industries	Houston	6,258	40,800
189	United Services Auto. Assn.	San Antonio	6,181	15,233
205	Halliburton	Dallas	5,741	57,200
208	Continental Airlines	Houston	5,670	37,800
210	Texas Utilities	Dallas	5,664	10,794
214	FoxMeyer Health	Carrollton	5,409	4,804
219	Dresser Industries	Dallas	5,331	29,200
229	Burlington Northern	Fort Worth	4,995	30,711
232	Tandy	Fort Worth	4,944	45,800
238	American General	Houston	4,841	12,900
252	Panhandle Eastern	Houston	4,585	5,500
271	Browning-Ferris Industries	Houston	4,315	37,000
287	Houston Industries	Houston	4,002	11,498
293	Lyondell Petrochemical	Houston	3,857	2,263
315	Central & South West	Dallas	3,623	8,057
330	Dell Computer	Austin	3,475	6,400
353	Centex	Dallas	3,215	6,395
387	Temple-Inland	Diboll	2,938	15,000
401	Transco Energy	Houston	2,816	4,542
404	NorAm Energy	Houston	2,801	6,840
430	Diamond Shamrock	San Antonio	2,621	6,400
434	Southwest Airlines	Dallas	2,592	16,818
439	Pennzoil	Houston	2,563	10,501
448	Baker Hughes	Houston	2,505	14,700
469	American Medical Holding	Dallas	2,382	30,200

Source: *FORTUNE*; May 15, 1995

Texas Companies on the *Business Week* 1000 List of America's Most Valuable Companies

Rank	Company	City	1995 Market Value ($ mil.)
3	Exxon	Irving	79,298
30	SBC Communications	San Antonio	25,354
87	J.C. Penney	Plano	9,733
96	Compaq Computer	Houston	9,005
104	Tenneco	Houston	8,565
108	Kimberly-Clark	Irving	8,325
112	Enron	Houston	8,059
127	Texas Utilities	Dallas	7,396
130	Texas Instruments	Dallas	7,299
147	American General	Houston	6,503
156	Browning-Ferris	Houston	6,113
187	SYSCO	Houston	5,201
196	Burlington Northern	Fort Worth	5,002
205	Burlington Resources	Houston	4,871
210	Houston Industries	Houston	4,719
211	Central & South West	Dallas	4,693
213	AMR	Fort Worth	4,638
215	Cooper Industries	Houston	4,589
230	Halliburton	Dallas	4,250
242	DSC Communications	Plano	4,087
267	Dresser Industries	Dallas	3,800
301	Panhandle Eastern	Houston	3,355
304	Enron Oil & Gas	Houston	3,335
330	Coastal	Houston	3,011
357	Temple-Inland	Diboll	2,738
361	Baker Hughes	Houston	2,697
364	Service Corp. International	Houston	2,668
370	Tandy	Fort Worth	2,607
376	Anadarko Petroleum	Houston	2,580
387	Vastar Resources	Houston	2,516
426	Pennzoil	Houston	2,185
454	First USA	Dallas	2,085
487	Lyondell Petrochemical	Houston	1,920
533	Southland	Dallas	1,704
538	Paging Network	Plano	1,686
539	Union Texas Petroleum	Houston	1,685
552	Dell Computer	Austin	1,622
555	BMC Software	Houston	1,616
576	Apache	Houston	1,536
585	E-Systems	Dallas	1,489
602	Brinker International	Dallas	1,428
628	Trinity Industries	Dallas	1,337
633	American National	Galveston	1,324
701	Southwestern PS	Amarillo	1,192
702	Fina	Dallas	1,198
718	La Quinta Inns	San Antonio	1,145
722	Oryx Energy	Dallas	1,138

Texas Companies on the *Business Week* 1000 List of America's Most Valuable Companies (continued)

Rank	Company	City	1995 Market Value ($ mil.)
728	Belo (A.H.)	Dallas	1,112
730	Triton Energy	Dallas	1,109
743	El Paso Natural Gas	El Paso	1,093
747	Stewart & Stevenson	Houston	1,089
803	Clear Channel	San Antonio	995
822	Weingarten Realty	Houston	956
834	Enserch	Houston	937
848	Valhi	Dallas	920
897	Property Trust	El Paso	845
900	TransTexas Gas	Houston	842
901	Sterling Software	Dallas	841
908	Mitchell Energy	The Woodlands	833
923	Santa Fe Energy	Houston	810
952	Valero Energy	San Antonio	776
958	Battle Mountain Gold	Houston	769
979	Western National	Houston	740
989	Centex	Dallas	727
990	Transco Energy	Houston	726
993	Diamond Shamrock	San Antonio	722
997	Energy Service	Dallas	716

Source: *Business Week*; March 27, 1995; market value calculated as of February 28, 1995

Texas Companies on the *FORTUNE* List of America's 100 Fastest-Growing Companies

Rank	Company	City	Sales Annual Growth (%)
21	Financial Industries	Austin	154
34	USA Waste Services	Dallas	120
56	VTEL	Austin	92
58	EZCORP	Austin	91
61	NetWorth	Irving	86
61	Renters Choice	Dallas	86
63	Drypers	Houston	85
64	Fresh America	Houston	84
64	U.S. Long Distance	San Antonio	84
89	Ultrak	Carrollton	72

Source: *FORTUNE*; April 17, 1995

Texas Companies on the *Forbes* 500 List of Largest Private Companies in the U.S.

Rank	Company	City	Sales ($ mil.)	Employees
20	H-E-B Grocery	San Antonio	4,850	25,000
47	Randall's Food Markets	Houston	2,321	9,600
68	Gulf States Toyota	Houston	1,743*	1,500
85	Grocers Supply Co	Houston	1,450*	1,200
91	Sammons Enterprises	Dallas	1,350*	4,000
99	Lennox International	Dallas	1,290*	8,000
188	ClubCorp	Dallas	843*	13,000
192	AmeriServ Food	Dallas	833	1,150
202	Brookshire Grocery	Tyler	811*	3,200
207	Hunt Consolidated/Hunt Oil	Dallas	800*	2,600
213	HB Zachry	San Antonio	791	8,050
214	Lincoln Property	Dallas	790	4,200
217	Minyard Food Stores	Coppell	780	3,650
224	GSC Enterprises	Sulphur Springs	757	1,365
231	Mary Kay Cosmetics	Dallas	737	2,400
257	Fiesta Mart	Houston	675	6,500
280	Enterprise Products	Houston	630*	982
316	Specialty Retailers	Houston	557	7,500
338	Home Interiors & Gifts	Dallas	526	1,250
340	MediaNews Group	Houston	525*	7,950
347	Ben E Keith	Fort Worth	513	1,350
348	Charlie Thomas Auto World	Houston	513	1,350
357	Austin Industries	Dallas	502	5,000
374	Riviana Foods	Houston	482	2,645
384	Glazer's Wholesale Distributors	Dallas	470*	1,000
409	Dal-Tile International	Dallas	441	3,200
414	Goodman Manufacturing	Houston	437*	1,700
421	Williamson-Dickie Manufacturing	Fort Worth	429	5,500
433	Placid Oil	Dallas	415	600
459	United Supermarkets	Lubbock	400*	2,100
469	Texas Olefins	Houston	386*	375
470	Chief Auto Parts	Dallas	385*	5,200
492	Southern Foods Group	Dallas	360*	1,900

*Estimated

Source: *Forbes*; December 5, 1994

Texas Companies on the *Inc.* 500 List of Fastest-Growing Private Companies

Rank	Company	City	Sales Growth 1989–93 (%)	1993 Sales ($ mil.)
8	Tivoli Systems	Austin	12,545	12.8
9	Duracom Computer Systems	Irving	11,876	15.1
12	Vektron International	Grand Prairie	11,273	11.8
30	Flood Data Services	Austin	5,639	7.0
95	AnTel	Plano	2,259	4.1
130	Max Distribution	Dallas	1,771	2.4
146	Datasys	Dallas	1,680	6.3
176	Topique Associates	Houston	1,406	3.9
193	OccuSystems	Dallas	1,311	47.0
202	Collins/Reisenbichler Architects	Dallas	1,253	2.7
206	HCFS	Dallas	1,220	2.5
212	Nest Entertainment	Irving	1,197	55.1
218	Daydots Label Co.	Fort Worth	1,171	4.5
269	Dominion Capital	Dallas	996	4.3
270	Keys Fitness Products	Dallas	994	15.1
319	Calais Home Corp. of Texas	Houston	829	24.2
322	Blue Whale Moving Co.	Austin	815	1.7
325	Operator Service	Lubbock	804	22.4
330	Saber Software	Dallas	788	13.1
353	ExecuTrain of Texas	Dallas	736	5.9
381	Kitty Hawk Group	DFW Airport	687	65.8
435	Roach Air	Fort Worth	596	4.9
436	SabreData	Austin	595	27.5
453	ProForma Watsonrise Business Systems	Arlington	574	1.9
470	HVJ Associates	Houston	562	1.9

Source: *Inc.*, October 1994

Largest Texas Companies in Austin, Dallas–Ft. Worth, Houston, and San Antonio

Austin	Sales ($ mil.)
The University of Texas System	4,030
Dell Computer Corporation	3,475
Tracor, Inc.	694
Southern Union Company	480
Whole Foods Market, Inc.	402
McCoy Corporation	400
The Continuum Company, Inc.	324
National Western Life Insurance Company	317
Southwest Texas State University	190
EZCORP, Inc.	168
Healthcare America, Inc.	150
Pedernales Electric Cooperative, Inc.	128
National Instruments Corporation	127
CompuAdd Computer Corporation	120
Intercontinental Life Corp.	115
CJC Holdings Inc.	110
Hart Graphics, Inc.	85
Summagraphics Corporation	79
Financial Industries Corporation	69
VTEL Corporation	54
Steck-Vaughn Publishing Corporation	54
Citizens, Inc.	49
Microelectronics & Computer Technology Corporation	40
Embree Construction Group, Inc.	33
Tivoli Systems Inc.	27

Dallas–Ft. Worth	Sales ($ mil.)
Exxon Corporation	113,904
J. C. Penney Company, Inc.	20,380
AMR Corporation	16,137
Texas Instruments Incorporated	10,315
Electronic Data Systems Corporation	10,052
Kimberly-Clark Corporation	7,364
Army & Air Force Exchange Service	7,100
The Southland Corporation	6,760
Halliburton Company	5,741
Texas Utilities Company	5,664
Dresser Industries, Inc.	5,331
FoxMeyer Health Corporation	5,177
Burlington Northern Santa Fe Corp.	4,995
Tandy Corporation	4,944
Central and South West Corporation	3,623
FINA, Inc.	3,421
Centex Corporation	3,278
CompUSA Inc.	2,813
Southwest Airlines Co.	2,592
Trinity Industries, Inc.	2,315

Dallas–Ft. Worth (continued)	Sales ($ mil.)
ENSERCH Corporation	1,857
Commercial Metals Company	1,666
Blue Cross and Blue Shield of Texas Inc.	1,505
Sammons Enterprises, Inc.	1,300
CompuCom Systems, Inc.	1,256
Contran Corporation	1,213
First USA, Inc.	1,082
Oryx Energy Company	1,082
Brinker International, Inc.	1,042
Zale Corporation	1,036
DSC Communications Corporation	1,003
Hunt Consolidated Inc.	1,000
Lennox International Inc.	1,000
Michaels Stores, Inc.	995
Memorex Telex N.V.	910
Baylor Health Care System	875
AmeriServ Food Co.	875
Aviall Inc.	863
Mary Kay Cosmetics Inc.	850
Valhi, Inc.	842
Texas Industries, Inc.	831
Minyard Food Stores Inc.	810
Wingate Partners LP	800
Lincoln Property Company	790
GSC Enterprises, Inc.	789
Club Corporation International	773
Dr Pepper/Seven-Up Companies, Inc.	769
NCH Corporation	735
Pier 1 Imports, Inc.	712
Harris Methodist Health System	681
Color Tile Inc.	675
A. H. Belo Corporation	628
Greyhound Lines, Inc.	616
Holly Corporation	615
Austin Industries Inc.	613
Capstead Mortgage Corporation	604
County Seat Stores Inc.	588
Redman Industries, Inc.	558
Rexene Corporation	538
Home Interiors & Gifts, Inc.	534
Chaparral Steel Company	532
Dr Pepper Bottling Company of Texas	532
Southwestern Life Corporation	530
United Insurance Companies, Inc.	529
Overhead Door Corporation	524
Glazer's Wholesale Drug Company Inc.	520
CellStar Corporation	518
Ben E. Keith Co.	513
Dal-Tile International Inc.	506
NeoStar Retail Group, Inc.	504

Largest Texas Companies in Austin, Dallas–Ft. Worth, Houston, and San Antonio (continued)

Dallas–Ft. Worth (continued)	Sales ($ mil.)
Atmos Energy Corporation	500
Haggar Corporation	491
Paging Network, Inc.	490
Justin Industries, Inc.	483
TNP Enterprises, Inc.	478
Sterling Software, Inc.	473
Coca-Cola Bottling Group-Southwest	470
Hollywood Casino Corporation	464
Williamson-Dickie Manufacturing Co.	450
INDRESCO Inc.	441
Triangle Pacific Corp.	410
Eljer Industries, Inc.	406
Chief Auto Parts Incorporated	400
Wyndham Hotel Company Ltd.	400
Southern Foods Groups Incorporated	395
D.R. Horton, Inc.	393
Keystone Consolidated Industries, Inc.	365
Tyler Corporation	358
Lone Star Technologies, Inc.	357
FFP Partners, L.P.	356
Darling International Inc.	354
Daisytek International Corporation	353
Associated Materials Incorporated	353
Software Spectrum, Inc.	352
Pillowtex Corporation	352
Foxworth-Galbraith Lumber Company	350
Palm Harbor Homes, Inc.	331
Presbyterian Healthcare System	321
Crown Sterling Suites	320
Integrated Floor Sources Inc.	320
Perot Systems Corporation	320
Heritage Media Corporation	318
Affiliated Computer Services, Inc.	313
American General Hospitality Inc.	300
Dallas Auto Auction Inc.	300
BancTec, Inc.	298
Cameron Ashley Inc.	296
Pratt Hotel Corporation	295
MorningStar Group, Inc.	292
AMRE, Inc.	286
Pro Group Holdings, Inc.	285
Cinemark USA Inc.	283
TIC United Corporation	275
Frozen Food Express Industries, Inc.	275
Lomas Financial Corporation	271
Transport Holdings Inc.	271
ShowBiz Pizza Time, Inc.	268
Snyder Oil Corporation	262
Cash America International, Inc.	262
Ensco International, Inc.	262

Dallas–Ft. Worth (continued)	Sales ($ mil.)
Tandycrafts, Inc.	257
Darr Equipment Company	250
Cyrix Corporation	246
The Bombay Company, Inc.	242
HCB Contractors	236

Houston	Sales ($ mil.)
Shell Oil Company	21,581
Tenneco Inc.	12,174
SYSCO Corporation	12,118
Compaq Computer Corporation	10,866
The Coastal Corporation	10,215
Enron Corp.	8,984
Star Enterprise	6,086
EOTT Energy Partners, L.P.	5,921
Continental Airlines, Inc.	5,670
American General Corporation	4,841
Cooper Industries, Inc.	4,588
Panhandle Eastern Corporation	4,585
Browning-Ferris Industries, Inc.	4,315
Houston Industries Incorporated	4,002
Lyondell Petrochemical Company	3,857
NGC Corporation	3,238
NorAm Energy Corp.	2,801
Pennzoil Company	2,563
Baker Hughes Incorporated	2,505
Randall's Food Markets, Inc.	2,400
MAXXAM Inc.	2,116
Sisters of Charity of the Incarnate Word Health Care System	2,027
Kaiser Aluminum Corporation	1,782
Gulf States Toyota, Inc.	1,743
Grocers Supply Co. Inc.	1,450
American National Insurance Company	1,395
Stewart & Stevenson Services, Inc.	1,138
Service Corporation International	1,117
Cooper Cameron Corporation	1,110
Burlington Resources Inc.	1,055
Tejas Gas Corporation	1,032
U.S. Home Corporation	995
NL Industries, Inc.	908
Mitchell Energy & Development Corp.	895
National Convenience Stores Incorporated	881
Tauber Oil Company	846
Vastar Resources, Inc.	817
Union Texas Petroleum Holdings, Inc.	770
Destec Energy, Inc.	727
Quanex Corporation	704
Sterling Chemicals, Inc.	701
Aectra Refining & Marketing Inc.	700
Fiesta Mart Inc.	675
Virginia Indonesia Co.	665

Largest Texas Companies in Austin, Dallas–Ft. Worth, Houston, and San Antonio (continued)

Houston (continued)	Sales ($ mil.)
Smith International, Inc.	654
Adams Resources & Energy, Inc.	635
Enterprise Products Company	630
Western National Corporation	616
Bank United of Texas FSB	614
Hines Interests L.P.	600
Camco International Inc.	590
Imperial Holly Corporation	587
Enron Oil & Gas Co.	572
Administaff Inc.	564
E-Z Serve Corporation	563
National-Oilwell	562
Southdown, Inc.	562
Specialty Retailers Inc.	557
Apache Corporation	546
Keystone International, Inc.	535
East Texas Distributing Inc.	525
APS Holding Corporation	524
Charlie Thomas Auto World	510
Living Centers of America, Inc.	499
Anadarko Petroleum Corporation	483
Memorial Healthcare System	471
The Methodist Hospital System	470
Howell Corporation	449
Rowan Companies, Inc.	438
BJ Services Company	435
Kirby Corporation	433
PM Realty Group	430
Riviana Foods Inc.	427
Goodman Manufacturing Corporation	425
Nabors Industries, Inc.	423
University of Houston	414
Seagull Energy Corporation	408
Santa Fe Energy Resources, Inc.	391
Aramco Services Co.	380
Texas Olefins Co.	375
American Rice, Inc.	373
Weatherford International Incorporated	372
Weekley Homes Inc.	360
Global Marine, Inc.	359
Wainoco Oil Corporation	354
Noble Drilling Corporation	352
Allwaste, Inc.	351
Wilson Industries Incorporated	350
BMC Software, Inc.	345
Space Industries International Inc.	340
TransTexas Gas Corporation	336
Harris County Hospital District	330
Owen Healthcare, Inc.	320
Gillman Companies	320
The Men's Wearhouse, Inc.	317
Oshman's Sporting Goods, Inc.	311
Diamond Offshore Drilling	308
Enterra Corporation	302
Stewart Information Services Corporation	302

Houston (continued)	Sales ($ mil.)
Vanguard Energy Corporation	300
Weiner's Stores, Inc.	300
Tejas Power Corporation	295
Academy Corporation	268
Plains Resources Inc.	257
Kent Electronics Corporation	254
E.R. Fant, Inc.	252
King Ranch, Inc.	250
Quintana Petroleum Corporation	250
Energy Ventures, Inc.	249
Sonat Offshore Drilling Inc.	243
Sterling Electronics Corporation	242
Zapata Corporation	241
Oceaneering International, Inc.	240
Cabot Oil & Gas Corporation	237
Hi-Lo Automotive, Inc.	235
Pool Energy Services Co.	234
Battle Mountain Gold Company	230
Fulbright & Jaworski L.L.P.	226
Stanley Stores Inc.	225
Northern Border Partners, L.P.	212
Vinson & Elkins L.L.P.	211
Daniel Industries, Inc.	204
Vallen Corporation	203
Gerland's Food Fair Inc.	200
Mundy Cos.	200

San Antonio	Sales ($ mil.)
SBC Communications Inc.	11,619
USAA	6,181
H. E. Butt Grocery Company	4,850
Associated Milk Producers, Inc.	2,629
Diamond Shamrock, Inc.	2,606
Valero Energy Corporation	1,837
Tesoro Petroleum Corporation	877
H. B. Zachry Company	750
Harte-Hanks Communications, Inc.	514
Luby's Cafeterias, Inc.	391
Curtis C. Gunn, Inc.	365
La Quinta Inns, Inc.	362
Aquila Gas Pipeline Corporation	329
Cullen/Frost Bankers, Inc.	282
Baptist Memorial Hospital System	275
Kinetic Concepts, Inc.	270
Ancira Enterprises Inc.	261
Rayco Ltd.	250
Southwest Research Institute Inc.	230
Santa Rosa Health Care Corp.	215
50-OFF Stores, Inc.	202
U.S. Long Distance Corp.	182
Clear Channel Communications, Inc.	173
Datapoint Corporation	173
UETA Inc.	150

State of Texas Profile

STATE OF TEXAS

OVERVIEW

The Lone Star State is the 2nd largest in area and population (after Alaska and California, respectively), but Texans have a sense of provincial pride that ranks it first in ALL respects. Famous for endless plains of cattle ranches and oil fields, the state has become as diverse economically as its marshy, wooded, hilly, desert, mountainous, flat landscape has always been. Business services, retail trade, government, and health services now provide most of the employment growth as the state has weaned itself from dependence on the oil and gas industry.

As a result, Texas has become more closely aligned with the national economy. Nevertheless, its geographic location, with Mexico to the south and the Gulf of Mexico to the southeast, allows Texas a distinct strategic advantage: easy access (across the border or via 13 major ports) to burgeoning foreign markets and the fast-growing Sunbelt.

The state's relatively low tax rate (there is no state income tax), competitive labor costs, and pro-business laws make relocation extremely attractive to out-of-state companies. Cultural diversity adds spice to a warm, friendly climate, juxtaposing grand opera, Tejano music dance halls, and county rodeos. Texas ranked first in job creation among the 10 most populous states from 1990 to 1995.

Perhaps the state's biggest challenge is how it will cope with the rapid influx of new residents and their demands on its institutions, infrastructure, and natural resources. More than 123,000 people were expected to move to Texas in 1994 and 1995. Austin, El Paso, Houston, and San Antonio are currently its fastest-growing metropolitan areas.

WHEN

Prehistoric Native Americans lived and hunted in Texas as early as 10,000 years ago. The first Europeans to reach the area were Spaniards, searching for legendary cities rich in gold, in the 1500s. ("Texas," or "Tejas," was the Spanish pronunciation of a Caddo Indian word meaning "friends.") In response to French territorial claims in the 1680s, the Spanish established several missions in East Texas. Primitive roads linked the outposts, which initially served to "civilize" the natives and later became the centers of the first towns.

Mexican independence from Spain (1821) heralded the first wave of English-speaking settlers. Mexico offered generous land deals to anyone who would settle its northern territory. However, in 1835 the Anglo settlers revolted, largely because of the government's ambivalence regarding their rights as Mexican citizens. On March 2, 1836, the new republic won independence after numerous battles, including the infamous siege of the Alamo.

Texas was annexed by treaty to the US in 1845 despite congressional misgivings concerning the area's massive debt and proslavery views. The economic stability of statehood, the protection of the US army, and a liberal land policy lured settlers, many from Europe. By 1860 Texas had over 600,000 citizens, most of whom were subsistence farmers. Cotton became an important cash crop.

Texas sided with the Confederacy during the Civil War (1861–65), providing the only regular route to Europe for Confederate goods — through Mexico. The final battle of the war was fought in South Texas, a month after General Robert E. Lee had surrendered.

In 1866 began the first of the legendary cattle drives up the Chisholm Trail, which led to Kansas and beyond. Meanwhile railroad construction in Texas began in earnest, and by the 1870s a steel ribbon reached south to Dallas and Austin and west from Houston to San Antonio. Cotton compresses, stockyards, and sawmills appeared in the railroad towns, processing growing volumes of agricultural goods bound for the East Coast and the Midwest. The railroads also brought heavy equipment from northern factories, spurring local industries.

In 1901 oil was discovered at Spindletop, near Beaumont. News of the first big gusher spread, and in 2 years oil production in Texas increased tenfold, to about 17 million barrels. In the 1920s manufacturing replaced agriculture as the state's chief industry, and in the 1950s oil production topped one billion barrels a year. Like the rest of the nation, Texas enjoyed an economic boom after WWII.

The 1973 OPEC oil embargo caused oil prices to skyrocket. Although the embargo ended in 1974, prices continued to rise, and Texas's economy, closely tied to oil, was buoyed as well. A collapse in oil prices, ill-considered lending practices by banks, and overbuilding led to a recession in the 1980s.

By the early 1990s the Texas economy turned around, aided by diversification, especially into high-tech industries. Passage of NAFTA greatly enhanced the state's position as an exporter and conduit for the rest of the US.

Official name: State of Texas
Admitted as a state: December 29, 1845
State capital: Austin
Motto: "Friendship"

WHO

Governor: George W. Bush (R)
Lieutenant Governor: Bob Bullock (D)
Speaker of the House: James E. "Pete" Laney (D)
Secretary of State: Antonio O. Garza Jr. (R)
Attorney General: Dan Morales (D)
Comptroller of Public Accounts: John Sharp (D)
Treasurer: Martha Whitehead (D)
Supreme Court Chief Justice: Thomas R. Phillips (R)
Commissioner of Agriculture: Rick Perry (R)
Commissioner of the General Land Office: Garry
  Mauro (D)
Railroad Commissioner: Barry Williamson,
  chairman (R)
US Senators: Phil Gramm (R), Kay Bailey Hutchison (R)

WHERE

Governor's Office: State Capitol, Rm. 2S.1, Austin, TX
  78701
Phone: 512-463-2000
Fax: 512-463-1849

Department of Commerce: 816 Congress Ave., Austin,
  TX 78701
Phone: 512-472-5059

Capitol Complex Visitors Center: (Old Land Office bldg.)
  112 E. 11th St., Austin, TX 78701
Phone: 512-305-8400

Texas is the 2nd largest state in the US (after Alaska),
comprising 266,807 square miles. The state has 254
counties and is larger than the entire northeastern US
— Connecticut, Delaware, Maine, Maryland, Massachusetts, New Hampshire, New Jersey, New York, Pennsylvania, Rhode Island, Vermont, Virginia, and West
Virginia — combined.

Largest Cities	1994 Estimated Population
Houston	1,721,225
Dallas	1,047,215
San Antonio	1,034,498
El Paso	567,900
Austin	530,123
Fort Worth	464,232
Corpus Christi	272,399
Lubbock	194,286
Garland	188,358
Irving	168,298

WHAT

	1994 GSP Distribution	
	$ bil.	% of total
Business & retail services	87.2	19
Wholesale & retail trade	78.0	17
Manufacturing	76.3	16
Finance, insurance & real estate	72.5	15
Transportation, communi- cation & public utilities	52.5	11
Government	52.0	11
Mining (oil & gas)	28.0	6
Construction	16.2	3
Agriculture	8.4	2
Total GSP	**471.1**	**100**

Selected Exports

Agricultural Products	Minerals
Cattle	Cement
Cotton	Clay
Grain sorghum	Stone

Durable Goods	Petroleum Products
Building materials	Natural gas
Clothing	Oil
Electronics	Plastics
Oil field equipment	Refined petrochemicals

HOW MUCH

	9-Year Growth	1985	1986	1987	1988	1989	1990	1991	1992	1993	1994
Population (mil.)	1.4%	16,275	16,563	16,624	16,669	16,807	16,987	17,349	17,656	18,022	18,378
GSP ($ bil.)	4.5%	316	298	305	332	353	382	396	420	443	471
GSP per capita ($)	3.1%	19,420	17,990	18,350	19,920	21,000	22,490	22,830	23,790	24,580	25,630
Personal income per capita ($)	4.4%	13,494	13,489	13,843	14,590	15,702	16,668	17,325	18,333	19,145	19,994
Employment growth (annual % change)	—	2.6	(1.5)	(0.7)	2.5	2.4	2.8	0.9	1.3	2.9	3.5

GSP per capita
1985–94
($)

Texas Statistics

Category	Statistic	Rank Among All States
Population and Housing		
Total persons:		
1993 (July 1)	18,031,000	3
Percent increase, 1990–93	6.2%	11
People per square mile, 1993	68.8	39
65 years old and over, 1993	10.2%	46
Foreign-born, 1990	9.0%	7
Persons 5 years old and over, speaking a language other than English, 1990	25.4%	3
Residing in a metro area, 1992	83.9%	13
Persons per household, 1993	2.75	5
Housing units:		
Built between 1980 and 1990	29.7%	6
With no telephone, 1990	8.6%	9
Vital Statistics and Health		
Infant deaths per 1,000 live births, 1991	7.7	37
Community hospitals, 1992:		
Beds per 100,000 people	331	—
Occupancy rate	56.3%	42
Average cost per patient per day	$933	11
Physicians per 100,000 people, 1992	179	34
People without health insurance, 1992	22.4%	2
Education		
Public elementary and secondary schools:		
Enrollment, percent increase, 1990–93 (est.)	1.5%	—
Teachers' average salaries, 1993	$29,900	34
High school graduates, percent increase, 1990–94 (est.)	0.2%	—
Educational attainment, persons 25 years old and over, 1990:		
High school or higher	72.1%	39
Bachelor's degree	13.9%	17
Advanced degree	6.5%	23
College enrollment, 1992:		
Full-time students	54.4%	—
Minority students	31.4%	4
Crime		
Violent crime rate per 100,000 people, 1992	806	10
Criminal justice expenditures per person, 1991	$237	27
Federal and state prisoners, percent increase, 1991–92	18.4%	1

Texas Statistics (continued)

Category	Statistic	Rank Among All States
Federal Funds and Social Insurance		
Federal funds, 1993:		
Funds for defense	$16.1 billion	3
Grants to state and local governments per person:		
Total	$612	—
Highway trust fund	$59	35
Percent of population receiving, 1992:		
Social Security	13.1%	—
Aid to Families with Dependent Children		
and/or Supplemental Security Income	4.4%	—
Labor Force		
Civilian labor force, 1993:		
Employment/population ratio	64.0%	23
Female participation rate	59.2%	32
Unemployment rate	7.0%	16
Income and Poverty		
Median household income, 1992	$28,282	33
Disposable personal income per capita, 1993	$17,116	27
Persons below poverty level, 1992	17.8%	8
Business		
Business failures, 1993	7,096	2
New business incorporations, 1992	34,011	4
Manufacturing, 1991:		
Value added	$78 billion	4
Value of shipments	$204 billion	2
Retail sales per household, percent		
change, 1991–92	6.9%	29
U.S. exports by state of origin, 1993	$45.3 billion	2
Miscellaneous		
Voting-age population casting votes		
for president, 1992	49.1%	46
Energy expenditures per person, 1991	$2,471	5
State government general expenditure		
per person, 1993	$1,741	50
Motor vehicles:		
State gasoline tax per gallon, 1993	20¢	20
Miles of travel per 1,000 miles of road, 1992	557	24
Deaths per 100 million vehicle miles, 1992	1.9	19
Farm land and buildings percent increase in average		
value per acre, 1992–93	1.1%	36
Hazardous waste sites, 1993	30	14

Source: U.S. Bureau of the Census, *Statistical Abstract of the United States: 1994*

Top Texas Companies

AMERICAN GENERAL CORPORATION

OVERVIEW

Houston-based American General is on the offensive to carry out the ambition of its chairman and CEO, Harold Hook: to double its size by the year 2000. Two recent acquisitions, 40% of Western National Corp. in 1994 and Franklin Life in 1995, helped propel American General into the top 10 among stock insurance companies, but another target, Unitrin, eluded capture.

Both of the acquisitions fit well with American General's core business lines. These include retirement annuities (through a variety of investment products, tax-deferred retirement plans, and retirement counseling services), consumer finance (consumer loans, home equity loans, retail financing, and private-label and bank credit cards), and life insurance (traditional and interest-sensitive policies).

American General has grown rapidly through acquisitions, and it had been in the forefront of the movement toward consolidation in the insurance industry. But rapid growth created problems in controlling and steering the company's many components and in melding their separate cultures.

To create a distinctive culture for the company, Hook (who owns a business management school) has instituted a system of his own, called Main Event Management. This system, which American General will use to assimilate Franklin Life into its organization, consists of centralized control and decentralized operations. American General sets goals, allocates capital, chooses key personnel, and monitors performance, while the subsidiaries receive the autonomy to carry out the programs.

WHEN

In 1925 the Commission of Appeals of Texas ruled that insurers could underwrite more than one line of insurance. One of the first to take advantage of the ruling was Gus Wortham, who formed American General Insurance Company in 1926 to provide both fire and casualty insurance.

In 1939 the company established its first subsidiary, American General Investment Corporation; its first acquisition was Houston-based Seaboard Life Insurance (1945). But American General didn't really take off until Benjamin Woodson joined the company in 1953. Woodson, formerly managing director of the National Association of Life Underwriters, used his contacts to find acquisitions to expand American General's life and health business. These included companies in Nebraska, Oklahoma, and Pennsylvania.

After concentrating on its life and health business through the 1950s, American General turned its attention to property/casualty insurance. In 1964 it doubled its size by acquiring Maryland Casualty Company in a stock swap. The move made American General a major property and casualty insurer with a presence across the US and in Canada.

In 1968 American General bought 1/3 of California-Western States Life Insurance (Cal-West), increasing its stake to 100% by 1975. Cal-West's Harold Hook became president in 1975, and in 1978 he succeeded Woodson as chairman.

In the 1980s the company changed its name to American General Corp. and diversified into

financial services. It also continued to make big acquisitions, buying NLT Corp. for $1.5 billion (1982) and Gulf United's insurance business for $1.2 billion (1984). In the late 1980s American General began shifting its emphasis, buying Manufacturers Hanover's consumer finance division in 1988 and selling its property and casualty business to Zurich Insurance Co. in 1989.

In 1990 Torchmark Corporation made a hostile takeover attempt, offering $50 per share. Hook won the ensuing proxy fight and then put American General up for sale. When no buyers appeared, he took the company off the market and set out to cut costs and boost earnings by consolidating operations and laying off more than 500 employees in 1991.

In 1993 a subsidiary, American General Investment, was ordered to pay $310 million in compensatory and punitive damages to Avia Development Group for breach of a joint venture agreement to build cargo facilities at 2 airports. The award was later reduced to $176.5 million.

After a 6-year acquisitions hiatus, the company bought Conseco's 40% interest in Western National Corp. in 1994 and then in 1995 acquired Franklin Life Insurance Co. from American Brands for $1.17 billion. Through much of 1994 and into early 1995 American General pursued Chicago-based Unitrin, an insurer and consumer lender, with a $2.6 billion hostile takeover offer. It abandoned its efforts because of continued resistance by Unitrin's management.

NYSE symbol: AGC
Fiscal year ends: December 31

WHO

Chairman and CEO: Harold S. Hook, age 63,
$1,960,000 pay
VC: Robert M. Devlin, age 54, $673,155 pay
President: James R. Tuerff, age 54, $749,616 pay
Chairman and CEO, American General Finance, Inc.:
Daniel Leitch III, age 61, $478,231 pay
**Chairman and CEO, The Variable Annuity Life
Insurance Co.:** Stephen D. Bickel, age 55,
$450,000 pay
**President and CEO, American General Life Insurance
Co.:** Robert S. Cauthen Jr., age 50
SVP and CFO: Austin P. Young, age 54
SVP and General Counsel: Jon P. Newton, age 53
Director Corporate Personnel: Joann Griffith
Auditors: Ernst & Young LLP

WHERE

HQ: 2929 Allen Pkwy., Houston, TX 77019-2155
Phone: 713-522-1111
Fax: 713-831-3028

American General provides insurance and other
financial services in all 50 US states, the District of
Columbia, Canada, Puerto Rico, and the Virgin Islands.

WHAT

	1994 Sales		1994 Pretax Income	
	$ mil.	% of total	$ mil.	% of total
Life insurance	1,932	39	399	37
Annuities	1,537	31	282	26
Consumer finance	1,491	30	392	37
Adjustments	(119)	—	(271)	—
Total	**4,841**	**100**	**802**	**100**

	1994 Assets	
	$ mil.	% of total
Cash & equivalents	45	0
Government securities	1,221	3
Mortgage-backed securities	10,032	21
Corporate bonds	14,291	31
Mortgage loans	2,651	6
Policy loans	1,197	3
Other investments	1,305	3
Net finance receivables	7,694	17
Deferred policy acquisition costs	2,731	6
Separate account assets	2,901	6
Other	2,227	5
Total	**46,295**	**100**

Selected Subsidiaries
American General Finance
American General Life and
Accident Insurance Co.
American General Life
Insurance Co.
The Franklin Life
Insurance Co.
The Variable Annuity
Life Insurance Co.
Western National Corp. (40%)

Selected Services
Annuities
Consumer finance
Consumer loans
Credit-related insurance
Home equity loans
Life insurance
Private-label credit cards
Retail financing
Visa and MasterCard

KEY COMPETITORS

Aetna
AIG
Blue Cross
Chubb
CIGNA
Citicorp
Countrywide Credit
Equitable
GEICO
General Re
Guardian Life Insurance
Household International
John Hancock
Kemper National
Insurance
Marsh & McLennan
MassMutual
MetLife
New York Life
Northwestern Mutual
Prudential
State Farm
Teachers Insurance
Travelers
USAA

HOW MUCH

	9-Year Growth	1985	1986	1987	1988	1989	1990	1991	1992	1993	1994
Assets ($ mil.)	8.9%	21,515	23,447	25,432	30,422	32,062	33,808	36,105	39.742	43,982	46,295
Net income ($ mil.)	0.8%	477	648	540	442	464	562	480	533	250	513
Income as % of assets	—	2.2%	2.8%	2.1%	1.5%	1.4%	1.7%	1.3%	1.3%	0.6%	1.1%
Earnings per share ($)	4.8%	1.60	2.17	1.86	1.72	1.88	2.35	2.13	2.45	0.94	2.45
Stock price – high ($)	—	18.13	23.38	22.38	18.44	19.25	25.32	22.50	29.38	36.50	30.50
Stock price – low ($)	—	12.38	16.69	13.63	13.69	14.75	11.75	14.00	20.13	26.25	24.88
Stock price – close ($)	5.5%	17.44	18.44	15.88	14.82	15.63	15.38	22.25	28.50	28.63	28.25
P/E – high	—	11	11	12	11	10	11	11	—	39	12
P/E – low	—	8	8	7	8	8	5	7	—	28	10
Dividends per share ($)	9.8%	0.50	0.56	0.63	0.70	0.75	0.79	1.00	1.04	1.10	1.16
Book value per share ($)	2.5%	13.58	15.32	16.15	17.18	18.53	18.57	19.86	—	23.99	17.03
Employees	(2.4%)	16,000	16,321	16,000	18,300	12,500	12,000	11,000	11,600	11,500	12,900

1994 Year-end:
Equity as % of assets: 7.5%
Return on equity: 11.9%
Return on assets: 3.0%
Long-term debt (mil.): $7,451
No. of shares (mil.): 203
Dividends
  Yield: 4.1%
  Payout: 47.3%
Market value (mil.): $5,736
Sales (mil.): $4,841

**Stock Price History
High/Low 1985–94**

AMR CORPORATION

OVERVIEW

American Airlines, the #1 US airline, is flying high again. Its improved economic performance helped lift Fort Worth–based AMR, American's holding company, to its first annual profit in 5 years in 1994. A combination of an expanding economy and cost-cutting measures have lifted the company's sales and productivity. The carrier has cut jet service to 30 cities, removed more than 90 jet aircraft from its fleet, and drastically reduced its payroll.

AMR also owns American Eagle, a group of 4 small regional airlines; operates the SABRE reservations system; and manages airport ground services, consulting, information, and telemarketing systems.

The air carrier is focusing on expanding its services to more than 20 key markets that cater to the business traveler, and it is increasing its services to Chicago, Dallas/Fort Worth, and Miami.

AMR ended 1994 on a down note with 2 fatal crashes of American Eagle planes, due in part to wing icing on its ATR planes. Under FAA restrictions AMR redeployed its ATR fleet to southern routes. American Airlines itself extended its safety record to 15 years and over 10 million flights since its last fatal accident.

In 1995 AMR planned to break into the large Chinese aviation market by selling travel-related services and technology to Chinese airlines.

WHEN

In 1929 Sherman Fairchild's Fairchild Aviation Corporation created a New York City holding company called the Aviation Corporation (AVCO). By 1930 AVCO owned about 85 small airlines, which together formed an unconnected coast-to-coast network. Hoping to consolidate this route structure, AVCO created American Airways in 1930.

In 1934 new postal regulations forced AVCO to split up its aircraft-making and transportation concerns. American Airlines was formed as a result, and, through an exchange of stock, it bought American Airways.

With former AVCO manager C. R. Smith at the helm, American surpassed United as the leading US airline in the late 1930s. The Douglas DC-3, built to Smith's specifications, was introduced into service by American in 1936 and was the first commercial airliner to pay its way on passenger revenues alone.

After WWII, American bought American Export Airlines (renamed American Overseas Airlines), with flights to northern Europe, but it sold this division to Pan Am in 1950. American formed subsidiary Americana Hotels in 1963 and introduced SABRE, the industry's first automated reservations system, in 1964. In 1968 Smith left American to serve President Johnson as secretary of commerce.

American bought Trans Caribbean Airlines in 1971, gaining routes to the Caribbean. In 1977 Americana Hotels bought the Howard Corporation's hotel properties and by 1978 operated 21 hotels and resorts in the US, Latin America, and Korea. Within 10 years most of the hotels were sold.

In 1979 American moved its headquarters from New York to Dallas/Fort Worth. Former

CFO Bob Crandall became president in 1980 and, using SABRE to keep track of mileage, introduced the industry's first frequent flyer program (AAdvantage) in 1981. In 1982 American created AMR Corporation as its holding company. After acquiring Nashville Eagle (commuter airline) in 1987, AMR established AMR Eagle to operate commuter services as American Eagle, buying 4 new commuter services in 1988 and 1989.

In 1989 AMR weathered an unsolicited takeover bid by Donald Trump and bought Eastern Air Lines's Latin American routes from Texas Air (now Continental Airlines). In 1991 AMR bought TWA's US–London routes and won DOT approval to fly to Manchester, England. AMR also bought Continental's Seattle–Tokyo route and Midway Airlines's gates at LaGuardia and Washington National airports. The new routes did not bring the expected financial results, and AMR scaled back its expansion.

In 1993, despite taking steps toward profitability, AMR asked its flight attendants for concessions. The resulting strike took the airline into the red and tied up Thanksgiving weekend travel; it ended when President Clinton persuaded the parties to go to arbitration. Most of the attendants' pay and labor issues were resolved in a 1995 agreement.

Reflecting its growing business activities in China, AMR opened an office in Beijing in 1994. The air carrier also announced a frequent flyer relationship with Japan Airlines.

A freak hail storm that swept through Dallas/Fort Worth International Airport in 1995 damaged 55 planes belonging to American Airlines and caused several days of canceled flights and high repair costs.

WHO

Chairman, President, and CEO: Robert L. Crandall, age 59, $600,000 pay
EVP; President, American Airlines: Donald J. Carty, age 48, $540,000 pay
EVP Operations, American Airlines: Robert W. Baker, age 50, $540,000 pay
SVP Marketing, American Airlines: Michael W. Gunn, age 49, $400,000 pay
SVP Corporate Services (HR): Thomas J. Kiernan
SVP Finance and Planning: Gerard J. Arpey, age 36
SVP Florida, Caribbean and Latin America, American Airlines: Peter J. Dolara
SVP International, American Airlines: Hans Mirka
SVP and General Counsel: Anne H. McNamara, age 47
President, AMR Eagle Inc.: Daniel P. Garton, age 38
VP Corporate Real Estate, American Airlines: A. Jaynne Allison
VP Employee Relations, American Airlines: Jane G. Allen
Corporate Secretary: Charles D. MarLett, age 40
Auditors: Ernst & Young LLP

WHERE

HQ: 4333 Amon Carter Blvd., Fort Worth, TX 76155
Phone: 817-963-1234
Fax: 817-967-9641
Reservations: 800-433-7300

American serves more than 170 worldwide destinations. American Eagle serves cities in the US, the Bahamas, and the Caribbean.

Hub Locations
Chicago
Dallas/Fort Worth
Miami
Nashville
San Juan

WHAT

	1994 Sales	
	$ mil.	% of total
Air Transport Group		
Passenger	13,616	80
Cargo	657	4
Other	622	4
SABRE Group	1,542	9
AMR Management Svcs.	535	3
Adjustments	(835)	—
Total	**16,137**	**100**

	1994 Aircraft	
	Owned	Leased
Airbus A300	10	25
Boeing 727	49	39
Boeing 757	40	41
Boeing 767	29	38
Fokker 100	66	9
McDonnell Douglas DC-10	19	5
McDonnell Douglas MD-11	17	—
McDonnell Douglas MD-80	119	141
Total	**349**	**298**

Selected Subsidiaries and Affiliates
American Airlines, Inc.
AMR Eagle, Inc. (commuter services)
AMR Investment Services (investment management)
AMR Services Corp. (ground services)
SABRE Computer Services (data processing)
SABRE Decision Technologies (consulting to travel and other industries)
SABRE Travel Information Network (reservations)

KEY COMPETITORS

Air France	Galileo International	Southwest
America West	IRI	Airlines
British Airways	JAL	TWA
Continental	KLM	UAL
Airlines	Lufthansa	USAir Group
Delta	Northwest Airlines	ValuJet Airlines

HOW MUCH

	9-Year Growth	1985	1986	1987	1988	1989	1990	1991	1992	1993	1994
Sales ($ mil.)	11.4%	6,131	6,018	7,198	8,824	10,480	11,720	12,887	14,396	15,816	16,137
Net income ($ mil.)	(0.1%)	346	279	198	477	455	(40)	(240)	(475)	(170)	343
Income as % of sales	—	5.6%	4.6%	2.8%	5.4%	4.3%	—	—	—	—	2.1%
Earnings per share ($)	(2.9%)	5.88	4.63	3.28	7.66	7.15	(0.64)	(3.54)	(6.35)	(2.23)	4.51
Stock price – high ($)	—	50.75	62.13	65.50	55.00	107.25	70.25	71.13	80.25	72.88	72.75
Stock price – low ($)	—	33.50	39.25	26.75	32.63	52.13	39.75	44.25	54.38	55.50	48.13
Stock price – close ($)	2.8%	41.38	53.63	35.25	53.63	58.00	48.38	70.50	67.50	67.00	53.25
P/E – high	—	9	13	20	7	15	—	—	—	—	16
P/E – low	—	6	9	8	4	7	—	—	—	—	11
Dividends per share ($)	—	0.00	0.00	0.00	0.00	0.00	0.00	0.00	0.00	0.00	0.00
Book value per share ($)	1.8%	37.17	42.30	45.58	53.50	60.54	59.83	55.50	44.41	42.17	43.50
Employees	8.6%	52,100	54,300	65,100	77,100	89,000	102,809	116,300	119,300	118,900	109,800

1994 Year-end:
Debt ratio: 71.8%
Return on equity: 10.6%
Cash (mil.): $777
Current ratio: 0.63
Long-term debt (mil.): $7,878
No. of shares (mil.): 76
Dividends
  Yield: —
  Payout: —
Market value (mil.): $4,042

Stock Price History
High/Low 1985–94

ARMY & AIR FORCE EXCHANGE

OVERVIEW

Wal-Mart and Price/Costco have their shopping clubs, but the Army & Air Force Exchange Service (AAFES) runs an exclusive shopping club of its own — exclusive, but not small. AAFES operates nearly 11,000 facilities, including retail stores, restaurants, theaters, and vending centers, at post exchanges (PXs) and base exchanges (BXs) on army and air force bases around the world.

Headquartered in Dallas, AAFES is a government agency that operates under the Department of Defense. Although it receives no funding from the DOD, AAFES pays neither taxes nor rent for US government property.

AAFES passes these savings on to its customers: average prices are more than 20% lower than competitors'. Eligible customers include active-duty military personnel, National Guard members, reservists, retirees, and their families. With the downsizing of the military, AAFES has seen its customer base shrink by about 11% over the past 2 years.

AAFES's profits go into a capital improvements fund to refurbish stores and into a Morale, Welfare & Recreation fund to pay for things such as libraries and youth centers. Although AAFES is headed by military personnel, it is staffed almost entirely by civilians.

WHEN

The methods used to provide US military personnel with personal items have evolved since the American Revolution. During the Revolution, peddlers, called sutlers, followed the army, selling items such as soap, razors, and tobacco. The practice lasted until after the Civil War, when sutlers were replaced by post traders. The post trader system was replaced in 1889 when the War Department authorized canteens at military bases.

The first US military exchanges were established in 1895, creating a system to supply military personnel with personal items on US Army bases around the world. The exchanges were run independently, with each division creating a PX to serve its unit. The post commander would assign an officer to run the PX (usually along with other duties) and would decide how profits were spent.

In 1941 the Army Exchange Service was created, and the system was reorganized. A 5-member advisory committee made up of civilian merchandisers was created to provide recommendations for the reorganization.

The restructuring made the system more like a chain store business. The independent PXs were bought by the War Department from the individual military organizations that ran them. Civilian personnel were brought in to staff the PXs, and a brigadier general was named to head an executive staff made up of army officers and civilians that provided centralized control of the system. The army also created a special school to train officers to run the exchanges.

During WWII sales at the PXs skyrocketed. The PXs also provided business for manufacturers who were unable to make certain products for civilian use because of rationing: a manufacturer making products for the PXs could get special permits to obtain materials that otherwise would have been rationed. Also during WWII the PXs added a catalog business so that soldiers could order gifts to send home to their families.

The exchange system has been run as a joint operation since 1947, when the Department of the Air Force was established. In 1948 the organization was renamed the Army & Air Force Exchange Service.

In 1960 the government decided to allow the overseas exchanges to provide more luxury items in an effort to keep soldiers from buying foreign-made goods. By the time the military had been cranked up again for the Vietnam War, big-ticket items such as televisions, cameras, and tape recorders were among the exchanges' hottest sellers. In 1967 AAFES moved its headquarters from New York to Dallas.

The number of people eligible to shop at the exchanges continued to grow. By 1991, with the military buildup for the Persian Gulf War and the passage of the National Defense Authorization Act, which opened up the exchanges to the National Guard and the Reserve, AAFES's customer base had grown to 14 million.

When the military began downsizing during the 1990s, AAFES reorganized to streamline its operations. In 1993 AAFES began a pilot program at recently closed Carswell Air Force Base in Fort Worth to keep its stores open so it could provide goods for some 100,000 military retirees living in the Dallas–Fort Worth area. In 1994 AAFES announced plans to spend $28 million on a new distribution center to modernize its Fort Gillem, Georgia, operations.

In 1995 Major General Robert Swarts retired as head of AAFES. He was succeeded by Major General Allen Bunger.

Government instrumentality
Fiscal year ends: 4th Monday in January

WHO

Chairman: Lieutenant General George T. Babbitt
Commander and CEO: Major General Allen D. Bunger
COO: James McKinney
EVP Sales Directorate: Bob Maddin
CFO: Kenneth C. Weaver
SVP Human Resources Directorate: Tom Harmon
General Counsel: Colonel William C. Kirk
Auditors: Ernst & Young LLP

WHERE

HQ: Army & Air Force Exchange Service,
3911 S. Walton Walker Blvd., Dallas, TX 75236
Phone: 214-312-2011
Fax: 214-312-3000

AAFES has operations in all 50 US states and in 25
countries and overseas areas.

	1994 Sales
	% of total
Continental US & Alaska	69
Europe	18
Pacific	12
Catalog sales	1
Total	**100**

	1994 Stores
	No.
Continental US	149
Europe	58
Pacific	17
Total	**224**

WHAT

	1994 Sales	
	$ mil.	% of total
Direct	6,400	90
Concession	700	10
Total	**7,100**	**100**

	1994 Sales
	% of total
Retail	80
Concessions	10
Food	7
Vending	2
Motion pictures & services	1
Total	**100**

KEY COMPETITORS

50-Off Stores
Ames
Best Buy
Circuit City
Dayton Hudson
Dillard
Edison Brothers
Federated
Fred Meyer
Home Depot
J. C. Penney
Kmart
Kroger
Lechters
May
Meijer
Melville
Mercantile Stores
Merck
Montgomery Ward
Navy Exchange Service
Price/Costco
Sears
Service Merchandise
Walgreen
Wal-Mart
Woolworth

HOW MUCH

	Annual Growth	1985	1986	1987	1988	1989	1990	1991	1992	1993	1994
Sales ($ mil.)	4.3%	4,881	4,918	5,187	5,855	6,195	6,777	7,422	7,501	7,263	7,100
Net income ($ mil.)	1.5%	236	171	229	260	233	354	340	330	301	270
Income as % of sales	—	4.8%	3.5%	4.4%	4.4%	3.8%	5.2%	4.6%	4.4%	4.1%	3.7%
Employees	(2.3%)	—	—	70,385	78,823	—	—	79,609	75,584	72,562	60,000

1994 Year-end:
Return on assets: 11.8%
Cash (mil.): —
Current ratio: 2.00
Total assets (mil.): $3,904

AAFES

Net Income
($ mil.)
1985–94

ASSOCIATED MILK PRODUCERS, INC.

OVERVIEW

Membership is slipping and so is market share, but you won't find AMPI crying over spilt milk — especially not when its farmers collect 15.5 billion pounds of the stuff. San Antonio–based Associated Milk Producers, Inc., the largest US milk cooperative, was responsible for 10% of the nation's milk supply in 1994, down 2% from the year before. AMPI had a 9% slice of the US cheese production and churned out 143 million pounds of butter. The cooperative's products can be found in grocery stores, convenience stores, restaurants, delis, and other food service operations.

AMPI's 12,698 member farms (down 48% in the past 10 years) are located in 20 states and organized into 3 operating regions, each of which manufactures, processes, and markets dairy items. Morning Glory Farms includes operations primarily in Illinois, Indiana, and Wisconsin and specializes in cheese production. The North Central and Southern Regions, meanwhile, produce a broader range of dairy products, including milk, cheese, butter, whey, ice cream, cottage cheese, sour cream, and yogurt.

While demand for dairy products has increased 19% in the past decade, milk prices have declined, brought down by oversupply despite sometimes drastic measures instituted by the US government. There are fewer than 190,000 dairy farms in the US, down from more than one million in the early 1960s.

AMPI's political action committee, C-TAPE (Committee for Thorough Agricultural Political Education), saw victories by 86% of the 284 US congressional candidates it backed in 1994. That year, the cooperative awarded more than $18 million in rebates to its members.

WHEN

In 1969, faced with declining income and milk consumption, about 100 dairy cooperatives in the Midwest and the South merged to form Associated Milk Producers, Inc. The membership elected John Butterbrodt, from a Wisconsin cooperative, as the first president and established headquarters in San Antonio, home of the largest cooperative, Milk Producers Association. Cooperatives throughout the central US clamored to join, and AMPI became the largest US dairy cooperative within 2 years of its formation.

Almost from the beginning AMPI became embroiled in the 2 main controversies involving dairy cooperatives: monopolistic practices and political contributions. In 1972 consumer advocate Ralph Nader alleged that the 3 main dairy cooperatives — AMPI, Dairymen, and Mid-America Dairymen — had illegally contributed $422,000 to President Nixon's re-election campaign in an attempt to obtain higher price supports (enacted in 1971) and an agreement that the administration would drop antitrust suits against the cooperatives. Watergate investigators subpoenaed Nixon's tapes, and AMPI was accused of bribery, destruction of evidence, and attempting to achieve "complete market dominance." In 1974 AMPI pleaded guilty to making illegal political contributions in 1968, 1970, and 1972. By 1975, 3 former AMPI employees had been convicted of various charges and Butterbrodt had resigned.

AMPI spent the last half of the 1970s quietly reorganizing; during this time it established its current regional management structure. In 1982 a suit for monopolistic practices, originally filed in 1971 by the National Farmers' Organization (NFO), finally reached the federal courts. The case was decided in favor of AMPI and 2 other large cooperatives, but before the year was out an appeals court reversed the decision, saying AMPI and its codefendants had conspired to eliminate competitive sellers of milk. In 1983 Congress rejected a bill to cut price supports for dairy farmers and instead adopted a program to pay farmers not to produce milk. Industry critics charged that the 3 major milk cooperatives had bought the legislation through large political contributions.

AMPI extended its dominance of the industry in 1985 by merging its central region, then called the Mid-States Region, with 2,200 members of Shawano, Wisconsin–based Morning Glory Farms Cooperative. In 1989 the US Supreme Court upheld the appeals court ruling in the NFO antitrust case.

In 1990 business soured for AMPI: it posted a $27 million loss. AMPI successfully lobbied the Department of Agriculture to strengthen dairy price supports in 1992.

The cooperative in 1994 became one of the first targets of a lawsuit stemming from the Family Leave Act. The Labor Department sued on behalf of a truck driver in New Mexico who was fired a week after he missed work while his wife was in early labor with triplets.

AMPI and rival cooperative Mid-America Dairymen ended their joint marketing pact in 1994 but resumed collaboration the next year.

Mutual company
Fiscal year ends: December 31

President: Irvin J. Elkin
General Manager: Noble Anderson
President, Morning Glory Farms Region: Robert Thompson
President, North Central Region: Mel Kunstleben
President, Southern Region: Bill Thornton
Manager, Morning Glory Farms Region: Jim Kasten
Manager, North Central Region: Mark Furth
Manager, Southern Region: Jim Carroll
Corporate Controller: Terry Krueger
Manager Human Resources: Charlie Warren
Auditors: Deloitte & Touche LLP

WHERE

HQ: 6609 Blanco Rd., PO Box 790287, San Antonio, TX 78279-0287
Phone: 210-340-9100
Fax: 210-340-9158

AMPI is divided into 3 regions. The Morning Glory Farms Region serves customers in Illinois, Indiana, Michigan, Ohio, and Wisconsin. The North Central Region serves customers in Iowa, Minnesota, Missouri, Nebraska, South Dakota, and Wisconsin. The Southern Region serves customers in Arkansas, Colorado, Kansas, Kentucky, Louisiana, Mississippi, Missouri, Nebraska, New Mexico, Oklahoma, Tennessee, and Texas.

| | 1994 Membership | |
Regions	No. of members	% of total
North Central	6,125	48
Morning Glory Farms	3,333	26
Southern	3,240	26
Total	**12,698**	**100**

| | 1994 Production | |
Regions	Lbs. mil.	% of total
Southern	8,100	52
North Central	4,500	29
Morning Glory Farms	2,900	19
Total	**15,500**	**100**

WHAT

| | 1994 Sales | |
	$ mil.	% of total
Milk products	2,587	98
Hauling & other	42	2
Total	**2,629**	**100**

| | 1994 Production |
	Lbs. mil.
Unprocessed milk	15,500
Cheese	576
Dried whey	243
Nonfat dry milk	185
Butter	143

Dairy Activities
Grade A milk production
Production and packaging of dairy products, canned cheese sauces, and other milk-based goods under the Morning Glory, New Holstein, State Brand, and other labels

Major Subsidiaries, Affiliates, and Investments
Farm Credit System Banks
Land O'Lakes, Inc.
Northland Foods Cooperative
Prairie Farms Dairy, Inc.

Membership Services
AMPI Investment Corp. (investment subsidiary of the Southern Region)
Member insurance

Political Activities
Committee for Thorough Agricultural Political Education (C-TAPE)
State political committees in the Southern Region

KEY COMPETITORS

Alpine Lace	MorningStar Group
Borden	Philip Morris
Dairyman's Co-op Creamery	Schreiber Foods
Dairymen	Shamrock Foods
Danone	Southern Foods
Darigold	Specialty Foods
Dean Foods	Universal Foods
Michael Foods	Wisconsin Dairies
Mid-America Dairymen	

HOW MUCH

	Annual Growth	1985	1986	1987	1988	1989	1990	1991	1992	1993	1994
Sales ($ mil.)	0.9%	2,416	2,489	2,710	2,777	2,987	3,063	2,768	2,835	2,692	2,629
Operating income ($ mil.)	(24.3%)	—	—	7	4	12	(27)	1	(13)	11	1
Member farms	(6.5%)	23,300	23,500	22,400	20,800	19,400	18,478	16,321	14,729	13,403	12,698
Milk deliveries (lbs. mil.)	(0.1%)	15,700	15,900	17,200	17,700	17,300	17,700	17,100	16,500	15,700	15,500
Employees	1.4%	—	—	—	—	4,200	4,500	4,319	4,364	4,199	4,500

Sales ($ mil.)
1985–94

BAKER HUGHES INCORPORATED

OVERVIEW

Baker Hughes serves the oil industry through 2 industry segments — Baker Hughes Oilfield Operations (drill bits, drilling fluids, and other equipment used in the drilling process; equipment and services involved in the completion and repair of oil and gas wells) and Baker Hughes Process Equipment Operations (process equipment for mining and other industries).

As Baker Hughes is the world's leading maker of rock drilling bits and the #1 provider of drilling services, its fortunes are tied to the state of the oil industry. Unfortunately, 1994 was not a good year for oil exploration and production, as industrywide the number of operating oil and gas rigs hovered around 700 (only about 100 more than 1993's all-time low and a far cry from 1981's peak of 4,500).

To provide oil companies with a "one-stop shop" of oil field equipment and services, Baker Hughes has reorganized in order to concentrate on its oil, gas, and process businesses. It has sold several business units to pay down debt. In 1994 it sold EnviroTech Measurement & Controls to Thermo Electron for $134 million.

WHEN

Howard Hughes Sr., developed the first oil well drill bit for rock in 1909. Hughes and partner Walter Sharp opened a plant in Houston, and Sharp & Hughes soon had a near monopoly on rock bits. When Sharp died in 1912, Hughes bought his half of the company, incorporating as Hughes Tool. Hughes held 73 patents when he died in 1924; the company passed to Howard Hughes Jr.

It is estimated that between 1924 and 1972 the tool company provided Hughes Jr. with $745 million in pretax profits, which he used to diversify into movies (RKO), airlines (TWA), and Las Vegas casinos. In 1972 Hughes sold the tool division of Hughes Tool to the public for $150 million. After 1972 the company expanded into above-ground oil production tools.

In 1913 oil well drilling contractor Carl Baker organized the Baker Casing Shoe Company in California to collect royalties on his 3 oil tool inventions. In 1918 Baker began to manufacture his own products. During the 1920s Baker expanded nationwide, began international sales, and formed Baker Oil Tools (1928). Sales increased sixfold between 1933 and 1941. In the late 1940s and the 1950s, Baker grew as oil drilling boomed.

During the 1960s Baker prospered despite fewer US well completions. Foreign sales increased from 19% to 33% of total revenues. Baker bought Kobe (oil field pumping equipment) in 1963 and diversified into mining equipment with the purchase of Galigher (1969) and Ramsey Engineering (1974). The company bought Reed Tool (oil well drill bits) in 1975. In 1979 revenues topped $1 billion for the first time.

Between 1982 and 1986, US expenditures for oil services fell from $40 billion to $9 billion. In 1987, when both Baker and Hughes faced declining revenues and Hughes had large debts from expansion, the 2 companies merged to form Baker Hughes. By closing plants and combining operations, the company cut annual expenses by $80 million and was profitable by the end of fiscal 1988. Several small acquisitions in 1989 included Bird Machine (process centrifuges) and EDECO Petroleum Services (pumps). The company bought Eastman Christensen (world leader in directional and horizontal drilling equipment) and acquired the instrumentation unit of Tracor Holdings in 1990.

In 1991 Baker Hughes spun off BJ Services (pumping services) to the public. That same year it sold the Eastern Hemisphere operations of Baker Hughes Tubular Services (BHTS) to Tuboscope. It sold Western Hemisphere operations of BHTS to ICO in 1992.

Also in 1992 Baker Hughes bought Teleco Oilfield Services, a pioneer in sophisticated directional drilling techniques, from Sonat Inc. for $350 million. In 1993 the company consolidated its drilling technologies businesses into a single unit, named Baker Hughes INTEQ, to package services more efficiently for its clients in the oil industry.

In 1994 Baker Performance Chemicals opened a new office in Seoul, South Korea; formed a new joint venture in Indonesia; and set up a new company in Peru. In that year Baker Hughes also reorganized its operations; it streamlined its geographical operating business units from 5 to 3 and merged its 4 technology groups into one cohesive unit.

In 1995 Baker Hughes completed the sale of EnviroTech Pumpsystems, which provides specialized pumps to the mining, chemical, and petrochemical markets, to the Weir Group of Glasgow, Scotland, for $210 million.

NYSE symbol: BHI
Fiscal year ends: September 30

WHO

Chairman, President, and CEO: James D. Woods, age 63, $1,417,835 pay
EVP; President, Baker Hughes Oilfield Operations: Max L. Lukens, age 46, $738,560 pay
SVP and General Counsel: Franklin Myers, age 42, $461,042 pay
SVP and CFO: Eric L. Mattson, age 43, $436,566 pay
VP; President, Baker Hughes Process Equipment Operations: Timothy J. Probert, age 43, $318,238 pay
VP; VP Technology and Market Development, Baker Hughes Oilfield Operations: Roger P. Herbert, age 48
VP Government Affairs: Arthur T. Downey, age 57
VP Investor Relations: Scott B. Gill, age 35
VP Human Resources: Phillip A. Rice, age 59
Controller: James E. Braun, age 35
Auditors: Deloitte & Touche LLP

WHERE

HQ: 3900 Essex Ln., Houston, TX 77027-5177
Phone: 713-439-8600
Fax: 713-439-8699

Baker Hughes operates 72 manufacturing plants around the world, of which 43 are located in the US.

	1994 Sales		1994 Operating Income	
	$ mil.	% of total	$ mil.	% of total
US	1,272	52	60	28
Europe	479	19	39	16
Other Western Hemisphere	362	14	60	28
Other regions	392	15	60	28
Total	**2,505**	**100**	**219**	**100**

WHAT

	1994 Sales		1994 Operating Income	
	$ mil.	% of total	$ mil.	% of total
Oilfield	2,111	84	158	72
Process	298	12	22	10
Disposed businesses	96	4	39	18
Total	**2,505**	**100**	**219**	**100**

Divisions and Selected Subsidiaries

Baker Hughes Oilfield Operations
Baker Hughes INTEQ (technical service, project management)
Baker Oil Tools (completion, production, workover, and fishing equipment and services)
Baker Performance Chemicals Inc. (specialty chemicals)
Centrilift (pumps, drives, speed controls, and cabling)
Hughes Christensen Co. (drill bits)

Baker Hughes Process Equipment Operations
Baker Hughes Process Systems (designs and supplies processing systems for water injection)
Bird Machine Company, Inc.(centrifugal and filtration equipment)
EIMCO Process Equipment Co. (separation technology and equipment)

KEY COMPETITORS

Alfa-Laval	Kaneb Services
Bechtel	Klockner-Humbollt-Deutch
Camco	LTV
Cooper Cameron	McDermott
Dorr-Oliver	Michael Baker
Dresser	Nabors Industries
Energy Service	Outokumpu
Fluor	Sala
FMC	Schlumberger
Halliburton	Serck Baker
Ingersoll-Rand	Smith International
Ingram	

HOW MUCH

	9-Year Growth	1985[1]	1986[1]	1987	1988	1989	1990	1991	1992	1993	1994
Sales ($ mil.)	3.8%	1,904	1,557	1,924	2,316	2,328	2,614	2,828	2,539	2,702	2,505
Net income ($ mil.)	(0.1%)	88	(19)	(255)	59	83	142	174	5	59	87
Income as % of sales	—	4.6%	—	—	2.6%	3.6%	5.4%	6.1%	0.2%	2.2%	3.5%
Earnings per share ($)	(8.9%)	1.25	(0.27)	(2.22)	0.45	0.64	1.06	1.26	0.00	0.34	0.54
Stock price – high ($)	—	18.88	17.88	27.38	19.88	27.63	34.75	31.00	25.38	29.63	22.13
Stock price – low ($)	—	14.13	8.88	11.13	12.13	13.63	21.75	17.88	15.88	18.50	17.00
Stock price – close ($)	0.2%	17.88	11.88	13.63	14.00	25.50	25.63	19.25	19.63	20.00	18.25
P/E – high	—	15	—	—	44	43	33	25	—	87	41
P/E – low	—	11	—	—	27	21	21	14	—	54	31
Dividends per share ($)	(7.4%)	0.92	0.81	0.23	0.46	0.46	0.46	0.46	0.46	0.46	0.46
Book value per share ($)	(2.4%)	14.43	9.67	7.78	8.10	8.31	10.36	11.17	11.84	11.44	11.60
Employees	(3.7%)	20,600	14,900	24,482	21,500	20,400	20,900	21,300	19,600	18,400	14,700

1994 Year-end:
Debt ratio: 28.5%
Return on equity: 5.4%
Cash (mil.): $69
Current ratio: 2.57
Long-term debt (mil.): $638
No. of shares (mil.): 141
Dividends
  Yield: 2.5%
  Payout: 85.2%
Market value (mil.): $2,571

Stock Price History High/Low 1985–94

[1] Figures are for Baker International Corporation only.

BROWNING-FERRIS INDUSTRIES, INC.

OVERVIEW

Like the Pac-Man of garbage, Browning-Ferris Industries (BFI) is gobbling up smaller waste disposal firms — 113 in 1994 — as that industry becomes increasingly consolidated. Among the company's 1994 purchases were UK-based Attwoods plc, the US's #4 waste company (won in a hostile takeover) and a 50% stake in Otto Waste Services, one of Germany's top trash haulers. Despite BFI's appetite, the Houston-based company remains the world's #2 waste management firm, after WMX Technologies.

BFI's fleet of 12,400 trucks collects solid waste in 45 states and 11 foreign countries. The company operates 110 waste transfer stations (50 company-owned), nearly 150 landfills, 28 medical-waste treatment facilities, and 136 recycling facilities worldwide.

BFI's fastest-growing business is recycling, an industry BFI veterans discounted when William Ruckelshaus became CEO in 1988. Anticipating increasing government regulation, Ruckelshaus nurtured BFI's recycling segment; its revenues soared from $9.6 million in 1990 to $359 million in 1994. President Bruce Ranck succeeded him as CEO in 1995.

In 1995 BFI began an aggressive ad campaign that targeted the company's rivals in the New York City refuse industry. BFI entered that city's market in 1993 and is now its largest waste collection company.

WHEN

Accountant Tom Fatjo and Harvard MBA Louis Waters founded American Refuse Systems in 1967 with a single truck, providing garbage collection to a Houston neighborhood. They saw that the 1960s clean-air laws created opportunities for large garbage businesses with the resources to comply with changing environmental regulations. In 1969 the company acquired construction equipment distributor Browning-Ferris Machinery and changed its name to Browning-Ferris Industries. BFI acquired a total of 157 waste disposal firms by 1973. That year BFI signed its first foreign contract to provide trash service in parts of Spain. Although it continued to expand its international presence, concentrating on Europe and the Far East, it lagged behind rival Waste Management, which picked up most of the lucrative international contracts.

BFI moved into a variety of peripheral businesses during the 1970s, including wastepaper recycling. In 1975 revenues and profits fell 18%, partly because of decreased demand for wastepaper, which had previously provided nearly half of the company's revenues. BFI spun off its wastepaper subsidiary, Consolidated Fibres, in 1976. In 1976 and 1977 BFI hiked prices across its entire operation, resulting in a 37% rise in earnings in 1977.

By 1980 BFI had become the 2nd largest US waste disposal company. It acquired 508 companies from 1981 to 1988, including hazardous-waste disposer CECOS International (1983). It formed a joint venture to market trash-burning power plants (1984) and entered the medical-waste field by buying 2 small firms (1986).

BFI paid fines of $1.35 million after pleading guilty to price fixing in 1987 and paid $2.5 million in 1988 and $1.55 million in 1990 to settle suits arising from environmental violations at Louisiana hazardous-waste sites. To improve its image, in 1988 BFI recruited William Ruckelshaus, a former EPA administrator, to take over as CEO. (As a US deputy attorney general, Ruckelshaus had resigned rather than follow Richard Nixon's directive to fire Watergate special prosecutor Archibald Cox.)

After the EPA denied BFI permits to restart 2 hazardous-waste operations in 1990, the company discontinued such operations altogether, writing off $295 million in the process. The company reserved another $246.5 million in 1991 for projected landfill closure and postclosure management costs resulting from new EPA regulations.

In 1993 BFI spent almost $140 million to buy more than 100 companies. It had announced plans to acquire rival Western Waste but backed out of the deal after it decided that the $400 million price tag was too high.

In 1994 the SEC accused BFI's former general counsel, Howard Hoover, of insider trading because he had sold about half his shares in the company a week before it announced lower earnings projections in 1991. BFI had fired Hoover several weeks after the sale was revealed in 1991.

BFI took garbage collection high-tech in 1995 when it contracted with MapInfo Corp. and software provider RoTec, to develop new collection routes to improve productivity and cut costs. That same year BFI Europe acquired Swiss waste collection and transport company Fritz Erismann AG. The company's Sunshine Canyon landfill near metropolitan Los Angeles was being readied for a fall 1995 opening.

NYSE symbol: BFI
Fiscal year ends: September 30

WHO

Chairman: William D. Ruckelshaus, age 63,
$1,143,546 pay
VC and Chief Marketing Officer: Norman A. Myers,
age 58, $639,096 pay
President, CEO, and COO: Bruce E. Ranck, age 46,
$657,638 pay (prior to promotion)
Chairman and President, BFI International, Inc.: Louis
A. Waters, age 56, $510,298 pay
President, Browning-Ferris Industries Europe, Inc.:
Eric A. Black
SVP and CFO: Jeffrey E. Curtiss, age 46, $361,197 pay
SVP Disposal Operations: Hugh J. Dillingham III,
age 45
SVP Corporate Development: J. Gregory Muldoon,
age 40
SVP and General Counsel: Rufus Wallingford, age 54
VP Sales and Marketing: Edward H. Hamlett
VP, Controller, and Chief Accounting Officer: David R.
Hopkins, age 51
VP Human Resources and Employee Relations:
Susan J. Piller
Auditors: Arthur Andersen & Co, SC

WHERE

HQ: 757 N. Eldridge, Houston, TX 77079
Phone: 713-870-8100
Fax: 713-870-7844

BFI operates in 650 locations in Asia, Australia, Europe,
the Middle East, New Zealand, and North America.

	1994 Sales		1994 Operating Income	
	$ mil.	% of total	$ mil.	% of total
US & Puerto Rico	3,294	76	427	78
Other countries	1,021	24	117	22
Total	**4,315**	**100**	**544**	**100**

WHAT

	1994 Sales	
	$ mil.	% of total
North America		
Solid waste collection	2,360	50
Solid waste transfer & disposal	885	19
Recycling	359	8
Medical waste	161	3
Other services	83	2
International	859	18
Adjustments	(392)	—
Total	**4,315**	**100**

Solid Waste Services

Collection (commercial/governmental/industrial/
residential collection)
Transfer and disposal (operation of 110 transfer stations
and 146 landfills)
Medical waste (collection and disposal, including 28
waste treatment sites)
Recycling (service for residential and commercial
customers, including collection, organic waste
treatment, and tire recycling)
Other services (including portable restroom services and
street and parking lot sweeping services)

KEY COMPETITORS

Allied Waste
American Waste
Bechtel
Canadian Pacific
Conrail
EnviroSource
Integrated Waste
 Services
International
 Technology

Mid-American Waste
Norcal Waste
Republic Waste
Safety-Kleen
Sanifill
TRW
Union Pacific
USA Waste Services
Western Waste
WMX Technologies

HOW MUCH

	9-Year Growth	1985	1986	1987	1988	1989	1990	1991	1992	1993	1994
Sales ($ mil.)	15.9%	1,145	1,328	1,657	2,067	2,551	2,968	3,183	3,288	3,495	4,315
Net income ($ mil.)	10.9%	112	137	172	227	263	250	65	176	197	284
Income as % of sales	—	9.8%	10.3%	10.4%	11.0%	10.3%	8.4%	2.0%	5.3%	5.6%	6.6%
Earnings per share ($)	7.4%	0.80	0.95	1.15	1.51	1.74	1.64	0.42	1.11	1.15	1.52
Stock price – high ($)	—	16.00	23.69	35.75	29.25	42.75	49.25	30.75	27.13	28.63	32.88
Stock price – low ($)	—	9.16	15.13	17.50	20.88	26.88	20.00	16.88	19.50	20.88	24.25
Stock price – close ($)	6.6%	16.00	22.38	28.00	27.38	38.75	22.25	21.75	26.13	25.75	28.38
P/E – high	—	20	25	31	19	25	30	73	24	25	22
P/E – low	—	12	16	15	14	15	12	40	18	18	16
Dividends per share ($)	10.8%	0.27	0.31	0.38	0.46	0.54	0.62	0.67	0.68	0.68	0.68
Book value per share ($)	13.3%	3.95	5.11	5.93	7.05	8.33	7.61	7.29	8.66	8.83	12.18
Employees	8.8%	17,300	18,000	18,200	21,500	25,500	25,200	27,000	29,400	31,600	37,000

1994 Year-end:
Debt ratio: 38.7%
Return on equity: 14.5%
Cash (mil.): $141
Current ratio: 1.01
Long-term debt (mil.): $1,459
No. of shares (mil.): 196
Dividends
 Yield: 2.4%
 Payout: 44.7%
Market value (mil.): $5,572

**Stock Price History
High/Low 1985–94**

BURLINGTON NORTHERN SANTA FE

OVERVIEW

Burlington Northern Santa Fe Corp. (BNSF) was created in 1995 by the $4 billion merger of Burlington Northern Inc. (BN) and Santa Fe Pacific (SFP). The Fort Worth–based railroad has over 31,000 miles of track stretching through 27 states and 2 Canadian provinces, serving some of the continent's richest coal-, grain-, and timber-producing regions.

The new company, which had combined revenues of about $7.7 billion, is led by chairman Gerald Grinstein (from BN) and CEO Robert Krebs (from SFP). In addition to expected reductions in operating and overhead costs, the merger will provide BNSF with increased access to key West Coast and Gulf Coast ports.

BN and SFP, now subsidiaries of the new railroad, both contribute strong intermodal businesses. These train-to-truck, train-to-ship, and truck-to-ship operations accounted for 15% of BNI's revenues in 1994 and compose one of SFP's fastest growth sectors. BN also brings its 180,000-square-foot, state-of-the-art Network Operations Center, which opened near Fort Worth in 1995.

BNSF's status as the nation's largest railroad will likely be shortlived, pending rival Union Pacific's purchase of Southern Pacific.

WHEN

BNI was largely created by James Hill, who bought the St. Paul & Pacific Railroad in Minnesota in 1878. By 1893 Hill had completed the Great Northern Railway, extending from St. Paul to Seattle. In 1894 he gained control of Northern Pacific (chartered in 1864), which had been built between Minnesota and Washington. With J. P. Morgan's help, in 1901 Hill acquired the Chicago, Burlington & Quincy (Burlington), whose routes included Chicago–St. Paul and Billings–Denver–Fort Worth–Houston. The Spokane, Portland & Seattle Railway (SP&S), completed in 1908, gave Great Northern an entrance to Oregon.

Hill intended to merge Great Northern, Northern Pacific, SP&S, and Burlington under his Morgan-backed Northern Securities Company, but in 1904 the Supreme Court found that Northern Securities had violated the Sherman Anti-Trust Act. The court dissolved the holding company, but Hill kept control of the individual railroads until he died in 1916. Hill's railroads produced some of America's best-known passenger trains. Great Northern's Empire Builder (now operated by Amtrak) began service between Chicago and Seattle in 1929. The 1934 Burlington Zephyr was the nation's first streamlined passenger diesel.

After years of deliberation, the ICC allowed Great Northern and Northern Pacific to merge in 1970 along with jointly owned subsidiaries Burlington and SP&S. The new company, Burlington Northern, acquired the St. Louis–San Francisco Railway in 1980, adding more than 4,650 miles to the BN rail network.

The company formed Burlington Motor Carriers (BMC) in 1985 to manage 5 trucking companies it had acquired. BN sold BMC in 1988 and spun off Burlington Resources, an independent holding company for its nonrailroad businesses (primarily natural gas, oil, minerals, construction, and forest products, including 1.8 million acres of land). In 1989 BN hired as CEO Gerald Grinstein, a former Western Airlines CEO with a knack for labor relations but with no experience running a railroad. In 1991 BN built a link into Mexico through a rail-barge joint venture with Mexican industrial firm Grupo Protexa. In 1993 BN's service was disrupted by midwestern summer flooding, one of the worst natural disasters to affect US railroads.

In 1994 BN and SFP announced their intention to merge. SFP's history dates back to 1859, when Cyrus Kurtz Holliday founded the Atchison and Topeka Railroad Co. (renamed the Atchison, Topeka & Santa Fe Railroad in 1863). By 1890 the railroad had grown into a 9,000-mile giant under president William Strong. The company reorganized in 1895 and in 1904 the new Atchison, Topeka & Santa Fe Railway Co. moved its headquarters to Chicago. Guided by strong leaders and a conservative financial policy, the Santa Fe (as it was called) prospered into the 1960s.

Santa Fe Industries agreed in 1983 to merge with Southern Pacific to create Santa Fe Southern Pacific Corporation. In 1988 the ICC ruled that the merger was anticompetitive, and the company sold Southern Pacific to Rio Grande Industries. It adopted the Santa Fe Pacific name in 1989. Between 1990 and 1994 SFP spun off its Catellus Development real estate and Santa Fe Energy Resources oil and gas subsidiaries as well as its 85% stake in gold producer Santa Fe Pacific Gold.

In 1994 BNI rival Union Pacific (UP) made a hostile bid for SFP but withdrew its offer for legal reasons in early 1995. Later that year BN and SFP received ICC approval to merge.

NYSE symbol: BNI
Fiscal year ends: December 31

WHO

Chairman: Gerald Grinstein, age 63, $1,482,527 pay (prior to merger)
President and CEO: Robert D. Krebs, age 53, $714,450 pay (prior to merger)
SVP Coal Business: John Q. Anderson, age 44
SVP and COO: Donald G. McInnes, age 54
SVP and Chief of Staff: Douglas J. Babb, age 43
SVP Consumer Business: Steven F. Marlier, age 49
SVP Industrial Business: Gregory T. Swienton, age 45
SVP and CFO: Denis E. Springer, age 49
SVP and Chief Information Officer: Charles Feld, age 53
SVP Law and General Counsel: Jeffrey Moreland, age 51
SVP Employee Relations: James B. Dagnon, age 55
Auditors: Coopers & Lybrand L.L.P.

WHERE

HQ: Burlington Northern Santa Fe Corporation, 3800 Continental Plaza, 777 Main St., Fort Worth, TX 76102-5384
Phone: 817-333-2000
Fax: 817-878-2377

Principal Cities Served

Albuquerque, NM	Kansas City, MO	St. Louis, MO
Billings, MT	Los Angeles, CA	San Diego, CA
Birmingham, AL		San Francisco, CA
Chicago, IL	Memphis, TN	Seattle, WA
Dallas, TX	Minneapolis– St. Paul, MN	Tulsa, OK
Denver, CO		Vancouver, British Columbia, Canada
El Paso, TX	Omaha, NE	
Fargo, ND	Pensacola, FL	Winnipeg, Manitoba, Canada
Fort Worth, TX	Phoenix, AZ	
Houston, TX	Portland, OR	

WHAT

	1994 BN Sales	
Items Transported	$ mil.	% of total
Coal	1,669	33
Agricultural commodities	830	16
Intermodal containers	772	15
Forest products	498	10
Chemicals	412	8
Metals	277	5
Consumer products	267	5
Mineral processors	208	4
Vehicles & machinery	190	4
Shortlines & other	(128)	—
Total	**4,995**	**100**

	1994 SFP Sales	
Freight Type	$ mil.	% of total
Intermodal	1,198	45
Carload commodities	620	23
Bulk products	598	22
Automotive	223	8
Other	42	2
Total	**2,681**	**100**

Subsidiaries
Burlington Northern Inc.
Santa Fe Pacific Corp.

KEY COMPETITORS

American Freightways	Ingram
American President	J.B. Hunt
Arkansas Best	Leaseway Transportation
Canadian Pacific	Norfolk Southern
C.H. Robinson	Roadway
Conrail	Schneider National
Consolidated Freightways	Southern Pacific Rail
CSX	TNT Freightways
Heartland Express	Union Pacific
Illinois Central	Yellow Corp.

HOW MUCH

	9-Year Growth	1985	1986	1987	1988	1989	1990	1991	1992	1993	1994
Sales ($ mil.)	(5.9%)	8,651	6,941	6,621	4,700	4,606	4,674	4,559	4,630	4,699	4,995
Net income ($ mil.)	(4.7%)	658	(525)	369	264	243	222	(306)	299	296	426
Income as % of sales	—	7.6%	—	5.6%	5.6%	5.3%	4.7%	—	6.5%	6.3%	8.5%
Earnings per share ($)	(6.5%)	8.03	(7.53)	4.93	3.49	3.19	2.89	(3.96)	3.35	3.06	4.38
Stock price – high ($)	—	72.63	82.38	84.25	80.38	32.38	39.25	41.88	47.38	58.88	66.63
Stock price – low ($)	—	46.25	46.50	40.00	56.00	21.38	22.25	26.25	33.25	42.00	46.50
Stock price – close ($)	(3.8%)	68.25	53.25	62.75	79.00	31.50	28.75	40.50	43.50	57.88	48.13
P/E – high	—	9	—	17	23	10	14	—	14	19	15
P/E – low	—	6	—	8	16	7	8	—	10	14	11
Dividends per share ($)	(0.9%)	1.30	1.55	2.00	2.20	1.45	1.20	1.20	1.20	1.20	1.20
Book value per share ($)	(11.4%)	63.13	47.84	50.80	12.31	14.30	16.29	13.76	15.80	17.82	21.29
Employees	(4.2%)	45,022	44,200	42,300	32,400	32,900	32,905	31,760	31,204	30,502	30,711

1994 Year-end:
Debt ratio: 44.8%
Return on equity: 24.5%
Cash (mil.): $27
Current ratio: 0.70
Long-term debt (mil.): $1,697
No. of shares (mil.): 89
Dividends
  Yield: 2.5%
  Payout: 27.4%
Market value (mil.): $4,294

Stock Price History High/Low 1985–94

Note: Data for Burlington Northern Inc.

CALTEX PETROLEUM CORPORATION

OVERVIEW

Dallas-based Caltex Petroleum is a 50-50 joint venture between Texaco and Chevron. Its subsidiaries and affiliates have operations in 61 countries, primarily in Africa, Australasia, Asia, and the Middle East. Caltex markets products through more than 18,000 retail outlets in 31 countries (including Australia, Japan, the Philippines, South Africa, and South Korea), fuels aircraft at 41 airports, and provides marine fuels and lubricants at 103 ports in 22 countries. Caltex boasts average market shares of 18% in motor fuels in the markets it serves.

With the growing economies in countries in the Asia/Pacific region, demand for petroleum products is expected to grow at 6–8% a year, and Caltex is focusing on increasing its refining and retailing capacity in that area. It is planning to invest over $8 billion in the next 5 years in the region, where it already sells more gasoline, diesel, and other refined products than any other Western oil company.

In 1994 Caltex launched a major study to assess a potential joint venture in China with Sinopec, the Chinese national petroleum body, to upgrade Sinopec's Nanjing Refinery. Caltex is expanding its retail service network in China and is building a $1.7 billion, 130,000-barrel-a-day refinery in Thailand (scheduled to commence full production in 1996).

WHEN

In the 1930s Standard Oil of California (Socal) had a problem most oil companies would only wish upon themselves: it had oil reserves in Bahrain with a potential 30,000-barrel-a-day production capacity. The problem was that Socal didn't have the marketing or refining network to sell the oil profitably.

While Socal's oil sat idly in the Bahrain soil, Texaco had its own problems. It had a large marketing network in Asia and Africa but lacked a crude supply in the eastern hemisphere; it was shipping its products from the US. Enter James Forrestal, head of the investment bank Dillon, Read, with plans for a little matchmaking. Forrestal brought together the 2 companies, and in 1936 they formed the California-Texas Oil Company.

The new company had barely taken its first steps when WWII disrupted operations. Caltex had moved drilling equipment into a promising field in Sumatra, but, after the war started, the Japanese took over the field and struck oil using Caltex's equipment.

Following the war, Caltex grew rapidly as oil demand began to climb. It formed companies in Malaysia, Thailand, and Yemen. Caltex also increased its refining capacity in Bahrain (1945), began a refinery construction and expansion program in other areas (1946), and bought Texaco's European and North African marketing facilities (1947).

In 1951 the company formed the Nippon Petroleum Refining Company as a joint venture with Nippon Oil to refine crude oil, supplied by Caltex, in Japan. Caltex also bought 50% of Japan's Koa Oil Company.

Caltex sold its European operations, which it had served from Saudi Arabia, to Socal and Texaco in 1967, allowing it to concentrate on building its presence in Africa, Asia, and Australasia. In 1968 Caltex entered Korea and formed the Honam Oil Refinery Company in a partnership with Lucky Chemical.

During the 1970s several of Caltex's Arab holdings were nationalized as an OPEC-spawned upheaval shook the oil industry, and in 1978 the Indian government nationalized Caltex Oil Refining (India) Ltd.

In 1982 the company moved its offices to Dallas from New York. In 1986 the company began a major modernization program of its refineries in Australia, the Philippines, and Singapore. That same year Caltex entered the real estate development business in Hong Kong when it began construction of a $176 million condominium and shopping complex on the site of a former petroleum products terminal. In 1988 the company created Caltex Services Corporation to provide technical support to Caltex companies.

P. T. Caltex Pacific Indonesia signed an agreement with the Indonesian government in 1992 to extend its production-sharing agreement in Sumatra through 2021.

In 1993, 3 Japanese refiners pulled out of a $9.5 billion joint venture with Caltex and Saudi Aramco, apparently because it would take at least 12 years to profit from the planned 3-refinery project. That same year Caltex formed a lubricants blending and marketing joint venture with Indian oil company IBP.

In 1994 the company built its first service station in Laos and opened offices in Vietnam and Indonesia.

In 1995 Caltex veteran David Law-Smith succeeded Patrick Ward as chairman and CEO.

Joint venture
Fiscal year ends: December 31

Chairman and CEO: David Law-Smith, age 55
SVP and CFO: Malcolm J. McAuley, age 57
SVP: John McPhail
SVP: G. J. Camarata
SVP: Matt W. Saunders
VP and General Counsel: Frank W. Blue
VP Human Resources: E. M. Schmidt
Auditors: KPMG Peat Marwick LLP

WHERE

HQ: 125 E. John Carpenter Fwy., PO Box 619500,
Irving, TX 75602-2750
Phone: 214-830-1000
Fax: 214-830-1156

Caltex has operations in 61 countries, primarily in
Africa, Asia, Australasia, and the Middle East. The
company markets products through more than 18,000
retail outlets in 31 countries, fuels aircraft at 41 airports,
and provides marine fuels and lubricants at 103 ports in
22 countries.

**International Supply
and Trading Offices**
Bahrain
Cape Town
Dallas
London
Singapore (HQ)
Tokyo

Refineries
Bahrain (40%)
Batangas (the Philippines)
Cape Town (South Africa)
Karachi (Pakistan, 12%)
Kurnell (Australia, 75%)
Marifu (Japan, 50%)
Mombasa (Kenya, 11.75%)
Muroran (Japan, 50%)
Negishi (Japan, 50%)
Osaka (Japan, 50%)
Pualau Merilimau (Singapore, 33.3%)
Sriracha (Thailand, 4.75%)
Whangarei (New Zealand, 8.57%)
Yocheon (South Korea, 50%)

WHAT

Real Estate Holdings
Riviera Gardens (apartments, shopping, restaurants;
Hong Kong)

Selected Subsidiaries and Affiliates
American Overseas Petroleum Ltd.
(coordinates activities of P. T. Caltex Pacific Indonesia)
Amoseas Indonesia Inc. (manages holdings in Indonesia)
Caltex Australia
Caltex Oil South Africa (refining and marketing)
Caltex Services Corp. (technical services to group
companies)
Caltex Services Private, Ltd. (tanker operations,
Singapore)
Honam Oil Refinery Company, Ltd. (refining and
marketing, Korea)
Honam Tanker Co.
Korea Tanker Co.
Koa Oil Company, Ltd. (refining, Japan)
Nippon Petroleum Refining Company, Ltd.
(refining, Japan)
P. T. Caltex Pacific Indonesia (oil and gas
exploration)
Singapore Refining Co.

KEY COMPETITORS

Amerada Hess	Mobil
Amoco	Nippon Seiro
Ashland, Inc.	Norsk Hydro
Atlantic Richfield	Occidental
British Petroleum	PDVSA
Broken Hill	PEMEX
Coastal	Pennzoil
Cosmo Oil	Petrobrás
Elf Aquitaine	Petrofina
ENI	Phillips Petroleum
Exxon	Repsol
Hutchison Whampoa	Royal Dutch/Shell
Idemitsu Kosan	Showa Shell Sekiyu
Imperial Oil	Swire Pacific
Jardine Matheson	TOTAL
Kerr-McGee	Unocal
Koch	USX–Marathon
Mitsubishi	YPF

HOW MUCH

	Annual Growth	1985	1986	1987	1988	1989	1990	1991	1992	1993	1994
Sales ($ mil.)	0.0%	14,784	9,526	10,186	10,277	11,507	15,147	15,445	17,281	15,409	14,751
Net income ($ mil.)	(0.2%)	701	568	472	471	609	601	839	720	720	689
Income as % of sales	—	4.7%	5.7%	4.6%	4.6%	5.3%	4.0%	5.4%	4.2%	4.7%	4.7%
Employees	1.0%	—	—	—	—	—	7,700	7,700	7,600	7,800	8,000

1994 Year-end:
Debt ratio: 15.6%
Return on equity: 15.3%
Cash (mil.): $251
Current ratio: 0.79
Long-term debt (mil.): $715

Net Income ($ mil.)
1985–94

CENTEX CORPORATION

OVERVIEW

The housing business, like land itself, is uneven. To be successful, a housing company has to find a way to smooth things out.

Dallas-based Centex Corporation, the US's largest home builder, smooths things out with a strategy of diversification that has helped keep it in business through the boom and bust cycles of the housing market for nearly 50 years. The company builds single-family houses in 44 major markets in every region of the continental US. Its other lines of business include mortgage banking, land ownership, commercial real estate development (through its 3333 Holding Corp.), and construction supply manufacturing (through its 49% interest in Centex Construction Products, which went public in 1995).

The company also entered into joint ventures in 1995 with the Charles Church Group to build luxury houses in the UK and with Kensington Cottages Corp. to build 2 living centers for people suffering from Alzheimer's disease and memory disorders.

Although the company's strategy of geographical diversification protects it from regional downturns, Centex was helpless in the face of the repeated interest rate increases of 1994. Without the gain the company received from Centex Construction Products, 1995 earnings would have declined even further than they did. But Centex sees good prospects for the construction products company in sales of cement, of which there is an incipient shortage, and wallboard for home renovations.

WHEN

Centex was founded in 1950 by Tom Lively and Ira Rupley, whose association in home construction had begun informally 5 years earlier. In 1949 they built their first large subdivision near Dallas. They named their company Centex and were soon ready to operate nationally. Their first out-of-state project was Elk Grove Village, a development of 7,000 houses near Chicago. By 1960 the company had built 25,000 houses.

Centex's involvement in construction products began in 1963 when it built its first cement plant. Its Fernley, Nevada, cement kiln was started up in 1964 (3 other plants were established nationwide in the next 24 years).

In 1966 Centex expanded into the commercial construction business with the purchase of J. W. Bateson Co. (now called Centex Bateson Construction Co.), a construction and contracting company that had operated in Dallas since 1936. Centex moved into mortgage banking in 1973, allowing it to combine home building with home financing. Also during the 1970s, when oil prices seemed destined to rise forever, the company invested in petroleum, forming a new subsidiary, Cenergy.

Centex expanded its contracting and construction segment in 1978 by acquiring Frank J. Rooney, Inc., a large general contractor in Florida, and later acquiring other contractors in California and Washington, DC.

Centex's early geographical focus was narrow. In 1979, 72% of the company's 9,600 homes were built in Texas. And by 1980 the company was leveraged to the hilt.

Larry Hirsch, a New York–reared lawyer who had been at the helm of a Houston

cement and energy company, became COO in 1984 (and CEO in 1988). In that year, after oil prices had begun to decline but before the collapse in 1986, Centex sold Cenergy. The early 1980s were a boom time for Texas real estate because deregulation left many S&L officers desperate to make loans, any loans. The market became overbuilt, and when credit began to dry up in 1986–87 after the spectacular failure of several Texas S&Ls, the Texas real estate market crashed. Centex was pinched, but because its fixed costs (personnel and leased equipment) were elastic, it survived on the sales from less depressed areas of the US. The Texas market began rebounding after 1991.

Centex Development Company (CDC) was established in 1987 as a custodian for $75.9 million worth of land that the company could not develop during the bust and whose carrying costs were a burden on its balance sheet. Centex also created a new subsidiary, Centex-Rodgers Construction, in Nashville, which focused on medical construction, then a growth area. In the 1990s Centex continued to diversify its building operations and to expand its mortgage banking operations.

In 1994 the company took its construction products division public, retaining a 49% interest. But it was a dicey year for home builders as increases in interest rates frightened many buyers off, so response to the IPO was notably subdued. After a 7-year experiment with thrift management, Centex sold off its S&Ls in 1994.

Centex completed its purchase of Dallas-based developer Vista Properties in 1995.

NYSE symbol: CTX
Fiscal year ends: March 31

WHO

Chairman and CEO: Laurence E. Hirsch, age 49,
$790,000 pay
**President and COO; Chairman, President, and CEO,
Centex Construction Group:** William J. Gillilan III,
age 49, $575,000 pay
President, CEO, and COO, Centex Real Estate:
Timothy R. Eller, age 46, $575,000 pay
CEO, CTX Mortgage: Carl N. Hearne
President, Nova Mortgage Credit: Richard L. Smith
EVP and CFO: David W. Quinn, age 53, $560,000 pay
**VP, Chief Legal Officer, General Counsel, and
Secretary:** Raymond G. Smerge, age 51, $345,500 pay
VP Finance and Controller: Michael S. Albright, age 47
VP Tax: Richard C. Harvey
VP Corporate Communications: Sheila E. Gallagher
Auditors: Arthur Andersen & Co, SC

WHERE

HQ: 3333 Lee Pkwy., Ste. 1200, Dallas, TX 75219
Phone: 214-559-6500
Fax: 214-559-6750

Centex builds houses in 44 markets in California,
Florida, Georgia, Illinois, Minnesota, New Mexico, North
Carolina, Ohio, South Carolina, Texas, Washington, and
the District of Columbia.

	1995 Houses Completed	
	No.	% of total
Southwest	3,674	28
East	2,921	23
Southeast	2,632	20
West	2,454	19
Midwest	1,283	10
Total	**12,964**	**100**

WHAT

	1995 Sales		1995 Operating Income	
	$ mil.	% of total	$ mil.	% of total
Home building	2,111	65	112	93
Contracting & construction services	1,060	32	(2)	—
Financial services	107	3	9	7
Total	**3,278**	**100**	**119**	**100**

Selected Subsidiaries
Centex Construction Group, Inc.
Centex Escrow Co.
Centex Insurance Agencies
Centex Real Estate
Centex Roofing Co.
Centex Senior Services
Centex Title Co.
CTX Commercial Loan Division
CTX Mortgage Co.
Metropolitan Title and Guaranty Co.
Nova Mortgage Credit Corp.

KEY COMPETITORS

Beazer Homes
Del Webb
Fleetwood
Kaufman and Broad
NVR
Pulte
Ryland
US Home
Weekley Homes

HOW MUCH

	9-Year Growth	1986	1987	1988	1989	1990	1991	1992	1993	1994	1995
Sales ($ mil.)	1.9%	2,767	2,530	2,884	3,632	4,039	4,404	2,166	2,503	3,214	3,278
Net income ($ mil.)	7.5%	48	44	24	40	62	44	35	61	85	92
Income as % of sales	—	1.7%	1.7%	0.8%	1.1%	1.5%	1.0%	1.6%	2.4%	2.7%	2.8%
Earnings per share ($)	9.8%	1.31	1.24	0.75	1.32	2.01	1.42	1.11	1.91	2.60	3.04
Stock price – high ($)[1]	—	13.44	20.25	17.81	14.75	20.94	22.13	23.31	32.88	45.25	45.75
Stock price – low ($)[1]	—	10.25	12.00	7.56	8.25	13.63	9.63	14.00	19.88	26.75	20.13
Stock price – close ($)[1]	6.7%	12.69	15.63	8.63	14.63	15.44	14.94	22.44	32.00	42.00	22.75
P/E – high	—	10	16	24	11	10	16	21	17	17	15
P/E – low	—	8	10	10	6	7	7	13	10	10	7
Dividends per share ($)	4.9%	0.13	0.13	0.13	0.13	0.20	0.20	0.20	0.20	0.20	0.20
Book value per share ($)	11.2%	9.17	10.23	12.12	13.28	14.85	16.07	16.99	18.57	21.12	23.80
Employees	3.7%	4,600	4,500	4,200	4,700	5,100	5,300	5,500	6,500	8,430	6,395

1995 Year-end:
Debt ratio: 54.4%
Return on equity: 13.8%
Cash (mil.): $24
Current ratio: —
Long-term debt (mil.): $223
No. of shares (mil.): 28
Dividends
  Yield: 0.9%
  Payout: 6.6%
Market value (mil.): $639

**Stock Price History[1]
High/Low 1986–95**

[1] Stock prices are for the prior calendar year.

CENTRAL AND SOUTH WEST

OVERVIEW

To stay current with a transforming industry, Central and South West Corp. (CSW) is altering the way it works. The Dallas-based public utility holding company has 4 electric subsidiaries: Central Power and Light (serving South Texas), Public Service Company of Oklahoma (PSO; about 2/3 of Oklahoma), Southwestern Electric Power (parts of Arkansas, Louisiana, and Texas), and West Texas Utilities.

CSW operates 38 generating plants serving more than 1.6 million customers within the 2nd largest geographical service area in the US. Kilowatt-hour (KWH) sales were up 3.5% in 1994, and the company expects growth to average 2.4% over the next 10 years.

CSW has also diversified into other energy-related fields, buying Transok (1961, gas pipelines) and forming subsidiaries such as CSW International (1994, overseas power plants).

In response to a changing regulatory environment and increased competition, CEO E. R. Brooks (who won a *Wall Street Journal* management award in 1993) began in 1993 to guide CSW through a 2-year restructuring. In order to enhance and expand CSW's core business, Brooks placed the electric utilities in CSW Electric, a new division. Power plant operations and administrative functions were folded into CSW Services, allowing the utilities to focus on customer service and marketing. The firm reassigned many employees to new jobs and reduced its ranks by 7%.

CSW is seeking the repeal of the Public Utility Holding Company Act (PUHCA). The company views PUHCA — which requires the firm to seek the SEC's approval before taking actions unrelated to its electric utility business — as the only barrier to its ability to compete.

WHEN

Utility magnate Samuel Insull and his brother Martin formed the Central & South West Utilities Company (CSU) as a subsidiary of their huge Middle West Utilities in 1925. CSU, in turn, united 5 firms that provided electric power, water, and gas for customers in Kansas, Louisiana, Mississippi, Oklahoma, and Texas.

PUHCA, passed in 1935, was intended to break the great electric utility trusts and required holding companies to register with the SEC. In 1947 CSU merged with one of its subsidiaries (American Public Service), changed its name to Central and South West Corporation, and was divested from Middle West.

The postwar building boom in the 1950s and the growth in the oil and natural gas industry in Oklahoma and Texas helped CSW reach over $200 million in sales by 1962. In 1961 the firm bought Transok Pipe Line to supply natural gas to PSO's power stations.

Within a decade CSW's revenues had more than doubled, to $425 million. All of its plants were fueled by natural gas and located mostly in rural areas. Thus the firm initially avoided the safety and environmental concerns associated with nuclear and coal-fired plants.

Led by chairman Silas Bent Phillips, CSW embarked on a major construction program in 1972. Despite an effort to diversify fuel sources, by 1978 the company was still 96% dependent on natural gas, and its fuel costs were 50% above competitors Houston Lighting & Power (HL&P) and Texas Utilities (TU), which had converted to lignite or still had cheap gas contracts in effect. So Phillips decided to interconnect CSW's utilities throughout their 4-state service area to make cheaper wholesale power available systemwide. Until then, the Texas power grid was completely independent of the US grid. HL&P and TU were loath to send power across state lines (which constituted interstate commerce and subjected them to federal regulation). After years of litigation, a compromise allowed CSW to convert the AC power to DC, transmit it across state lines, then reconvert it to AC, while the feds looked the other way.

CSW's 25% ownership of the South Texas Nuclear Project mired the firm in spiraling construction costs during the 1980s. Generating Unit 1 went on line in 1988, 8 years behind schedule. Unit 2 was powered up in 1989.

In 1991 president E. R. Brooks was named chairman and CEO. The next year the federal Energy Policy Act fundamentally changed the industry by opening once-exclusive service areas to wholesale competition.

Then in 1993 CSW and El Paso Electric (EPE) agreed to merge as a way of pulling the latter out of bankruptcy. In 1994 the restructuring of CSW began in earnest, and 2 subsidiaries were formed: CSW Communications and CSW International.

Citing a breach of agreement, CSW tore up plans to buy EPE in June 1995. In reality, the 2 years between the merger announcement and breakup saw widespread changes in the electric utility industry; regulatory policies changed and competition grew, making EPE worth less than the agreed upon $2.2 billion.

NYSE symbol: CSR
Fiscal year ends: December 31

WHO

Chairman, President, and CEO: E. R. Brooks, age 57, $620,342 pay
EVP: T. V. Shockley III, age 50, $405,082 pay
EVP: Harry D. Mattison, age 58, $391,153 pay
SVP and General Counsel: Ferd. C. Meyer Jr., age 55, $328,603 pay
SVP and CFO: Glenn D. Rosilier, age 47, $318,255 pay
VP Corporate Services (HR): Venita McCellon-Allen
Auditors: Arthur Andersen & Co, SC

WHERE

HQ: Central and South West Corporation,
1616 Woodall Rodgers Fwy., Dallas, TX 75202-1234
Phone: 214-777-1000
Fax: 214-777-1033

	1994 Electric Sales	
	$ mil.	% of total
Texas	1,900	62
Oklahoma	736	24
Louisiana	245	8
Arkansas	184	6
Total	**3,065**	**100**

WHAT

	1994 Sales	
	$ mil.	% of total
Residential electric	1,156	32
Commercial electric	836	23
Industrial electric	733	20
Wholesale electric	204	6
Other electric	136	4
Gas & other	558	15
Total	**3,623**	**100**

1994 Energy Marketed		
	KWH (mil.)	% of total
Industrial	18,869	33
Residential	16,368	28
Commercial	13,463	24
Wholesale	7,133	12
Other	1,501	3
Total	**57,334**	**100**

1994 Electric Generating Capacity		
	MW	% of total
Natural gas	8,246	59
Coal & lignite	4,702	33
Nuclear	630	4
Plant in storage	557	4
Hydroelectric & oil	42	—
Total	**14,177**	**100**

Nonutility Subsidiaries
CSW Communications (designs, builds, and maintains telecommunications networks)
CSW Energy (develops and operates independent power and cogeneration projects)
CSW International (develops and operates foreign independent power and cogeneration projects)
Transok (intrastate [Oklahoma] natural gas pipeline and marketing)

KEY COMPETITORS

Cajun Electric Power Coop.
Central Louisiana Electric
City of Austin
Destec Energy
El Paso Electric
Empire District Electric
Entergy
Houston Industries
Lower Colorado River Authority
Magic Valley Electric Coop.
North Plains Electric Coop.
Northeast Texas Electric Coop.
Oklahoma Gas and Electric
Pedernales Electric Coop.
Rusk County Electric Coop.
Southwestern Electric Power
Southwestern Public Service
Texas Utilities
TNP Enterprises

HOW MUCH

	9-Year Growth	1985	1986	1987	1988	1989	1990	1991	1992	1993	1994
Sales ($ mil.)	3.3%	2,711	2,555	2,436	2,512	2,549	2,744	3,047	3,289	3,687	3,623
Net income ($ mil.)	2.2%	340	355	402	356	337	386	401	404	281	412
Income as % of sales	—	12.5%	13.9%	16.5%	14.2%	13.2%	14.1%	13.2%	12.3%	7.6%	11.4%
Earnings per share ($)	1.6%	1.81	1.88	1.96	1.72	1.63	1.90	1.99	2.03	1.39	2.08
Stock price – high ($)	—	14.06	18.75	20.25	17.38	20.13	23.00	27.19	30.00	34.25	30.88
Stock price – low ($)	—	10.81	13.25	13.50	14.75	14.88	18.31	20.75	24.25	28.25	20.13
Stock price – close ($)	5.7%	13.75	17.13	14.75	16.00	20.06	22.00	27.00	29.13	30.25	22.63
P/E – high	—	8	10	10	10	9	10	14	15	25	15
P/E – low	—	6	7	7	9	9	10	10	12	20	10
Dividends per share ($)	6.0%	1.01	1.07	1.14	1.22	1.30	1.38	1.46	1.54	1.62	1.70
Book value per share ($)	3.6%	11.64	12.45	13.26	13.75	14.07	14.57	15.05	15.54	15.55	16.01
Employees	(1.8%)	9,469	9,202	8,894	8,478	8,423	8,377	8,581	8,595	8,707	8,055

1994 Year-end:
Debt ratio: 56.7%
Return on equity: 13.8%
Cash (mil.): $27.0
Current ratio: 0.56
Long-term debt (mil.): $2,940
No. of shares (mil.): 191
Dividends
   Yield: 7.5%
   Payout: 81.7%
Market value (mil.): $4,313

Stock Price History
High/Low 1985–94

THE COASTAL CORPORATION

OVERVIEW

Diversified energy giant Coastal Corporation has $10 billion in assets but is not coasting into the future. The Houston-based company has operations in natural gas marketing, transmission, and storage; petroleum refining, marketing, and distribution; oil and gas exploration; coal mining; chemicals; independent power production; and trucking.

Coastal's most profitable business is the interstate transmission of natural gas. Through its ANR Pipeline subsidiary it operates 2 major pipeline systems (over 19,000 miles in total length), one in the Midwest and one in the Rocky Mountain region and Kansas.

Through subsidiary Coastal Mart and branded marketers, Coastal conducts retail marketing in 37 states through 1,457 Coastal branded outlets. The company is investing $150 million to upgrade its 3 wholly owned refineries in Aruba, New Jersey, and Texas in order to increase their capacity to produce middle distillates, such as gasoline.

Coastal is also increasing its international operations. In 1994 and 1995 it signed deals to develop tracts in central Peru and the South China Sea. It also set up a 1995 joint venture agreement to construct and operate an electric plant in Wuxi City, China.

WHEN

After spending boyhood summers working in the oil fields, serving as a bomber pilot in WWII, and earning a mechanical engineering degree from Texas A&M, Oscar Wyatt started a small natural gas gathering business in 1951 in Corpus Christi, Texas.

In 1955 the company became Coastal States Gas Producing Company. It collected and distributed natural gas from oil fields in southern Texas. In 1962 Coastal purchased Sinclair Oil's Corpus Christi refinery and pipeline network. Also in the early 1960s, a Coastal subsidiary, Lo-Vaca Gathering, supplied natural gas to Texas cities and utilities. During the energy crisis of the early 1970s, Lo-Vaca curtailed its natural gas supplies and then raised prices. Unhappy customers sued Coastal, and regulators in 1977 ordered Lo-Vaca to refund $1.6 billion. To finance the settlement, Coastal spun off Lo-Vaca as Valero Energy.

Meanwhile, the combative Wyatt, who would earn a reputation as one of the swashbuckling corporate raiders of the 1980s, had been expanding Coastal through a series of deals. Coastal won Rio Grande Valley Gas, a small South Texas pipeline (1968), and then in 1973 mounted a successful $182 million hostile bid for Colorado Interstate Gas and changed its name to Coastal States Gas Corporation. With aggressive acquisitions, Coastal moved into low-sulfur Utah coal (Southern Utah Fuel, 1973), New England pipelines (Union Petroleum, 1973), California refining (Pacific Refining, 1976), and Florida petroleum marketing and transportation (Belcher Oil, 1977; renamed in 1990). In 1980 Coastal adopted its present name. Wyatt tried to snare Texas Gas Resources (1983) and Houston Natural Gas (1984). These bids were thwarted, but when the companies bought back stock

owned by Coastal to defend themselves, Coastal made money.

In 1985 Coastal purchased American Natural Resources in a $2.5 billion hostile takeover. In 1989, just before Wyatt stepped down as CEO, Coastal bid $2.6 billion for Texas Eastern, but that company sold out to white knight Panhandle Eastern.

Before the 1991 Gulf War, Wyatt courted the Iraqis, attempting to trade Coastal's refining and marketing assets for a steady supply of Iraq's crude oil. Wyatt and Coastal director John B. Connally, former US secretary of the treasury, met with Saddam Hussein and flew hostages out of Baghdad. Wyatt's statements against Operation Desert Storm drew harsh US criticism. In 1992 Coastal cut staff and inventory and closed a Kansas refinery after its Refining and Marketing Group posted a $192 million operating loss.

In 1993 Coastal announced plans to build the 600-mile SunShine Pipeline in Florida. Coastal also signed contracts with Peoples Gas System and Florida Power Corporation to supply Florida with natural gas. That same year construction was completed on the Empire State Pipeline. The 156-mile pipeline system, in which Coastal holds a 45% interest, runs from Niagara Falls to Syracuse, New York.

In 1994 the company announced a $100 million expansion of its refinery complex in Aruba, in the Caribbean.

In 1995 Coastal agreed to buy Maverick Markets, a chain of 102 gasoline-selling convenience stores in South Texas. The largest concentration of these stores (35) is in Corpus Christi. Also that year, Coastal signed a project development agreement with Habibullah Energy to build and manage a 140-megawatt power plant in the Pakistani city of Quetta.

NYSE symbol: CGP
Fiscal year ends: December 31

Chairman and CEO: Oscar S. Wyatt Jr., age 70,
$1,049,093 pay
VC: Harold Burrow, age 80
President, COO, and CFO: David A. Arledge, age 50,
$703,873 pay
EVP Natural Gas: James F. Cordes, age 54, $722,223 pay
EVP Refining, Engineering, and Chemicals: James A.
King, age 55, $418,823 pay
EVP Crude Oil Supply and Marketing: Sam F.
Willson Jr., age 65, $409,062 pay
SVP and General Counsel: Carl A. Corrallo, age 51
SVP: Jeffrey A. Connelly, age 48
SVP Finance: Donald H. Gullquist, age 51
SVP and Controller: Coby C. Hesse, age 47
SVP Coal: James L. Van Lanen, age 50
SVP Exploration and Production: Jerry D. Bullock,
age 65
SVP Marketing: Dan J. Hill, age 54
SVP Retail Marketing: Jack C. Pester, age 60
SVP Special Projects: Kenneth O. Johnson, age 74
SVP and Secretary: Austin M. O' Toole, age 59
VP Product Supply and Transportation: Edward A.
Moré, age 46
VP Crude Oil Supply and Marketing: Thomas M. Wade,
age 42
VP Employee Relations: E. C. Simpson, age 59
Auditors: Deloitte & Touche LLP

WHERE

HQ: Coastal Tower, 9 Greenway Plaza, Houston, TX
77046-0995
Phone: 713-877-1400
Fax: 713-877-6754

Coastal conducts marketing and distribution operations
around the world. The company and its branded
marketers operate 1,457 Coastal outlets in 37 states.

WHAT

	1994 Sales		1994 Operating Income	
	$ mil.	% of total	$ mil.	% of total
Refining & marketing	6,459	62	153	21
Natural gas	3,076	29	431	59
Coal	451	4	98	13
Exploration & production	299	3	42	6
Other	208	2	9	1
Adjustments	(278)	—	—	—
Total	**10,215**	**100**	**733**	**100**

Selected Subsidiaries

**Refining, Marketing,
and Distribution**
Coastal Fuels Marketing,
Inc.
Coastal Refining &
Marketing, Inc.

Natural Gas
ANR Pipeline Co.
ANR Storage Co.
Coastal Gas Services Co.
Colorado Interstate Gas Co.

Coal
ANR Coal Co.
Coastal States Energy Co.

Exploration and Production
ANR Production Co.
CIG Exploration, Inc.
Coastal Oil & Gas Corp.

Other
ANR Freight System, Inc.
Coastal Power Production Co.

KEY COMPETITORS

Amerada Hess	Exxon	Petrofina
Amoco	Kaneb Services	Phillips Petroleum
Ashland, Inc.	Koch	Shell Oil
Atlantic Richfield	Mobil	Sonat, Inc.
British Petroleum	Natural Gas	Southland
Broken Hill	Occidental	Sun Company
Chevron	Oryx	Tenneco
Columbia Gas	Panhandle	Texaco
Diamond Shamrock	Eastern	TOTAL
DuPont	PDVSA	Unocal
Elf Aquitaine	PEMEX	USX-Marathon
Enron	Pennzoil	Valero Energy

HOW MUCH

	9-Year Growth	1985	1986	1987	1988	1989	1990	1991	1992	1993	1994
Sales ($ mil.)	3.8%	7,275	6,668	7,429	8,187	8,271	9,381	9,549	10,063	10,136	10,215
Net income ($ mil.)	5.6%	142	72	113	157	170	226	96	(127)	116	233
Income as % of sales	—	2.0%	1.1%	1.5%	1.9%	2.1%	2.4%	1.0%	—	1.2%	2.3%
Earnings per share ($)	2.7%	1.61	0.56	1.40	1.80	1.81	2.15	0.92	(1.23)	1.02	2.05
Stock price – high ($)	—	17.47	16.03	25.69	22.50	33.09	39.63	36.75	30.00	31.38	33.75
Stock price – low ($)	—	12.47	12.72	14.03	19.84	22.00	29.25	23.75	22.00	23.50	24.75
Stock price – close ($)	4.4%	17.41	15.56	17.34	22.84	33.09	32.25	24.63	23.88	28.25	25.75
P/E – high	—	11	29	18	13	18	18	40	—	31	17
P/E – low	—	8	23	10	11	12	14	26	—	23	12
Dividends per share ($)	11.5%	0.15	0.18	0.22	0.27	0.27	0.40	0.40	0.40	0.40	0.40
Book value per share ($)	8.0%	11.71	11.75	12.84	14.25	17.36	19.21	19.67	19.33	21.77	23.43
Employees	0.1%	16,200	16,500	17,800	19,000	13,100	13,900	16,500	16,600	16,000	16,300

1994 Year-end:
Debt ratio: 61.7%
Return on equity: 9.8%
Cash (mil.): $74
Current ratio: 0.97
Long-term debt (mil.): $3,720
No. of shares (mil.): 105
Dividends
  Yield: 1.6%
  Payout: 19.5%
Market value (mil.): $2,697

**Stock Price History
High/Low 1985–94**

COMPAQ COMPUTER CORPORATION

OVERVIEW

Compaq, which in 1995 slipped to #2 in the US PC market (after Packard Bell), is fighting to regain the top spot. Among the weapons in its arsenal are a low-cost manufacturing agreement with Taiwanese subcontractors and a barrage of new products. Also in 1995 Compaq filed a suit accusing Packard Bell of selling new computers that incorporate used parts (a charge Packard Bell denies).

Despite rapid sales growth in early 1995, Compaq, which sells primarily to corporate clients, is having trouble competing in 2 key areas: low-end home computers and laptop models. Instead of relying on its own highly touted manufacturing, the company has decided to put its name on home models made by Mitac International and laptops made by

Inventec Group (both of Taiwan). Compaq is risking consumer disfavor in return for low cost and a reliable inventory.

It was Compaq's in-house manufacturing that cost the company its top market share in the first place: rivals such as Packard Bell, Dell, and Gateway, which use Pentium-based components made by Intel, introduced the faster machines while Compaq was still relying on 486-based models as the top of its line.

Not to worry. In early 1995 Compaq made its biggest product introduction ever, rolling out more than 100 new items, many with Pentium chips and built-in networking and systems management capabilities. A recent pact with NexGen for Pentium clones should increase Compaq's margins even more.

WHEN

Joseph R. (Rod) Canion and 2 other ex–Texas Instruments engineers started Compaq in Houston in 1982 to manufacture and sell portable IBM-compatible computers. Compaq's first portable was developed from a prototype the 3 sketched on a paper place mat when they first discussed the product idea.

Compaq shipped its first computer in 1982 and in 1983 (the year it went public) recorded sales of $111 million — unprecedented growth for a computer start-up. Compaq's success was due in part to emphasis on leading-edge technology. In 1983 Compaq introduced a portable computer — 18 months before IBM did — and in 1986 it was first out with a computer based on Intel's 386 chip. However, Compaq delayed introduction of its laptop until the prototype's display and battery technologies met engineering specifications. Although introduced late (1988), Compaq's SLT/286 laptop with its crisp display screen became an immediate success.

To sell its products, Compaq capitalized on the extensive base of dealers and suppliers built up around the IBM PC. Rather than establish a large sales force, Compaq gave exclusive rights to dealers for sales and service of its products and by 1990 had a network of 3,800 retailers in 152 countries. The dealer channel proved to be effective. In 1988 Compaq became the first company to exceed the $2 billion sales mark within 6 years of its first product introduction (1982–88). Sales in 1989 rose to $2.9 billion.

In 1989 the company dropped Businessland, its 2nd largest reseller (after ComputerLand), as an authorized dealer after Businessland demanded preferential discounts. Compaq

reauthorized Businessland as a dealer in 1990 after it agreed to abide by Compaq's policies. In 1991 Compaq bought a 13% interest in engineering workstation maker Silicon Graphics and paid $50 million for access to its graphics technology. Compaq also took a lead role in creating a 21-company alliance, Advanced Computer Environment (ACE), to establish a standard for Reduced Instruction Set Computing (RISC) computers to compete with those of Sun and IBM.

Economic recession and stiff price competition slashed Compaq's revenues in 1991. Founder and CEO Canion (an engineer) was forced to resign; he was replaced with Eckhard Pfeiffer (a salesman). The next year Compaq withdrew from ACE and sold back its stake in Silicon Graphics and its 20% interest in Conner Peripherals (bought in 1986) for an $80 million profit. Late in 1992 Compaq introduced the world's fastest PC server, the Compaq SYSTEMPRO/XL. In 1993 Compaq and Microsoft announced a joint venture to develop pen-based PCs, mobile computing, and multiprocessor computers and servers.

By 1994 Compaq had become the world's top manufacturer of personal computers, passing IBM and Apple to take 10% of the market. That same year the company announced a joint venture with video conferencing developer Picturetel Corporation to design and build personal conferencing products.

In 1995 Compaq established a unit to develop multimedia software products. The previous year the company had acquired a 4% stake in home improvement software publisher Books That Work.

NYSE symbol: CPQ
Fiscal year ends: December 31

WHO

Chairman: Benjamin M. Rosen, age 62
President and CEO: Eckhard Pfeiffer, age 53, $3,550,000 pay
SVP Systems: Gary Stimac, age 43, $1,000,000 pay
SVP Europe, Middle East, and Africa: Andreas Barth, age 50, $914,298 pay
SVP North America: Ross A. Cooley, age 54, $890,000 pay
SVP Finance and CFO: Daryl J. White, age 47, $835,000 pay
SVP Desktop PC Division: John T. Rose
SVP Portable PC Division: Hugh Barnes
SVP Corporate Operations: Gregory E. Petsch, age 44
SVP, General Counsel, and Secretary: Wilson D. Fargo, age 50
SVP Human Resources: Hans W. Gutsch, age 51
Auditors: Price Waterhouse LLP

WHERE

HQ: 20555 SH 249, Houston, TX 77070
Phone: 713-370-0670
Fax: 713-374-1740

Compaq has manufacturing facilities in Brazil, China, Scotland, and Singapore. The company sells and supports its products in more than 100 countries.

	1994 Sales		1994 Operating Income	
	$ mil.	% of total	$ mil.	% of total
US & Canada	5,473	50	533	41
Europe	3,829	35	470	36
Other regions	1,564	15	292	23
Adjustments	—	—	(1)	—
Total	**10,866**	**100**	**1,294**	**100**

WHAT

	1994 Sales
	% of total
Desktop PCs	58
Portable PCs	25
PC systems	17
Total	**100**

Computer Peripherals
COMPAQ ProLiant

Desktop PCs
COMPAQ Deskpro Series
COMPAQ Presario
COMPAQ ProLinea Series

PC Systems
COMPAQ ProSignia
COMPAQ Systempro

Portables
COMPAQ Concerto
COMPAQ Contura
COMPAQ LTE Lite

Software
Rack Builder
TabWorks

KEY COMPETITORS

Acer	Fujitsu	NEC
Advanced Logic Research	Gateway 2000	Oki
Apple	Hewlett-Packard	Olivetti
AST	Hitachi	Packard Bell
AT&T	Hyundai	Philips
Canon	IBM	Sharp
Casio	Intel	Siemens
CompuAdd	Machines Bull	Sun Microsystems
Data General	Matsushita	Toshiba
DEC	Micron Technology	Unisys
Dell		Wang

HOW MUCH

	9-Year Growth	1985	1986	1987	1988	1989	1990	1991	1992	1993	1994
Sales ($ mil.)	40.7%	504	625	1,224	2,066	2,876	3,599	3,271	4,100	7,191	10,866
Net income ($ mil.)	47.0%	27	43	136	255	333	455	131	213	462	867
Income as % of sales	—	5.3%	6.9%	11.1%	12.4%	11.6%	12.6%	4.0%	5.2%	6.4%	8.0%
Earnings per share ($)	40.5%	0.15	0.22	.60	1.05	1.29	1.70	0.50	0.84	1.78	3.21
Stock price – high ($)	—	2.37	3.60	13.07	10.95	18.73	22.60	24.73	16.61	25.22	42.13
Stock price – low ($)	—	1.02	1.94	3.21	6.99	9.87	11.82	7.37	7.41	13.90	24.13
Stock price – close ($)	37.8%	2.21	3.21	9.22	9.93	13.24	18.77	8.78	16.23	24.60	39.50
P/E – high	—	16	16	22	10	15	13	50	20	14	13
P/E – low	—	7	9	5	7	8	7	15	9	8	8
Dividends per share ($)	—	0.00	0.00	0.00	0.00	0.00	0.00	0.00	0.00	0.00	0.00
Book value per share ($)	36.4%	0.86	1.13	1.95	3.52	4.97	7.88	7.64	8.37	10.48	14.07
Employees	25.6%	1,850	2,200	4,000	6,900	9,500	11,400	11,600	11,300	10,541	14,372

1994 Year-end:
Debt ratio: 7.5%
Return on equity: 27.4%
Cash (mil.): $471
Current ratio: 2.56
Long-term debt (mil.): $300
No. of shares (mil.): 261
Dividends
  Yield: —
  Payout: —
Market value (mil.): $10,311

Stock Price History
High/Low 1985–94

COMPUCOM SYSTEMS, INC.

OVERVIEW

Dallas-based CompuCom is one of the largest PC resellers and network integration companies in the US. It caters primarily to large corporate customers, providing product procurement and configuration, network integration, and technical support from its more than 40 sales and service locations nationwide. Venture capital firm Safeguard Scientifics owns about 2/3 of CompuCom's stock.

CompuCom sells several lines of PCs, including Apple, Compaq, and IBM, as well as peripherals, software, and networking products from such suppliers as DEC, Intel, Microsoft, Novell, and Synoptics.

CompuCom's low-cost, direct sales format enables the company to price competitively. It can purchase, configure, deliver, and service microcomputer and network products for less

than a customer would pay to buy directly from a manufacturer. In addition, CompuCom has recently centralized its sales offices into a customer center in Dallas. Customers can dial a toll-free number to obtain information about product availability, pricing, and shipping.

With the rapid growth of computer networking, CompuCom is focusing on expanding its networking and service businesses. It is working to become what it calls an "end-to-end" services provider, helping customers purchase their computer systems, configuring the computers, integrating those PCs into a network, and then providing training, network management services, and a help desk when customers have questions. It boosted its service workforce by about 70% in 1994.

WHEN

CompuCom was founded by Stanley Sternberg in Michigan in 1981 to make factory automation products. Originally called CytoSystems, the company changed its name in 1983 to Machine Vision International (MVI) to reflect its focus on designing artificial vision systems for computers. Its main customers were Detroit automakers, who used MVI's automated inspection guidance systems to control industrial robots.

By the mid-1980s MVI was one of the largest machine vision companies in the US. In 1984 Safeguard Scientifics bought 31.5% of the company; Safeguard had been founded in 1953 by Warren Musser and Frank Diamond to raise funds for small, promising businesses. Looking to raise more capital for MVI, Safeguard and MVI's management took it public in 1985. However, MVI soon ran into trouble as the machine vision industry began to cool off. General Motors, the company's biggest customer, cut its orders, and MVI lost more than $13 million in 1986. Safeguard chairman Musser became chairman of MVI and began to shift the company's focus.

In 1987 MVI acquired New Jersey–based computer retailer TriStar Data Systems and Office Automation. The company moved its headquarters to New Jersey, adopted its present name, and shifted the thrust of its business to selling and supporting microcomputer systems.

CompuCom exited the machine vision business in 1988 to focus on computer retailing. That same year the company acquired CompuShop, a Dallas-based computer retailer,

from Bell Atlantic. CompuCom then moved its headquarters to Dallas. James Dixon, CEO of CompuShop, became president of CompuCom. In 1989 the company named former CompuCraft head Avery More president and co-CEO; Dixon was named co-CEO and chairman. More made the key decision to abandon minicomputers and shift operations to a networked PC platform.

With the acquisition of the Computer Factory in 1991, the company became an authorized Apple dealer and gained a foothold in the northeastern US. Also that year it expanded its presence in the western US with the acquisition of retailer Photo & Sound Company. CompuCom considered expanding into discount superstore retailing but decided to focus on what More called its "bread and butter" — direct sales to large and medium-sized corporate customers. The retail outlets of the Computer Factory were sold.

In 1992 CompuCom expanded its networking business when it bought network integrator MicroSolutions. When More left the company in 1993 to start a venture capital firm, Eureka Ventures, COO Ed Anderson became CEO; Dixon remained chairman.

As part of its strategy to expand its networking and service business, CompuCom has acquired several network service companies, including San Francisco–based International Micronet Systems in 1994. In early 1995 it bought 3 network integrators: New Jersey–based Allerion, Houston's Trellis/ Hayes/Micronet, and Minneapolis-based Benchmark Network Systems.

Nasdaq symbol: CMPC
Fiscal year ends: December 31

WHO

Chairman: James W. Dixon, age 48, $620,000 pay
President and CEO: Edward R. Anderson, age 48, $620,000 pay
EVP Sales: Daniel F. Brown, age 49, $465,500 pay
SVP Finance and CFO; President, ClientLink: Robert J. Boutin, age 37, $300,000 pay
SVP and COO, ClientLink: James H. Hamilton
SVP Services: Alfred Chong
VP Information Services and Chief Information Officer: Jack D. Dowling
VP Technology Management: A. David Shay
VP Product Management: Jack B. Smyth
VP CompuCom Technology Services: Robert C. Donalson
VP Product Integration Networking Group: David W. Hall
VP Services Integration: Brian P. O'Connell
VP Distribution Services: David I. Robinson
VP Finance and Corporate Controller: M. Lazane Smith
VP Human Resources: Mark S. Esselman
Treasurer: Daniel L. Celoni
Auditors: KPMG Peat Marwick LLP

WHERE

HQ: 10100 N. Central Expwy., Dallas, TX 75231-1800
Phone: 214-265-3600
Fax: 214-265-5220

Distribution Facilities
Stockton, California
Woolwich, New Jersey

WHAT

Selected Microcomputer Brands Sold
3Com
Apple
Compaq
DEC
Hewlett-Packard
IBM
NEC
Toshiba

Selected Software Brands Sold
Lotus
Microsoft
Novell
WordPerfect

Subsidiaries
ClientLink, Inc.
CompuCom Properties, Inc.
The Computer Factory Inc.
International Micronet Systems

KEY COMPETITORS

Arthur Andersen
Baker & Taylor
Circuit City
CompuAdd
CompUSA
Computer Horizons
Compuware
Control Data Systems
Dataflex
DEC
Dell
EDS
Egghead
Entex
Gateway 2000
IBM
InaCom
Ingram
Intelligent Electronics
Merisel
Micro Warehouse
MicroAge
Perot Systems
Random Access
Software Spectrum
Tandy
Tiger Direct
Vanstar
Wang

HOW MUCH

	Annual Growth	1985	1986	1987	1988	1989	1990	1991	1992	1993	1994
Sales ($ mil.)	72.7%	9	3	43	159	271	343	529	713	1,016	1,256
Net income ($ mil.)	—	(4)	(14)	0	2	2	4	5	7	11	15
Income as % of sales	—	—	—	0.2%	1.0%	0.6%	1.0%	0.9%	1.0%	1.1%	1.2%
Earnings per share ($)	—	(0.51)	(1.25)	0.01	0.06	0.06	0.13	0.16	0.22	0.29	0.34
Stock price – high ($)	—	7.13	5.75	3.38	2.50	2.25	2.13	3.56	2.88	4.63	7.25
Stock price – low ($)	—	4.38	0.50	0.38	1.13	1.13	0.75	1.31	1.44	2.19	2.75
Stock price – close ($)	(5.1%)	5.00	0.50	2.13	1.50	1.13	1.31	2.25	2.19	4.06	3.13
P/E – high	—	—	—	—	42	38	16	22	13	16	21
P/E – low	—	—	—	—	19	19	6	8	7	8	8
Dividends per share ($)	—	0.00	0.00	0.00	0.00	0.00	0.00	0.00	0.00	0.00	0.00
Book value per share ($)	14.0%	0.68	(0.49)	0.42	0.72	0.81	0.93	1.14	1.39	1.78	2.21
Employees	34.1%	—	—	253	540	590	683	1,061	1,156	1,542	1,975

1994 Year-end:
Debt ratio: 59.2%
Return on equity: 22.6%
Cash (mil.): $4
Current ratio: 2.06
Long-term debt (mil.): $137
No. of shares (mil.): 34
Dividends
  Yield: —
  Payout: —
Market value (mil.): $105

**Stock Price History
High/Low 1985–94**

COMPUSA INC.

OVERVIEW

Almost counted out by some analysts, Dallas-based CompUSA has risen from the mat and come back fighting. The nation's largest computer retailer, CompUSA posted a $17 million loss in fiscal 1994 after expanding too rapidly.

The company has installed a new management team led by James Halpin and instituted a number of changes designed to transform the company from an entrepreneurial daredevil into a stable, mature corporation. In addition to decreasing the rate of new store openings (and even closing some old stores), changes included a new emphasis on training and customer services, consolidation of inventory and pricing at the corporate level, and a new focus on the home market rather than the hard-core "techie" market. In order to facilitate this change, the company began remodeling its stores to make them less intimidating to computer neophytes and adding informational programs and events.

The makeover seems to have helped. CompUSA's sales were up 31%, to $2.8 billion, and its same-store sales rose 10.3% in fiscal 1995. However, CompUSA doesn't have time to rest on its laurels. It faces stiff competition from both computer superstores, including Tandy's Computer City, and consumer electronics chains, including Best Buy and Circuit City.

CompUSA plans to continue to focus on "nontechie" computer buyers. To entice parents it has introduced to many of its stores a CompKids area, which features hundreds of edutainment software titles that kids can try before they buy.

WHEN

CompUSA was founded in 1984, when 23-year-old Mike Henochowicz (a native of South Africa and former Highland Appliance salesman) and 33-year-old Errol Jacobson invested $2,000 to open Soft Warehouse, an 800-square-foot software store near Dallas.

When the business opened, profit margins on computer programs were huge, and deep discounting, with little competition, still offered good profits. Soft Warehouse prospered by offering a wide selection of titles. In 1985 Henochowicz and Jacobson opened their first superstore in Dallas.

While the superstore concept was booming in other retail areas, it was a fairly new concept in the computer world. In the early 1980s buyers often did not know very much about computers and would go to one store to purchase hardware and another to buy software, relying on each store's technical expertise to guide their buying decisions. Soft Warehouse's one-stop-shopping concept coincided with the rise of savvy buyers who knew what they wanted. Soft Warehouse let them explore many options under one roof.

In 1988 the partners opened a 24,000-square-foot store in Atlanta. In 1989 Dubin Clark & Co., a private investment firm, bought a 50% interest in Soft Warehouse and brought in Nathan Morton, a former SVP of Home Depot, as the new COO. With the influx of capital, Morton immediately began an expansion program by opening stores in Houston, Los Angeles, Philadelphia, Miami, San Diego, and Washington, DC — all in 1989. In 1990 Morton became CEO, and Soft Warehouse attempted an IPO but abandoned the effort when the Persian Gulf War dampened the market.

Decisions by Dell in 1990 and Apple in 1991 to sell their products through Soft Warehouse built the company's credibility. Because it was then selling computer hardware as well as software, in 1991 Soft Warehouse adopted the name CompUSA to reflect its broader product lines and national expansion. Also in 1991 CompUSA successfully launched its IPO. The 2 founders left the company about that time to pursue other interests. By 1992 the company operated 31 stores in 21 markets.

To manage its growth, CompUSA restructured in May 1993 and created an international division to service its planned worldwide markets. Morton became chairman, while James Halpin (former president of HomeBase) was named president.

Just 7 months later, Morton resigned amid board dissatisfaction with CompUSA's poor earnings, which analysts blamed on inefficiencies stemming from rapid growth. Under Morton CompUSA had become extremely decentralized — individual stores were responsible for buying and pricing. Halpin became CEO and killed plans for an international division. He also began staff cutbacks and instituted centralized buying (decentralization had resulted in such great inefficiencies that in late 1994 the company had to auction off excess inventory).

In 1995 CompUSA opened its first stand-alone customer training centers, in Boston and Seattle.

NYSE symbol: CPU
Fiscal year ends: Last Saturday of June

WHO

Chairman: Giles H. Bateman
President and CEO: James F. Halpin, age 43, $451,805 pay
EVP and COO: Harold F. Compton, age 47
EVP Merchandising: Lawrence N. Mondry, age 34, $236,000 pay
EVP, CFO, and Treasurer: James Skinner, age 41
SVP Services and Administration: Paul Poyfair, age 42
SVP Marketing and Advertising: Ronald Gilmore, age 39
VP, General Counsel, and Secretary: Mark R. Walker, age 37
VP Direct Sales: Stanley R. Schiller, age 58
VP Real Estate: Ronald D. Strongwater, age 51
VP Human Resources: Mel McCall, age 51
Auditors: Ernst & Young LLP

WHERE

HQ: 14951 N. Dallas Pkwy., Dallas, TX 75240
Phone: 214-383-4000
Fax: 214-383-4276

	1994 Stores
	No.
California	13
Ohio	6
Texas	6
Florida	5
Georgia	4
New Jersey	4
New York	4
Illinois	3
Maryland	3
Massachusetts	3
Michigan	3
Pennsylvania	3
Virginia	3
Other states	16
Total	**76**

WHAT

Selected Products
Connectivity products
Data storage devices
Laptop computers
Microcomputers
Modems
Monitors
Printers

Selected Brands
Apple
Compaq
DEC
Dell
Hewlett-Packard
Sony
Texas Instruments
Toshiba

KEY COMPETITORS

Anam Group	J&R Music
Barnes & Noble	Kmart
Best Buy	Micro Center
CDW Computer Centers	Micro Warehouse
Circuit City	MicroAge
CompuCom	Montgomery Ward
Dell	NeoStar
Egghead	Office Depot
ELEK-TEK	Office Max
Entex	Price/Costco
Fretter	Sears
Fry's Electronics	Service Merchandise
Future Shop	Staples
Gateway 2000	Supercom
Global Directmail	Tandy
Good Guys	Tiger Direct
InaCom	Vanstar
Inmac	Wal-Mart
Intelligent Electronics	

HOW MUCH

	Annual Growth	1985	1986	1987	1988	1989	1990	1991	1992	1993	1994
Sales ($ mil.)	82.4%	—	—	32	67	137	300	544	821	1,342	2,146
Net income ($ mil.)	—	—	—	0	2	2	2	(11)	8	12	(17)
Income as % of sales	—	—	—	0.9%	2.9%	1.2%	0.5%	—	1.0%	0.9%	(0.8)%
Earnings per share ($)	—	—	—	—	—	0.01	0.16	(1.58)	0.62	0.67	(0.92)
Stock price – high ($)	—	—	—	—	—	—	—	23.75	40.50	37.00	22.25
Stock price – low ($)	—	—	—	—	—	—	—	15.00	19.25	17.88	6.75
Stock price – close ($)	(11.3%)	—	—	—	—	—	—	21.50	28.00	19.88	15.00
P/E – high	—	—	—	—	—	—	—	—	65	55	—
P/E – low	—	—	—	—	—	—	—	—	31	27	—
Dividends per share ($)	—	—	—	—	—	—	—	0.00	0.00	0.00	0.00
Book value per share ($)	—	—	—	—	—	—	—	(2.05)	5.55	8.80	7.91
Employees	70.5%	—	—	—	—	543	1,208	1,782	2,767	5,086	7,819

1994 Year-end:
Debt ratio: 52.0%
Return on equity: —
Cash (mil.): $23
Current ratio: 2.00
Long-term debt (mil.): $153
No. of shares (mil.): 18
Dividends
  Yield: —
  Payout: —
Market value (mil.): $277

**Stock Price History
High/Low 1991–94**

CONTINENTAL AIRLINES, INC.

OVERVIEW

Good idea, bad result. Continental's bold move to compete with low-cost, no-frills carriers like Southwest, through its CALite short-haul (flights of 2 hours or less) carrier, spun out of control last year. Far from making money, the carrier ran up a 1994 loss of $166.5 million on its CALite service. Continental decided to pull out of the short-haul business in 1995.

CEO Gordon Bethune's other strategies aimed at cutting costs and improving productivity have proved more successful. Continental and its affiliates, which serve over 100 cities in the US and 54 in Asia, Australia, Europe, and Latin America, have been clipping the wings of underperforming flights; the company cut its Munich route in 1994. Con-

centrating on its strengths, the firm expanded its services on core routes in Europe, Micronesia, and Latin America. The airline now offers 164 flights per week to Mexico (and 10 destinations) and 71 weekly flights to Central and South America, more service than any other US carrier. Continental also has a code-sharing deal with Alitalia.

Continental's majority owners include Air Canada (18.7%) and Air Partners (24.8%), a limited partnership, led by Texan David Bonderman, that also has a stake in America West.

Bethune received a bonus of $1.5 million in 1994 as part of a deal to keep him with the carrier after rival United tried to recruit him.

WHEN

Houston-based Trans Texas Airways began serving Texas communities in 1947. It became Texas International in 1968 and served the West Coast and Mexico by 1970. However, the company was unable to compete with major airlines on interstate routes or with commuter airlines in Texas and faced bankruptcy by 1972, when Frank Lorenzo's Jet Capital Corporation gained control. With Lorenzo at the helm, Texas International had netted over $3 million by 1976. In 1980 Lorenzo formed Texas Air, a holding company for Texas International and a newly created New York–Washington, DC, shuttle, New York Air.

In 1981 Texas Air bought 50% of Continental Airlines (founded as Varney Speed Lines in 1934), which operated in the western US, Mexico, and the Pacific. Continental's employees tried to block the takeover, but Texas Air bought the rest of the company in 1982. Continental had lost over $500 million between 1978 and 1983. In 1983, when Lorenzo's efforts to wrest wage concessions from the airline's unions resulted in a strike, Lorenzo maneuvered the airline into Chapter 11, abrogating union contracts. Continental emerged from bankruptcy in 1986 as a nonunion, low-fare carrier with the industry's lowest labor costs.

That year Texas Air bought Eastern Air Lines (founded as Pitcairn Aviation in 1927). WWI ace Eddie Rickenbacker had run Eastern from 1935 until his retirement in 1963. Losses and union disputes in the 1960s and 1970s forced Eastern's CEO, Frank Borman (a former astronaut), to sell in 1986. That year Texas Air also bought People Express Airlines and Frontier Airlines.

In 1988 Lorenzo sold Eastern's Air Shuttle to Donald Trump, but in 1989 mounting losses and a machinists' strike forced Eastern into bankruptcy. In 1990 the bankruptcy court removed Texas Air from Eastern's management, appointing Martin Shugrue as trustee. Texas Air then changed its name to Continental Airlines Holdings. Lorenzo resigned as chairman, president, and CEO after selling his stake in the company to SAS for a substantial premium plus $19.7 million in salary and severance pay. After Lorenzo's resignation, Hollis Harris, former president of Delta Air Lines, was named CEO.

With fuel prices up and traffic down, Continental followed Eastern into bankruptcy late in 1990. Eastern held on until January 1991, when increasing losses forced it to liquidate. Harris, who opposed new cost-cutting efforts, left Continental in 1991 and was replaced by former CFO Robert Ferguson. In 1991 Continental sold its Seattle–Tokyo route to AMR for $145 million.

Out of bankruptcy in 1993, Continental began pursuing the ill-fated strategy of muscling into the short-haul market, with a high level of employee cooperation that would have been unthinkable in earlier years.

Bethune was appointed CEO in late 1994, replacing Ferguson, the chief proponent of the ill-starred CALite strategy. In 1995 Bethune managed to secure a deal with Boeing whereby the airplane maker agreed to defer delivery of 24 jets in 1995 and 1996 (for a savings of $200 million). Continental also persuaded General Electric, its primary lender, to defer principal payments in 1995 and 1996, saving an additional $140 million.

NYSE symbol: CAIB
Fiscal year ends: December 31

Chairman: David Bonderman, age 52
President and CEO: Gordon M. Bethune, age 53,
  $2,221,154 pay
COO: Gregory D. Brenneman, age 33
SVP Strategic Business Units: Daniel P. Garton, age 38,
  $349,992 pay
SVP and CFO: Lawrence W. Kellner, age 36
SVP, General Counsel, and Secretary: Jeffery A. Smisek,
  age 40
SVP Operations: C. D. McLean, age 54
SVP European Operations: Barry P. Simon, age 52
SVP Airport Services: Mark A. Erwin, age 39
SVP Inflight Service: D. Sam Coats, age 54
SVP Human Resources: David A. Loeser, age 40
President and CEO, Continental Micronesia: Donald J.
  Breeding, age 60
President and CEO, Continental Express: Jonathan
  Ornstein, age 37
President, System One: William S. Diffenderffer, age 44
VP Reservations: Larry D. Goodwin
VP Marketing and Sales: Bonnie Reitz
VP Route Planning and Scheduling: David N. Siegel
Auditors: Ernst & Young LLP

WHERE

HQ: 2929 Allen Pkwy., Houston, TX 77019
Phone: 713-834-5000
Fax: 713-834-2087
Reservations: 800-525-0280

Continental flies to more than 100 cities in the US and
to 60 destinations in Asia, Australia, Europe, and Latin
America.

Hub Locations
Cleveland
Houston
Newark

WHAT

	1994 Sales	
	$ mil.	% of total
Passenger	5,036	89
Cargo, mail & other	634	11
Total	**5,670**	**100**

Major Affiliate
Continental Micronesia, Inc. (91%, air service in the
  Pacific)

	Aircraft	
	Owned	Leased
A300	2	19
Boeing 727	1	64
Boeing 737	32	79
Boeing 747	—	5
Boeing 757	—	11
DC-9	3	28
DC-10	—	19
MD-80	10	57
Total	**48**	**282**

KEY COMPETITORS

Air France
Alaska Air
All Nippon Airways
America West
AMR
British Airways
Delta
Galileo International
IRI
JAL
Kiwi Air
KLM

Lufthansa
Midwest Express
Northwest Airlines
SAS
Singapore Airlines
Southwest Airlines
Swire Pacific
TWA
UAL
USAir Group
ValuJet Airlines
Virgin Group

HOW MUCH

	Annual Growth	1985	1986	1987	1988	1989	1990	1991	1992	1993	1994
Sales ($ mil.)	12.6%	1,944	4,407	8,626	8,552	6,650	6,184	5,487	5,494	5,775	5,670
Net income ($ mil.)	—	49	42	(466)	(719)	(908)	(2,403)	(306)	(125)	(1,017)	(619)
Income as % of sales	—	2.5%	1.0%	—	—	—	—	—	—	—	—
Earnings per share ($)	—	—	—	—	—	—	—	—	—	(23.15)	(23.76)
Stock price – high ($)	—	—	—	—	—	—	—	—	—	30.50	27.25
Stock price – low ($)	—	—	—	—	—	—	—	—	—	13.00	7.50
Stock price – close ($)	(54.9%)	—	—	—	—	—	—	—	—	20.50	9.25
P/E – high	—	—	—	—	—	—	—	—	—	—	—
P/E – low	—	—	—	—	—	—	—	—	—	—	—
Dividends per share ($)	—	—	—	—	—	—	—	—	—	0.00	0.00
Book value per share ($)	(86.2%)	—	—	—	—	—	—	—	—	28.23	3.89
Employees	1.0%	—	—	—	35,649	31,400	34,800	36,300	38,300	43,100	37,800

1994 Year-end:
Debt ratio: 94.1%
Return on equity: —
Cash (mil.): $396
Current ratio: 0.41
Long-term debt (mil.): $1,038
No. of shares (mil.): 27
Dividends
  Yield: —
  Payout: —
Market value (mil.): $247

**Stock Price History
High/Low 1993–94**

COOPER INDUSTRIES, INC.

OVERVIEW

A corporate tune-up — including the spin-off of Cooper Cameron, its sputtering petroleum equipment segment — has Cooper Industries running smoothly again. The giant manufacturer had suffered from slowdowns in the construction and energy industries, and in 1994 a $313 million write-off for the Cooper Cameron deal negatively affected net income.

Cooper has realigned its numerous subsidiaries into 3 business segments. Its Automotive Products division includes name-brand manufacturers Anco and Champion. In late 1994 Cooper added Abex Friction Products (brake materials) and Zanxx (lighting components) to its auto parts makers.

Cooper's Electrical Products segment includes Buss (fuses) and Halo (lighting fixtures). Its Tools and Hardware unit includes

Crescent (wrenches), Kirsch (drapery hardware), and Diamond (pliers and wrenches).

With construction and industrial production both up in early 1995, Cooper's Electrical Products and Tools and Hardware segments showed revenue increases. Auto segment sales were helped by recent acquisitions.

Cooper Cameron, which had accounted for about 1/4 of its parent's revenues, was spun off in early 1995. That spring it won a $72 million Shell Oil contract for North Sea wellhead and production equipment. In mid-1995 Cooper Cameron became an independent company.

A struggle between Cooper and the United Steelworkers continued in 1995 despite a National Labor Relations Board decision ordering Cooper to recognize the union as a bargaining agent for employees at a Pennsylvania plant.

WHEN

In 1833 Charles Cooper sold a horse for $50 and borrowed additional money to open a foundry with his brother Elias in Mount Vernon, Ohio. Known as C. & E. Cooper, the company made plows, hog troughs, maple syrup kettles, stoves, and wagon boxes.

In the 1840s Cooper began making steam engines for use in mills and on farms; it later adapted the engines for wood-burning locomotives. In 1868 the company built its first Corliss steam engine and in 1875 introduced the first steam-powered farm tractor. By 1900 Cooper's steam engines were sold in the US and overseas. In 1909 Cooper introduced an internal combustion engine-compressor for natural-gas pipelines.

In the 1920s Cooper became the biggest seller of compression engines for oil and gas pipeline transmission. A 1929 merger with Bessemer (small gas and diesel engines) created Cooper-Bessemer, whose diesel engines powered marine vessels. Cooper was hurt badly by the Depression; sales fell 90% in 1931. The success of a new turbocharged diesel to power locomotives revived revenues.

Diversification began in the late 1950s with the purchase of Rotor Tools (1959). Cooper adopted its current name in 1965 and moved its headquarters to Houston in 1967. The company went on to acquire 20 other companies, including its "tool basket": Lufkin Rule (measuring tapes, 1967), Crescent (wrenches, 1968), and Weller (soldering tools, 1970).

The purchase of Gardner-Denver in 1979 gave Cooper a strong position in oil-drilling and mining equipment, and the 1981 acquisi-

tion of Crouse-Hinds was a significant diversification into electrical materials. Another 1981 purchase was Kirsch (drapery hardware). The decline in oil prices in the early 1980s caused sales to drop more than 35% between 1981 and 1983, but Cooper remained profitable because of its tools and electrical products.

The electrical segment expanded further with the 1985 purchase of McGraw-Edison, maker of both consumer products (Buss fuses) and heavy transmission gear for electrical utilities. Cooper bought RTE (electrical equipment, 1988), Cameron Iron Works (oil-drilling equipment, 1989), and Ferramentas Belzer do Brasil (hand-tool maker, 1992).

Expanding into automotive parts, Cooper bought Champion Spark Plug (1989) and Moog (auto replacement parts, 1992).

Tough times have forced Cooper to shake out nonessential or underperforming product lines. From 1991 to 1993 the company completed 11 divestitures, using the proceeds to help finance acquisitions of 13 complementary lines and streamline manufacturing.

In 1993 Cooper sold Belden Inc. (electrical wires and cables) through a public offering, keeping a 9.6% share in the company. That same year Cooper made 5 product-line acquisitions, which included Hawker Fusegear of the UK (electrical fuses), Triangle Tool Group (nonpower hand tools), and Fail-Safe Lighting Systems (security lighting). In 1994 the company spun off Gardner-Denver Industrial Machinery and sold Cameron Forged Products.

John Riley was named CEO in 1995. Chairman Robert Cizik is slated to retire in 1996.

NYSE symbol: CBE
Fiscal year ends: December 31

Chairman: Robert Cizik, age 64, $895,000 pay
President, CEO, and COO: H. John Riley Jr., age 54, $487,500 pay (prior to promotion)
EVP Operations: Michael J. Sebastian, age 64, $377,500 pay
EVP Operations: Ralph E. Jackson Jr., age 53, $285,938 pay
EVP Operations: Larry W. McCurdy, age 59, $275,000 pay
SVP Finance and CFO: D. Bradley McWilliams, age 53
SVP, General Counsel, and Secretary: Diane K. Schumacher, age 41
SVP Human Resources: Carl J. Plesnicher Jr., age 57
Auditors: Ernst & Young LLP

WHERE

HQ: First City Tower, Ste. 4000, Houston, TX 77002
Phone: 713-739-5400
Fax: 713-739-5555

Cooper manufactures and sells automotive and electrical products, hardware, and tools worldwide.

	1994 Sales	
	$ mil.	% of total
US	3,493	77
Other countries	1,062	23
Adjustments	33	—
Total	**4,588**	**100**

	1994 Manufacturing Facilities
	No. of Plants
US	82
Europe	19
Other Americas	18
Other regions	6
Total	**125**

WHAT

	1994 Sales		1994 Operating Income	
	$ mil.	% of total	$ mil.	% of total
Electrical products	2,035	44	326	53
Automotive prods.	1,622	35	190	31
Tools & hardware	898	20	103	16
Other	33	1	(41)	—
Total	**4,588**	**100**	**578**	**100**

Selected Products

Automotive
ACI electric motors
Anco windshield wipers
Belden wire and cable
Champion spark plugs
Everco heating products
Precision universal joints
Wagner lighting products
Zanxx lighting products

Electrical Products
Arrow Hart wiring devices
Buss and Edison fuses
Crouse-Hinds industrial lighting
Edison indoor and outdoor lighting

Halo recessed and track lighting
Kyle distribution switchgear
Metalux fluorescent lighting

Tools and Hardware
Apex impact sockets
Crescent wrenches
Diamond farrier tools
Kirsch drapery hardware
Lufkin measuring tapes
Nicholson files and saws
Plumb hammers
Weller soldering equipment
Wiss cutting products

KEY COMPETITORS

ABB
Arrow Automotive
Black & Decker
Borg-Warner Automotive
Dana
Danaher
Eaton
Echlin
Emerson
Fastenal

Federal-Mogul
General Electric
General Signal
Hastings Manufacturing
Illinois Tool Works
Ingersoll-Rand
Masco
Newell Co.
PACCAR
Philips

Robert Bosch
Siemens
Snap-on Tools
Standard Products
Stanley Works
Tenneco
Textron
Waxman
Westinghouse

HOW MUCH

	9-Year Growth	1985	1986	1987	1988	1989	1990	1991	1992	1993	1994
Sales ($ mil.)	4.6%	3,067	3,433	3,586	4,258	5,129	6,222	6,163	6,159	6,274	4,588
Net income ($ mil.)	—	135	148	174	224	268	361	393	361	367	(20)
Income as % of sales	—	4.4%	4.3%	4.8%	5.3%	5.2%	5.8%	6.4%	5.9%	5.9%	—
Earnings per share ($)	—	1.39	1.52	1.73	2.20	2.49	2.81	3.01	2.71	2.75	(0.64)
Stock price – high ($)	—	21.19	25.75	37.25	31.38	40.00	46.00	58.00	59.38	54.75	52.25
Stock price – low ($)	—	14.00	17.81	19.50	25.06	26.88	31.25	38.50	41.75	45.63	31.63
Stock price – close ($)	5.5%	21.00	20.69	27.75	27.00	40.00	41.13	57.25	47.38	49.25	34.00
P/E – high	—	15	17	22	14	16	16	19	22	20	—
P/E – low	—	10	12	11	11	11	11	13	15	17	—
Dividends per share ($)	6.3%	0.76	0.79	0.83	0.89	0.98	1.06	1.14	1.22	1.30	1.32
Book value per share ($)	5.3%	14.58	14.66	15.91	17.47	24.75	27.66	29.96	24.99	25.84	23.16
Employees	(1.3%)	46,000	40,200	43,200	46,300	58,100	57,500	53,900	52,900	49,500	40,800

1994 Year-end:
Debt ratio: 36.0%
Return on equity: —
Cash (mil.): $25
Current ratio: 1.58
Long-term debt (mil.): $1,362
No. of shares (mil.): 117
Dividends
  Yield: 3.9%
  Payout: —
Market value (mil.): $3,979

Stock Price History
High/Low 1985–94

DELL COMPUTER CORPORATION

OVERVIEW

Dell, the world's #7 personal computer maker, is back on track after pulling out of retail stores and reconfiguring its notebook computer operations. The Texas-based company is one of the world's 2 leading mail-order computer vendors (Gateway 2000 is its main rival).

Dell's turnaround came in 1994 after it abandoned Wal-Mart and other retail stores to refocus on its mail-order origins. The company took a $40 million charge in early 1994 to kill its troubled notebook computer line; later that year it released the Latitude notebook to general acclaim. The company offered its first Pentium-based notebook in 1995.

Dell's earnings rose in 1995, partially on the strength of its notebook computers, which jumped to 9% of sales. The company also benefited from its early entry into the Pentium-based PC market and from its introduction of innovative products such as lithium-ion notebook batteries, which last longer than conventional batteries.

Dell is now setting its sights on overseas opportunities (one of the most promising horizons for computer sales). The company is doubling capacity at its Irish plant and building a new facility in Malaysia to serve the Asian market. The company is also expanding the meaning of "mail order" by marketing its wares on the Internet.

The Dell family owns 30% of the company's stock.

WHEN

At the age of 13, Michael Dell was already a successful businessman. From his parents' home in Houston, Dell ran a mail-order stamp trading business that, within a few months, grossed over $2,000. At 16 he sold subscriptions to the *Houston Post* and at 17 bought his first BMW. When he enrolled at the University of Texas in 1983, he was thoroughly bitten by the business bug.

Although Dell started college as a pre-med major, he found time to establish a business selling random-access memory (RAM) chips and disk drives for IBM PCs. Dell bought his products at cost from IBM dealers, who, at the time, were required to order from IBM large monthly quotas of PCs, which frequently exceeded demand. Dell resold his stock through newspapers (and later through national computer magazines) at 10–15% below retail.

By April 1984 Dell's dorm-room computer components business was grossing about $80,000 a month — enough to convince him to drop out of college. At about that time he started making and selling his own IBM clones under the brand name PC's Limited. Drawing on his previous sales experience, Dell sold his machines directly to end-users rather than through retail computer outlets, as most manufacturers did. By eliminating the retail markup, Dell could sell his PCs at about 40% of the price of an IBM.

The company was plagued by management changes during the mid-1980s. Renamed Dell Computer, it added international sales offices in 1987. In 1988 it started selling to government agencies and added a sales force to serve larger customers. That year Dell went public in a $34.2 million offering.

Dell tripped in 1990, reporting a 64% drop in profits. Sales were growing — but so were costs, mostly because of Dell's efforts to design a PC using proprietary components and RISC chips. Also, the company's warehouses were oversupplied. But within a year Dell turned itself around by cutting inventories and coming out with 8 new products.

In 1990 Dell entered the retail arena by allowing Soft Warehouse Superstores (now CompUSA) to sell its PCs at mail-order prices. In 1991 the company struck a similar deal with Staples, an office supply chain. Also that year Dell opened a plant in Limerick, Ireland.

In 1992 Xerox agreed to sell Dell machines in 19 Latin American countries. That same year Dell sold a new line of PCs through Price Club (now Price/Costco). The following year Dell opened subsidiaries in Japan and Austria and began selling PCs through Best Buy's 117 US stores, located in 16 states.

Dell introduced a new line of servers, called PowerEdge, in 1994. That same year Dell suspended sales in retail stores and signed deals with resellers in Indonesia and Korea to sell its products. Late in 1994 Joel Kocher — Dell's wunderkind president of worldwide sales, marketing, and services, who had led the company's marketing efforts since 1987 — left to become COO of Artisoft, maker of networking products such as LANtastic. .

In 1995 Dell introduced the OptiPlex DGX system, its first dual-processor desktop computer. It also reduced prices on its workhorse Dimension series PCs. Also that year a suit was filed accusing Dell of selling new computers containing used parts (Compaq has accused rival Packard Bell of a similar tactic).

Nasdaq symbol: DELL
Fiscal year ends: Saturday nearest January 31

WHO

Chairman and CEO: Michael S. Dell, age 30,
$818,032 pay
VC: Morton L. Topfer, age 58, $566,015 pay
SVP Finance and Information Systems; CFO: Thomas
J. Meredith, age 45, $524,308 pay (prior to promotion)
SVP Product Group: Eric F. Harslem, age 49,
$651,153 pay
SVP; General Manager, Dell Americas: Richard N.
Snyder, age 50
VP and General Manager — Asia: Phillip E. Kelly,
age 37
VP and General Manager — Europe: Martyn R. Ratcliffe,
age 33
VP Advanced Systems Group: Terry Klein
VP and Corporate Controller: Catherine P. Thompson
General Counsel and Secretary: Thomas B. Green,
age 40
VP Human Resources: Julie A. Sackett, age 51
Auditors: Price Waterhouse LLP

WHERE

HQ: 9505 Arboretum Blvd., Austin, TX 78759-7299
Phone: 512-338-4400
Fax: 512-728-3653

Dell sells 64 computer systems in 7 product families as
well as a variety of computer software and peripheral
products through the company's DellWare and
ReadyWare programs. Dell computer products are sold
in more than 125 countries.

	1995 Sales % of total
Americas	69
Europe	27
Other regions	4
Total	**100**

WHAT

	1995 Sales % of total
Desktop systems	85
Notebooks	9
Servers	6
Total	**100**

Selected Dell Products

Desktop Systems	Servers
Dimension family	Performance family
NetPlex family	PowerEdge family
OptiPlex family	Series family

Notebooks
Latitude family

Third-Party Products

CD-ROM drives	Printers
Modems	Removable storage devices
Monitors	Scanners
Networking hardware	Software
PCMCIA cards	Speakers
Power accessories	Tape backup systems

KEY COMPETITORS

Acer	Hewlett-	NeoStar
Advanced Logic	Packard	Oki
Research	Hitachi	Olivetti
Apple	Hyundai	Packard Bell
AST	IBM	Philips
AT&T	Machines Bull	Sharp
Compaq	Matsushita	Siemens
CompuAdd	Micron	Sun
CompUSA	Micro	Microsystems
Data General	Warehouse	Tandy
DEC	Micron	Toshiba
Fujitsu	Technology	Unisys
Gateway 2000	NEC	

HOW MUCH

	Annual Growth	1986	1987	1988	1989	1990	1991	1992	1993	1994	1995
Sales ($ mil.)	67.2%	34	70	159	258	389	546	890	2,014	2,873	3,475
Net income ($ mil.)	73.2%	1	2	9	14	5	27	51	102	(36)	140
Income as % of sales	—	2.9%	3.2%	5.9%	5.6%	1.3%	5.0%	5.7%	5.0%	—	4.0%
Earnings per share ($)	58.5%	0.05	0.13	0.48	0.53	0.18	0.91	1.40	2.59	(1.06)	3.15
Stock price – high ($)[1]	—	—	—	—	8.34	6.92	12.59	24.18	48.38	49.88	47.38
Stock price – low ($)[1]	—	—	—	—	5.25	3.42	3.08	10.51	15.00	15.88	19.13
Stock price – close ($)[1]	35.3%	—	—	—	6.67	3.67	12.34	17.09	48.00	22.63	41.00
P/E – high	—	—	—	—	16	38	14	17	19	—	15
P/E – low	—	—	—	—	10	19	3	8	6	—	6
Dividends per share ($)	—	—	—	—	0.00	0.00	0.00	0.00	0.00	0.00	0.00
Book value per share ($)	35.2%	—	—	—	2.69	2.83	3.86	7.66	10.02	12.42	16.42
Employees	32.6%	—	—	—	1,175	1,500	2,050	2,970	4,650	5,980	6,400

1995 Year-end:
Debt ratio: 14.8%
Return on equity: 25.0%
Cash (mil.): $527
Current ratio: 1.96
Long-term debt (mil.): $113
No. of shares (mil.): 40
Dividends
  Yield: —
  Payout: —
Market value (mil.): $1,627

Stock Price History[1]
High/Low 1989–95

[1] Stock prices are for the prior calendar year.

DIAMOND SHAMROCK, INC.

OVERVIEW

Far from being a diamond in the rough, Diamond Shamrock has been more rough than diamond in the 1990s. Headquartered in San Antonio, the regional refiner and marketer of petroleum products has had flat sales since 1990. Diamond Shamrock owns approximately 3,800 miles of pipelines that bring crude oil into refineries and take refined products to 16 terminals across the Southwest.

The company sells over 1.5 billion gallons of gasoline per year through more than 2,000 Diamond Shamrock branded retail outlets in Texas, Colorado, Louisiana, New Mexico, and 4 other states. Other businesses include petrochemical processing; hydrous ammonia production; and natural gas liquids storage, marketing, and distribution. Diamond Shamrock also owns Northern American InteleCom, a provider of phone service to prison inmates.

In 1996 Diamond Shamrock plans to complete a pipeline into Denver (connecting the city with its McKee, Texas, refinery), which is expected to save $200,000 a month in gasoline trucking costs. The company is also building a pipeline to El Paso to enable expansion into the Arizona and northern Mexico markets.

WHEN

In 1910 T. R. Evans and a group of Pittsburgh businessmen formed the Diamond Alkali Company to produce chemicals for the glass industry. With $1.2 million in capital, the company established a plant in Painesville, Ohio, in 1912, that soon began producing caustic soda, chromates chlorine, chlorinated paraffins, and coke. With the outbreak of WWI, the demand for canning glass increased, lifting Diamond's sales. Oversupply of soda ash in 1915 led the firm to use it to produce caustic soda and find new uses for it, such as soap and detergents.

In 1925 the firm began producing calcium carbonates and cement, and in 1929 it began marketing chlorine and hydrogen, by-products of a new industrial process involving the electrolysis of salt.

Following the Depression, J. T. Richards led the company in a revival of fortunes. In 1936 the company began making magnesium oxide, a component of incendiary bombs that was much in demand during WWII. The government chose Diamond as one of 12 magnesium plants to supply its armaments. Diamond moved its headquarters from Pittsburgh to Cleveland in 1948 to be closer to its major manufacturing center in Painesville.

The company continued to diversify in the 1950s, moving into organic chemicals, plastics, and chromic acids. The Korean War also brought a renewed growth in magnesium production. Expanding overseas, Diamond joined 3 foreign companies in building a $15 million caustic chlorine plant in Brazil in 1961. In 1962 it formed a joint venture with French firm Prosim to make water treatment chemicals.

In 1967 Diamond Alkali merged with Shamrock Oil & Gas, an oil, gas, and fertilizer producer and marketer. The new company was named Diamond Shamrock. To comply with FTC regulations, Diamond Shamrock sold its Bessemer Cement division to Louisville Cement Co. for $20 million.

Diamond Shamrock's core oil and gas business expanded in the 1970s. Between 1972 and 1977 its acres under exploration more than doubled, to 2.5 million acres. The company branched into coal production with the purchase of Falcon Seaboard in 1979 and Amherst Coal in 1981. It merged with Natomas Company in a $1.2 billion stock swap in 1983 that gave it access to gas and oil wells in Canada, Indonesia, and the North Sea.

In 1984 Diamond Shamrock agreed to spend $412 million to clean up its dioxin-contaminated New Jersey plant, which had produced dioxin-based Agent Orange during the Vietnam War. This setback was followed by a disastrous 1985 when low energy prices and poor results by its Natomas subsidiary forced the company to post losses of $605 million.

Smelling blood, corporate raider T. Boone Pickens made a hostile takeover bid for Diamond Shamrock in 1986. In a defensive move the company spun off its refining and marketing arm (which retained the Diamond Shamrock name). The exploration and production parent company changed its name to Maxus. The new Diamond Shamrock (based in San Antonio) went public in 1987. (Maxus was bought by Argentine oil firm YPF in 1995.)

The company entered the petrochemicals business in 1989 by becoming a 33% partner in a propane-propylene operation in Mount Belviu, Texas. In the 1990s the company has pursued a strategy of adding refineries, expanding pipelines, and increasing retail gasoline outlets in the Southwest. It built 17 retail outlets and acquired 26 others in 1994 (including 18 in Colorado and 6 in El Paso). It acquired 21 retail gas stations from Bar-F Enterprises of Las Cruces, New Mexico, in 1995.

NYSE symbol: DRM
Fiscal year ends: December 31

WHO

Chairman, President, and CEO: Roger R.
Hemminghaus, age 58, $838,258 pay
EVP: William R. Klesse, age 48, $329,419 pay
EVP: J. Robert Mehall, age 52, $329,419 pay
SVP, Group Executive, and General Counsel: Timothy
J. Fretthold, age 45, $329,419 pay
SVP; President, Marketing: A. W. O'Donnell, age 62,
$329,419 pay
SVP; President, Refining: J. E. Prater, age 56,
$329,419 pay
VP and Controller: Gary E. Johnson, age 59
VP Product Supply: Thomas A. Lyons, age 45
VP South America: Patrick W. McConahy, age 44
VP Planning and Development: Joseph C. Shockney,
age 57
VP and Treasurer: Robert C. Becker, age 53
VP Human Resources: Penelope Rhude Viteo, age 42
Auditors: Price Waterhouse LLP

WHERE

HQ: 9830 Colonnade Blvd., San Antonio, TX 78230
Phone: 210-641-6800   **Fax:** 210-641-8687

Diamond Shamrock sells petroleum products through
more than 2,000 retail outlets in 8 states. Its 810
company-operated outlets are located in Colorado,
Louisiana, New Mexico, and Texas.

	1994 Company-Operated Retail Outlets	
	No.	% of total
Texas	632	78
Colorado	119	15
Louisiana	37	4
New Mexico	22	3
Total	**810**	**100**

WHAT

	1994 Sales		1994 Operating Profit	
	$ mil.	% of total	$ mil.	% of total
Refining & wholesale	1,321	51	147	64
Retail	974	37	59	25
Other	311	12	26	11
Total	**2,606**	**100**	**232**	**100**

	1994 Retail Outlets	
	No.	% of total
Jobber operated (franchised)	1,206	60
Company owned	496	25
Company operated	314	15
Total	**2,016**	**100**

**Selected Petroleum
  Products and Services**
Distribution
Marketing
Refining
Supply

Natural gas and
  petrochemical storage
  and distribution
Northern American
  InteleCom (telephone
  services for correctional
  institutions)

Other
Ammonia production

Propane/propylene
  production

KEY COMPETITORS

Amerada Hess	Exxon	PDVSA
Amoco	Koch	Petrofina
Ashland, Inc.	LDDS	Repsol
AT&T	Communications	Shell Oil
Atlantic Richfield	MCI	Southland
Chevron	MESA Inc.	Star
Circle K	Mobil	Enterprise
Coastal	National	Sun Co.
E Z Mart	Convenience	Texaco
E-Z Serve	Occidental	TOTAL
Eastman Chemical		

HOW MUCH

	Annual Growth	1985	1986	1987	1988	1989	1990	1991	1992	1993	1994
Sales ($ mil.)	6.0%	—	1,637	1,741	1,804	2,091	2,708	2,576	2,603	2,555	2,606
Net income ($ mil.)	—	—	(25)	11	54	60	78	37	26	33	76
Income as % of sales	—	—	—	0.6%	3.0%	2.9%	2.9%	1.4%	1.0%	1.3%	2.9%
Earnings per share ($)	—	—	(0.85)	0.47	2.08	2.10	2.78	1.36	0.92	1.04	2.34
Stock price – high ($)	—	—	—	18.25	17.00	28.50	27.75	26.63	23.63	27.38	30.00
Stock price – low ($)	—	—	—	7.38	8.63	14.88	17.25	18.13	15.63	17.00	23.38
Stock price – close ($)	16.8%	—	—	8.75	15.25	25.00	19.25	19.25	18.50	24.25	26.02
P/E – high	—	—	—	39	8	14	10	20	26	26	13
P/E – low	—	—	—	16	4	7	6	13	17	16	10
Dividends per share ($)	8.5%	—	—	0.30	0.40	0.44	0.49	0.52	0.52	0.52	0.53
Book value per share ($)	10.4%	—	—	10.20	14.79	11.11	13.84	15.28	15.18	18.28	20.38
Employees	(6.5%)	11,696	7,265	3,400	4,000	5,000	5,000	6,000	6,000	6,300	6,400

1994 Year-end:
Debt ratio: 46.6%
Return on equity: 13.6%
Cash (mil.): $27
Current ratio: 1.44
Long-term debt (mil.): $509
No. of shares (mil.): 29
Dividends
  Yield: 2.0%
  Payout: 22.6%
Market value (mil.): $752

**Stock Price History
High/Low 1987–94**

DRESSER INDUSTRIES, INC.

OVERVIEW

With more than 100 manufacturing plants in some 50 countries, Dallas, Texas–based Dresser Industries is one of the largest energy service companies in the world, offering everything from drill bits to gas pumps to pipe coating services. Through joint venture Dresser-Rand, the company makes compressors and other industrial machinery. Engineering and construction services are provided through M. W. Kellogg, whose specialty is liquefied natural gas (LNG) liquefaction facilities and LNG receiving terminals. Approximately 61% of Dresser's sales are to customers outside of North America.

The company has shuffled the deck with recent acquisitions and divestitures in order to improve its position in the highly competitive drilling industry.

The 1994 purchases of Baroid and Wheatley TXT for $930 million allow Dresser's drilling operations to offer more services and equipment to drillers and strengthen its global presence. The divestiture of its stakes in Western Atlas International (a provider of oil and gas services), M-I Drilling Fluids, and IRI International (a manufacturer of mobile drilling rigs) helped raise approximately $720 million in cash that same year.

The company is banking on increased demand for its services from growing oil and gas markets in Asia, the Middle East, Latin America, and Africa.

WHEN

Solomon Dresser arrived in the oil boom town of Bradford, Pennsylvania, in 1878 with a consumptive wife and 4 children. He eked out a living in oil field jobs. He also tinkered with an invention, and in 1880 Dresser was granted a patent for a cap packer, a device that prevents crude oil from mixing with other fluids in a well. In the 1880s and 1890s, he perfected a coupling that used fitted rubber to prevent leaks in pipeline connections.

As the natural gas industry grew, so did demand for the reliable Dresser coupling. The family firm prospered even after Solomon's death in 1911, but his heirs, anxious to pursue other interests, sold the company to W. A. Harriman & Company in 1928, and the investment banker took Dresser public. Soon after, 3 Harriman executives — including Roland Harriman, son of the founder, and Prescott Bush, father of future US president George Bush — were discussing the vacant Dresser presidency. Just then, an old Yale friend, Neil Mallon, dropped by the office, and Harriman tapped Mallon for the top post.

During Mallon's 41-year career with Dresser, the company grew into an oil field conglomerate. Bryant Heating and Manufacturing was the first acquisition (bought in 1933 and sold in 1949). When Dresser tried to develop a high-speed compressor for gas pipelines, it purchased Clark Brothers (compressors, 1937). It later abandoned its compressor research, but Olean, New York–based Clark became a company cornerstone. Dresser moved its headquarters to Dallas in 1950. Acquisitions ranged from Magnet Cove (drilling "mud" lubricant for oil well holes, 1949) to Symington-Wayne (gasoline pumps, 1968).

In 1983, after an oil services boom had peaked, CEO Jack Murphy refocused on the petroleum business, balancing upstream (exploration and production) and downstream (refining and marketing) services and products. In 1986 Dresser formed a joint venture (now 51%-owned) with Ingersoll-Rand called Dresser-Rand (compressors, gas turbines). Dresser bought M. W. Kellogg Company (refinery engineering, 1988) and the diamond drill bit product line of Baker Hughes (1990).

In 1992 Dresser spun off its industrial products and equipment operations as INDRESCO to Dresser's shareholders. That same year Dresser acquired AVA International (oil field safety valves and well-completion equipment) and pooled its pump operations with Ingersoll-Rand to form a minority-held (49%) joint venture, Ingersoll-Dresser Pump. In 1993 Dresser bought Bredero Price Pipe (pipe coating) and TK Valve (oil and gas production ball valves).

In 1994 Dresser sold its 29.5% stake in Western Atlas and acquired Houston, Texas–based Baroid (offshore and drilling services and products). To get the purchase approved by antitrust regulators, in 1994 Dresser sold M-I Drilling Fluids to Smith International and placed the diamond drilling bit business of Baroid unit DBS on the auction block.

In 1995 Dresser was awarded a $300 million contract to provide Statoil, the Norwegian oil and gas company, with external and internal coatings for its new gas pipelines in the North Sea. Also that year Dresser signed a contract to prepare design and engineering work on an LNG project in Oman. The project is 51%-owned by the government of Oman and 34%-owned by Royal Dutch/Shell and others.

NYSE symbol: DI
Fiscal year ends: October 31

WHO

Chairman and CEO: John J. Murphy, age 63, $1,748,700 pay
VC and CFO: Bill D. St. John, age 63, $946,360 pay
President and COO: William E. Bradford, age 60, $959,600 pay
SVP Operations; Chairman, President, and CEO, M. W. Kellogg: Donald C. Vaughn, age 58, $890,059 pay
SVP Operations: James L. Bryan, age 58, $541,575 pay
VP: George A. Helland Jr., age 57
VP and General Counsel: Clinton E. Ables, age 55
VP Washington Counsel: Ardon B. Judd Jr., age 58
VP Human Resources: Paul M. Bryant, age 48
VP Tax: David R. Smith, age 48
VP Corporate Counsel and Secretary: Rebecca R. Morris, age 49
Treasurer: Paul W. Willey, age 57
Assistant Treasurer: Richard T. Kernen
Assistant Secretary: Stanley E. McGlothlin
Auditors: Price Waterhouse LLP

WHERE

HQ: 2001 Ross Ave., PO Box 718, Dallas, TX 75201
Phone: 214-740-6000
Fax: 214-740-6584

Dresser operates manufacturing, marketing, and service facilities serving more than 80 countries.

	1994 Sales		1994 Operating Income	
	$ mil.	% of total	$ mil.	% of total
US	1,802	34	171	37
Europe	1,069	20	58	13
Latin America	722	14	53	12
Canada	262	5	31	7
Other regions	1,476	27	147	31
Total	**5,331**	**100**	**460**	**100**

WHAT

	1994 Sales		1994 Operating Income	
	$ mil.	% of total	$ mil.	% of total
Hydrocarbon processing	2,416	45	218	47
Oil field services	1,653	31	157	34
Engineering services	1,265	24	85	19
Adjustments	(3)	—	—	—
Total	**5,331**	**100**	**460**	**100**

Hydrocarbon Processing
Compressors
Control products for process, power, and gas distribution industries
Electric motors
Gas and diesel engines
Gas and steam turbines
Gasoline and diesel fuel dispensing systems
Generators
Pumps

Oil Field Services
Drilling fluid
Drilling services
Offshore services
Oil field and mining rock bits
Pipe coating services
Production tools

Engineering Services
Engineering and construction for hydrocarbon processing industries

Selected Joint Ventures
Dresser-Rand (51%, compressors and turbines)
Ingersoll-Dresser Pump (49%, pumps)

KEY COMPETITORS

ABB
Baker Hughes
Bechtel
BJ Services
Caterpillar
Cooper Cameron
Deere
DSI Industries
Fluor
FMC
Friedrich Krupp
General Electric
Halliburton
Keystone International
LTV
McDermott
Nabors Industries
Peter Kiewit Sons'
Raytheon
Schlumberger
Smith International
Western Atlas

HOW MUCH

	9-Year Growth	1985	1986	1987	1988	1989	1990	1991	1992	1993	1994
Sales ($ mil.)	2.9%	4,111	3,661	3,120	3,942	3,956	4,480	4,670	3,797	4,216	5,331
Net income ($ mil.)	—	(196)	1	43	146	163	174	140	35	127	362
Income as % of sales	—	—	0.0%	1.4%	3.7%	4.1%	3.9%	3.0%	0.9%	3.0%	6.8%
Earnings per share ($)	—	(1.29)	0.01	0.29	1.06	1.21	1.29	1.04	0.26	0.92	1.98
Stock price – high ($)	—	12.13	10.19	17.81	17.81	24.00	28.13	28.50	23.63	25.38	24.88
Stock price – low ($)	—	8.38	7.00	8.81	11.25	14.50	16.50	16.25	17.25	17.25	18.50
Stock price – close ($)	8.5%	9.06	9.69	13.13	14.69	22.44	20.88	20.13	18.00	20.75	18.88
P/E – high	—	—	—	61	17	20	22	27	91	28	13
P/E – low	—	—	—	30	11	12	13	16	66	19	9
Dividends per share ($)	5.7%	0.40	0.35	0.20	0.28	0.45	0.55	0.60	0.60	0.60	0.66
Book value per share ($)	(2.2%)	10.80	10.67	10.75	11.19	11.88	13.01	13.11	6.93	6.86	8.88
Employees	(5.0%)	46,200	39,700	30,800	30,700	31,436	33,133	31,839	27,380	25,926	29,200

1994 Year-end:
Debt ratio: 23.4%
Return on equity: 28.1%
Cash (mil.): $515
Current ratio: 1.61
Long-term debt (mil.): $461
No. of shares (mil.): 183
Dividends
  Yield: 3.5%
  Payout: 33.3%
Market value (mil.): $2,681

**Stock Price History
High/Low 1985–94**

ELECTRONIC DATA SYSTEMS

OVERVIEW

The way to a consultant's heart is through his wallet. In 1995 Electronic Data Systems (EDS), after a year of negotiations, finally found the number that overcame the objections of A.T. Kearney's partners to a merger between the companies. It was $600 million in cash and stock, which works out to over $4.5 million for each of Kearney's approximately 130 partners.

The merger is intended to propel EDS's struggling management consulting business into the major leagues of international consulting. The unit was started in 1993 and has been gobbling up MBAs ever since, but it needed the name recognition and experience that only an established firm like Kearney could provide in order to draw clients.

Plano, Texas–based EDS believes that high-profile consultancy is an important complement to its primary business: the design of data management systems for companies in many fields, including the insurance, automotive, financial, and communications industries, as well as for the government. One of the largest data processing companies in the US, EDS (founded by Ross Perot) had been a wholly owned subsidiary of General Motors for 11 years when GM announced in 1995 that it would spin off EDS as an independent company. GM accounted for 35% of EDS's 1994 revenues (down from 73% in 1986).

EDS has been losing market share in its traditional market of outsourcing and is putting more emphasis on reengineering.

WHEN

After 10 years with Big Blue, disgruntled salesman Ross Perot founded Electronic Data Systems in 1962. IBM executives had pooh-poohed Perot's idea to provide companies with electronic data processing management services, taking computer and data management worries off clients' hands.

It took Perot 5 months to find his first customer, Collins Radio of Cedar Rapids, Iowa. EDS pioneered the long-term, fixed-price contract with Frito-Lay in 1963, writing a 5-year contract instead of the 60- to 90-day contracts usually offered by service companies.

The company entered Medicare and Medicaid claims processing (mid-1960s), insurance company data processing (1963), and data management for banks (1968). EDS went on to become the #1 provider of data management services in all 3 of these markets.

EDS went public in 1968. It bought Wall Street Leasing (computer services) and established Regional Data Centers and central data processing stations, pioneering the concept of distributed processing in the early 1970s.

In 1976 EDS signed its first offshore contract, in Saudi Arabia, and also signed a contract with the government of Iran. But by 1978 Iran was 6 months behind in its payments, and EDS halted operations. When 2 EDS employees were later arrested, amid the disorder of the Islamic revolution, Perot assembled a rescue team to get them out of the country. The 2 employees were eventually released, and the team aided in their flight from Iran.

In the mid-1970s EDS began moving toward the installation of computer systems and away from the management of them.

In 1984, on its 22nd anniversary (and Perot's birthday), General Motors bought EDS for $2.5 billion. GM promised EDS its independence as well as contract work managing its lumbering data processing system. EDS prospered, but the differing managerial styles of Perot and GM chairman Roger Smith resulted in an uneasy alliance that ended in divorce. GM bought Perot's EDS shares in 1986 for over $700 million. Perot formed competitor Perot Systems Corporation in 1988. Perot's company has barely dented EDS's sales.

Lester Alberthal became CEO, and through the rest of the 1980s he lessened EDS's dependence on GM by diversifying widely.

In 1990 EDS bought the UK's SD-Scicon. The next year IBM, facing declining profits (and looking more green than blue), entered the profitable data management industry.

EDS won an FAA contract worth $508 million in 1993, and the next year the company began, on a small scale, selling new housebrand personal computers. Also in 1993 the company launched its management consulting service as a way of leveraging the contacts it makes in its systems business, but it was a slow, money-losing startup.

The company scored a major hit in 1994 when Xerox contracted with EDS to manage most of its information technology needs (worth $3 billion). A bid to move into multimedia communications via an alliance with Sprint collapsed because issues relating to EDS's independence from GM and the value of the company itself were not resolved.

In 1995 EDS acquired, A.T. Kearney and FCI, a securities industry consultant.

WHO

Chairman, President, and CEO: Lester M. Alberthal Jr.,
age 50
SVP and Secretary: John R. Castle Jr.
SVP and CFO: Joseph M. Grant
SVP: Paul J. Chiapparone
SVP: Gary J. Fernandes
SVP: Jeffrey M. Heller
SVP: Dean Linderman
SVP Personnel: G. Stuart Reeves
VP and General Counsel: D. Gilbert Friedlander
Auditors: KPMG Peat Marwick LLP

WHERE

HQ: Electronic Data Systems Corporation,
5400 Legacy Dr., Plano, TX 75024-3199
Phone: 214-604-6000
Fax: 214-605-6798

EDS has operations in over 30 countries.

	1994 Sales	
	$ mil.	% of total
US	7,376	74
Europe	1,831	18
Other regions	753	8
Adjustments	92	—
Total	**10,052**	**100**

WHAT

	1994 Sales	
	$ mil.	% of total
Systems & other contracts	9,960	99
Interest & other	92	1
Total	**10,052**	**100**

	1994 Sales	
	$ mil.	% of total
Outside customers	6,413	64
GM & subsidiaries	3,547	35
Interest & other	92	1
Total	**10,052**	**100**

Products and Services
Computer Services
    Corporate outsourcing
    Data-center management
    Networking
    Reengineering
Insurance
    Claims underwriting (through National Heritage
        Insurance Company, a wholly owned subsidiary)
Management consulting

Selected Customers
American Express
Apple Computer
Banco Santander
General Motors
Gruppo S&M
Kooperativa Förbundet
Rockwell International
Southland
Spectradyne
USTravel
Xerox

KEY COMPETITORS

ADP	Continuum
American Software	Coopers & Lybrand
Arthur Andersen	Deloitte & Touche
Arthur D. Little	Ernst & Young
AT&T	IBM
Bain & Co.	MCI
Booz, Allen	Perot Systems
Cap Gemini Sogeti	Policy Management Systems
Computer Sciences	Technology Solutions

HOW MUCH

	9-Year Growth	1985	1986	1987	1988	1989	1990	1991	1992	1993	1994
Sales ($ mil.)	12.6%	3,442	4,366	4,423	4,844	5,467	6,109	7,099	8,219	8,562	10,052
Net income ($ mil.)	17.7%	190	261	323	384	435	497	563	636	724	822
Income as % of sales	—	5.5%	6.0%	7.3%	7.9%	8.0%	8.1%	7.9%	7.7%	8.5%	8.2%
Earnings per share ($)	17.8%	0.39	0.53	0.67	0.79	0.91	1.04	1.17	1.33	1.51	1.71
Stock price – high ($)	—	11.63	12.38	12.75	11.22	14.41	20.06	33.06	34.00	35.88	39.50
Stock price – low ($)	—	5.13	6.13	6.00	8.38	10.63	12.19	17.50	25.25	26.00	27.50
Stock price – close ($)	15.8%	10.25	6.25	9.63	11.22	13.66	19.31	31.50	32.88	29.25	38.38
P/E – high	—	30	23	19	14	16	19	28	26	24	23
P/E – low	—	13	12	9	11	12	12	15	19	17	16
Dividends per share ($)	28.6%	0.05	0.10	0.13	0.17	0.24	0.28	0.32	0.36	0.40	0.48
Book value per share ($)	26.1%	1.09	1.64	2.16	2.88	3.69	4.56	5.46	6.39	7.52	8.79
Employees	6.4%	40,000	45,000	44,000	47,500	55,000	59,900	65,800	70,500	70,000	70,000

1994 Year-end:
Debt ratio: 22.4%
Return on equity: 20.9%
Cash (mil.): $758
Current ratio: 1.17
Long-term debt (mil.): $1,021
No. of shares (mil.): 482
Dividends
    Yield: 1.3%
    Payout: 28.1%
Market value (mil.): $18,485

**Stock Price History
High/Low 1985–94**

ENRON CORP.

OVERVIEW

Houston-based Enron is North America's #1 buyer and seller of natural gas and has a vision of becoming the world's #1 natural gas provider. To accomplish this ambitious task, the company is organized into 5 major subsidiaries. Enron Operations handles about 15% of the natural gas consumed in the US and 4% of the natural gas liquids. It builds and manages worldwide natural gas transportation, power generation, liquids, and clean fuels facilities.

Enron Capital & Trade Resources manages the world's largest portfolio of natural gas–related risk management contracts (futures and swaps) and is the leading supplier of natural gas to the US electric generation industry.

Enron Development and Enron Global Power & Pipelines build and operate power plants and pipelines in such emerging-market economies as China, Guatemala, and the Philippines. The company also operates a natural gas pipeline in Argentina and has signed a deal with Russia's Gazprom to help the state-owned company market gas in Europe. Enron Oil and Gas (80%-owned) is one of the world's largest independent oil and gas exploration companies.

The company currently owns energy facilities in 15 countries and is developing power projects in another 15. Enron employees own approximately 14% of the company.

WHEN

Enron traces its history through 2 well-established natural gas companies — InterNorth and Houston Natural Gas (HNG).

InterNorth started out in 1930 as Northern Natural Gas, an Omaha, Nebraska, gas pipeline company. By 1950 Northern had doubled its capacity and in 1960 it started processing and transporting natural gas liquids. The company changed its name to InterNorth in 1980. In 1983 it spent $768 million to buy Belco Petroleum, adding 821 billion cubic feet of natural gas and 67 million barrels of oil to its reserves. At the same time the company (with 4 partners) was building the Northern Border Pipeline to link Canadian fields with US markets.

HNG, formed in 1925 as a South Texas natural gas distributor, served more than 55,000 customers by the early 1940s. It started developing oil and gas properties in 1953 and bought Houston Pipe Line Company in 1956. Other major acquisitions included Valley Gas Production, a South Texas natural gas company (1963), and Houston's Bammel Gas Storage Field (1965). In the 1970s the company started developing offshore fields in the Gulf of Mexico, and in 1976 it sold its original gas distribution properties to Entex. In 1984 HNG, faced with a hostile takeover attempt by Coastal Corporation, brought in former Exxon executive Kenneth Lay as CEO. Lay refocused the company on natural gas, selling $632 million worth of unrelated assets. He added Transwestern Pipeline (California) and Florida Gas Transmission, and by 1985 the firm operated the only transcontinental gas pipeline.

In 1985 InterNorth bought HNG for $2.4 billion, creating the US's largest natural gas pipeline system (38,000 miles). Soon after,

Lay became chairman/CEO of newly named Enron (1986), and the company moved its headquarters from Omaha to Houston. Laden with $3.3 billion of debt (most related to the HNG acquisition), Enron sold 50% of Citrus Corporation (owner of Florida Gas Transmission, 1986), 50% of Enron Cogeneration (1988), and 16% of Enron Oil & Gas (1989).

In 1990 the company bought CSX Energy's Louisiana production facilities, which helped to increase Enron's production of natural gas liquids by nearly 33%. In 1991 Enron closed a deal with Tenneco to buy that company's natural gas liquids/petrochemical operations for $632 million.

In 1992 Enron signed a contract with Sithe Energies Group to supply $4 billion worth of natural gas over 20 years to a planned upstate New York cogeneration plant. Also in 1992 Enron and 3 partners acquired a 70% interest in the 3,800-mile Transportadora de Gas del Sur pipeline in Argentina. Enron acquired the Louisiana Resources Company and several other gas businesses, including a 540-mile pipeline, from the Williams Companies for $170 million in 1993.

In 1994 Enron renamed its gas services subsidiary Enron Capital & Trade Resources. Also in 1994 Enron completed a $90 million extension of the Argentinian natural gas pipeline, and in 1995 the $1 billion, 815-mile expansion of the Florida Gas Transmission pipeline was completed, linking the Mobile Bay production field to key consumer markets in southwest Florida. A wave of nationalism in India in 1995 led a state government there to terminate an Enron-backed, $2.8 billion power plant project already under construction.

NYSE symbol: ENE
Fiscal year ends: December 31

WHO

Chairman and CEO: Kenneth L. Lay, age 52,
$2,190,000 pay
VC: John A. Urquhart, age 66
President and COO: Richard D. Kinder, age 50,
$1,500,044 pay
**Managing Director, North American Operations,
Enron Capital & Trade Resources:** Ronald J. Burns,
age 41, $821,000 pay
EVP and Chief of Staff: Edmund P. Segner III, age 41,
$650,000 pay
**Managing Director, International Operations, Enron
Capital & Trade Resources:** Rodney L. Gray, age 42,
$638,000 pay
SVP and General Counsel: James V. Derrick Jr., age 50
SVP Government Affairs and Public Policy: Terence H.
Thorn
**SVP Chief Information, Administrative, and
Accounting Officer:** Jack I. Tomkins, age 45
President, Enron Services Corp.: James G. Barnhart
VP Finance and Treasurer: Kurt S. Huneke, age 41
VP Human Resources: Philip J. Bazelides
Auditors: Arthur Andersen & Co, SC

WHERE

HQ: 1400 Smith St., Houston, TX 77002-7369
Phone: 713-853-6161
Fax: 713-853-3129

Enron operates natural gas pipelines in North and South
America and operates energy projects worldwide.

	1994 Sales		1994 Operating Income	
	$ mil.	% of total	$ mil.	% of total
US	7,604	85	609	85
Other countries	1,380	15	107	15
Total	**8,984**	**100**	**716**	**100**

WHAT

	1994 Sales		1994 Operating Income	
	$ mil.	% of total	$ mil.	% of total
Domestic gas				
& power services	7,166	81	164	22
Trans. & operation	938	10	327	43
International gas				
& power services	392	4	72	9
Exploration & prod.	488	5	195	26
Adjustments	—	—	(42)	—
Total	**8,984**	**100**	**716**	**100**

Gas Services
Intrastate natural gas
pipelines
Natural gas–fired power
plants (North America)
Price risk management
and financing
arrangements
Purchasing and marketing
of natural gas, natural
gas liquids (NGLs), and
power

**Transportation and
Operation**
Crude oil transportation
Natural gas liquid plant
and power facility
construction,
management, and
operation

Natural gas transmission
Pipeline construction,
management, and
operation

**International Gas and
Power Services**
Natural gas liquids
marketing
Power plant, NGL facility,
and pipeline development
(outside North America)

Exploration and Production
Natural gas and crude oil
exploration and
production

Gas Processing
NGL extraction (North
America)

KEY COMPETITORS

British Gas	NGC	Sonat
Coastal	NOVA	Tejas Gas
Columbia Gas	Occidental	Tenneco
Gaz de France	Panhandle Eastern	USX–Delhi
Koch	Phillips Petroleum	Valero Energy

HOW MUCH

	9-Year Growth	1985	1986	1987	1988	1989	1990	1991	1992	1993	1994
Sales ($ mil.)	(0.6%)	9,458	7,453	5,916	5,708	9,836	13,165	13,520	6,325	7,972	8,984
Net income ($ mil.)	—	(128)	29	(39)	73	201	177	217	284	316	438
Income as % of sales	—	—	0.4%	—	1.3%	2.0%	1.3%	1.6%	4.5%	4.0%	4.9%
Earnings per share ($)	—	(2.89)	0.66	(0.86)	1.54	3.85	3.44	2.04	2.42	1.25	1.70
Stock price – high ($)	—	13.66	12.66	13.38	10.75	15.25	15.69	19.22	25.06	37.00	34.63
Stock price – low ($)	—	9.75	8.44	7.75	8.72	8.88	12.56	12.41	15.31	22.19	26.75
Stock price – close ($)	11.7%	11.25	9.88	9.78	9.16	14.41	13.69	17.50	23.19	29.00	30.50
P/E – high	—	—	19	—	7	4	5	9	10	30	20
P/E – low	—	—	13	—	6	2	4	6	6	18	16
Dividends per share ($)	2.3%	0.62	0.62	0.62	0.62	0.62	0.62	0.63	0.67	0.71	0.76
Book value per share ($)	5.0%	7.01	5.46	5.02	7.39	7.69	8.02	8.43	9.97	9.93	10.89
Employees	(5.8%)	11,911	7,200	6,900	6,895	6,900	6,962	7,400	7,780	7,100	6,978

1994 Year-end:
Debt ratio: 49.3%
Return on equity: 16.8%
Cash (mil.): $132
Current ratio: 0.83
Long-term debt (mil.): $2,805
No. of shares (mil.): 252
Dividends
  Yield: 2.5%
  Payout: 44.7%
Market value (mil.): $7,676

**Stock Price History
High/Low 1985–94**

EOTT ENERGY PARTNERS, L.P.

OVERVIEW

Houston-based EOTT Energy Partners is one of the largest independent gatherers and marketers of crude oil in North America. EOTT purchases crude oil produced from approximately 23,000 leases in 17 states, principally in the Gulf Coast, Southwest, Rocky Mountain, and midcontinent regions of the US. The company collects crude oil from leases and wells and takes it to refineries. It also purchases crude oil from Canada and has a network of oil pipelines and trucking operations across the US.

The company processes crude oil through 3rd-party processing arrangements, primarily with Paramount Petroleum, the major crude oil processor for its West Coast operations. EOTT also markets crude oil and uses 3rd-party carrier pipeline systems to distribute refined products (such as fuel oil, jet fuel, and unleaded gasoline).

EOTT struck out on its own in 1994, separating from its former parent, Enron, before the latter's major investment in a $3 billion power plant in India ran into political trouble there in 1995. According to some analysts, Enron, which has restructured its operations around its core natural gas businesses, would have preferred to sell all of its oil trading group but was unable to get the price it wanted. By setting up EOTT as a separate stock entity, Enron reduced its exposure and risk to price changes in the oil market. An Enron subsidiary, EOTT Energy Corp., acts as general partner of EOTT and holds approximately 39% of the company.

EOTT is eyeing new market services, such as risk management and financial products, as part of its expanding portfolio of products and services. The company also is planning on making additional acquisitions.

WHEN

EOTT's origins can be traced to Houston Natural Gas (HNG) and Northern Natural Gas, forebears of EOTT's parent, Enron Corp.

In 1925 HNG was formed as a natural gas distributor. By 1940 it was serving more than 55,000 customers in South Texas. It began developing oil and gas fields in 1953 and bought the Houston Pipe Line Company in 1956. The company began developing offshore fields in the Gulf of Mexico in the 1970s, and in 1976 it sold its original gas distribution properties to Entex. In 1984, Coastal Corporation tried to take over HNG, prompting the HNG board to bring in former Exxon executive Kenneth Lay as CEO to help fend off the bid. Lay focused HNG on natural gas, selling $632 million worth of noncore assets that year.

Omaha, Nebraska–based Northern Natural Gas, a gas pipeline company, was formed in 1930. By 1950 Northern had doubled its capacity, and in 1960 it started processing and transporting natural gas liquids. The company changed its corporate name to InterNorth in 1980, and in 1983 it spent $768 million to acquire Belco Petroleum. This purchase added 821 billion cubic feet of natural gas and 67 million barrels of oil to the company's reserves.

In 1985 InterNorth bought HNG for $2.4 billion, creating the US's largest natural gas system (38,000 miles). Lay became chairman and CEO of the newly named Enron in 1986 and moved its corporate headquarters from Omaha to Houston.

While natural gas forms the core of Enron's business, it is by no means the only asset that Enron has developed under Lay's leadership. In 1987 the company purchased a crude oil terminal and transportation facility from Fairway Crude, Inc. In 1988 Enron bought Tesoro Petroleum's gathering and transportation businesses, and in 1991 it bought Tenneco's natural gas liquids and petrochemicals operations for $632 million. In 1993 Enron acquired Shell Pipe Line Corp.'s eastern New Mexico crude oil pipeline system (including 500,000 barrels of tank storage).

By the mid-1990s Enron had established itself as North America's #1 buyer and seller of natural gas, with plans to become the world's leading supplier. To finance Enron's expansion plans in that market, the company sold some of its noncore assets. In 1993 Enron sold 87% of Northern Border Partners L.P. (an interstate pipeline systems operator) for $217 million. Enron combined its EOTT (Enron Oil Trading & Transportation) Energy and Enron Products Marketing Company and created EOTT Energy Partners as a separate public company in 1994. The IPO raised approximately $200 million.

To stem the refining margin losses from its West Coast operation in 1995, EOTT renegotiated its contract with its key processor, Paramount Petroleum. To protect itself from fluctuations in refining margins, EOTT agreed to sell crude oil to Paramount and then market the fuels and take a share of the revenues.

NYSE symbol: EOT
Fiscal year ends: December 31

WHO

Chairman: Edward O. Gaylord, age 63, $7,560,190 pay
President and CEO: Philip J. Hawk, age 41,
$340,000 pay
SVP and General Manager, West Coast Business: Mark
R. Milano, age 42, $187,624 pay
**VP and General Manager, Crude Oil Marketing and
Lease Acquisition:** Steven M. Myers, age 41,
$195,634 pay
VP Strategic Planning and Trading Controls: Gary W.
Luce, age 35, $164,168 pay
VP Finance and Business Development: Walter Z.
Berger, age 39
VP Operations: Douglas P. Huth, age 48
VP and General Counsel: Stephen W. Duffy, age 41
VP and Controller: Marian E. Ragland, age 43
VP Human Resources and Administration: Mary Ellen
Coombe, age 44
Auditors: Arthur Andersen & Co, SC

WHERE

HQ: 1330 Post Oak Blvd., Houston, TX 77056
Phone: 713-993-5200 **Fax:** 713-993-5873

EOTT purchases crude oil produced from approximately
23,000 leases in 17 states, principally in the Gulf Coast,
Southwest, Rocky Mountain, and midcontinent regions
of the US. It also purchases crude oil from Canada.
EOTT has oil pipeline and/or trucking operations in
Alabama, Arkansas, California, Colorado, Florida,
Kansas, Louisiana, Mississippi, Missouri, Montana,
Nebraska, New Mexico, North Dakota, Oklahoma, Texas,
Utah, and Wyoming.

WHAT

	1994 Sales	
	$ mil.	% of total
North American crude oil	5,041	82
West Coast operations	740	12
Refined products marketing	372	6
Adjustments	(232)	—
Total	**5,921**	**100**

Selected Products and Services
Crude oil and refined petroleum products
  Gathering
  Processing
  Purchasing
  Resale
  Storage
  Trading
  Transporting

Selected Affiliates
EOTT Energy Canada Limited Partnership
EOTT Energy Operating Limited Partnership
EOTT Energy Pipeline Limited Partnership

KEY COMPETITORS

Abraxas Petroleum	Occidental
Ashland, Inc.	Oryx
Atlantic Richfield	Pennzoil
British Petroleum	Phillips Petroleum
Chevron	Repsol
Coastal	Shell Oil
Diamond Shamrock	Scurlock Permian
Elf Aquitaine	Snyder Oil
Exxon	Sun Co.
FINA	Texaco
Imperial Oil	TOTAL
Koch	Unocal
Mobil	

HOW MUCH

	Annual Growth	1985	1986	1987	1988	1989	1990	1991	1992	1993	1994
Sales ($ mil.)	(6.9%)	—	—	—	—	—	7,886	8,236	7,697	6,359	5,921
Net income ($ mil.)	—	—	—	—	—	—	(14)	28	(19)	20	21
Income as % of sales	—	—	—	—	—	—	—	0.3%	—	0.3%	0.4%
Earnings per share ($)	—	—	—	—	—	—	—	—	—	—	0.71
Stock price – high ($)	—	—	—	—	—	—	—	—	—	—	20.13
Stock price – low ($)	—	—	—	—	—	—	—	—	—	—	14.75
Stock price – close ($)	—	—	—	—	—	—	—	—	—	—	15.25
P/E – high	—	—	—	—	—	—	—	—	—	—	28
P/E – low	—	—	—	—	—	—	—	—	—	—	21
Dividends per share ($)	—	—	—	—	—	—	—	—	—	—	1.70
Book value per share ($)	—	—	—	—	—	—	—	—	—	—	9.33
Employees	—	—	—	—	—	—	—	—	—	—	900

1994 Year-end:
Debt ratio: 26.3%
Return on equity: 13.3%
Cash (mil.): $2
Current ratio: 1.10
Long-term debt (mil.): $13
No. of shares (mil.): 17
Dividends
  Yield: 11.1%
  Payout: 239.4%
Market value (mil.): $259

**Stock Price History
High/Low 1994**

EXXON CORPORATION

OVERVIEW

Exxon is the world's largest publicly owned integrated oil company, with oil reserves of 6.6 billion barrels and gas reserves of 42.2 trillion cubic feet. In addition to conducting worldwide oil and gas exploration and production, it produces and sells petrochemicals, mines coal and other minerals, and owns 60% of a Hong Kong electric power generating station.

The company is continuing to focus on lowering costs and selling nonstrategic assets. It has sold about $1 billion in assets per year since 1990, and staffing levels are half of 1981

levels. Exxon's finances have been buoyed by its chemical division, whose profits more than doubled to $954 million in 1994.

Exxon spends about 1/3 of its refining and retail operations capital on the fast-growing Asia/Pacific region.

Despite slick work in cleaning up the *Exxon Valdez* oil spill, on which it spent approximately $2.5 billion, Exxon was slapped with a $5 billion punitive damage verdict by a federal court in Alaska in 1994, a judgment it plans to appeal.

WHEN

John D. Rockefeller, a commodity trader, started his first oil refinery in 1863 in Cleveland. Realizing that the price of oil at the well would shrink with each new strike, Rockefeller chose to monopolize oil refining and transportation. He raised $1 million in loans and investments and in 1870 formed the Standard Oil Company. In 1882 Rockefeller and his associates created the Standard Oil Trust, which allowed Rockefeller and 8 others to dissolve existing Standard Oil affiliates and set up new, ostensibly independent companies in different states, including the Standard Oil Company of New Jersey (Jersey Standard).

Initially capitalized at $70 million, the Standard Oil Trust controlled 90% of the petroleum industry. In 1911, after 2 decades of political and legal wrangling, the Supreme Court disbanded the trust into 34 companies, the largest of which was Jersey Standard. In that year John Archbold took over as president of Jersey Standard and commenced more active exploration efforts.

Walter Teagle took over the presidency in 1917, secretly bought half of Humble Oil of Texas (1919), and expanded into South America. In 1928 Jersey Standard joined in the Red Line Agreement, which reserved most Middle East oil for a handful of companies. Congressional investigation of a prewar research pact giving Farben of Germany patents for a lead essential to the development of aviation fuel in exchange for a formula for synthetic rubber (never received) led to Teagle's resignation in 1942.

The 1948 purchase of a 30% interest in Arabian American Oil Company for $74 million, combined with a 7% share of Iranian production acquired in 1954, made Jersey Standard the world's largest oil company.

Other US companies still using the Standard Oil name objected to Jersey Standard

marketing in their territories as Esso (derived from the initials S.O. for Standard Oil). To end the confusion, Jersey Standard became Exxon in 1972. The name change cost $100 million.

In the 1970s nationalization of oil assets by producing countries reduced Exxon's access to oil. Despite increased exploration in the 1970s and 1980s, Exxon's reserves shrank faster than new reserves could be found.

The oil tanker *Exxon Valdez*, under the command of Joseph Hazelwood, spilled nearly 11 million gallons of oil into Alaska's Prince William Sound in 1989. In 1991 Exxon agreed to settle criminal charges resulting from the spill. Payments to the US government and the state of Alaska totaled $1.1 billion. Exxon spent billions on coastal cleanup operations.

In 1992 Exxon announced a $900 million expansion of its Sriracha refinery in Thailand and an agreement with Mobil to develop an 86-million-acre area in Siberia. Also in 1992 Arthur Seale, a former security official with Exxon, pleaded guilty to the kidnapping and murder of Sidney Reso, president of Exxon's international division. He was sentenced to life plus 125 years in prison.

In 1994 a federal jury in Alaska found that Exxon's "recklessness" caused the grounding of the *Exxon Valdez*.

In that same year Exxon and Pertamina, the Indonesian state oil company, agreed on terms to develop the giant Natuna gas field (50%-owned by Exxon), which contains an estimated 45 trillion cubic feet of natural gas.

In 1995 the company awarded 10 contracts worth approximately $200 million to 6 Malaysian companies to construct natural gas platforms and pipelines. Also that year Exxon signed a $15 billion agreement to develop 3 oil and natural gas fields off Sakhalin Island in Russia. Drilling is expected to get underway sometime in 1996.

NYSE symbol: XON
Fiscal year ends: December 31

WHO

Chairman and CEO: Lee R. Raymond, age 56, $1,850,000 pay
President: Charles R. Sitter, age 64, $1,285,000 pay
SVP: Robert E. Wilhelm, age 54, $900,000 pay
SVP: H. J. Longwell, age 53, $695,833 pay (prior to promotion)
SVP: Edwin J. Hess, age 61
VP Investor Relations and Secretary: T. P. Townsend, age 58
VP and Treasurer: Edgar A. Robinson, age 61
VP Medicine and Occupational Health: T. J. McDonagh, age 63
VP and Controller: W. B. Cook, age 59
VP and General Counsel: C. W. Matthews Jr., age 50
VP Public Affairs: A. W. Atkiss, age 55
VP Human Resources: Daniel S. Sanders, age 55
General Manager Corporate Planning: S. F. Goldmann, age 50
Auditors: Price Waterhouse LLP

WHERE

HQ: 225 E. John W. Carpenter Fwy., Irving, TX 75062-2298
Phone: 214-444-1000
Fax: 214-444-1505

Exxon conducts operations in the US and in more than 100 other countries.

	1994 Sales		1994 Net Income	
	$ mil.	% of total	$ mil.	% of total
US	22,651	21	1,560	31
Other Western Hemisphere	16,875	15	370	7
Other regions	70,429	64	3,195	62
Adjustments	3,949	—	(25)	—
Total	**113,904**	**100**	**5,100**	**100**

WHAT

	1994 Sales		1994 Net Income	
	$ mil.	% of total	$ mil.	% of total
Petroleum & natural gas	100,409	89	4,171	81
Chemicals	9,544	8	954	19
Other	3,951	3	(25)	—
Total	**113,904**	**100**	**5,100**	**100**

Petroleum and Natural Gas
Upstream operations
  Oil and gas exploration and production
Downstream operations
  Lubricants
  Refining
  Service stations

Chemicals
Aromatics
Fuel and lubricant additives

Performance chemicals for oil field operations
Plasticizers
Polyethylene and polypropylene plastics
Solvents
Specialty resins
Specialty rubbers

Other Activities
Coal and mineral mining
Power generation

KEY COMPETITORS

Amerada Hess
Amoco
Ashland, Inc.
Atlantic Richfield
British Gas
British Petroleum
Broken Hill
Caltex Petroleum
Chevron
Circle K
Coastal
Diamond Shamrock
Dow Chemical
DuPont
Eastman Chemical
Elf Aquitaine
Enron

FINA
Huntsman Chemical
Imperial Oil
Koch
Lyondell Petrochemical
Mobil
Norsk Hydro
NOVA
Occidental
Oryx
Panhandle Eastern
PDVSA
PEMEX
Pennzoil

Petrobrás
Phillips Petroleum
Repsol
Shell Oil
Sinclair Oil
Southland
Star Enterprise
Sun Company
Texaco
TOTAL
Union Carbide
Unocal
USX–Marathon
YPF

HOW MUCH

	9-Year Growth	1985	1986	1987	1988	1989	1990	1991	1992	1993	1994
Sales ($ mil.)	2.3%	92,869	76,555	83,335	88,563	96,285	116,940	116,492	117,106	111,211	113,904
Net income ($ mil.)	0.5%	4,870	5,360	4,840	5,260	2,975	5,010	5,600	4,810	5,280	5,100
Income as % of sales	—	5.2%	7.0%	5.8%	5.9%	3.1%	4.3%	4.8%	4.1%	4.7%	4.5%
Earnings per share ($)	2.6%	3.23	3.71	3.43	3.95	2.32	3.96	4.45	3.82	4.21	4.07
Stock price – high ($)	—	27.94	37.06	50.38	47.75	51.63	55.13	61.88	65.50	69.00	67.38
Stock price – low ($)	—	22.06	24.19	30.88	36.63	41.50	44.88	49.63	53.75	57.75	56.13
Stock price – close ($)	9.2%	27.56	35.06	38.13	44.00	50.00	51.75	60.88	61.13	63.13	60.75
P/E – high	—	9	10	15	12	22	14	14	17	16	17
P/E – low	—	7	7	9	9	18	11	11	14	14	14
Dividends per share ($)	5.9%	1.73	1.80	1.90	2.15	2.30	2.47	2.68	2.83	2.88	2.91
Book value per share ($)	4.5%	19.90	22.29	24.38	24.64	23.36	25.78	27.42	26.57	28.02	29.68
Employees	(5.7%)	146,000	102,000	151,000	101,000	104,000	104,000	101,000	95,000	91,000	86,000

1994 Year-end:
Debt ratio: 25.3%
Return on equity: 14.4%
Cash (mil.): $1,775
Current ratio: 0.84
Long-term debt (mil.): $8,831
No. of shares (mil.): 1,242
Dividends
  Yield: 4.8%
  Payout: 71.5%
Market value (mil.): $75,452

Stock Price History
High/Low 1985–94

FINA, INC.

OVERVIEW

Dallas-based FINA is the publicly traded US subsidiary of Belgian oil, gas, and chemical conglomerate Petrofina S. A., which owns about 85% of FINA's Class A common stock and 100% of its Class B common stock.

FINA is an integrated oil and gas company with broad upstream (exploration and production) and downstream (refining and marketing) operations. Most of the company's 31.7 million barrels of crude oil reserves are located in the Permian Basin of West Texas, and the majority of FINA's 348 billion cubic feet of natural gas reserves are located in the Gulf of Mexico, the Texas Rio Grande Valley, and in Louisiana.

FINA owns and operates 2 refineries, with a total output of 215,000 barrels a day, in Port Arthur and Big Spring, Texas. It sells gasoline through more than 2,600 branded retail outlets located in 11 southeastern and southwestern states, most of which are owned by independent distributors.

The company also markets natural gas, jet and diesel fuel, and other petroleum-based products, and it manufactures and markets petrochemicals and plastics.

Over the last few years, FINA has concentrated on streamlining its operations. Since 1990 it has cut its workforce by more than 30%.

WHEN

Petrofina S.A. created its US subsidiary, American Petrofina, in 1956. Petrofina S.A. was founded in 1920 by a group of Belgian investors. The group acquired interests in Romanian oil fields from Germany, which was forced to surrender the fields following WWI. Petrofina expanded throughout Europe during the 1920s and 1930s, but it suffered 2 major blows in the 1940s — first, the invasion of Belgium by Hitler's armies, and 2nd, the Communists' seizure of the Romanian oil fields after the Iron Curtain dropped. To recover, Petrofina looked abroad and moved into the US.

Following the formation of American Petrofina, the company acquired Panhandle Oil. Most of Panhandle's 1.25 million barrels of oil production came from its Texas fields.

American Petrofina quickly added more holdings through acquisitions. In 1957 it purchased American Liberty Oil for $24 million, and in 1958 it bought Petro-Atlas and its subsidiary El Dorado Refining from Atlas Corporation. That same year it acquired Reco Oil. By 1960 American Petrofina had more than 1,100 oil wells, and it refined more than 36,000 barrels of crude oil per day.

Expansion continued on many fronts during the 1960s. In 1963 it doubled its refining capacity when it acquired Cosden Petroleum and its Big Spring, Texas, refinery for $90 million. It also added to its oil and gas holdings when it paid $20 million for Breckenridge, Texas–based Graridge Corporation (1966).

American Petrofina expanded its gas station holdings during the 1960s. In 1964 it bought 42 outlets in East Texas and western Louisiana from Bell Oil; the stations were then leased back to Bell in a marketing agreement. American Petrofina also diversified into petrochemicals, signing a joint venture agreement with Borg-Warner Chemicals to build a styrene monomer plant in Carville, Louisiana, in 1968.

In 1969 the company greatly expanded its petroleum marketing holdings in a 10-state region in and around the Rocky Mountains when it bought 132 of Tenneco's service stations and 250 outlets owned by distributors of Tenneco gasoline.

The company continued its expansion in the 1970s. In 1973 it paid Standard Oil of Ohio $100 million for a refinery in Port Arthur, Texas, and a subsidiary that operated some 1,500 service stations in the southeastern US. It also acquired Wintershall Oil and Gas from Germany's BASF for $20 million in 1979. During the late 1970s the company sold its refineries in North Texas and in Kansas to concentrate on its West Texas and Gulf Coast refining facilities, which it began modernizing in 1980.

The company added to its chemical operations in 1984 with the acquisition of ARCO Chemical's 470 million-pound-per-year polypropylene plant in La Porte, Texas. In 1988 it expanded its upstream operations when it paid Tenneco $602 million for that company's Gulf Coast and Southwest exploration and production business, which had estimated reserves of 28 million barrels of crude oil and 437 billion cubic feet of natural gas.

In 1991 American Petrofina changed its name to FINA, Inc. The company bought Hoechst Celanese's high-density polyethylene business in 1992.

In 1995 FINA announced a major discovery at its King Bee well in Mississippi that could add up to 40 million barrels to its reserves.

AMEX symbol: FI
Fiscal year ends: December 31

WHO

Chairman: Paul D. Meek, age 64
President and CEO: Ron W. Haddock, age 54, $613,872 pay
VP: H. Patrick Jack, age 43, $299,518 pay
VP: Neil A. Smoak, age 49, $299,119 pay
VP: Michael J. Couch, age 43, $247,017 pay
VP, CFO, and Treasurer: Yves Bercy, age 49, $237,180 pay
VP, Secretary, and General Counsel: Cullen M. Godfrey, age 49
VP: S. Robert West, age 55
Controller: James D. Grier, age 53
General Manager Human Resources: Bill Bonnett
Auditors: KPMG Peat Marwick LLP

WHERE

HQ: FINA Plaza, 8350 N. Central Expwy., Dallas, TX 75206
Phone: 214-750-2400
Fax: 214-750-2508

Selected Properties

Chemical Plants
Bayport, TX (high-density polyethylene)
Carville, LA (polystyrene)
Carville, LA (styrene monomer, 50%)
La Porte, TX (polypropylene)
Mont Belvieu, TX (propylene splitter, 33%)

Refineries
Big Spring, TX
Port Arthur, TX

WHAT

	1994 Sales		1994 Operating Inc	
	$ mil.	% of total	$ mil.	% of tot
Refining, supply & transportation & marketing	1,982	58	42	20
Chemicals	890	26	171	80
Exploration, production & natural gas marketing	549	16	(16)	—
Other	16	0	(16)	—
Total	**3,437**	**100**	**181**	**100**

	1994 Sales
	% of total
Gasoline	29
Petrochemicals & plastics	28
Distillates	20
Natural gas	14
Other	9
Total	**100**

Selected Products
Asphalt	Jet fuel
Diesel fuel	Natural gas
Gasoline	Petrochemicals
Heavy oils	Plastics

KEY COMPETITORS

Amerada Hess	Eastman	Phillips
Amoco	Chemical	Petroleum
Ashland, Inc.	Enron Corp.	Shell Oil
Atlantic Richfield	Exxon	Southland
Chevron	Koch	Sun Co.
Coastal	Mobil	Texaco
Diamond Shamrock	Occidental	Union Carbide
Dow Chemical	Oryx	Unocal
DuPont	PDVSA	USX–Marathon

HOW MUCH

	9-Year Growth	1985	1986	1987	1988	1989	1990	1991	1992	1993	1994
Sales ($ mil.)	4.0%	2,422	2,021	2,510	2,651	3,057	3,979	3,339	3,409	3,516	3,437
Net income ($ mil.)	—	(10)	(25)	83	133	96	126	42	24	70	102
Income as % of sales	—	—	—	3.3%	5.0%	3.1%	3.2%	1.3%	0.7%	2.0%	3.0%
Earnings per share ($)	—	(0.43)	(1.02)	3.16	5.04	3.15	4.06	1.36	0.78	2.26	3.27
Stock price – high ($)	—	31.25	26.50	37.50	36.38	45.00	42.38	45.50	38.44	35.50	39.88
Stock price – low ($)	—	22.50	19.19	21.00	29.19	33.63	35.50	32.69	29.56	30.13	32.00
Stock price – close ($)	4.7%	22.63	21.56	29.06	34.44	37.31	40.63	35.00	30.13	34.38	34.19
P/E – high	—	—	—	12	7	14	10	34	49	16	12
P/E – low	—	—	—	7	6	11	9	24	38	13	10
Dividends per share ($)	6.2%	1.05	0.00	0.25	1.30	1.60	1.60	1.60	1.60	1.60	1.80
Book value per share ($)	3.9%	26.08	24.81	27.71	31.44	34.30	36.76	36.51	34.58	35.23	36.70
Employees	(2.4%)	3,439	3,358	3,369	3,595	3,694	3,997	3,665	3,369	3,224	2,770

1994 Year-end:
Debt ratio: 36.2%
Return on equity: 9.1%
Cash (mil.): $4
Current ratio: 1.20
Long-term debt (mil.): $531
No. of shares (mil.): 31
Dividends
  Yield: 5.3%
  Payout: 55.0%
Market value (mil.): $1,066

Stock Price History
High/Low 1985–94

...on, Texas–based FoxMeyer Health (known until 1994 as National Intergroup, formerly National Steel) is the parent company of FoxMeyer Corporation, one of the largest and oldest pharmaceutical distribution companies in the US. Distribution companies have become one of the most important parts of the pharmaceuticals business because, in an age of increased scrutiny of health care costs, they have the buying power to get advantageous prices from manufacturers for their independent pharmacy clients. Other clients include drugstore chains, hospitals and other medical facilities, and managed care companies. The company also offers marketing support and distributes nonpharmaceutical personal care and health products.

In recent years FoxMeyer has developed a number of pharmacy-related managed care services, which are part of its CareStream unit. These services include order, inventory, and billing software; claims processing services; benefits plan management; and drug utilization databases (which are helpful in determining the efficacy of treatment).

FoxMeyer also owns 17% of Ben Franklin Retail Stores, a general merchandise store franchiser that has boosted its sales by emphasizing craft supplies. Until a 1995 spinoff of its Ben Franklin shares to FoxMeyer stockholders, it owned about 68% of the franchiser.

Recent earnings have fluctuated as the company struggled to shed its steel and aluminum businesses and establish a new identity in distribution and health care services. Co-CEOs Abbey Butler and Melvyn Estrin, individually and through their Centaur Group partnership, control over 27% of FoxMeyer.

WHEN

National Steel Company was created by the 1929 merger of Great Lakes Steel Co., Weirton Steel Co., and Hanna Iron Ore Company. The company survived the Depression and in the succeeding decades expanded and diversified, adding subsidiaries overseas and buying or starting up a variety of steel and aluminum companies, including mining interests, trading, and transportation businesses.

In the 1970s, however, the postwar era of US domination of world manufacturing came to an end. Increased competition from the recently rebuilt steel industries of Japan and Germany (as well as the increased production costs and the decreased demand that followed the oil shocks of the 1970s) sent US steel companies, including National Steel, into a slump.

In 1982, seeking a mechanism for greater diversification, chairman Howard Love (whose father had also been a National Steel executive) restructured the company to form a new holding company, National Intergroup (NII), as National Steel's parent.

In 1984 Love began selling NII's steel assets; he sold Weirton to its employees and 50% of National Steel to Japan's NKK. Hoping to profit from the hot businesses of the 1980s, the company formed a consulting and software subsidiary, GENIX. In 1985 NII bought Permian Corp., a crude oil gathering and shipping business, just in time for the crash of the oil industry in 1986. Then Love went looking for a pharmaceuticals distributor, because the business was not capital intensive and used a relatively small labor force.

After unsuccessfully attempting to buy Bergen Brunswig, Love turned his attention to FoxMeyer, then the 3rd largest pharmaceuticals distributor in the US. FoxMeyer's predecessor was created in 1977 by wheeler-dealer William Y. Tauscher as the parent company for a number of small drug distributors, including Fox-Vliet, which had been founded in 1903. In 1981 Tauscher acquired Meyer Brothers, another distribution company, and the company became FoxMeyer in 1983. Within 3 years it had added 8 more drug distributors and Tauscher was looking for a buyer for the company. Love and Tauscher found each other in 1986 and made the deal despite indications that FoxMeyer was overpriced and the industry itself was on the brink of a new round of consolidation and competition.

By 1987, with FoxMeyer in trouble, oil prices off, and problems arising in melding the managements of National Steel and NKK, NII went into technical default. A series of management upheavals followed, taking their toll on results. More subsidiaries were sold off, the company successively reduced its holdings in National Steel (selling the last of its stock in 1991), and FoxMeyer began to recover.

In 1990 a stockholder revolt led to the ascendancy of Butler and Estrin, who raised money by taking FoxMeyer public in 1991. In 1994 NII was renamed FoxMeyer Health Corporation and the company repurchased all public shares of FoxMeyer. In 1995 FoxMeyer Health said that it would consider spinning off its CareStream operations.

NYSE symbol: FOX
Fiscal year ends: March 31

Co-chairman and Co-CEO: Abbey J. Butler, age 58, $1,504,761 pay
Co-chairman and Co-CEO: Melvyn J. Estrin, age 52, $1,504,761 pay
President and COO: Thomas L. Anderson, age 46, $371,080 pay
SVP and CFO: Peter B. McKee, age 57, $216,753 pay
VP and Controller: Edward L. Massman, age 36, $150,869 pay
SVP, General Counsel, and Secretary: Kevin J. Rogan, age 43
VP Human Resources: Sandra K. Stevens
Auditors: Deloitte & Touche LLP

WHERE

HQ: 1220 Senlac Dr., Carrollton, TX 75006
Phone: 214-446-4800
Fax: 214-446-4499

	1995 Facilities	
	FoxMeyer	Ben Franklin*
Ohio	3	5
California	2	4
Missouri	2	—
Florida	1	4
Massachusetts	1	3
Indiana	—	3
Michigan	—	3
New York	—	9
Other states	16	2
Total	**25**	**33**

* Company-owned only

WHAT

	1995 Sales		1995 Operating Income	
	$ mil.	% of total	$ mil.	% of total
FoxMeyer	4,822	93	32	86
Ben Franklin	355	7	5	14
Adjustments	—	—	31	—
Total	**5,177**	**100**	**68**	**100**

	1995 Pharmaceutical Sales	
	$ mil.	% of total
Independent drugstores	1,683	35
Drugstore chains	1,489	31
Hospitals/medical facilities	1,231	25
Other	419	9
Total	**4,822**	**100**

Selected Operations

Ben Franklin Retail Stores, Inc. (17.3%)
General retail and craft stores

CareStream
Billing and payment management software
Drug utilization databases
Electronic claims processing services
Managed care services
Order and inventory management software
Pharmacy benefits plan management

FoxMeyer Corp.
Health and beauty products distribution
Pharmaceuticals distribution

KEY COMPETITORS

Amber's Stores	Krelitz
Bergen Brunswig	McKesson
Bindley Western	Michaels Stores
Cardinal Health	Moore Medical
D & K Wholesale Drug	Owens & Minor
Kmart	Wal-Mart

HOW MUCH

	9-Year Growth	1986	1987	1988	1989	1990	1991	1992	1993	1994	1995
Sales ($ mil.)	9.1%	2,370	4,541	3,355	3,081	2,755	2,879	3,411	4,852	5,409	5,177
Net income ($ mil.)	—	(15)	(32)	(25)	(27)	23	(89)	25	1	30	42
Income as % of sales	—	—	—	—	—	0.8%	—	0.7%	—	0.5%	0.8%
Earnings per share ($)	—	(0.66)	(2.46)	(1.40)	(1.48)	0.83	(13.53)	0.91	(0.24)	1.10	1.52
Stock price – high ($)	—	33.63	28.50	20.50	20.50	20.88	19.00	20.88	15.38	15.88	18.75
Stock price – low ($)	—	24.00	13.00	10.25	12.13	12.13	11.00	12.38	11.13	12.25	13.25
Stock price – close ($)	(6.6%)	27.38	14.00	12.00	17.38	14.38	13.88	14.25	12.75	13.25	14.88
P/E – high	—	—	—	—	—	25	—	23	—	14	12
P/E – low	—	—	—	—	—	15	—	14	—	11	9
Dividends per share ($)	(100.0%)	0.25	0.31	0.25	0.06	0.00	0.00	0.00	0.05	0.00	0.00
Book value per share ($)	(8.3%)	39.59	34.64	32.66	31.45	32.77	19.97	18.91	18.28	17.47	18.17
Employees	(4.0%)	6,965	7,492	7,204	5,875	4,697	2,354	3,138	3,020	2,847	4,804

1995 Year-end:
Debt ratio: 47.0%
Return on equity: 15.7%
Cash (mil.): $35
Current ratio: 1.57
Long-term debt (mil.): $423
No. of shares (mil.): 17
Dividends
  Yield: —
  Payout: —
Market value (mil.): $249

Stock Price History
High/Low 1986–95

¹ Stock prices are for the prior calendar year.

HALLIBURTON COMPANY

OVERVIEW

One of the world's biggest energy, engineering, and construction services companies, Dallas-based Halliburton operates 3 business segments. The company's energy services business provides a wide range of equipment, products, and services from drilling equipment for oil exploration to construction and maintenance services for oil refineries. Halliburton's engineering and construction unit, led by Brown & Root, provides services for industrial and government customers, including oil and chemical companies, electric power generators, and manufacturing firms. The company's insurance subsidiary, Highlands Insurance, issues property and casualty insurance.

The company has reorganized itself over the past 2 years, selling noncore assets and streamlining its operations. In 1994 the firm sold its gas-compression unit to Tidewater Compression Service for $205 million and its troubled geophysical business to Western Atlas for $190 million. It is also considering divesting its insurance business, which broke even in 1994 after 2 years of losses.

In 1994 Brown & Root was contracted to provide logistical support to the US military in its peacekeeping mission in Haiti.

WHEN

Erle Halliburton began his oil career in 1916, when he went to work for Perkins Oil Well Cementing. Discharged for suggesting too many new ideas, Halliburton left for Burkburnett, Texas, in 1919 and started his Better Method Oil Well Cementing Company. Halliburton used cement to hold a steel pipe in a well, which kept oil out of the water table. Although his contribution is widely recognized today, it was considered nonessential then. In 1921, the same year he moved to Duncan, Oklahoma, he recorded his first profit — of 50¢. In 1924 he incorporated as Halliburton Oil Well Cementing Company.

Between the 1950s and 1970s, Halliburton built up its oil service business by buying companies with expertise throughout the oil and gas market. It acquired Welex, a well-logging company (1957), and Houston-based Brown & Root construction company (1966), which had expertise in offshore platforms. It bought Ebasco Services, an electric utility engineering company with expertise in nuclear plants (1973), but the Justice Department forced its sale (1976), fearing that Halliburton's 20% share of the utility engineering market would limit competition.

The investments in Welex and Brown & Root left Halliburton well positioned to benefit from the oil boom of the 1970s. Later that decade, as drilling costs surged, Halliburton became the leader in stimulating old and abandoned wells by developing new techniques for fracturing deep formations.

When the oil industry slumped in 1982, Halliburton avoided further energy investments, instead cutting employment by more than half, while rivals Schlumberger and Dresser bought distressed companies at bargain prices. Another Halliburton business was not faring well, either: in 1985 Brown & Root, already suffering a scarcity of new construction projects, settled out of court for $750 million for mismanagement of the South Texas Nuclear Project.

Halliburton began reinvesting in oil and gas services, buying 60% of Texas Instruments's Geophysical Services (GSI), and Geosource, another geophysical service company (1988). Halliburton also bought Gearhart Industries (wireline services) and merged it with Welex to form Halliburton Logging Services. It purchased the remaining interest in GSI in 1991.

Halliburton opened an office in Moscow in 1991 and has since established joint enterprises throughout the former Soviet Union. Also in 1991 Brown & Root was chosen by Tokyo-based Sanpo Land Industrial as the prime contractor for an $8 billion luxury resort to be located near Nagoya, Japan.

In 1993 Halliburton acquired Smith International's directional drilling and services business for $240 million in stock. That same year the firm signed a joint venture deal with China National Petroleum Corporation to provide oil and gas field equipment and services.

In 1994 Brown & Root was named contractor for the Gulf–South Asia Gas Project, a $3.2 billion pipeline stretching from Qatar to Pakistan. In that same year Brown & Root started building a floating production platform for BHP Petroleum in the Dai Hung Field in the waters off Vietnam.

In 1995 Halliburton set the record for the world's deepest horizontal well (18,860 feet) with a Mobil well in Germany. Former US defense secretary Dick Cheney was named president and CEO in August 1995.

NYSE symbol: HAL
Fiscal year ends: December 31

WHO

Chairman: Thomas H. Cruikshank, age 63,
$1,200,000 pay
President and CEO: Richard B. Cheney, age 54
VC and COO: W. Bernard Pieper, age 62, $842,500 pay
VC: Dale P. Jones, age 58, $750,000 pay (prior to
promotion)
President and CEO, Halliburton Energy Services:
Kenneth R. LeSuer, age 59, $635,837 pay
President and CEO, Brown & Root, Inc.: Tommy E.
Knight, age 56, $622,500 pay
President and CEO, Highlands Insurance: Harold G.
Duble
EVP and General Counsel: Lester L. Coleman, age 52
EVP and CFO: David J. Lesar, age 42
VP Government Relations: George L. Gleason
VP and Corporate Secretary: Susan S. Keith
VP and Treasurer: C. Robert Fielder
VP Legal: Robert M. Kennedy
VP Investor Relations: Guy T. Marcus
VP Administration (Personnel): Karen S. Stuart
Auditors: Arthur Andersen & Co, SC

WHERE

HQ: 3600 Lincoln Plaza, Dallas, TX 75201
Phone: 214-978-2600
Fax: 214-978-2611

Halliburton conducts business in the US and in more
than 100 other countries.

	1994 Sales		1994 Operating Income	
	$ mil.	% of total	$ mil.	% of total
US	3,416	60	172	61
Europe	961	15	(22)	—
Other regions	1,363	25	108	39
Adjustments	—	—	(23)	—
Total	**5,740**	**100**	**235**	**100**

WHAT

	1994 Sales		1994 Operating Income	
	$ mil.	% of total	$ mil.	% of total
Engineering & construction	2,996	52	67	26
Energy services	2,514	44	191	74
Insurance services	230	4	0	—
Adjustments	—	—	(23)	—
Total	**5,740**	**100**	**235**	**100**

Engineering and Construction Services
Construction
Engineering
Environmental services
Facilities operation and maintenance
Project management

Energy Services
Cementing, casing equipment, and water control services
Drilling systems and services

Logging and perforating
Pressure pumping equipment and services
Software
Specialized completion and production equipment and services
Well control
Well testing and reservoir evaluation services

Insurance Services
Casualty
Property

KEY COMPETITORS

ABB
Baker Hughes
Bechtel
BJ Services
Black and Veatch
Camco
CBI Industries
CSX
Dresser
Duke Power
Fluor
FMC

General Electric
Jacobs Engineering
Litton Industries
McDermott
Morrison Knudsen
Nabors Industries
Ogden
Perini
Peter Kiewit Sons'

Raytheon
Schlumberger
Siemens
Turner Industries
Union Pacific
Western Atlas
Westinghouse
WMX Technologies

HOW MUCH

	9-Year Growth	1985	1986	1987	1988	1989	1990	1991	1992	1993	1994
Sales ($ mil.)	2.1%	4,781	3,527	3,836	4,839	5,661	6,926	7,019	6,566	6,351	5,740
Net income ($ mil.)	22.3%	29	(515)	48	85	134	197	27	(124)	(161)	178
Income as % of sales	—	0.6%	—	1.3%	1.8%	2.4%	2.8%	0.4%	—	—	3.1%
Earnings per share ($)	21.5%	0.27	(4.85)	0.45	0.81	1.26	1.85	0.25	(1.15)	(1.43)	1.56
Stock price – high ($)	—	33.88	28.00	43.13	36.50	44.50	58.75	55.25	36.88	44.00	37.25
Stock price – low ($)	—	24.50	17.38	20.13	24.38	27.50	38.75	25.50	21.75	25.75	27.88
Stock price – close ($)	2.1%	27.50	24.38	24.75	28.00	42.75	45.63	28.50	28.75	31.88	33.13
P/E – high	—	—	—	96	45	35	32	—	—	—	24
P/E – low	—	—	—	45	30	22	21	—	—	—	18
Dividends per share ($)	(6.3%)	1.80	1.20	1.00	1.00	1.00	1.00	1.00	1.00	1.00	1.00
Book value per share ($)	(4.7%)	26.30	20.30	19.77	19.80	19.90	21.04	20.24	17.80	16.55	17.02
Employees	(1.4%)	64,955	46,909	48,600	61,400	65,500	77,000	73,400	69,200	64,700	57,200

1994 Year-end:
Debt ratio: 25.8%
Return on equity: 9.3%
Cash (mil.): $647
Current ratio: 2.42
Long-term debt (mil.): $643
No. of shares (mil.): 114
Dividends
  Yield: 3.0%
  Payout: 64.1%
Market value (mil.): $3,780

Stock Price History
High/Low 1985–94

H. E. BUTT GROCERY COMPANY

OVERVIEW

Based in San Antonio, H. E. Butt Grocery Company (H-E-B) is the largest private company in Texas and the 20th largest private company in the US. H-E-B over 220 supermarkets under the names H. E. Butt Food Stores, Pantry Foods, MarketPlace, and Central Market.

H-E-B is focusing on its customers' increasing demand for freshly prepared, ready-to-eat food products. In 1992 H-E-B opened the City Kitchen. This San Antonio facility prepares and distributes freshly prepared food products to its stores. H-E-B also opened the 60,000-square-foot Central Market in Austin, featuring a large produce department and a wide assortment of upscale food products.

H-E-B sells more than 2,000 products ranging from milk to cough syrup under its own private-label brands. The company is establishing H-E-B as its premium brand and Hill Country Fare as its value brand. H-E-B recently introduced its own sodas, including H-E-B Cola, Diet Cola, Lemon Lime, and Dr. B, and H-E-B Premium Blend Coffee.

CEO Charles Butt is the younger son of Howard E. Butt Sr., the company's namesake.

WHEN

Charles C. Butt and his wife, Florence, moved to Kerrville, in the Texas Hill Country, in 1905 in hopes that the climate would help Charles's tuberculosis. Since Charles was unable to work, Florence began peddling groceries door-to-door for A&P. Later that year she opened a grocery store, C. C. Butt Grocery, in Kerrville. Florence, a dyed-in-the-wool Baptist, refused to carry such articles of vice as tobacco, and she extended easy credit to fellow believers.

The family lived over the store, and all 3 of the Butt children worked there. The youngest son, Howard, began working in the store full-time in his teens. After a stint in the navy during WWI, he returned to take over the store.

At first Howard made little more profit than his mother, and his first attempt at expansion failed for want of capital. By adopting modern marketing methods like price tagging and by overcoming their moral objections to tobacco, the Butts earned enough to finance expansion. In 1927 Howard opened a 2nd store in Del Rio, in West Texas. In the next few years, he bought 3 Piggly Wiggly stores in the Rio Grande Valley and opened new stores. He gained patron loyalty by making minimal markups on staples. In 1928 the headquarters moved to Harlingen in South Texas.

In 1935 Howard (who had adopted the middle name Edward) rechristened the chain the H. E. Butt Grocery Company, and in 1940, in view of the company's strength in South Texas, he moved the headquarters to Corpus Christi. Howard put his 3 children to work for the company.

Howard Jr. and his younger brother, Charles, were rivals for succession until Howard Jr. decided that his interests lay in faith and philanthropy. He took over the H. E. Butt Foundation from his mother while Charles was groomed for succession.

In the 1960s H-E-B seemed stuck in a time warp. While others followed up-to-the-minute targeting or decorating strategies, H-E-B plodded along with a down-market image.

In 1971 Howard Sr. resigned and Charles took over, bringing in fresh management. But this was not enough. Studies showed that the reasons for H-E-B's lagging market share were its refusal to stock alcohol and its policy of Sunday closing. In 1976 it abandoned these policies. It also drastically lowered its prices, undercutting competitors and driving many independents out of business. Beginning in 1979 H-E-B fought off Kroger's entry into several Texas markets, allegedly by cutting its prices below cost in the contested markets and paying for it by raising prices in other markets. H-E-B won these price wars and emerged the dominant player in its major markets.

H-E-B's first superstore, which opened in Austin in 1979, was 56,000 square feet and offered a variety of general merchandise, photofinishing, and a pharmacy. In the 1980s H-E-B concentrated on building more of these superstores. It also added video rental centers in its stores and extended the chain to include 35 freestanding locations called Video Central. In 1985 H-E-B moved its headquarters from Corpus Christi to San Antonio.

In 1991 the company opened H-E-B MarketPlace in San Antonio. This 93,000-square-foot concept store offers restaurants, a wood-burning pizza oven, and the company's largest produce department. In 1993 the company sold 33 video stores to Hollywood Entertainment of Portland, Oregon, for $30.5 million. In 1994 H-E-B opened its Houston Retail Support Center, designed to provide additional retail support to some of its stores.

In 1995 H-E-B began phasing out its Park Lane, Park Manor, and Village Park brands.

Private company
Fiscal year ends: October 31

WHO

Chairman, President, and CEO: Charles C. Butt
EVP and COO: James F. Clingman
SVP Marketing: Robert A. Neslund
SVP Distribution and Manufacturing: Charles W. Sapp
VP and Secretary: Wesley D. Nelson
VP Store Operations, San Antonio: Paul Madura
VP Store Operations, Central Texas: John Butler
VP South Texas Division: Greg Souquette
Chief Administrative Officer and CFO: Jack Brouillard
VP Human Resources: Louis M. Laguardia
Auditors: Arthur Andersen & Co, SC

WHERE

HQ: 646 S. Main Ave., San Antonio, TX 78204
Phone: 210-246-8000
Fax: 210-246-8169

H-E-B operates grocery and related stores throughout Texas. The company also operates milk, ice cream, and tortilleria and tortilla chip plants, bakeries, and a photo processing plant.

	1994 Stores	
	No.	% of total
San Antonio area	34	15
Houston area	26	11
Other areas	168	74
Total	**228**	**100**

WHAT

	1994 Stores	
	No.	% of total
H. E. Butt Food Stores	162	71
Pantry Foods	64	29
MarketPlace	1	—
Central Market	1	—
Total	**228**	**100**

HEBCO (real estate and development operation)

Selected Brands and Products

H-E-B Brand
Aluminum foil
Bacon
Bread
Canned vegetables
  Sliced pineapple
  Stewed tomatoes
  Sweet peas
  Tomato paste
  Whole kernel corn
  Whole tomatoes
Charcoal
Cough and cold products
Dr. B (original soda)
Eggs
Milk products
Premium blend coffee
Yogurt

Hill Country Fare
Bathroom tissue
Bread
Canned vegetables and fruit
Cereals
Detergents
Napkins

KEY COMPETITORS

Albertson's
Brookshire Brothers
Brookshire Grocery
Circle K
Drug Emporium
Eckerd
Fiesta Mart
Handy Andy Supermarkets
Kmart
Kroger
Minyard Food Stores
National Convenience
Pay 'N Save
Randall's
Rice Food Markets
Southland
Stanley Stores
United Supermarkets
Walgreen
Wal-Mart
Whole Foods Market
Winn-Dixie

HOW MUCH

	Annual Growth	1985	1986	1987	1988	1989	1990	1991	1992	1993	1994
Sales ($ mil.)	10.7%	1,936	2,055	2,105	2,312	2,586	2,900	3,162	3,204	4,500	4,850
Employees	21.4%	—	—	—	—	9,485	10,000	12,000	12,000	19,772	25,000

Sales ($ mil.)
1985–94

H·E·B

HOUSTON INDUSTRIES INCORPORATED

OVERVIEW

Houston Industries is a holding company for one of the largest electric utilities in the US, Houston Lighting & Power (HL&P), which provides electric service to more than 1.4 million customers in a 5,000-square-mile area on the Texas Gulf Coast.

After a foray into cable televison, the company has turned off the TV and is doing some traveling instead. In 1995 it sold its cable television businesses, KBLCOM and Paragon Communications (formerly a 50/50 joint venture with Time Warner), to Time Warner in a deal valued at $2.2 billion. Houston Industries received about $1 billion of the entertainment

company's preferred stock (convertible into 5% of Time Warner's equity) and Time Warner assumed about $1.2 billion of Houston Industries' debt. KBLCOM and Paragon serve about 1.6 million subscribers.

Houston Industries is exiting the cable business to focus on electricity through both HL&P and its Houston Industries Energy (HI Energy) subsidiary, which pursues domestic and international independent natural gas power projects and invests in privatized foreign electric utilities. HI Energy is looking at power projects in fast-growing markets, including India and Latin America.

WHEN

Houston Industries was formed as a holding company in 1976, but its history, through HL&P, goes back to the 19th century. The company's earliest predecessor, Houston Electric Lighting and Power, was formed in 1882 by a group including Emanuel Raphael, cashier at Houston Savings Bank, and Mayor William R. Baker.

Faced with financial difficulties, the company changed hands a number of times, with affiliates of General Electric owning the company twice. GE's financial arm, United Electric Securities Company, took control of the company in 1901. That same year the company became Houston Lighting and Power. United Electric sold HL&P in 1906. In 1922 National Power & Light Company (NP&L) bought HL&P. NP&L was a subsidiary of Electric Bond & Share Company, which in turn was a public utility holding company that had been spun off by General Electric.

HL&P became an independent company in 1942 when National Power & Light was forced to sell it in order to comply with the 1935 Public Utility Holding Company Act.

Following WWII, HL&P began a major expansion of its power supply to meet the growing demands of the booming petroleum industry. The company continued its expansion during the 1950s and 1960s. HL&P also built a "power highway" connecting it with other Texas utilities from the Red River to the Gulf of Mexico.

Beginning in the 1970s HL&P began looking into nuclear energy as a way to meet its growing power needs. In 1973 HL&P became managing partner (with 30.8% ownership) in a joint venture to build a nuclear power plant on the Texas Gulf Coast. Construction on the South Texas Project, with partners Central

Power and Light Company and the cities of Austin and San Antonio, began in 1975 and was scheduled for completion in 1982. Its price tag was estimated at under $1 billion.

By 1980 the plant was 4 years behind schedule, and soon the lawsuits began flying. In 1982 HL&P and its partners sued construction company Brown & Root, receiving a $700 million settlement in 1985. In 1983 the city of Austin sued HL&P for $419 million in damages. HL&P won that suit in 1989. The power plant finally began commercial operation in 1988, with final cost estimated at $5.8 billion.

In the meantime the company had to tend to other business. In 1986 it diversified into cable television, forming the Enrcom (later Paragon Communications) in a joint venture with American Television and Communications Corp., a subsidiary of Time Inc. In 1988 Houston Industries bought Canadian cable company Rogers Communications for $1.27 billion. Houston Industries made its first foray into the international power market in 1992 as part of a consortium that bought 51% of an electric distribution system in Argentina.

The Nuclear Regulatory Commission put the South Texas Project on its "Watch List" of troubled plants (which calls for increased inspections) in 1993 after both units at the plant went out of service because of technical problems. The units came back on-line a year later.

In 1994 Houston Industries formed a joint venture with Chewton Glen Energy to build a 20-megawatt electricity plant fueled by scrap tires in Ford Heights, Illinois.

In 1995 Houston Industries Energy acquired a 90% stake in Argentina's Santiago del Estero electric utility system for $15 million. The system serves more than 100,000 customers in north-central Argentina.

WHO

Chairman and CEO (Principal Financial Officer): Don D. Jordan, age 62, $1,594,373 pay
President and COO: Don D. Sykora, age 64, $1,099,348 pay
SVP, General Counsel, and Corporate Secretary: Hugh Rice Kelly, age 52, $514,320 pay
SVP Government and Regulatory Affairs: Raymond J. Snokhous, age 65
VP; President and COO, Houston Lighting & Power: R. Steve Letbetter, age 46, $567,525 pay
VP; President and COO, Houston Industries Energy: Lee W. Hogan, age 50, $550,650 pay
VP and Treasurer: William A. Cropper, age 55
VP Governmental Relations: B. Bruce Gibson, age 41
VP Strategic Planning and Administration: Stephen W. Naeve, age 47
Group VP Nuclear, Houston Lighting & Power: William T. Cottle, age 49
Group VP Operations, Houston Lighting & Power: Jack D. Greenwade, age 55
Comptroller: Mary P. Ricciardello, age 39
VP Human Resources, Houston Lighting & Power: Susan D. Fabre, age 39
Auditors: Deloitte & Touche LLP

WHERE

HQ: 5 Post Oak Park, 4400 Post Oak Pkwy., Houston, TX 77027
Phone: 713-629-3000
Fax: 713-629-3129

Houston Lighting & Power has 11 electric generating stations serving its Houston-area customers. HL&P buys coal primarily from the Powder River Basin of Wyoming. Houston Industries Energy has power projects in the US, Argentina, and India.

WHAT

1994 Electricity Sales	$ mil.	% of total
Residential	1,586	40
Industrial	1,185	29
Commercial	1,029	26
Street lighting	26	1
Sales to other utilities	26	1
Other	122	3
Adjustments	(228)	—
Total	**3,746**	**100**

	1994 Sales		1994 Operating Income	
	$ mil.	% of total	$ mil.	% of total
Electricity sales & utility services	3,746	94	998	99
Cable television	256	6	15	1
Adjustments	—	—	(1)	—
Total	**4,002**	**100**	**1,012**	**100**

1994 Energy Sources	% of total
Coal & lignite	43
Natural gas	34
Purchased power	16
Nuclear	7
Total	**100**

KEY COMPETITORS

Duke Power
FPL
General Electric
NIPSCO
Pacific Enterprises
Pacific Gas and Electric
SCEcorp
Southern Co.
Westinghouse

HOW MUCH

	9-Year Growth	1985	1986	1987	1988	1989	1990	1991	1992	1993	1994
Sales ($ mil.)	(0.2%)	4,062	3,536	3,628	3,650	3,790	4,179	4,444	4,596	4,324	4,002
Net income ($ mil.)	(1.4%)	464	425	435	395	414	340	417	434	416	407
Income as % of sales	—	11.4%	12.0%	12.0%	10.8%	10.9%	8.1%	9.4%	9.4%	9.6%	10.2%
Earnings per share ($)	(3.1%)	4.42	3.81	3.74	3.34	3.32	2.67	3.28	2.63	3.20	3.32
Stock price – high ($)	—	29.50	37.00	39.38	33.88	35.88	37.13	44.38	46.88	49.75	47.75
Stock price – low ($)	—	21.75	27.25	26.50	26.63	26.75	30.63	34.63	40.13	42.50	30.00
Stock price – close ($)	2.7%	28.00	34.75	30.00	28.00	35.00	36.75	44.25	45.88	47.63	35.63
P/E – high	—	7	10	11	10	11	14	14	18	16	14
P/E – low	—	5	7	7	8	8	12	11	15	13	9
Dividends per share ($)	1.6%	2.60	2.76	2.86	2.94	2.96	2.96	2.96	2.98	3.75	3.00
Book value per share ($)	0.2%	26.74	27.19	28.33	28.75	29.05	28.45	26.63	25.36	25.06	27.30
Employees	(0.5%)	12,060	12,060	11,506	11,599	12,878	13,084	13,289	11,576	11,350	11,498

1994 Year-end:
Debt ratio: 72.6%
Return on equity: 12.3%
Cash (mil.): $10
Current ratio: 0.26
Long-term debt (mil.): $4,223
No. of shares (mil.): 123
Dividends
  Yield: 8.4%
  Payout: 90.4%
Market value (mil.): $4,397

Stock Price History
High/Low 1985–94

J. C. PENNEY COMPANY, INC.

OVERVIEW

"It is our objective to have the customer think of J. C. Penney first for every category of merchandise we compete in," says new CEO James Oesterreicher. He succeeded William Howell (who remains chairman) at the beginning of 1995 to take the helm of the Plano, Texas–based retailer. Oesterreicher is taking control of a company that has been on something of a roll lately; sales and profits have been on the rise for 3 years.

The new chief is working to boost Penney's market share by cutting costs to keep prices down. He also plans to continue the

company's emphasis on private-label products (including Arizona jeans, Stafford men's suits, and Worthington women's business casual clothing), which account for about half its merchandise.

The company is also expanding internationally, looking to develop new markets because it sees the US as "over-stored." It is opening stores in Chile and Mexico and has its eyes on Japan, China, and the Middle East. It already offers mail-order service in Iceland, Brazil, and Russia. Penney also operates drugstores, an insurance company, and a credit bank.

WHEN

In 1902 James Cash Penney and 2 former employers opened The Golden Rule, a dry goods store, in Kemmerer, Wyoming. Penney bought out his partners in 1907 and opened stores that sold high-demand soft goods in small towns. Basing his customer service policy on his Baptist heritage, he held employees (called "associates") to a high moral code. Managers, usually former sales clerks, were offered 1/3 partnerships in the stores.

The company incorporated in Utah in 1913 as the J. C. Penney Company, with headquarters in Salt Lake City, but moved to New York City in 1914 to aid buying and financial operations. In the 1920s the company expanded to nearly 1,400 stores and went public in 1929. The company grew during the Depression on the strength of its reputation for high quality and low prices.

With Penney riding the postwar boom, by 1951 sales in the more than 1,600 stores had surpassed $1 billion. Penney introduced credit plans in 1958. In 1963 the company added hard goods, which, with the purchase of General Merchandise Company (1962, Milwaukee, mail order) allowed it to compete with Sears and Montgomery Ward.

The company bought Treasure Island discount stores in 1962 (sold in 1981) and formed JCPenney Insurance from companies it bought in the mid-1960s. Penney bought Thrift Drug in 1969 and continued to grow. In 1973, 2 years after James Cash Penney's death, there were 2,053 stores.

In the 1970s Penney began its first, ill-fated foray overseas by buying chains in Belgium and Italy in hopes of duplicating its US formula — giant department stores. But there was local resistance to the large stores. The company took until 1987 to extricate itself.

Penney bought First National Bank (Harrington, Delaware; 1983), renamed JCPenney National Bank (1984), to issue MasterCard and Visa cards. The company refocused on soft goods during the 1980s. In 1983 Penney stopped selling automotive services, restaurants, appliances, paint, hardware, and fabrics. In 1987 it discontinued sporting goods, consumer electronics, and photographic equipment.

The company entered the cable television shopping market twice between 1987 and 1991 but was not successful. In 1988 JCPenney Telemarketing was started to take catalog phone orders and provide telemarketing services for other companies. Also in 1988 the company moved its headquarters from New York to Texas.

In the 1980s Penney tried to move upmarket, enlisting Halston to produce a fashion line for the store. The fashion world viewed this as a betrayal; the Penney line failed, and it effectively ended Halston's career. Thereafter, unable to enlist any famous names, the company developed its own, including Hunt Club, St. John's Bay, and Worthington, which have developed considerable cachet abroad.

Penney began a marketing program targeted at minorities in 1993. In 1994 it settled a class action lawsuit that charged Penney had illegally calculated pension benefits. As part of the settlement, the company agreed to change the way it determines benefits for employees and retirees.

After facing many delays (including the devaluation of the peso), Penney opened its first Mexican store in 1995 in the Plaza San Agustin mall in Monterrey. Also that year, the company acquired 7 stores in the Washington, DC, area from bankrupt Woodward & Lothrop.

NYSE symbol: JCP
Fiscal year ends: Last Saturday in January

WHO

Chairman: William R. Howell, age 59, $1,801,644 pay
VC and CEO: James E. Oesterreicher, age 53, $672,277 pay (prior to promotion)
President and COO: W. Barger Tygart, age 59, $602,345 pay
SEVP; Director, Personnel and Company Communications: Gale Duff-Bloom, age 55
President, JCPenney Stores: John T. Cody Jr., age 55, $445,744 pay
President, Merchandising Worldwide: Thomas D. Hutchens, age 54, $439,820 pay
President, Catalog and Distribution: William E. McCarthy, age 53
EVP and CFO: Robert E. Northam, age 64, $680,096 pay
EVP; Director, Support Services: Terry S. Prindiville, age 59
EVP, Secretary, and General Counsel: Charles R. Lotter, age 57
SVP; Director, Financial Services and Government Relations: Ted L. Spurlock, age 56
SVP; Director, Planning and Information Systems: David V. Evans, age 51
VP and Treasurer: Leo A. Gispanski
VP and Controller: Donald A. McKay
VP; Director, Communications: Russell H. Longyear
VP; Director, Personnel: Jay F. Hundley
Auditors: KPMG Peat Marwick LLP

WHERE

HQ: 6501 Legacy Dr., Plano, TX 75024-3698
Phone: 214-431-1000
Fax: 214-431-1977

J. C. Penney operates 1,233 JCPenney retail stores and 526 Thrift Drug drugstores throughout all 50 states and Puerto Rico, as well as 6 distribution centers.

WHAT

	1995 Sales	
	$ mil.	% of total
JCPenney stores	15,023	74
Catalog	3,817	19
Drugstores	1,540	7
Total	**20,380**	**100**

	1995 Stores	
	No.	% of total
JCPenney stores	1,233	70
Drugstores	526	30
Total	**1,759**	**100**

Major Product Lines	Selected Subsidiaries
Accessories	JCPenney Insurance
Family apparel	JCPenney National Bank
Home furnishings	Thrift Drug, Inc.
Jewelry	
Shoes	

KEY COMPETITORS

American Stores
Ames
Clothestime
Dayton Hudson
Dillard
Dress Barn
Eckerd
Federated
Fred Meyer
J. Crew
Jos. A. Bank
Kmart
Lands' End
L.L. Bean
Longs
May
Melville
Men's Wearhouse

Mercantile Stores
Montgomery Ward
Nordstrom
Paul Harris Stores
Price/Costco
Rex Stores
S & K Famous Brands
Sears
Service Merchandise
Spiegel
Stein Mart
Thrifty PayLess
Today's Man
TJX
Venture Stores
Walgreen
Wal-Mart

HOW MUCH

	9-Year Growth	1986	1987	1988	1989	1990	1991	1992	1993	1994	1995
Sales ($ mil.)	4.5%	13,747	14,740	15,332	15,296	16,103	16,365	16,201	18,009	18,983	20,380
Net income ($ mil.)	11.5%	397	530	608	807	802	577	264	777	889	1,057
Income as % of sales	—	2.9%	3.6%	4.0%	5.3%	5.0%	3.5%	1.6%	4.3%	4.7%	5.2%
Earnings per share ($)	13.2%	1.33	1.77	2.06	2.96	2.93	2.17	0.99	2.95	3.55	4.05
Stock price – high ($)[1]	—	14.44	22.09	33.00	27.88	36.63	37.81	29.13	40.19	56.38	59.00
Stock price – low ($)[1]	—	11.16	13.16	17.63	19.00	25.19	18.69	21.25	25.38	35.38	41.13
Stock price – close ($)[1]	13.9%	13.88	18.06	21.69	25.31	36.38	22.13	27.50	38.88	52.63	44.63
P/E – high	—	11	13	16	9	13	17	29	14	16	15
P/E – low	—	8	7	9	6	9	9	22	9	10	10
Dividends per share ($)	11.9%	0.59	0.62	0.71	0.94	1.09	1.32	1.32	1.32	1.41	1.62
Book value per share ($)	6.2%	13.60	14.50	15.10	13.23	17.78	18.29	17.20	19.11	21.59	23.31
Employees	1.5%	177,000	176,000	181,000	190,000	198,000	196,000	185,000	192,000	193,000	202,000

1995 Year-end:
Debt ratio: 49.1%
Return on equity: 20.4%
Cash (mil.): $261
Current ratio: 2.11
Long-term debt (mil.): $3,335
No. of shares (mil.): 227
Dividends
  Yield: 3.6%
  Payout: 40.0%
Market value (mil.): $10,131

**Stock Price History[1]
High/Low 1986–95**

[1] Stock prices are for the prior calendar year.

KIMBERLY-CLARK CORPORATION

OVERVIEW

It's women and children first, but Kimberly-Clark isn't abandoning ship. Far from it, the Dallas-based maker of Kotex and New Freedom feminine care products and Huggies disposable diapers (#1 in the US) brought aboard a new first mate in 1995: Scott Paper. In buying the competing maker of facial tissue, paper towels, and toilet paper for $7.4 billion, Kimberly-Clark becomes a $10.9 billion company, narrowing the gap between it and the #1 paper products maker, Procter & Gamble.

Kimberly-Clark is gearing up for an expansion of its consumer product tissue lines. Its Kleenex tissue is the #1 US brand, with a 45% market share. Kimberly-Clark also makes Depend incontinence care products and Pull-Ups training pants, and it makes and markets paper towels, industrial wipes, and health care products, including disposable surgical gowns and sterile wrapping for surgical instruments.

The company, which owns about 700,000 acres of timberland, also makes groundwood printing papers and paper specialty products for the tobacco, electronics, and other industries. The company also owns about 30% of Milwaukee-based regional airline Midwest Express Holdings. Kimberly-Clark owned the other 70% as well until a 1995 IPO. The airline was originally set up in the 1980s as a means to transport Kimberly-Clark employees.

The company plans to exit its pulp and newsprint mills in Alabama and Ontario, Canada. The peso crisis in Mexico hurt its Mexican subsidiary's performance in 1995.

WHEN

In 1872 John Kimberly, Charles Clark, Havilah Babcock, and Frank Shattuck founded Kimberly, Clark & Company in Neenah, Wisconsin, to manufacture newsprint from rags. After incorporating as Kimberly & Clark Company (1880), the company built a pulp and paper plant on the Fox River (1889). The town of Kimberly, Wisconsin — named in John Kimberly's honor — formed as a result.

In 1914 the company developed cellucotton, a cotton substitute used by the US army as surgical cotton during WWI. Army nurses began using cellucotton pads as disposable sanitary napkins, and in 1920 the company introduced Kotex, the first disposable feminine hygiene product. Kleenex, the first throw-away handkerchief, followed in 1924, and soon many Americans were referring to all sanitary napkins and facial tissues as Kotex and Kleenex, respectively. In 1926 the company joined with The New York Times Company to build a newsprint mill (now Spruce Falls Power and Paper) in Ontario. In 1928 the company adopted its present name and was listed on the NYSE.

Kimberly-Clark expanded internationally during the 1950s, opening plants in Mexico, Germany, and the UK. During the 1960s the company began operations in 17 more foreign locations.

Before retiring in 1971 Guy Minard (CEO since 1968) sold the 4 mills that handled Kimberly-Clark's unprofitable coated-paper business and entered the paper towel and disposable diaper markets. Minard's successor, Darwin Smith, introduced Kimbies diapers in 1968, but they leaked and were withdrawn from the market. An improved version of Kimbies came out in 1976, followed by Huggies, a premium-priced diaper with elastic leg bands, in 1978.

From its corporate flight department, the company formed Midwest Express Airlines in 1984. Smith moved Kimberly-Clark's headquarters from Neenah to Dallas in 1985. From 1988 to 1989 he served as chairman and president of the King Ranch while still acting as chief executive of Kimberly-Clark.

In 1991 Kimberly-Clark, along with The New York Times Company, sold Spruce Falls Power and Paper. Smith retired as chairman in 1992. Wayne R. Sanders, who was largely responsible for designing Huggies Pull-Ups (introduced in 1989) succeeded Smith. Also in 1992 Procter & Gamble (P&G) settled out of court with Kimberly-Clark for an undisclosed sum. P&G had been charged with trying to dominate the US diaper market illegally. In 1994 the company entered into a joint venture with an Argentinian firm to make personal care products in that country. That year the firm also bought the feminine care products units of VP-Schickedanz (Germany) and Handan Comfort and Beauty Group (China).

The company introduced Huggies Supreme diapers with Velcro tabs in 1994. To save costs, it agreed in 1995 to have all of its domestic trucking handled by Schneider National Carriers. Also that year the company purchased the leading Czech manufacturer of feminine care products and 51% of the tissue and feminine care assets of Peru-based Unicel SA.

NYSE symbol: KMB
Fiscal year ends: December 31

Chairman and CEO: Wayne R. Sanders, age 47,
$1,134,384 pay
EVP: James G. Grosklaus, age 59, $542,400 pay
Group President, North American Consumer Products:
Thomas J. Falk, age 36, $476,877 pay
Group President, North American Consumer Products:
Kathi P. Seifert, age 45
EVP: James T. McCauley, age 56, $475,600 pay
President, European Consumer and Service &
Industrial Operations: John A. Van Steenberg, age 47
SVP and CFO: John W. Donehower, age 48
SVP Law and Government Affairs: O. George Everbach,
age 56
SVP: Larry M. Farrar
SVP: Robert A. Underhill
VP and Secretary: Donald M. Crook
VP and Controller: Randy J. Vest
VP Human Resources: Bruce J. Olson
Auditors: Deloitte & Touche LLP

WHERE

HQ: PO Box 619100, Dallas, TX 75261-9100
Phone: 214-830-1200
Fax: 214-830-1490

Kimberly-Clark has plants in the US and 25 foreign
countries. Its products are sold in 150 countries.

	1994 Sales		1994 Operating Income	
	$ mil.	% of total	$ mil.	% of total
US	5,439	73	817	88
Europe	1,075	15	(59)	—
Asia/Latin America	544	7	80	9
Canada	388	5	25	3
Adjustments	(82)	—	(44)	—
Total	**7,364**	**100**	**819**	**100**

WHAT

	1994 Sales		1994 Operating Income	
	$ mil.	% of total	$ mil.	% of total
Consumer prods.	5,911	79	656	76
Newsprint & paper	1,099	15	188	22
Air transportation	410	6	19	2
Adjustments	(56)	—	(44)	—
Total	**7,364**	**100**	**819**	**100**

Consumer Products
Baby wipes (Huggies)
Bathroom tissue (Delsey,
Kleenex)
Commercial wipes
(Kimwipes)
Disposable diapers
(Huggies, Pull-Ups,
UltraTrim)
Disposable surgical gowns
and accessories
(Kimguard)
Facial tissue (Kleenex)
Feminine hygiene
products (Kotex, New
Freedom, Lightdays)

Incontinence products
(Depend, Poise)
Paper napkins (Kleenex)
Paper towels (Hi-Dri)
Pulp

Newsprint and Paper
Business and writing papers
(Neenah)
Newsprint
Printing papers
Technical papers
Tobacco industry papers

Air Transportation
Midwest Express Airlines
(30%)

KEY COMPETITORS

Boise Cascade
Champion International
Diplomat
Drypers
DSG
Fletcher Challenge
Fort Howard
Georgia-Pacific
International Paper
James River
Johnson & Johnson

Mead
Paragon Trade Brands
Pope & Talbot
Procter & Gamble
Rayonier
Sandoz
Stone Container
Tambrands
Union Camp
Weyerhaeuser

HOW MUCH

	9-Year Growth	1985	1986	1987	1988	1989	1990	1991	1992	1993	1994
Sales ($ mil.)	6.8%	4,073	4,303	4,885	5,394	5,734	6,407	6,777	7,091	6,973	7,364
Net income ($ mil.)	9.0%	267	269	325	379	424	432	508	345	511	535
Income as % of sales	—	6.6%	6.3%	6.7%	7.0%	7.4%	6.7%	7.5%	4.9%	7.3%	7.3%
Earnings per share ($)	9.6%	1.46	1.47	1.87	2.36	2.63	2.70	3.18	2.15	3.18	3.33
Stock price – high ($)	—	17.50	23.16	31.63	32.88	37.69	42.88	52.25	63.25	62.00	60.00
Stock price – low ($)	—	11.25	15.84	19.69	23.06	28.69	30.75	38.00	46.25	44.63	47.00
Stock price – close ($)	13.0%	16.75	19.97	25.00	29.13	36.75	42.00	50.69	59.00	51.88	50.38
P/E – high	—	12	16	17	14	14	16	16	29	19	18
P/E – low	—	8	11	11	10	11	11	12	22	14	14
Dividends per share ($)	13.1%	0.58	0.61	0.70	0.78	1.18	1.35	1.45	1.64	1.70	1.75
Book value per share ($)	6.1%	9.52	10.45	9.80	11.60	12.93	14.01	15.74	13.63	15.27	16.20
Employees	1.7%	36,648	36,490	37,357	38,328	39,664	39,954	41,286	42,902	42,131	42,707

1994 Year-end:
Debt ratio: 39.6%
Return on equity: 21.2%
Cash (mil.): $24
Current ratio: 0.88
Long-term debt (mil.): $930
No. of shares (mil.): 160
Dividends
  Yield: 3.5%
  Payout: 52.6%
Market value (mil.): $8,070

Stock Price History
High/Low 1985–94

KING RANCH, INC.

OVERVIEW

With 142 years under its Texas-sized belt, 825,000-acre King Ranch is showing that it's not too old to try something new. The fabled ranch, which is larger than Rhode Island and managed from its corporate headquarters in the Woodlands (near Houston), is trying its luck with a new CEO, a new tourism venture, and a new breed of cattle.

Jack Hunt, former CEO of Tejon Ranch (at 270,000 acres, it's California's largest piece of private property), took over as president and top executive of privately held King Ranch in 1995. The spread he now oversees includes not only cattle ranching on 4 noncontiguous ranches in 6 South Texas counties, but also oil

and gas exploration and development as well as diversified farming and other operations.

King Ranch introduced a new breed of beef cattle in 1995. The Santa Cruz, which is 1/4 Gelbvieh, 1/4 Red Angus, and 1/2 Santa Gertrudis, took 7 years to develop and is highly fertile. Undertakings announced in 1994 by King Ranch include "eco-tours" through the ranch (home to more than 200 animal species) and a 1/3 interest in an Ecuadorian oil-and-gas venture with Australia's Broken Hill Proprietary. Plans to build a power plant in Ecuador hit a snag in 1995 when local opponents objected to plans to burn imported diesel instead of Ecuadorian fuel.

WHEN

The King Ranch was founded in 1853 by New York City runaway Richard King, a former steamboat captain, and his wife, Henrietta, the cultivated daughter of a Brownsville missionary. On the advice of his friend Robert E. Lee, King used his profits from steamboating to buy land — miles of flat, brush-filled coastal plain and desert south of Corpus Christi that was valued at pennies an acre.

In 1854 King relocated the residents of an entire drought-ravaged village in Mexico to the ranch and employed them as ranch hands, known ever after as *kiñenos* ("King's men"). In 1858 King and his wife built their homestead at a site recommended by Lee.

King Ranch endured attacks from Union guerrillas during the Civil War and from Mexican bandits after the war. In 1867 the ranch used its famed Running W brand for the first time. After King's death in 1885, Corpus Christi attorney Robert Kleberg, who had married King's daughter Alice, managed the 1.2 million–acre ranch for his mother-in-law.

Henrietta died in 1925, and 3/4 of the ranch was left to Alice. Before Robert's death in 1932, control of the ranch was passed to sons Richard and Bob. In 1933 Bob negotiated an exclusive and lucrative oil-and-gas lease with Houston-based Humble Oil, which later became part of Exxon. In 1935, to protect the ranch, the Klebergs incorporated.

While Richard served in Congress, Bob ran the ranch until his death in 1974. He developed the Santa Gertrudis, the first breed of cattle ever created in the US, by crossing beefy British shorthorn cattle with Indian Brahmas. The new beef breed was better suited to the hot, dry South Texas climate.

Kleberg made King Ranch a leading breeder of quarter horses, used to work cattle, and Thoroughbreds, which he raced. Kleberg bought Kentucky Derby winner Bold Venture (1938) and Idle Hour Stable, a Kentucky breeding farm (1946). In 1946 a King Ranch horse, Assault, won racing's Triple Crown.

When Bob Kleberg died, the family asked Princeton graduate James Clement, husband of one of the founders' great-granddaughters, to become CEO. Bypassed was Robert Shelton, a King relative and orphan whom Kleberg had raised as his own son. Shelton severed ties with the ranch and the family in 1977 over a lawsuit he filed, and partially won, against Exxon, alleging underpayment of royalties. (Clement and Shelton died within days of each other in 1994.)

Under Clement the King Ranch became a multinational corporation. In 1980 it formed King Ranch Oil and Gas to explore for and produce oil and gas in 5 states and the Gulf of Mexico. In 1988 Clement retired, and Kimberly-Clark executive Darwin Smith became CEO, the first unrelated by blood or marriage to the founders. Smith left after only one year, and the reins passed to Roger Jarvis, a petroleum geologist who headed the corporation's oil and gas operations, then to Jack Hunt in 1995.

In 1993 the US Navy announced plans to put transmitter antenna towers on the King Ranch as part of a radar system designed to track drug-carrying aircraft.

The great-great-grandson of a business partner of Richard King sued in 1995 for 15,000 acres of ranch land he said King and Robert Kleberg had swindled from his family in 1883.

Private company
Fiscal year ends: December 31

Chairman: Abraham Zaleznik
President and CEO: Jack Hunt, age 50
VP: Stephen J. "Tio" Kleberg, age 50
VP and Treasurer: Mark Kent
VP, General Counsel, and Secretary: Larry Worden
VP, Controller, and Assistant Secretary: James E. Savage
VP Audit: James B. Spear
Director: James H. Clement Jr.
Director: John D. Alexander
Director: John H. Duncan
Personnel Manager: Rickey Blackman

WHERE

HQ: 10055 Grogan's Mill Rd., Ste. 100, The Woodlands, TX 77380
Phone: 713-367-7300
Fax: 713-367-7332

King Ranch operates ranching and farming interests in South Texas as well as in Arizona, Florida, Kentucky, and Brazil.

US Agricultural Operations
King Ranch — Arizona
King Ranch Farm (Lexington, KY)
King Ranch Farms — Florida (Belle Glade, FL)
King Ranch Feedyard (Kingsville, TX)
King Ranch (Kingsville, TX)

WHAT

Selected Ranch Animals

Cattle
Monkey (foundation sire of the Santa Gertrudis breed)
Running W "A" herd

Quarter Horses
Mr San Peppy
Old Sorrel
Peppy
Peppy San Badger
Wimpy

Thoroughbred Horses
Assault (1946 Triple Crown winner)
Bold Venture
Chicaro
Gallant Bloom
High Gun
Middle Ground (1950 Kentucky Derby and Belmont Stakes winner)

Farming

Citrus
Cotton
Milo
Sod
Sugar cane

Selected Subsidiaries

King Ranch Holdings, Inc.
King Ranch Oil and Gas, Inc.
Kingsville Lumber Co. (retail building material)
Kingsville Publishing Co. (newspaper)
Robstown Hardware Co. (farm equipment)

KEY COMPETITORS

Amerada Hess	Koch
Amoco	K.S.A. Industries
Atlantic Richfield	Lane Industries
AZTX Cattle	Louisiana Land
British Petroleum	Mitchell Energy
Broken Hill	Mobil
Burlington Resources	Norsk Hydro
Cactus Feeders	Occidental
Calcot	Oryx
Castle Energy	PDVSA
CENEX	PEMEX
CF Industries	Pennzoil
Chevron	Petrobrás
Elf Aquitaine	Phillips Petroleum
Enron Corp.	Repsol
EOTT Energy Partners	Shell Oil
FINA	Southern States Co-op
Flying J	Sunkist
Friona Industries	Tejon Ranch
GROWMARK	Texaco
Howell Corp.	TOTAL
Imperial Oil	Unocal
International Thoroughbred Breeders	USX–Marathon
Kerr-McGee	YPF

HOW MUCH

	Annual Growth	1985	1986	1987	1988	1989	1990	1991	1992	1993	1994
Estimated sales ($ mil.)	9.3%	—	—	—	—	160	160	165	330	250	250
Employees	14.9%	—	—	—	—	350	350	350	700	360	700

Estimated Sales ($ mil.) 1989–94

LYONDELL PETROCHEMICAL COMPANY

OVERVIEW

Formerly a subsidiary of oil giant Atlantic Richfield (ARCO), Houston-based Lyondell Petrochemical was spun off to the public in 1989 and is still 49.9%–owned by ARCO. One of the US's largest petrochemical companies, Lyondell is an integrated petrochemical and petroleum processor and manufacturer.

Lyondell's Channelview, Texas, petrochemical complex produces ethylene, propylene, butadiene, methanol, specialty chemicals, and other products used in everything from trash bags and milk containers to paints and tires. The company conducts some of its refining operations through LYONDELL-CITGO Refining, a joint venture with CITGO Petroleum (a subsidiary of Petróleos de Venezuela), in which it holds an approximate 90% stake. LYONDELL-CITGO refines a number of petrochemical products, including aromatics, gasoline, heating oil, jet fuel, and motor oil. The raw material for this processing — heavy Venezuelan crude oil — is supplied by LAGOVEN, a Petróleos de Venezuela affiliate. Recent improvements to LYONDELL-CITGO facilities led to record processing rates in 1995.

An improving US economy fueled demand for petrochemical products in 1994. The company's methanol sales were particularly strong. In response, the firm increased its unit capacity 6%, to 248 million gallons per year.

WHEN

It wasn't exactly a model of efficiency. Located 16 miles apart on the Texas Gulf Coast, Atlantic Richfield's Houston refinery and its Channelview petrochemical complex were run by offices in Los Angeles and Philadelphia, respectively.

The operations were losing ground in the competitive Gulf Coast market, and ARCO Chemical was contemplating selling the petrochemical complex. However, Bob Gower, SVP of planning, convinced the company that the 2 Houston-area properties could be run together. In 1985 ARCO set up Lyondell Petrochemical Corporation (soon changed to Lyondell Petrochemical Company) as a wholly owned division, with Gower as CEO.

The refining facility that Gower and Lyondell got dated back to 1919, when Sinclair Oil & Refining Company had built a crude oil refinery in Houston. What was to become Lyondell's petrochemical complex was a petrochemical plant built on the Lyondell Country Club in Channelview by Texas Butadiene and Chemical Corporation in 1955. Sinclair Petrochemical, a subsidiary of Sinclair Oil, which had become a subsidiary of Richfield Oil Corporation in 1936, bought the petrochemical plant in 1962.

In 1966 Richfield and Atlantic Refining Company merged. Following the merger, the refinery became part of ARCO Products Company and the petrochemicals plant joined ARCO Chemical Company.

When ARCO Chemical was considering selling the petrochemical complex, Gower argued that there were synergies between the refinery and the petrochemical plant that could be exploited. The plant used inputs such as gas oil produced at the refinery, and the refinery used byproducts such as gasoline produced by the plant.

Gower proved to be right. By the 4th quarter of its first year, Lyondell was showing a profit. From the beginning Gower focused on making Lyondell flexible and efficient. The company upgraded its refinery so it could handle any kind of crude oil in the world. Gower also reduced Lyondell's work force by over 1,000 workers (including 75% of its executive staff) through voluntary layoffs in 1985.

With Lyondell's profits jumping over 340% between 1987 and 1988, ARCO decided to sell the company to the public. In 1989 ARCO sold 50.1% of Lyondell in an IPO worth $1.4 billion. However, before the sale ARCO had Lyondell pay it $500 million, leaving the fledgling company saddled with debt.

Lyondell persevered, and during 1989 the company upgraded its petrochemical facilities to increase capacity. In 1990 the firm acquired 2 chemical plants from Rexene Products Company. In 1992 Lyondell became the first major US refiner to recycle used motor oil into gasoline. In 1993 the company entered into an agreement with CDTECH to develop petrochemical technologies.

In 1994 ARCO completed a 3-year, $1 billion debt offering that gives ARCO the option to reduce its stake in Lyondell. Also that year Lyondell began upgrading its Houston refinery to increase its processing capacity from 130,000 to 200,000 barrels per day.

In 1995 the company signed an agreement to acquire Occidental Chemical Corp.'s Alathon high-density polyethylene business.

NYSE symbol: LYO
Fiscal year ends: December 31

WHO

Chairman and CEO: Robert G. Gower, age 57,
$1,258,203 pay
President and COO: Dan F. Smith, age 48, $792,175 pay
SVP, General Counsel, and Secretary: Jeffrey R.
Pendergraft, age 46, $381,830 pay
SVP, CFO, and Treasurer: Russell S. Young, age 46,
$374,456 pay
**SVP Petrochemicals Business Management and
Marketing:** Debra L. Starnes, age 42, $328,634 pay
**VP; VP Marketing, Supply, and Evaluations,
LYONDELL-CITGO Refining Company Ltd.:** Robert
H. Isé
VP Quality, Supply, and Planning: John R. Beard,
age 42
VP Channelview Operations: W. Norman Phillips Jr.,
age 40
VP Olefins: Clifton B. Currin Jr., age 40
VP and Controller: Joseph M. Putz, age 54
VP Human Resources: Richard W. Park, age 55
Auditors: Coopers & Lybrand L.L.P.

WHERE

HQ: 1221 McKinney St., Ste. 1600, Houston, TX 77010
Phone: 713-652-7200
Fax: 713-652-7430

Lyondell operates a petrochemical complex in
Channelview, Texas. LYONDELL-CITGO operates a
refinery on the Houston ship channel, a storage facility
at Mont Belvieu, Texas, and a lube oil blending and
packaging plant in Birmingport, Alabama.

WHAT

	1994 Sales		1994 Operating Income	
	$ mil.	% of total	$ mil.	% of total
Refined products	2,074	54	54	12
Petrochemicals	1,783	46	413	88
Adjustments	—	—	(43)	—
Total	**3,857**	**100**	**424**	**100**

Refining
Aromatics (benzene, paraxylene, orthoxylene, toluene)
Industrial products (coke, residual fuel, sulfur)
Light products (diesel fuel, gasoline, heating oil, jet fuel)
Lubricants (base oils, industrial lubricants, motor oils,
process oils, white oils)

Petrochemicals
Aromatics (benzene, toluene)
Olefins (butadiene, ethylene, propylene)
Oxygenated products (methanol, MTBE)
Polymers (low-density polyethylene, polypropylene)
Specialty products (DCPD, isoprene, piperylenes, resin
oil)

Subsidiaries
Lyondell Refining Company
LYONDELL-CITGO Refining Company Ltd. (90%)

KEY COMPETITORS

A. Schulman	Exxon	PEMEX
Amerada Hess	FINA	Pennzoil
Amoco	Formosa	Petrobrás
Ashland, Inc.	Plastics	Phillips
British Petroleum	Huntsman	Petroleum
Broken Hill	Chemical	Repsol
Chevron	Imperial Oil	Shell Oil
Coastal	Koch	Sun Energy
Dow Chemical	Mobil	Texaco
DuPont	Norsk Hydro	TOTAL
Eastman Chemical	Occidental	Unocal
Elf Aquitaine	Oryx	USX–Marathon

HOW MUCH

	Annual Growth	1985	1986	1987	1988	1989	1990	1991	1992	1993	1994
Sales ($ mil.)	3.1%	—	3,010	3,931	4,696	5,361	6,499	5,735	4,809	3,850	3,857
Net income ($ mil.)	7.2%	—	128	123	543	374	356	222	26	4	223
Income as % of sales	—	—	4.2%	3.1%	11.6%	7.0%	5.5%	3.9%	0.5%	0.1%	5.8%
Earnings per share ($)	(9.9%)	—	—	—	—	4.67	4.45	2.78	0.32	0.06	2.78
Stock price – high ($)	—	—	—	—	—	33.50	21.50	26.13	25.88	29.50	33.00
Stock price – low ($)	—	—	—	—	—	16.75	13.13	14.63	21.13	16.75	20.63
Stock price – close ($)	3.8%	—	—	—	—	21.50	14.63	22.63	24.63	21.25	25.88
P/E – high	—	—	—	—	—	7	5	9	81	—	12
P/E – low	—	—	—	—	—	4	3	5	66	—	7
Dividends per share ($)	(5.6%)	—	—	—	—	1.20	4.10	1.75	1.80	1.35	0.90
Book value per share ($)	48.3%	—	—	—	—	0.11	0.48	1.53	(0.08)	(1.10)	0.79
Employees	4.8%	—	1,911	1,874	2,000	2,070	2,250	2,270	2,312	2,283	2,263

1994 Year-end:
Debt ratio: 92.1%
Return on equity: —
Cash (mil.): $52
Current ratio: 1.61
Long-term debt (mil.): $707
No. of shares (mil.): 80
Dividends
 Yield: 3.5%
 Payout: 32.4%
Market value (mil.): $2,070

**Stock Price History
High/Low 1989–94**

...ary Kay's success is changing Russia's colors from communist red to capitalist pink. With about $850 million in company sales after commissions, Mary Kay is the largest direct-seller of skin care products in the US. Mary Kay sells its cosmetics and other products through 400,000 direct-sales "consultants" in the US and 23 foreign countries.

Mary Kay is now spreading its can-do style in Russia, where it generated sales of $9 million in 1994. The company expected to have 17,000 consultants and sales of $27 million there in 1995. Russia already ranks #4 in sales among the company's foreign markets.

Founded by a woman — Mary Kay Ash — for women, Mary Kay has a mostly female workforce. Despite the addition of men (fewer than 100) to its sales force, the company's mission has always been to provide the "best career opportunity to women." Among others, Ash gave a career boost to her sister-in-law, Mary Crowley, founder of Home Interiors and Gifts; that company was bought by Hicks Muse Tate & Furst for $1 billion in 1994.

Mary Kay's consultants demonstrate the company's 9 product lines in small groups of prospective clients who invite friends. Consultants can earn bonuses, such as earrings, flowered china, purses, or even the company's trademark pink Cadillacs.

Ash and her family own a majority of the company.

WHEN

Before founding her own company in 1963, Mary Kay Ash worked as a sales representative for Stanley Home Products. Impressed with the prize awarded the top saleswoman at a Stanley convention — an alligator handbag — Ash was determined to win the next year's prize, and she did. After she had worked at Stanley for 11 years, a male assistant was made her boss after less than a year on the job. Because Ash was tired of not receiving recognition, she and her 2nd husband used their life savings ($5,000) to go into business for themselves. Although her husband died of a heart attack shortly before the opening of the company's first headquarters, Ash, with her 2 grown sons, forged ahead.

Ash bought a cosmetics formula invented years earlier by a hide tanner. (The mixture was originally used to soften leather, but when the tanner noticed how the formula made his hands look younger, he began applying the mixture to his face, with great results.) Ash kept her first line simple — 10 products — and packaged her products in pink to contrast with the typical black and red toiletry cases of the day. With more attractive packaging, she believed, the products could be more openly displayed. Ash also enlisted consultants, who were to hold "beauty shows" with 5 or 6 women in attendance. The idea was that, with such small numbers, consultants could spend more time with clients individually. The company grossed $198,000 in its first year.

In 1966 Ash bought a pink Cadillac that was much admired by employees. She began awarding the cars as prizes the next year. (By 1981 orders were so large, almost 500, that GM dubbed a color "Mary Kay Pink.")

When the company went public in 1968, Ash became a millionaire. That same year the company launched its first fragrance, Snare. In 1969 Mary Kay began foreign operations, in Australia. Over the next 20 years the company entered Argentina, Canada, West Germany, and the UK.

The company grew steadily through the 1970s. Ash published her autobiography, *Mary Kay*, in 1981, mainly as a motivational tool. It came complete with tips on how to save time (eat lunch in your office) and gain your husband's support (don't talk to him too much about your work) and favorite words of wisdom ("Flowers leave their fragrance on the hand which bestows them").

In 1985 Ash and her family reacquired the company through a $315 million LBO. In the late 1980s the company, weighted with debt, lost money. A number of steps were taken to boost sales, income, and public image, including the introduction of recyclable packaging and empowerment groups (called Creative Action Teams). The company also began advertising in women's magazines (after a 5-year hiatus) to counter its old-fashioned image. In 1989 Avon rebuffed a buyout offer by Mary Kay, and both companies halted the practice of animal testing.

Mary Kay introduced a line of bath and body products in 1991, the result of a joint venture with International Flavors & Fragrances. The company's Skin Revival System, introduced in late 1993, raked in $80 million in its first 6 months on the market.

In 1995 Mary Kay joined Xenometrix in a research project to develop a skin irritation test that uses living cells outside the body.

Private company
Fiscal year ends: December 31

WHO

Chairman Emeritus: Mary Kay Ash
Chairman: Richard R. Rogers
CEO: John P. Rochon
President (US): Larry Harley
President (International): Amy DiGeso
President of the Americas, SVP Global HR: Tim Wentworth
EVP Manufacturing Group: Patrick E. Howard
SVP Marketing: Curran David Durand
SVP Information Systems: Trey Bradley
SVP Chief Scientific Officer: Myra O. Barker
SVP, Secretary, and General Counsel: Sheila O'Connell-Cooper
CFO: Ron Smith
Chief Administrative Officer: Ray Patrick
Auditors: Ernst & Young LLP

WHERE

HQ: 8787 Stemmons Fwy., Dallas, TX 75247
Phone: 214-630-8787
Fax: 214-905-5699
Consultant Directory: 800-627-9529 (800-MARYKAY)

Mary Kay Cosmetics Inc. employs over 400,000 direct-sales consultants who sell the company's merchandise in the US and 23 other countries. Mary Kay has foreign offices and warehouse facilities in Buenos Aires; Madrid; Mexico City; Monterrey, Mexico; Munich; Taipei, Taiwan; Toronto; and Victoria, Australia.

	1994 Sales
	% of total
US	90
Canada	6
Other countries	4
Total	**100**

WHAT

Selected Products
Beauty accessories
Body care products
Cosmetics
Fragrances
Hair care products
Skin care products
Sun protection products
Toiletries

Partnerships
Richmont Capital Partners (with New Arrow Corp. and J.R. Investments Corp.; owns 7.2% of Royal Appliance Manufacturing Co.)

KEY COMPETITORS

Alberto-Culver	Johnson & Johnson
Allou	Johnson Publishing
Aloette	The Limited
Amway	Liz Claiborne
Avon	L'Oréal
Body Shop	MacAndrews & Forbes
Carter-Wallace	Maybelline
Chattem	Nature's Sunshine
Colgate-Palmolive	Nu Skin International
Dep	Nutrition For Life
Estée Lauder	Perrigo
FoxMeyer Health	Procter & Gamble
Gillette	Regis
Helen of Troy	S.C. Johnson
Helene Curtis	Schering-Plough
Henkel	Shiseido
Herbalife	Soft Sheen Products
Jean Philippe Fragrances	Unilever

HOW MUCH

	Annual Growth	1985	1986	1987	1988	1989	1990	1991	1992	1993	1994
Sales ($ mil.)	14.6%	249	255	326	406	450	487	520	613	737	850
Net income ($ mil.)	—	21	(33)	(3)	9	20	—	—	15	34	—
Income as % of sales	—	8.4%	—	—	2.2%	4.4%	—	—	2.4%	4.6%	—
Direct-sales consultants	11.9%	145,493	141,113	—	—	192,804	208,009	225,000	300,000	325,000	400,000
Employees	8.3%	—	1,265	—	—	1,400	1,722	1,900	2,100	2,400	2,400

Sales ($ mil.) 1985–94

MAXXAM INC.

OVERVIEW

MAXXAM, corporate raider Charles Hurwitz's Houston-based holding company, is a controversial tangle of savvy business strategies, stunning financial turnarounds, legally contentious deals, and environmentally insensitive operations. The company is involved in aluminum mining and production, timber products, real estate investment, and horse racing.

MAXXAM's top revenue source is 58.9%-owned Kaiser Aluminum, a publicly traded company (NYSE: KLU) that produced 84% of MAXXAM's 1994 revenues. Hurwitz guided Kaiser through a major industry slump in 1990 to make it the world's #2 producer of alumina, the raw material of aluminum, in 1995. Kaiser's operations include bauxite mines, refining operations to convert bauxite to alumina, and smelters to produce aluminum. In 1994 Kaiser produced nearly 3 million tons of

aluminum and shipped 399,000 tons of fabricated aluminum products.

MAXXAM's timber industry operations accounted for 12% of 1994 revenues. Its Pacific Lumber subsidiary owns about 198,000 acres of old-growth redwood and Douglas fir timberlands in Humboldt County, California. Hurwitz is exploring the sale of Pacific Lumber, which has been besieged by environmental lawsuits since MAXXAM acquired it in 1986. Its selling price could top $1 billion.

Among MAXXAM's real estate interests are commercial and residential properties in Arizona, California, and Texas, and Palmas del Mar, a Puerto Rican resort. MAXXAM also has a stake in the Sam Houston Race Park, a Thoroughbred and quarter horse track near Houston that filed for bankruptcy in 1995.

Hurwitz owns 31% of MAXXAM.

WHEN

Robert McCulloch, an oil wildcatter and developer of the chain saw, founded MAXXAM in 1955 as the Cuban American Oil Company. In 1960 the company became McCulloch Oil Corp. of California. McCulloch drilled numerous wells but made no big strikes.

McCulloch began investing in real estate developments during the 1960s, starting with Lake Havasu City, an Arizona resort. Lake Havasu City was put on the map in 1968 when McCulloch purchased the London Bridge and had it reassembled in the Arizona desert. During the late 1960s and 1970s, McCulloch Oil continued to diversify, acquiring coal, gas, oil, real estate, and silver mining operations. With Lake Havasu City a success, the company also started developments at Fountain Hills, Arizona; Pueblo West, Colorado; and Spring Creek, Nevada.

McCulloch Oil began experiencing legal and financial setbacks in the 1970s. With the real estate industry in recession, the company took a $60 million write-off in 1976. The following year McCulloch died of drug and alcohol abuse and his son Robert Jr. pleaded guilty to fraud charges related to the company's real estate sales in Colorado.

Charles Hurwitz of Houston stepped into the picture the year following McCulloch's death. Hurwitz, a former Bache & Company stockbroker, had already established himself as a wheeler-dealer in insurance, investments, and real estate ventures. In 1978 Hurwitz bought 13% of McCulloch stock. By 1980 he was chairman and CEO and had filled top

management with his allies. That year the company became MCO Holdings.

Through MCO, Hurwitz created a puzzle of interlocking holdings. MCO purchased 37% of the Maxxam Group, one of Hurwitz's investment partnerships, in 1982. In 1983 MCO began investing in United Financial Group, which included United Savings Association of Texas. (The FDIC has sued Hurwitz alleging he allowed the S&L to fail in 1988.) MCO, through Maxxam, acquired Pacific Lumber in 1986 in a takeover engineered with Michael Milken and Ivan Boesky. To cover acquisition costs, MCO doubled Pacific Lumber's logging output of California redwood, angering environmentalists. In 1988 MCO purchased the outstanding shares of Maxxam and the companies merged as MAXXAM, Inc. Also that year MAXXAM paid $930 million, (raised by selling junk bonds) to acquire a majority interest in Kaiser Aluminum Corp.

During the early 1990s MAXXAM purchased numerous properties from the Resolution Trust Corporation. In 1991 environmental issues again threatened Pacific Lumber operations when the spotted owl and marbled murrelet (a small sea bird) were named to the endangered species list; both nest in Humboldt County. In 1992 MAXXAM lost a bidding war for bankrupt Continental Airlines.

Shareholders cried foul in 1995 when Sam Houston Race Park filed bankruptcy and then, in a reorganization plan, formed a new investment group that would increase MAXXAM's stake, cutting out other investors.

AMEX symbol: MXM
Fiscal year ends: December 31

Chairman, President, and CEO: Charles E. Hurwitz, age 54, $1,058,880 pay
Chairman and CEO, Kaiser Aluminum: George T. Haymaker Jr.
President and CEO, Pacific Lumber: John A. Campbell
President and CEO, MAXXAM Property: James D. Noteware
EVP and CFO: Paul N. Schwartz, age 48, $481,715 pay
SVP and General Counsel: Anthony R. Pierno, age 62, $595,144 pay
SVP: John T. La Duc, age 52, $343,000 pay
VP, Secretary, and Deputy General Counsel: Byron L. Wade, age 48, $299,495 pay
VP Federal Government Affairs: Robert E. Cole, age 48
VP Public Relations: Robert W. Irelan, age 58
VP and Chief Personnel Officer: Diane M. Dudley, age 54
Auditors: Arthur Andersen & Co, SC

WHERE

HQ: 5847 San Felipe St., Ste. 2600, Houston, TX 77057
Phone: 713-975-7600
Fax: 713-267-3701

MAXXAM's operations include bauxite and aluminum operations in Australia, Ghana, Jamaica, the US, and Wales. The company's timber production is concentrated in Northern California. Its real estate interests are in Arizona, California, Texas, and Puerto Rico.

	1994 Sales		1994 Operating Income	
	$ mil.	% of total	$ mil.	% of total
US	1,566.3	74	(55.3)	—
Caribbean	201.0	9	(0.1)	—
Africa	180.0	9	18.3	29
Other regions	168.4	8	44.4	71
Total	**2,115.7**	**100**	**7.3**	**100**

WHAT

	1994 Sales		1994 Operating Income	
	$ mil.	% of total	$ mil.	% of total
Aluminum ops.	1,781.5	84	(50.3)	—
Forest products	249.6	12	79.1	—
Real estate ops.	84.6	4	(10.0)	—
Adjustments	—	—	(11.5)	—
Total	**2,115.7**	**100**	**7.3**	**—**

Manufacturing Subsidiaries and Selected Products

Britt Lumber	**Pacific Lumber**
Wooden fencing products	Logs
	Lumber
Kaiser Aluminum (58.9%)	Wood chips
Alumina/bauxite	
Fabricated aluminum products	
Primary aluminum	

Selected Real Estate and Other Operations

MAXXAM Property Co. and MCO Properties (development and commercial real estate investment in Arizona, California, Colorado, New Mexico, and Texas)

Palmas del Mar Properties (resort, time-sharing, and land development and sales in Puerto Rico)

Sam Houston Race Park (46.0%, Thoroughbred and quarter horse racing facility near Houston)

KEY COMPETITORS

Alcan	Pechiney S.A.
Alcoa	Plum Creek Timber
Alumax	Pope & Talbot
Anschutz	RCL Industries
Commonwealth Aluminum	Reynolds Metals
Eel River	Sierra Pacific
Georgia-Pacific	Silgan
Glencore Ltd.	Tredegar Industries
IP Timberlands	Union Camp
Louisiana-Pacific	Weyerhaeuser
Norsk Hydro	

HOW MUCH

	Annual Growth	1985	1986	1987	1988	1989	1990	1991	1992	1993	1994
Sales ($ mil.)	41.9%	91	108	59	519	2,423	2,361	2,255	2,203	2,031	2,116
Net income ($ mil.)	—	8	(29)	1	18	117	144	58	(7)	(132)	(117)
Income as % of sales	—	9.1%	—	2.0%	3.4%	4.8%	6.1%	2.6%	—	—	—
Earnings per share ($)	—	1.18	(5.16)	0.20	2.10	12.46	15.19	6.08	(0.77)	(13.95)	(12.35)
Stock price – high ($)	—	15.00	16.75	17.75	25.75	51.00	67.50	54.75	43.50	38.88	44.50
Stock price – low ($)	—	12.75	8.88	8.00	7.75	23.38	26.38	26.00	22.25	21.75	29.50
Stock price – close ($)	9.4%	13.75	9.38	8.00	24.38	47.00	31.13	29.38	27.50	36.75	30.88
P/E – high	—	13	—	89	12	4	4	9	—	—	—
P/E – low	—	11	—	40	4	2	2	4	—	—	—
Dividends per share ($)	—	0.00	0.00	0.00	0.00	0.00	0.00	0.00	0.00	0.00	0.00
Book value per share ($)	—	16.26	11.20	11.42	13.66	27.02	45.82	52.95	51.01	(17.80)	(31.65)
Employees	17.3%	3,300	3,300	1,700	12,700	9,804	10,661	9,967	12,379	13,795	13,860

1994 Year-end:
Debt ratio: 120.5%
Return on equity: —
Cash (mil.): $85
Current ratio: 1.61
Long-term debt (mil.): $1,583
No. of shares (mil.): 9
Dividends
  Yield: —
  Payout: —
Market value (mil.): $269

Stock Price History High/Low 1985–94

NGC CORPORATION

OVERVIEW

Like the natural gas it markets, NGC Corporation is expanding rapidly. Formerly known as Natural Gas Clearinghouse, Houston-based NGC changed its name in 1995 after it bought Trident NGL, a leading fully integrated natural gas liquids company, for more than $338 million. The acquisition helped increase NGC's market share. NGC, which went public following the deal, is one of North America's largest natural gas and natural gas liquids gathering, processing, transportation, and marketing firms, with assets of more than $37 billion.

Other subsidiaries of the company include Accord Energy (an energy marketer in the UK, jointly owned by British Gas), Electric Clearinghouse (an electric power marketer), Hub Services (an operator of 3 transportation and interchange facilities known as gas marketing hubs), NGC Oil Trading and Transportation (a crude oil marketer), and Novagas Clearinghouse (a natural gas and natural gas liquids marketer in Canada, jointly owned by NOVA Corp). British Gas and NOVA each hold 33% of NGC. CEO Chuck Watson owns 6% of the company's stock.

The combination of natural gas, natural gas liquids, crude oil, and electricity marketing forms the basis for the company's continuing growth as a full-service, one-step provider of energy products and services. With 10% of the North American gas market, NGC plans to have a 12% share by 1998.

In 1995 NGC acquired Ozark Gas Transmission System, an interstate pipeline (266 miles of 20-inch mainline pipe) connecting Arkansas to eastern Oklahoma.

WHEN

NGC was originally one of several independent companies in the natural gas market that emerged in the wake of government deregulation of the industry. In 1978 the passage of the Natural Gas Policy Act reduced the interstate pipeline companies' control over the gathering, transportation, and marketing of natural gas. Federal Energy Regulatory Commission (FERC) Order 380, set down in 1984, made the price of gas bought from 3rd parties competitive with pipeline gas prices.

Natural Gas Clearinghouse was founded in late 1984 to match sellers and buyers of gas without taking title of the gas. C. L. "Chuck" Watson was appointed the company's CEO and president in 1985 (he became chairman in 1989). The company grew dramatically with the increasing deregulation of the 1980s. FERC Orders 436, 497, and 500 made larger volumes of gas available to independent marketers. By 1988 Natural Gas Clearinghouse had gas sales of 1.3 billion cubic feet per day; by 1990 this had risen to approximately 2.3 billion cubic feet per day.

The company developed financial instruments (such as natural gas futures) to provide its customers with a hedge against the wide fluctuations in the price of natural gas. By 1990 Natural Gas Clearinghouse was trading natural gas futures on the New York Mercantile Exchange. In that year it also formed NGC Oil Trading and Transportation, a crude oil marketing subsidiary. Natural Gas Clearinghouse was the first independent gas marketer to act as an exclusive supply agent for a large local distribution company. It also expanded into other natural gas markets by buying assets in gas gathering and processing facilities.

Natural Gas Clearinghouse expanded further following the implementation of FERC Order 636 in 1992. This order requires most interstate pipeline companies to separately offer merchant sales, transportation, and storage services to all gas shippers on terms comparable to those the pipeline companies offer to their affiliates. With the low-price advantage taken away from interstate pipeline companies, Natural Gas Clearinghouse targeted opportunities for increased gas sales at local distribution companies.

In 1993 the company formed 3 natural gas market area hubs (regional centers for natural gas transactions) with 3 major gas utilities in California, Illinois, and Pennsylvania.

Natural Gas Clearinghouse expanded internationally in 1994 through partnerships with NOVA Corp. of Canada (Novagas Clearinghouse, natural gas and natural gas liquids marketing services) and British Gas (Accord Energy, energy marketing). It also set up an electric power marketing subsidiary (Electric Clearinghouse) in 1994 as part of its strategy to become a comprehensive energy trader, and in anticipation of increased deregulation in the electric industry.

In 1995 the company acquired Trident, changed its name to NGC, and began trading on the NYSE. NGC subsequently agreed to combine Novagas Clearinghouse with NOVA subsidiary Pan-Alberta Gas. The deal created a gas marketing company selling roughly 2.8 billion cubic feet of natural gas per day.

NYSE symbol: NGL
Fiscal year ends: December 31

WHO

Chairman, President, and CEO: C. L. Watson, age 45, $2,575,000 pay
VC; Chairman and CEO, Trident NGL: Bruce M. Withers Jr., age 68, $508,000 pay
SVP; President, Clearinghouse: Stephen W. Bergstrom, age 37, $772,250 pay
SVP; President, Trident NGL: James T. Hackett, age 41, $537,458 pay
SVP, General Counsel, and Secretary: Kenneth E. Randolph, age 38, $291,078 pay
SVP, CFO, and Treasurer: H. Keith Kaelber, age 46
VP Human Resources: M. B. Barton
Auditors: Arthur Andersen & Co, SC

WHERE

HQ: 13430 Northwest Fwy., Ste. 1200, Houston, TX 77040
Phone: 713-507-6400
Fax: 713-507-3871

Gas Marketing Hubs
Transportation and interchange facilities located near an interconnection of 2 or more interstate pipelines: California Energy Hub, Chicago Hub, Ellisburg-Leidy Northeast Hub (Pennsylvania)

Regional Marketing Offices

Boston	Pittsburgh
Englewood, CO	Portland, OR
Mexico City	Rosemont, IL
Phoenix	Tulsa

WHAT

	1994 Sales	
	$ mil.	% of total
Gas marketing	2,626	79
Crude oil marketing	504	15
Natural gas liquid marketing	104	3
Gas gathering and processing	87	3
Adjustments	(83)	—
Total	**3,238**	**100**

	1994 Sales
	% of total
Local distribution companies	38
End user	19
Independent marketer	15
Pipeline affiliate	6
Major producer/affiliate	6
Other	6
Total	**100**

Selected Subsidiaries
Accord Energy Ltd. (UK, energy marketing)
Electric Clearinghouse, Inc. (electric power marketing)
Hub Services, Inc. (gas marketing hubs)
Natural Gas Clearinghouse (natural gas marketing)
NGC Oil Trading and Transportation, Inc. (crude oil marketing)
Novagas Clearinghouse Ltd. (Canada, natural gas and natural gas liquids marketing services)
Trident NGL, Inc. (natural gas liquids marketing services)

KEY COMPETITORS

American Oil and Gas
Aquila Gas Pipeline
Coastal
Columbia Gas
Cornerstone Natural Gas
Enron
KCS Energy
Occidental
Panhandle Eastern
Parker & Parsley Petroleum
Phillips Petroleum
Sonat Inc.
Tejas Gas
Tenneco
TransTexas Gas
U. S. Gas Transportation
USX–Delhi
Valero Energy
Western Gas
Williams Cos.

HOW MUCH

	Annual Growth	1985	1986	1987	1988	1989	1990	1991	1992	1993	1994
Sales ($ mil.)	16.9%	—	—	—	—	—	1,732	2,099	2,493	2,791	3,238
Net income ($ mil.)	10.4%	—	—	—	—	—	28	39	44	46	42
Income as % of sales	—	—	—	—	—	—	1.6%	1.8%	1.8%	1.6%	1.3%
Employees	172.3%	—	—	—	—	—	—	—	—	—	1,070

1994 Year-end:
Debt ratio: 17.8%
Return on equity: —
Cash (mil.): $15.2
Current ratio: 1.10
Long-term debt (mil.): $33.0

Sales ($ mil.)
1990–94

NORAM ENERGY CORP.

OVERVIEW

NorAm (known as Arkla before a 1994 corporate renaming) has set about establishing itself as a national natural gas heavyweight, rather than the regionally focused company its earlier Arkansas/Louisiana moniker indicated. With the acquisition in recent years of gas companies with assets in Mississippi and Minnesota, the company has developed the 3rd largest base of natural gas customers in the US, and its services cover North America from the Canadian border to the Mexican border. Its 3 natural gas distribution divisions are Entex

(Louisiana, Mississippi, Texas), Arkla (Arkansas, Louisiana, Oklahoma, and Texas), and Minnegasco (Minnesota). Natural gas sales accounted for 92% of total sales in 1994. NorAm's other subsidiaries are engaged in transportation and chemical and petroleum products. It moved its headquarters from Shreveport to Houston in 1994.

Despite an unusually warm winter in 1994 that caused a decline in gas distribution sales, total revenues were up, with gas pipeline sales turning in a 38% improvement that year.

WHEN

In 1928 Southern Cities Distributing Company was set up in Shreveport, Louisiana, to acquire and operate natural gas companies. It merged with 4 Arkansas and Louisiana gas concerns in 1934 to form Arkansas Louisiana Gas Company (ALG), a subsidiary of Cities Service Company. In 1936 ALG bought Little Rock Gas & Fuel. In 1944, citing the Public Utility Holding Company Act, the SEC forced Cities Service to divest ALG. Litigation and hearings delayed the reorganization of the company. ALG went public in 1952.

In 1954 Wilton "Witt" Stephens, the patriarch of one of the South's wealthiest families, bought 51% of ALG. He became president and chairman 3 years later. Stephens, who grew up on a farm south of Little Rock, had helped his brother Jackson create the largest investment bank outside Wall Street. He also emerged as the undisputed kingmaker in Arkansas politics as a fund-raiser and organizer for 6-term governor Orval Faubus. Under Stephens's control the company expanded its gas operations in Kansas, Louisiana, Oklahoma, and Texas. In 1963 ALG built a new pipeline connecting its central gas system in Arkansas with new gas fields in Oklahoma. But volatile oil prices and money-losing fertilizer and plywood operations dragged profits down in the late 1960s.

The early 1970s, with its energy shortages and oil embargoes, caused the company's finances to deteriorate further. In 1973 Stephens stepped down and appointed hand-picked successors Sheffield Nelson and Donald Wier as co-CEOs. Despite subsequent efforts from Stephens to control company strategy through his allies on the board, Nelson and Wier took the company in a new direction. They sold off the unprofitable plywood and fertilizer operations and invested heavily (and successfully) in natural gas exploration. In addition, ALG managed to negotiate contracts

at bargain prices with a range of gas producers before the 1978 Natural Gas Policy Act eroded the interstate pipeline companies' control over the gathering, transportation, and marketing of natural gas. This act and subsequent deregulation opened the door for independent gas firms to challenge established interstate pipeline companies like ALG for market share.

In 1981 ALG changed its corporate name to Arkla and signed a long-term contract with the Central Louisiana Electric Co. Under this contract Arkla agreed to sell the electric utility 100 million cubic feet of gas daily, greatly reducing Arkla's oversupply of gas.

In 1983 Thomas McLarty (who later became President Clinton's first chief of staff) was appointed Arkla president. He reorganized it into independent business units (natural gas distribution, transmission, and exploration and production). In 1988 Arkla acquired Entex, which serves 1.2 million customers in the Houston area, in a $500 million stock swap. The company also acquired Diversified Energies in 1990.

Federal Energy Regulation Commission Order 636 (issued in 1992) required interstate pipeline companies to "unbundle" its services — to separately offer its sales, transportation, and storage services to all gas shippers on terms comparable to those the pipeline companies offered to their affiliates. The low-price advantages taken away from interstate pipeline companies by this order increased the competitive pressure on Arkla.

The newly named NorAm expanded its operations in 1995. It formed a partnership with Grupo Gutsa to develop local distribution companies and regional pipelines in Mexico, and it also applied for permission from state authorities to branch into the telecommunications business in Arkansas and Oklahoma.

NYSE symbol: NAE
Fiscal year ends: December 31

WHO

Chairman and CEO: T. Milton Honea Jr., age 62, $498,909 pay
EVP and CFO: Michael B. Bracy, age 53, $407,000 pay
SVP, General Counsel, and Secretary: Hubert Gentry Jr., age 63, $387,500 pay
SVP Planning and Treasurer: William H. Kelly, age 55
SVP Human Resources and Administrative Services: Rick L. Spurlock, age 49
President, NorAm Energy Services: William A. Kellstrom, age 53, $371,004 pay
President and COO, Arkansas Louisiana Gas Co. (Arkla): Michael H. Means, age 46
President and COO, Entex: Robert N. Jones, age 42
President and COO, Minnegasco: Gary N. Petersen
President and COO, Mississippi River Transportation; EVP, Arkla Pipeline Group: Michael T. Hunter, age 44
VP and Controller: Jack W. Ellis II, age 41
Auditors: Coopers & Lybrand L.L.P.

WHERE

HQ: 1600 Smith, 11th Fl., PO Box 2628, Houston, TX 77252-2628
Phone: 713-654-5100
Fax: 713-654-7511

NorAm Energy distributes and transmits natural gas in 6 states in the midwestern, southern, and southwestern US.

	1994 Customers	
	Communities served	% of total
Arkansas	376	28
Texas	365	28
Minnesota	221	17
Louisiana	178	13
Oklahoma	95	7
Mississippi	91	7
Total	**1,326**	**100**

WHAT

	1994 Sales	
	$ mil.	% of total
Natural gas sales	2,578	92
Gas transportation	173	6
Chemical & petroleum products	5	0
Other	45	2
Total	**2,801**	**100**

	1994 Customers	
	No. (thou.)	% of total
Entex	1,376	51
Arkla	721	27
Minnegasco	612	22
Total	**2,709**	**100**

Natural Gas Distribution Divisions
Entex (Louisiana, Mississippi, Texas)
Arkla (Arkansas, Louisiana, Oklahoma, and Texas)
Minnegasco (Minnesota)

Other Subsidiaries
Mississippi River Transmission Corp.
NorAm Energy Services
NorAm Gas Transmission

KEY COMPETITORS

Coastal
Columbia Gas
Enron Corp.
ENSERCH Corp.
NGC
Panhandle Eastern
Sonat Inc.
Southwestern Energy
Tejas Gas
Transco Energy
TransTexas Gas
U. S. Gas Transportation
USX–Delhi
Valero Energy
Western Gas
Williams Cos.
Zapata

HOW MUCH

	Annual Growth	1985	1986	1987	1988	1989	1990	1991	1992	1993	1994
Sales ($ mil.)	12.2%	993	1,000	1,188	1,996	2,246	2,436	2,708	2,717	2,909	2,801
Net income ($ mil.)	(3.1%)	66	64	78	117	(84)	106	13	(29)	40	49
Income as % of sales	—	6.6%	6.4%	6.6%	5.9%	—	4.3%	0.5%	—	1.4%	1.8%
Earnings per share ($)	(13.8%)	1.30	1.20	1.25	1.30	(1.07)	1.10	0.05	(0.30)	0.26	0.34
Stock price – high ($)	—	24.25	21.13	26.50	20.63	27.75	27.25	20.25	12.38	10.63	9.00
Stock price – low ($)	—	16.25	16.00	15.63	17.75	20.00	18.50	9.75	6.88	7.38	5.25
Stock price – close ($)	(12.4%)	17.63	19.00	18.00	20.13	27.25	20.00	12.50	8.50	7.88	5.38
P/E – high	—	19	18	21	16	—	25	—	—	41	27
P/E – low	—	13	13	13	14	—	17	—	—	28	15
Dividends per share ($)	(13.9%)	1.08	1.08	1.08	1.08	1.08	1.08	1.08	0.48	0.28	0.28
Book value per share ($)	(7.4%)	9.54	10.65	10.72	8.41	6.67	10.04	7.61	4.77	4.72	4.79
Employees	9.3%	—	—	3,659	6,440	6,729	10,000	9,100	7,187	6,907	6,840

1994 Year-end:
Debt ratio: 70.2%
Return on equity: 8.4%
Cash (mil.): $18
Current ratio: 0.46
Long-term debt (mil.): $1,414
No. of shares (mil.): 123
Dividends
  Yield: 5.2%
  Payout: 82.4%
Market value (mil.): $659

Stock Price History High/Low 1985–94

ORYX ENERGY COMPANY

OVERVIEW

A mixture of bad timing, bad decisions, and bad luck has seen Oryx, once the largest US independent oil and gas exploration company, slide down the slippery slope to financial crisis. Oryx explores for, develops, produces, and markets crude oil and natural gas. The Dallas-based company boasts reserves of over 720 million barrels-of-oil equivalent. About 61% of Oryx's reserves are in the US, inherited when the company was spun off from Sun in 1988.

An aggressive and experienced management team gained the company a reputation as a high flyer with the financial ability to develop fields in far-flung places such as Ecuador, Indonesia, and the North Sea. But the company overreached itself, and since the bottom fell out of the oil market following the Gulf War

crisis, the firm has been furiously jettisoning assets and constantly restructuring in an attempt to keep itself financially viable.

Since 1988 Oryx has cut the number of its employees from 4,000 to 1,200 and sold more than $1 billion in oil properties in an effort to drastically reduce its losses. The firm continued to cut costs in 1994 with salary freezes and a 20% reduction in the exploration budget.

CEO Robert Hauptfuhrer retired in 1994 and was replaced by former COO and 30-year company veteran Robert Keiser. Keiser's new strategy has the company focusing on lower-risk, shorter-cycle-time projects, mainly in the Gulf of Mexico, and on cutting Oryx's debt by $400 million in 1995.

WHEN

In the early 1960s Seagram, run by Canada's Bronfman family, branched out beyond distilleries and acquired Texas Pacific Oil and oil and gas properties in the Southwest. In the 1970s the Sun Company, long a leading independent oil refiner and marketer under the Sunoco banner, branched out beyond oil and gas into medical equipment and other nonpetroleum ventures. In 1980 Seagram and Sun ended their branching out. Sun bought Seagram's Texas Pacific assets for $2.39 billion.

Oil prices collapsed in 1986, and in 1988 Sun spun off its domestic oil and gas exploration assets as Sun Exploration and Production (Sun E&P). Robert Hauptfuhrer, Sun's president, elected to jump to the new, Dallas-based company.

Sun E&P chairman Hauptfuhrer and president James McCormick led a brisk makeover of the company. The number of managerial reports was slashed by 28%, and the levels of management between thinking about doing something and doing something were decreased. Management also tackled rifts between exploration and production divisions.

Within 2 years of its creation, Sun E&P slashed the cost of finding the average barrel-of-oil equivalent by 53%. The same company that replaced only 42% of its reserves in 1986 replaced 311% in 1990.

In 1989 Sun E&P changed its name to Oryx Energy. Like the antelope in its logo, Oryx was leaping, first into the Austin Chalk formation of Texas and then into international exploration. Oryx modified offshore drilling techniques and used them in the all-but-abandoned Austin Chalk's Pearsall Fields.

Many oil companies had left the area because wells averaged only 5 barrels of oil a day. With the new technology of horizontal drilling (in which the drilling veers parallel to the surface), an Oryx well in the summer of 1989 produced 1,300 barrels a day.

In a purchase completed in 1990, Oryx paid $1.1 billion for British Petroleum properties in the UK's North Sea and in Ecuador, Gabon, Indonesia, and Italy. In late 1990 it repurchased 25 million of its shares held by Glenmede, the trust for Sun's founding family, the Pews. To whittle debt from those deals, Oryx sold California oil and gas properties to ARCO and Unocal (1990).

Oryx sold its oil and gas interests in the Midway-Sunset Field and a steam cogeneration facility for $534 million in 1991. In 1992 the company sold its South Texas natural gas liquids to Valero for $83 million.

In 1993 the company sold its nonproducing mineral rights in Oklahoma and Arkansas, totaling 20,600 acres, to Panhandle Royalty. That same year Oryx boosted its holdings in the Ninian field in the North Sea by 8.2% (to 29.5%).

In 1994 the company signed 2 agreements with the government of Kazakhstan to develop oil and gas reserves near the Caspian Sea. In that same year Oryx swapped some of its potentially profitable oil fields in the North Sea with Conoco for nearby fields already producing oil. This move enabled Oryx to save $200 million in development costs and to tap into cash-producing fields.

In 1995 the company sold its Indonesian oil and gas assets for $67 million.

NYSE symbol: ORX
Fiscal year ends: December 31

Chairman, CEO, and President: Robert L. Keiser,
age 52, $358,712 pay
EVP Exploration and Production: Jerry W. Box, age 56,
$251,368 pay
EVP Finance and CFO: Edward W. Moneypenny, age 53,
$244,400 pay
VP Marketing: William P. Stokes Jr., age 53, $191,516 pay
VP, General Counsel, and Secretary: William C.
Lemmer, age 50
Treasurer: David F. Chavenson, age 42
General Auditor: Sherri T. Durst, age 45
Director Human Resources: Frances G. Heartwell
Auditors: Coopers & Lybrand L.L.P.

WHERE

HQ: 13155 Noel Rd., Dallas, TX 75240-5067
Phone: 214-715-4000
Fax: 214-715-3798 (Investor Relations)

Oryx explores for and produces oil and gas from wells in
Algeria, Australia, Ecuador, Indonesia, Kazakhstan, the
North Sea (UK), and the US.

	1994 Sales		1994 Operating Income	
	$ mil.	% of total	$ mil.	% of total
US	624	58	152	65
UK	355	33	82	35
Indonesia	79	7	(5)	—
Other countries	24	2	(19)	—
Total	**1,082**	**100**	**210**	**100**

	1994 Exploratory Wells	
	No.	% of total
US	5	21
Other countries	19	79
Total	**24**	**100**

WHAT

	1994 Wells Drilled			
	Exploratory		Developmental	
	No.	% of total	No.	% of total
Dry	18	75	5	10
Gas	3	13	26	50
Oil	3	12	21	40
Total	**24**	**100**	**52**	**100**

Major Projects

Exploration	Development
Algeria	Ecuador
Australia	Gulf of Mexico
Gulf of Mexico	UK (North Sea)
Kazakhstan	
UK (North Sea)	

KEY COMPETITORS

Amerada Hess	Koch
Amoco	Mitchell Energy
Anadarko Petroleum	Mobil
Ashland, Inc.	Norsk Hydro
Atlantic Richfield	Occidental
British Petroleum	PDVSA
Broken Hill	PEMEX
Burlington Resources	Pennzoil
Castle Energy	Petrobrás
Chevron	Phillips Petroleum
Coastal	Repsol
DuPont	Shell Oil
Elf Aquitaine	Sinclair Oil
Enron	Sun Company
Exxon	Texaco
FINA	TOTAL
Hunt Oil	Unocal
Imperial Oil	USX-Marathon

HOW MUCH

	Annual Growth	1985	1986	1987	1988	1989	1990	1991	1992	1993	1994
Sales ($ mil.)	(1.0%)	—	—	1,161	1,070	1,140	1,940	1,484	1,275	1,080	1,082
Net income ($ mil.)	—	—	—	158	(305)	54	225	19	73	(93)	(78)
Income as % of sales	—	—	—	11.1%	—	4.5%	11.6%	1.3%	5.2%	—	—
Earnings per share ($)	—	—	—	1.70	(2.89)	0.51	2.26	0.08	0.74	(1.01)	(0.80)
Stock price – high ($)	—	—	—	—	28.00	46.25	54.88	40.38	27.25	26.25	20.00
Stock price – low ($)	—	—	—	—	23.13	25.50	34.75	22.00	16.75	16.25	10.63
Stock price – close ($)	(12.2%)	—	—	—	25.88	44.38	36.13	25.63	19.63	17.25	11.88
P/E – high	—	—	—	—	—	91	24	—	37	—	—
P/E – low	—	—	—	—	—	50	15	—	23	—	—
Dividends per share ($)	—	—	—	0.00	0.30	1.20	1.20	1.20	0.80	0.40	0.00
Book value per share ($)	—	—	—	14.87	15.24	14.17	7.72	6.62	8.11	6.90	(3.45)
Employees	(15.8%)	—	—	4,000	3,200	2,900	2,700	2,500	1,600	1,300	1,200

1994 Year-end:
Debt ratio: 100.0%
Return on equity: —
Cash (mil.): $10
Current ratio: 0.37
Long-term debt (mil.): $1,546
No. of shares (mil.): 102
Dividends
Yield: —
Payout: —
Market value (mil.): $1,211

**Stock Price History
High/Low 1988–94**

PANHANDLE EASTERN CORPORATION

OVERVIEW

Houston-based Panhandle Eastern operates one of the US's largest natural gas transmission systems. Its more than 34,000 miles of pipeline stretch from gas gathering areas in the southeastern and western US and in Canada to markets in the Upper Midwest and Northeast. With its 1994 merger with gas gathering company Associated Natural Gas, Panhandle Eastern has become one of the largest gas gatherers and marketers in the US.

Panhandle Eastern's 4 transmission subsidiaries deliver nearly 2.5 trillion cubic feet of natural gas a year (roughly 12% of the US's gas consumption). The company also imports and re-gasifies Algerian liquefied natural gas for sale in the US through its subsidiary Trunkline LNG.

The deregulation of the gas industry, which requires companies to "unbundle" their services — separating out sales, transportation, and gathering and storage functions — was a major reason for Panhandle's merger with Associated Natural Gas. While Panhandle had a strong business in transportation, where rates remain regulated, it wanted to expand into the less regulated business of gas gathering. The addition of Associated brings more than 9,000 miles of gathering pipelines and a presence in western markets.

The company plans to continue building its supply-area activities, including gathering, storage, and marketing, and to expand into new markets, including the UK and South America.

WHEN

Panhandle Eastern first appeared in 1929 as Interstate Pipe Line Company. Renamed Panhandle Eastern Pipe Line Company in 1930, it completed its first pipeline in 1931, which extended 2,100 miles from the Texas Panhandle to eastern Illinois by the end of 1939.

In 1951 the company started building its 2nd major pipeline system (Trunkline Gas Company), linking the Gulf Coast to Panhandle Eastern's system in Illinois.

In 1959 Panhandle Eastern bought Anadarko Production Company, an oil-and-gas exploration firm. It then joined National Distillers and Chemical to form National Helium in 1961, which built a helium extraction plant near Liberal, Kansas, in 1963.

Trunkline extended its system to the Indiana-Michigan border through 2 more pipelines, and by the end of 1969 the combined Panhandle-Trunkline system supplied natural gas to 12 states and Canada.

Hoping to reduce the effects of gas shortages, Panhandle Eastern entered into a 20-year contract for liquefied natural gas (LNG) with Algerian supplier Sonatrach in 1975. It also bought a coal mining firm (Youghiogheny and Ohio Coal, 1976) and an oil drilling firm (Dixilyn Corporation, 1977), which owned 1/3 of an offshore contractor, Dixilyn Godager Company (renamed Dixilyn-Field Godager, 1979). Panhandle Eastern completed its acquisition of Dixilyn-Field in 1980.

The company adopted the name Panhandle Eastern Corporation in 1981 and, in response to falling gas prices, suspended its Algerian LNG contract in 1983. Sonatrach subsequently filed for international arbitration.

In 1986, after rejecting a takeover bid from Wagner and Brown (a Midland, Texas–based oil and gas firm), Panhandle Eastern spun off Anadarko to its stockholders. In 1987 the company charged $460 million against earnings as part of its settlement with Sonatrach (which included a 20-year contract to buy LNG from Sonatrach). Also in 1987 the company shut down Youghiogheny and Ohio Coal and Dixilyn-Field (both were sold in 1990).

In 1989, when Texas Eastern Corporation (TEC, another Houston-based pipeline company) faced a hostile takeover by Coastal Corporation, Panhandle Eastern agreed to buy the company for $3.2 billion. Founded in 1947, Texas Eastern operated a gas pipeline extending from the Gulf Coast to the eastern seaboard. Panhandle Eastern took on $2.6 billion of debt to finance the TEC acquisition ($1.7 billion was retired that year through the sale of TEC's nonpipeline assets).

In 1991 the company's Texas Eastern Transmission Corporation (TETCO) joined 2 other pipeline operators to form Liberty Pipeline Company, a project designed to connect existing lines to high-need areas of Long Island and New York City.

Panhandle Eastern formed a new subsidiary in 1993, 1 Source Corporation, to provide customized gas transportation management services. In 1994 Panhandle subsidiary Centana Energy acquired several assets from a unit of Texas-based Mitchell Energy & Development, including a pipeline, a storage facility, and a processing plant.

In 1995 Paul Anderson succeeded Dennis Hendrix as CEO. Hendrix remains chairman.

NYSE symbol: PEL
Fiscal year ends: December 31

WHO

Chairman: Dennis R. Hendrix, age 55
VC: George L. Mazanec, age 59, $529,414 pay
President and CEO: Paul M. Anderson, age 50,
$531,964 pay (prior to promotion)
President, Algonquin Gas Transmission Co.: Richard
Perkins, age 54
President, Associated Natural Gas Corp.: Donald H.
Anderson, age 47
President, Panhandle Eastern Pipeline Co.: Steven M.
Roverud, age 56
President, Texas Eastern Transmission Corp.: Fred J.
Fowler, age 49
President, Trunkline Gas Co.: L. B. Gatewood, age 48
SVP: James B. Hipple, age 61, $403,827 pay
SVP and General Counsel: Carl B. King, age 52,
$390,333 pay
SVP and CFO: Paul F. Ferguson, age 46
VP Investor Relations: Brad Porlier
VP Human Resources: Dan R. Hennig, age 54
Corporate Secretary: Robert W. Reed, age 51
Auditors: KPMG Peat Marwick LLP

WHERE

HQ: 5400 Westheimer Ct., PO Box 1642, Houston, TX
77251-1642
Phone: 713-627-5400
Fax: 713-627-4145

Primary Market Areas

Connecticut	Missouri
Delaware	New Jersey
Illinois	New York
Indiana	Ohio
Iowa	Pennsylvania
Kentucky	Rhode Island
Maryland	Vermont
Massachusetts	Virginia
Michigan	West Virginia

WHAT

	1994 Sales	
	$ mil.	% of total
Market and supply services	2,893	63
Natural gas transmission	1,637	36
Other	55	1
Total	**4,585**	**100**

Market and Supply Services Group
Associated Natural Gas Corp.
Associated Natural Gas Inc. (ANGI)
Associated Transport and Trading Co. (ATTCO)
Centana Energy Corp. (gas extraction, gathering,
processing, and marketing)

Natural Gas Transmission Group
1Source Development Co.
1Source Information Services Co.
Algonquin Gas Transmission Co.
Panhandle Eastern Pipe Line Co. (PEPL)
Texas Eastern Transmission Corp. (TETCO)
Trunkline Gas Co.

Other Activities
Midland Cogeneration Venture (14.3%)
National Methanol Co. (25%, Saudi Arabia)
Northern Border Partners, L.P. (8.5%, gas transmission
system extending from Canada through Montana to
Iowa)
TEPPCO Partners, L.P. (transportation and storage of
petroleum products)
Trunkline LNG Co. (storage and regasification terminal
for liquefied natural gas)

KEY COMPETITORS

Amoco	Exxon	Sun Co.
Ashland	Koch	Tenneco
Chevron	NGC	USX–Delhi
Coastal	Occidental	Williams Cos.
Columbia Gas	Phillips	
Enron	Petroleum	
ENSERCH Corp.		

HOW MUCH

	9-Year Growth	1985	1986	1987	1988	1989	1990	1991	1992	1993	1994
Sales ($ mil.)	5.3%	2,889	2,250	1,653	1,307	2,781	2,988	2,454	2,342	2,121	4,585
Net income ($ mil.)	6.8%	125	(542)	108	(172)	58	(218)	85	187	148	225
Income as % of sales	—	4.3%	—	6.5%	—	2.1%	—	3.5%	8.0%	7.0%	4.9%
Earnings per share ($)	(6.7%)	2.83	(11.06)	2.04	(3.13)	0.82	(2.46)	0.86	1.74	1.29	1.51
Stock price – high ($)	—	41.50	50.25	34.75	27.38	30.75	29.75	16.50	19.75	27.25	25.50
Stock price – low ($)	—	32.38	24.25	18.25	21.00	20.50	10.38	9.88	12.88	16.75	18.25
Stock price – close ($)	(7.0%)	38.00	27.75	20.75	25.63	29.88	12.50	15.38	16.75	23.75	19.75
P/E – high	—	15	—	17	—	38	—	19	11	21	17
P/E – low	—	11	—	9	—	25	—	12	7	13	12
Dividends per share ($)	(10.6%)	2.31	2.23	2.00	2.00	2.00	1.40	0.80	0.80	0.80	0.84
Book value per share ($)	(10.9%)	38.42	18.93	19.40	14.06	16.21	12.80	12.32	12.65	13.88	13.65
Employees	(0.4%)	5,700	4,250	3,800	3,170	6,078	6,000	5,300	5,000	4,900	5,500

1994 Year-end:
Debt ratio: 53.8%
Return on equity: 12.2%
Cash (mil.): $33
Current ratio: 0.86
Long-term debt (mil.): $2,364
No. of shares (mil.): 149
Dividends
    Yield: 4.3%
    Payout: 55.6%
Market value (mil.): $2,945

**Stock Price History
High/Low 1985–94**

PENNZOIL COMPANY

OVERVIEW

Under the leadership of CEO James Pate, Houston-based Pennzoil has sold ailing businesses and refocused on 3 core areas: oil and gas exploration, motor oils, and Jiffy Lube oil change outlets. The company still has an interest in the sulfur business internationally but sold its domestic operations to Freeport-McMoRan in 1995.

Pennzoil owns Jiffy Lube International, the world's largest franchiser of quick lube centers with 52% of the US market. Its motor oil (which promises to act like liquid ball bearings) is the top-selling motor oil in the US. The company is taking advantage of the prominence of its market-leading brands with some strategic alliances. In 1995 it teamed up with Prestone, the #1-selling antifreeze in the

US, in a joint marketing agreement. In an arrangement with Sears it plans to expand its Jiffy Lube quick oil change operation by opening units in over half of the Sears Auto Center locations across the US (approximately 456) over the next 3 years.

The company is looking for growth in oil and exploration from major international projects. Pennzoil signed an agreement with Azerbaijan in 1994 to develop the Guneshli oil field in the Caspian Sea. Pennzoil Canada acquired Canadian oil and gas company Co-enerco Resources that year, increasing Pennzoil's presence in the North American natural gas market. Also that year the company signed contracts for oil and gas projects in Egypt and Qatar.

WHEN

The post-WWII oil boom in West Texas attracted brothers J. Hugh and Bill Liedtke and a Connecticut scion named George Bush. Eager to make their fortunes, they formed Zapata Petroleum. Zapata hit big, with more than 120 producing wells in its Jameson Field.

Zapata expanded with a subsidiary that drilled in the Gulf of Mexico. In 1959 Bush bought out the subsidiary and moved to Houston, where he later embarked on a political career that eventually took him to the White House. The Liedtkes set their sights on South Penn Oil of Oil City, Pennsylvania — a rusty relic from the 1911 dissolution of Standard Oil. Enlisting the support of J. Paul Getty, they took control of South Penn in 1963, merged it with Zapata, renamed it Pennzoil in honor of the lubricant it sold, and moved the headquarters to Houston.

In 1965 J. Hugh Liedtke engineered the historic takeover of Shreveport-based United Gas Pipeline, 5 times the size of Pennzoil. Though blessed with a large pipeline system and vast mineral interests, United Gas was hampered by lethargic management.

Using a takeover tactic that would break ground for a generation of corporate raiding, Liedtke launched a hostile cash tender offer. Pennzoil invited United Gas shareholders to sell their shares at a price higher than the market price. Shareholders tendered 5 times the number of shares that Pennzoil wanted to buy. Undaunted, the Liedtkes raised the additional funds to buy 42% of United Gas stock. They spun off a scaled-down United in 1974.

In the late 1960s Pennzoil financed speculative drilling by selling, directly to the public,

stock in subsidiary companies. Shareholders in the subsidiaries were given some security, with rights to Pennzoil stock if the risky drilling proved unsuccessful.

In 1983 J. Hugh Liedtke hoped to purchase Getty Oil, the company begun by his old benefactor, and thought he had a deal. Texaco bought Getty instead. Pennzoil sued, and in 1985 a Texas jury awarded a record $10.5 billion in damages. Texaco sought refuge in bankruptcy court, emerging after settling with Pennzoil for $3 billion.

Liedtke stepped down as CEO in 1988 but remained chairman as Pennzoil determined how to spend its booty. In 1989 Pennzoil spent $2.1 billion for 8.8% of Chevron, but Liedtke denied that his company had a takeover in mind. Chevron wasn't convinced and filed suit in 1989 to keep him at bay. Much of the suit was dismissed in 1990, and by year's end Pennzoil had increased its stake to 9.4%, just under Chevron's poison pill threshold.

In 1992 Pennzoil swapped $1.2 billion of its Chevron stock for 266 of Chevron's oil and gas properties primarily located in the Gulf of Mexico and along the Gulf Coast. The swap ended litigation between the 2 companies. Also in 1992 Pennzoil spun off filter maker Purolator, raising about $206 million.

In 1994 Pennzoil signed a joint venture agreement with Conoco to build a lube oil hydrocracker at Conoco's refinery in Louisiana. Pennzoil's weak 1994 results included a $500 million write-down on back taxes and losses on the sale of its sulfur subsidiary.

In 1995 Pennzoil teamed up with Citicorp to set up loans for lube center operators.

NYSE symbol: PZL
Fiscal year ends: December 31

WHO

Chairman, President, and CEO: James L. Pate, age 59, $830,500 pay
Group VP, Oil and Gas: Thomas M. Hamilton, age 51, $395,100 pay
Group VP Finance and Treasurer (CFO): David P. Alderson II, age 45, $290,700 pay
Group VP Accounting and Controller: Mark A. Malinski, age 39, $289,800 pay
Group VP Administration (HR): Terry Hemeyer, age 56
Group VP Products Manufacturing: William M. Robb, age 50
Group VP Products Marketing: William E. Welcher, age 62
General Counsel: James W. Shaddix, age 48, $294,900 pay
Corporate Secretary: Linda F. Condit, age 47
Auditors: Arthur Andersen & Co, SC

WHERE

HQ: Pennzoil Place, PO Box 2967, Houston, TX 77252-2967
Phone: 713-546-4000
Fax: 713-546-6639

Exploration and Production: Drilling in the US (primarily in California, Louisiana, Pennsylvania, Texas, and Utah) and in Canada, Indonesia, and Qatar.

Franchise Operations: 1,132 Jiffy Lube service centers in the US; 9 overseas.

Products: 2 refineries — Oil City, Pennsylvania, and Shreveport, Louisiana. Pennzoil motor oil and lubricants are sold in 60 countries.

Sulfur: Pennzoil operates an international sulfur business. It owns and operates a sulfur terminal in Antwerp, Belgium.

WHAT

	1994 Sales		1994 Operating Income	
	$ mil.	% of total	$ mil.	% of total
Motor oil & refined products	1,510	56	42	—
Oil & gas	834	32	(5)	—
Franchise ops.	258	10	3	—
Sulfur	72	2	(57)	—
Other	(111)	—	55	—
Total	**2,563**	**100**	**38**	**—**

Selected Brand Names
Gumout car care products
Pennzoil gasoline (7 US states)
Pennzoil motor oil and lubricants
Wolf's Head lubricants

Selected Subsidiaries
Jiffy Lube International, Inc. (quick lubrication shops)
Pennzoil Exploration and Production Co. (oil and gas)
    Pennzoil Gas Marketing Co.
Pennzoil Products Co. (refining, processing, and marketing of automotive products, industrial specialties, and motor oil)
Richland Development Corp. (real estate)
    Inco Real Estate Co.

KEY COMPETITORS

Amerada Hess	Exxon	Phillips Petroleum
Amoco	FINA	Quaker State
Ashland, Inc.	Imperial Oil	Repsol
Atlantic Richfield	Koch	Shell Oil
British Petroleum	Mobil	Sinclair Oil
Broken Hill	Norsk Hydro	Sun Company
Chevron	Occidental	Texaco
Coastal	Oryx	TOTAL
Diamond Shamrock	PDVSA	Unocal
DuPont	PEMEX	USX-Marathon
Elf Aquitaine	Petrobrás	

HOW MUCH

	9-Year Growth	1985	1986	1987	1988	1989	1990	1991	1992	1993	1994
Sales ($ mil.)	1.5%	2,239	1,889	1,809	2,274	2,215	2,367	2,685	2,357	2,782	2,563
Net income ($ mil.)	—	113	69	44	(187)	104	94	70	29	160	(284)
Income as % of sales	—	5.0%	3.7%	2.4%	—	4.7%	4.0%	2.6%	1.2%	5.8%	—
Earnings per share ($)	—	2.20	1.28	0.69	(5.22)	2.42	2.37	1.73	0.71	3.80	(6.16)
Stock price – high ($)	—	72.00	91.00	95.00	79.13	88.88	89.50	76.50	57.50	70.75	56.38
Stock price – low ($)	—	40.50	48.13	38.50	65.25	71.63	61.75	52.13	43.13	49.38	43.00
Stock price – close ($)	(4.0%)	64.00	67.00	71.00	71.75	88.63	66.00	56.38	50.00	53.38	44.13
P/E – high	—	33	71	138	—	37	38	44	81	19	—
P/E – low	—	18	38	56	—	30	26	30	61	13	—
Dividends per share ($)	3.5%	2.20	2.20	2.20	2.70	3.00	3.00	3.00	3.00	3.00	3.00
Book value per share ($)	4.1%	18.23	16.78	15.06	35.67	35.23	31.10	28.79	28.99	32.80	26.11
Employees	2.7%	8,320	6,257	6,153	10,021	6,103	7,859	8,145	9,125	9,901	10,501

1994 Year-end:
Debt ratio: 67.6%
Return on equity: —
Cash (mil.): $25
Current ratio: 1.08
Long-term debt (mil.): $2,175
No. of shares (mil.): 46
Dividends
  Yield: 6.8%
  Payout: —
Market value (mil.): $2,036

**Stock Price History
High/Low 1985–94**

RANDALL'S FOOD MARKETS, INC.

OVERVIEW

Randall's Food Markets is in good spirits these days. Not only is the company a solid 2nd behind H. E. Butt among Texas-based supermarket chains, but now Randall's sells beer and wine as well. The difficult decision to end 28 years of teetotaling shows that the chain is serious about being a grocery force beyond its home market in Houston.

The company's stores operate throughout the eastern half of Texas under the names Randalls, Tom Thumb, and Simon David. The chain, which produces its own line of private-label foods, including milk, bread, and potato chips, is known for its services (such as the use of security guards to monitor parking lots

to make customers feel safe) and was one of the first grocery store operators to allow customers to purchase goods with credit cards.

The recent acquisitions of Tom Thumb and AppleTree Market stores, which took Randall's into Austin and Dallas, have forced the company to restructure its management. Although founder Robert Onstead and his son Randall (the company's president) share a fondness for top-down management, the chain has created separate management teams for stores in the Houston, Dallas, and Austin markets and has begun delegating more authority.

The Onstead family owns 67% of Randall's; private investors own the rest.

WHEN

The first Randalls store was opened in the late 1940s by Jack Randall under the name Randall's Super Valu. At first the venture was unsuccessful, and the small chain was sold in 1964.

Robert Randall Onstead (no relation to Jack Randall) had first entered the grocery business in the mid-1950s when he went to work for his father-in-law, who owned 3 Houston grocery stores. In 1966 Onstead, Randall Barclay, and Norman Frewin, who had worked together for the Randall's Super Valu chain, founded Randall's Food Markets with 2 Randalls food stores in Houston and $85,000 in mostly borrowed money. Within 3 months sales at the 2 stores rose from $18,000 per week to $38,000 per week.

Over the next few years, Randall's opened additional stores; by 1983 there were 25, and the company's market share in Houston had risen to 11% (from 4% in 1978). Randall's had blossomed during this time because of Onstead's strategy of copying the smaller gourmet stores then becoming popular in the eastern US, placing great service above all else, and locating his stores in upper- to upper-middle-class neighborhoods. In 1984 Onstead expanded into nearby Pasadena and Galveston, and Houston market share rose to 16%.

The store count reached 29 in 1985. That year the company also introduced its first of many "Flagship" stores — upscale, specialty groceries with amenities such as coffee bars. By 1986 Randall's, with more than $600 million in annual sales, was 2nd in Houston only to Kroger. In 1987 the company debuted a "New Generation" concept store, more than tripling store size to between 70,000 and 80,000 square feet. Having saturated the up-

scale markets in Houston, Onstead decided to lure middle-income families with the new design and new locations. By 1991 the company had $1 billion in sales and, with a 21% market share and 44 stores (having taken advantage of a gutted Houston real estate market), had surpassed its main competitor.

In 1992 the company acquired Cullum Cos., the highly leveraged Dallas-based supermarket operator that ran 59 Tom Thumb, Simon David, and Page grocery/drug stores, among others, with a reputation very similar to that of Randall's. Also in 1992 Randall's embarked upon an aggressive push into the Austin area. Seven Tom Thumb stores were acquired there that year, and in 1993 the company bought 12 supermarkets from AppleTree, which was operating under Chapter 11.

In 1993 the company sold a Dallas warehouse, acquired with the Cullum purchase, to Fleming (its supplier) for more than $50 million. In 1994 Randall's began mulling alternatives to buy-one-get-one promotions, which the chain said were hurting its margins. Also in 1994, Randall's began experimenting with sales of computer software and audio books.

From the founding of Randall's Food Markets in 1966, Onstead had steadfastly refused to stock his stores with beer or wine, citing his father-in-law's alcoholism. When the company purchased Tom Thumb, however, it inherited that chain's beer and wine categories, and competition led management in 1994 to allow stores under the Randalls name to stock alcoholic beverages — in a back corner.

In 1995 the company began moving all of Tom Thumb's corporate operations to Houston but said it had no plans to eliminate the Tom Thumb name at its Dallas stores.

Private company
Fiscal year ends: June 30

WHO

Chairman and CEO: Robert R. Onstead Sr., age 63
President and COO: R. Randall Onstead Jr.
EVP Finance: Bob L. Gowens
EVP Administration (HR): Ronnie W. Barclay
SVP Merchandising and Logistics: Joseph Livorsi
SVP Operations: Tom Arledge
SVP Corporate Development: Mike Calbert
SVP Treasury and Secretary: Lee Straus
VP and Manager, Houston: John Sullivan
VP and Manager, Austin: Dale Pawlik
VP and Manager, Dallas: Mark Prestridge
Corporate VP Public Relations: Cindy Crane Garbs
Corporate VP, Randall's Properties Inc.: Joe Rollins
Corporate VP Benefits and Risk Management: Jan
  Schilmoeller
Auditors: Arthur Andersen & Co., SC

WHERE

HQ: 3663 Briarpark Dr., Houston, TX 77042
Phone: 713-268-3500
Fax: 713-268-3601

Randall's Food Markets operates more than 120
supermarkets exclusively in Texas (in Austin, Bryan/
College Station, Dallas, Fort Worth, Houston, Killeen,
Lufkin, San Marcos, and Sherman) under the names
Randalls, Simon David, and Tom Thumb.

WHAT

	1994 Stores
	No.
Randalls	67
Tom Thumb	51
Simon David	3
Total	**121**

Store Concepts
Conventional store (food and drug combination)
Flagship (upscale specialty goods, introduced 1985)
New Generation (large, open grocery stores; 70,000–
  80,000 sq. ft.; introduced 1987)

In-Store Services
Bakery
Bank
Catering
Coffee shop
Deli
Film developing
Florist
FTD and Teleflora delivery service
Gourmet counter
Pharmacies
Prepared food counter
Produce Row
Seafood market
Sushi bar (selected stores)
Ticketmaster
UPS mailing
Video rental shop

KEY COMPETITORS

Albertson's
Blockbuster
Brookshire Brothers
Brookshire Grocery
Circle K
Drug Emporium
Eckerd
Fiesta Mart
Food Lion
Gerland's Food Fair
Handy Andy Supermarkets
H. E. Butt
Hollywood Entertainment
Kmart
Kroger
Minyard Food Stores
National Convenience
Pay 'N Save
Price/Costco
Revco
Rice Food Markets
Southland
Stanley Stores
Super Club North America
United Supermarkets
Walgreen
Wal-Mart
Whole Foods Market
Winn-Dixie

HOW MUCH

	Annual Growth	1985	1986	1987	1988	1989	1990	1991	1992	1993	1994
Estimated sales ($ mil.)	16.7%	600	650	675	800	900	1,000	1,100	2,250	2,400	2,400
Estimated employees	—	—	—	—	—	—	—	7,000	16,000	18,000	21,000

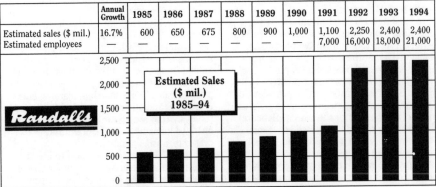

Estimated Sales
($ mil.)
1985–94

Randalls

SBC COMMUNICATIONS INC.

OVERVIEW

SBC Communications (formerly Southwestern Bell) continues to place calls outside of its traditional telephone business. Based in San Antonio, SBC has cellular operations in Boston, Chicago, Dallas/Fort Worth, St. Louis, and Washington, DC. SBC has expanded its cellular operations in Texas (Austin, El Paso, and Houston) through an alliance with GTE and purchased cellular systems in New York State (Albany, Buffalo, Glens Falls, Ithaca, Rochester, Syracuse, and Utica).

Internationally, the company has acquired a 10% stake in a national cellular carrier in France and a 40% stake in a Chilean telecommunications company. SBC also provides other telecommunications services and products and directory advertising. In 1994 nontraditional telephone operations accounted for 35% of the company's earnings.

SBC is adjusting its strategy for the future interactive television market. Even though the company tried (in vain) to sell its 2 cable systems in the Washington, DC, area, SBC has formed an alliance with Microsoft to develop the software for SBC's interactive video trial in Richardson, Texas, in late 1995. The company also formed a venture with Walt Disney and 2 other Baby Bells, Ameritech and BellSouth, to provide television programming, including on-demand videos, interactive games, and shopping over telephone lines.

In addition, SBC provides voice messaging services called CallNotes in selected markets and has introduced its own VISA credit card.

WHEN

Southwestern Bell was once an arm of AT&T, providing local communications services in its present region. Telephone service first arrived in Southwestern Bell territory in 1878, just 2 years after the telephone was invented. One man responsible for early growth of telephony in this region was George Durant, who located 12 customers for St. Louis's first telephone exchange. This grew into Bell Telephone Company of Missouri.

Meanwhile, the Missouri and Kansas Telephone Company had also been established. The first president of Southwestern Bell, Eugene Nims, negotiated the merger of Missouri and Kansas and Southwestern Bell into the Southwestern Telephone System around 1912. Southwestern Bell became part of AT&T in 1917; Nims served as president from 1919 to 1929. After WWII, demand for new telephone lines grew rapidly. By 1945 Southwestern Bell was providing service to one million telephones; by the 1980s this number had grown nearly tenfold.

In 1983 AT&T was split from the Bell Operating Companies, and Southwestern Bell became a separate legal entity; it began operations in 1984. At the time of the breakup, Southwestern Bell received local phone service rights in 5 states, Southwestern Bell Mobile Systems (cellular service provider), the directory advertising business, and a 1/7 share in Bell Communications Research (Bellcore), the R&D arm shared by the Bell companies. The company set up its telecommunications and publishing groups later.

Southwestern Bell concentrated much of its diversification effort in mobile communica-

tions. The company purchased operations from Metromedia (1987), which included paging in 19 cities and 6 major cellular franchises. Southwestern Bell also bought paging assets from Omni Communications (1988).

By 1988 the company had deployed more lines than any other for an integrated voice and data phone service known as ISDN.

In 1990 Southwestern Bell joined with France Télécom and Grupo Carso (mining, manufacturing, and tobacco) to purchase 20.4% of Teléfonos de México (Telmex), the previously state-owned telephone monopoly, for a total of $1.76 billion. The company's stake in the venture represents about 10% of Telmex.

In 1993 Southwestern Bell sold a 25% (it's now up to 50%) interest in its UK cable television and telephone operations to Cox Cable; it also sold its Metromedia Paging unit. That same year Southwestern Bell and Panasonic offered a new wireless telephone called FreedomLink, which can be used as a cellular phone outside of an office and as a cordless phone inside the office. In 1994 Southwestern Bell acquired 2 Washington, DC–area cable systems from Hauser Communications for $650 million. Also in 1994 Southwestern Bell and Cox Communications canceled their planned cable TV partnership, blaming cuts in cable rates and other new regulations issued by the FCC. That same year Southwestern Bell changed its name to SBC Communications and ceased printing operations.

In 1995 SBC announced plans to invest $90 million in South African cellular provider MTN. SBC will own 15.5% of the company.

NYSE symbol: SBC
Fiscal year ends: December 31

WHO

Chairman and CEO: Edward E. Whitacre Jr., age 53, $1,952,000 pay
President, Southwestern Bell Operations: Royce S. Caldwell, age 56, $695,100 pay
President, SBC Operations: Charles E. Foster, age 58, $607,600 pay
SEVP External Affairs: William E. Dreyer, age 56, $628,500 pay
SEVP and General Counsel: James D. Ellis, age 51
SVP Corporate Communications: Linda S. Mills, age 44
SVP Strategic Planning and Corporate Development: James S. Kahan, age 47
SVP Federal Relations: Thomas M. Barry, age 50
SVP, Treasurer, and CFO: Donald E. Kiernan, age 54
SVP Human Resources: Cassandra C. Carr, age 50
President and CEO, Mobile Systems: Stan Sigman
President and CEO, Southwestern Bell Yellow Pages: R. McRae Geschwind, age 53
President and CEO, Telecom: Dick G. Boerger, age 54
President and CEO, SBC International Operations: John H. Atterbury III, age 46
Auditors: Ernst & Young LLP

WHERE

HQ: 175 E. Houston, San Antonio, TX 78205-2233
Phone: 210-821-4105
Fax: 210-351-2071

SBC Communications provides telephone services in Arkansas, Kansas, Missouri, Oklahoma, and Texas and cellular service in 61 domestic markets. The company owns interests in operations in Australia, Chile, France, Israel, Mexico, South Africa, South Korea, and the UK.

WHAT

	1994 Sales	
	$ mil.	% of total
Local service	5,788	50
Network access	2,857	25
Directory advertising	947	8
Long distance service	917	8
Other	1,110	9
Total	**11,619**	**100**

Subsidiaries and Affiliates
Associated Directory Services, Inc.
Bell Communications Research, Inc. (1/7)
SBC International, Inc. (holding company)
SBC Media Ventures, Inc. (cable TV)
SFR (10%, France)
Southwestern Bell Messaging Services (automated voice messaging services under brand name CallNotes)
Southwestern Bell Mobile Systems, Inc. (cellular phone services)
Southwestern Bell Technology Resources (research, development, and technology assessment)
Southwestern Bell Telecommunications, Inc. (communications equipment)
Southwestern Bell Telephone Company
Teléfonos de México, SA de CV (Telmex, 10%)
VTR SA (telecommunications company, 40%, Chile)

KEY COMPETITORS

Air Touch	Century Telephone	TCI
Alcatel Alsthom	Dun & Bradstreet	Teléfonos de
American Business	GTE	Chile
Information	MCI	Telephone and
Ameritech	MFS	Data Systems
AT&T	Communications	U.S. Long
Bell Atlantic	Motorola	Distance
BellSouth	NYNEX	U S WEST
BT	Pacific Telesis	WorldCom
Cable & Wireless	Sprint	

HOW MUCH

	9-Year Growth	1985	1986	1987	1988	1989	1990	1991	1992	1993	1994
Sales ($ mil.)	3.6%	8,460	7,902	8,003	7,259	8,730	9,113	9,332	10,015	10,690	11,619
Net income ($ mil.)	5.8%	996	1,023	1,047	1,013	1,093	1,101	1,157	1,302	1,282	1,649
Income as % of sales	—	11.8%	12.9%	13.1%	14.0%	12.5%	12.1%	12.4%	13.0%	12.0%	14.2%
Earnings per share ($)	5.7%	1.67	1.71	1.74	1.76	1.82	1.84	1.93	2.17	2.14	2.74
Stock price – high ($)	—	14.73	19.38	22.75	21.31	32.19	32.38	32.94	37.38	47.00	44.38
Stock price – low ($)	—	11.39	13.16	10.75	16.50	19.44	23.63	24.50	28.31	34.19	36.75
Stock price – close ($)	12.3%	14.23	18.69	17.19	20.19	31.94	28.00	32.31	37.00	41.50	40.38
P/E – high	—	9	11	13	12	18	18	17	17	22	16
P/E – low	—	7	8	6	9	11	13	13	13	16	13
Dividends per share ($)	5.3%	0.98	1.05	1.14	1.22	1.29	1.36	1.41	1.45	1.51	1.56
Book value per share ($)	1.2%	12.36	12.99	13.62	11.80	13.92	14.31	14.76	15.51	12.68	13.72
Employees	(2.1%)	71,000	61,770	67,100	64,930	66,200	66,690	61,218	59,500	58,400	58,750

1994 Year-end:
Debt ratio: 47.4%
Return on equity: 20.7%
Cash (mil.): $365
Current ratio: 0.67
Long-term debt (mil.): $5,848
No. of shares (mil.): 609
Dividends
  Yield: 3.9%
  Payout: 56.9%
Market value (mil.): $24,595

Stock Price History High/Low 1985–94

SHELL OIL COMPANY

OVERVIEW

Shell Oil's gamble to pour money into new oil exploration wells in the Gulf of Mexico (nicknamed the "Dead Sea" by some oilmen for its lack of new oil finds in the 1980s) turned out to be more than a shell game. A string of major finds in the gulf's deep waters since the late 1980s has revived Shell Oil's prospects. By 1997 these new finds are expected to bring it $1 billion a year in oil production.

Shell Oil is one of the largest petroleum refiners and crude oil and natural gas producers in the US. The Houston-based company is a subsidiary of one of the world's leading petroleum and natural gas companies (Royal Dutch/Shell Group). Shell Oil is 100%-owned by Shell Petroleum, which is owned 60% by Royal Dutch Petroleum of the Netherlands and 40% by the "Shell" Transport and Trading Company of the UK.

The company searches for, develops, produces, purchases, transports, and markets crude oil and natural gas. It also manufactures, purchases, markets, and transports oil and chemical products. The majority of Shell Oil's US production of crude oil is in California, West Texas, the Gulf of Mexico, and along the Gulf Coast. Natural gas production is concentrated in South Texas, Michigan, and along the Gulf Coast. At the end of 1994, Shell Oil had crude oil reserves of more than 1.2 billion barrels.

The company has been in the midst of a major restructuring aimed at making it the lowest-cost producer in the US.

WHEN

The Royal Dutch/Shell Group began importing gasoline from Sumatra to the US in 1912 to take advantage of the breakup of the Standard Oil trust and the expanding automobile industry. That year it formed American Gasoline in Seattle and Roxana Petroleum in Oklahoma. Refineries were established in New Orleans in 1916 and Wood River, Illinois, in 1918.

In 1922 Royal Dutch/Shell consolidated all of its US operations into a 65%-owned holding company, Shell Union Oil Co. Shell products were available nationwide by 1929. That same year the company built a refinery in Houston.

During WWII the company shared its aviation fuel technology and produced chemicals used to make synthetic rubber. Shell Oil adopted its present corporate name in 1949.

Shell Oil moved its headquarters to Houston in 1970. In 1979 the company substantially boosted its oil reserves by acquiring Belridge Oil. The Royal Dutch/Shell Group acquired 100% of Shell Oil in 1985, but shareholders sued, claiming Shell Oil's assets were undervalued in the deal. In 1990 a judge awarded the shareholders $110 million.

While other major companies fled the Gulf of Mexico, viewing it as an unproductive region, Shell and a few independent companies focused on gulf exploration. In 1987 the company set a world drilling record with an exploratory well in 7,520 feet of water in the gulf. In 1989 the company hit pay dirt in the Gulf of Mexico with its discovery of the massive 700-million-barrel Mars Field.

An explosion in 1991 at Shell Oil's Norco, Louisiana, refinery crippled production and contributed to a 39% drop in profits. In mid-1991 the company announced cuts of 10–15% in its US workforce, to be made over the next year. Stricter US environmental regulations have caused Shell Oil to reduce its activities in the US while looking overseas for new sources of oil. The company sold its 125,000-barrels-per-day refinery in Wilmington, California, in 1991 and increased its production in Syria and its exploration efforts in Yemen and China.

Shell Oil exchanged its coal mining subsidiary for a 25% interest in the purchaser, Zeigler Coal Holding, in 1992 (which it sold in 1994). That same year the company entered a joint venture with PEMEX, the Mexican national oil company, concerning Shell Oil's Deer Park, Texas, refinery; Shell Oil operates the facility while PEMEX provides supplies of crude oil. Late in 1992 Shell Oil acquired the polyester resins business of Goodyear Tire and Rubber, including its principal product, polyethylene terephthalate (PET), used in the manufacture of food containers, beverage bottles, and other packaging materials.

In 1993 Frank Richardson retired as president and was succeeded by Philip Carroll, a 32-year Shell Oil veteran. In 1994 the company began production in the Auger field off the coast of Louisiana.

By 1994 the Gulf of Mexico represented 40% of the company's net domestic production of oil and gas, even though the new finds were mostly still in the developmental stage. Shell Oil holds interests in 653 gulf tracts, including 46 acquired in 1994 alone.

In 1995, responding to US government pressure and trade sanctions, Shell pulled out of a tentative deal to develop oil fields in Iran.

NYSE symbol: SC
Fiscal year ends: December 31

President and CEO: Philip J. Carroll
President, Shell Chemical Co.: Michael H. Grasley
President, Shell Services Co.: J. P. Parrish
President, Shell Oil Products: James M. Morgan
President, Shell Exploration and Production: Jack E. Little
VP Special Assignment: L. L. Smith
VP and General Counsel: S. A. Lackey
VP Finance and CFO: P. G. Turberville
VP and General Tax Counsel: S. C. Stryker
VP Government Affairs: S. E. Ward
VP Human Resources: Bert W. Levan
Treasurer: T. M. Botts
Controller: N. J. Caruso
Corporate Secretary: J. B. Edrington
Auditors: Price Waterhouse LLP

WHERE

HQ: One Shell Plaza, Houston, TX 77002
Phone: 713-241-6161
Fax: 713-241-4044

Shell Oil operates in the US and in other countries, including Brazil, China, Syria, and Yemen. The company has 6 operating facilities, in Anacortes, Washington; Deer Park, Texas; Martinez, California; Norco, Louisiana; Odessa, Texas; and Wood River, Illinois.

1994 Net Crude and Condensate Produced

	Thou. barrels daily	% of total
Gulf of Mexico	133	33
California	133	33
Texas	48	12
Louisiana	9	2
Michigan	7	2
Other US states	25	6
Other countries	43	12
Total	**398**	**100**

1994 Wells Drilled

	No.	% of total
US	240	98
Other countries	4	2
Total	**244**	**100**

WHAT

	1994 Sales		1994 Operating Income	
	$ mil.	% of total	$ mil.	% of total
Oil	15,733	73	698	70
Chemical	4,075	19	303	30
Oil & gas exploration & production	1,490	7	(8)	—
Other	325	1	(113)	—
Adjustments	(42)	—	—	—
Total	**21,581**	**100**	**880**	**100**

Selected Subsidiaries and Affiliates
Saudi Petrochemical Co. (minority interest, Saudi Arabia)
Shell Chemical Co.
Shell Oil Products Co.
Shell Pipe Line Corp.

Selected Brand Names
EPON (epoxy resin systems)
ETD (franchise convenience stores)
KRATON (thermoplastic elastomers)
NONATEL (pulp and paper surfactants for recycled paper)
REPETE (polyester resin)
SHELLVIS (viscosity index improvers)

KEY COMPETITORS

Amoco	Lyondell Petrochemical
Ashland, Inc.	Mobil
Atlantic Richfield	Occidental
British Petroleum	Oryx
Caltex Petroleum	PDVSA
Chevron	PEMEX
Coastal	Pennzoil
Diamond Shamrock	Petrobras
Dow Chemical	Phillips Petroleum
DuPont	Quick Trip
Enron Corp.	Racetrac Petroleum
Exxon	Sun Co.
EZ Serve	Texaco
FINA	Unocal
Huntsman Chemical	USX–Marathon
Imperial Oil	YPF
Koch	

HOW MUCH

	9-Year Growth	1985	1986	1987	1988	1989	1990	1991	1992	1993	1994
Sales ($ mil.)	0.6%	20,474	17,338	21,199	21,399	21,948	24,790	22,411	21,702	21,092	21,581
Net income ($ mil.)	(12.3%)	1,650	883	1,230	1,204	1,405	1,036	20	445	781	508
Income as % of sales	—	8.1%	5.1%	5.8%	5.6%	6.4%	4.2%	0.1%	2.1%	3.7%	2.4%
Employees	(5.3%)	35,167	32,641	33,184	32,432	31,338	31,637	29,437	25,308	22,212	21,496

1994 Year-end:
Return on assets: 2.0%
Cash (mil.): $617
Current ratio: 0.85
Total assets (mil.): $26,379

Net Income
($ mil.)
1985–94

THE SOUTHLAND CORPORATION

OVERVIEW

Seller of Slurpees, Big Gulps, and more lottery tickets than any other US retailer, Dallas-based Southland Corporation owns 7-Eleven, the #1 convenience store chain in the world. Even with hundreds of store closings in recent years, the company still operates or franchises more than 5,600 US and Canadian stores under the 7-Eleven banner and other names. Through a licensing agreement, Seven-Eleven Japan runs more than 5,800 7-Elevens, while licensees in the US and 19 other countries operate more than 3,200 stores.

In 1994 the company saw its first increase in same-store merchandise sales since 1988.

That may be a sign that 7-Eleven's efforts to rejuvenate its stores are paying off. The chain's stores now offer fresh baked goods, dairy products, and fruits and vegetables in an attempt to snag working customers who want healthy basics for their families at reasonable prices but don't have time to spend at the supermarket. The company has also been improving the lighting inside and outside its stores and has been installing new security systems. New store openings are expected to exceed closings by 1997.

Japanese retailer Ito-Yokado owns 64% of Southland's stock.

WHEN

Claude Dawley, son of an ice company pioneer, formed the Southland Ice Company in Dallas in 1927 to buy 4 other Texas ice plant operations. Ice was both a rare commodity and a basic necessity during Texas summers for storing and transporting food and, especially, beer. Dawley was backed in his bid by Chicago utility magnate Martin Insull.

One of the ice operations Dawley bought was Consumers Ice, where a young employee, Joe Thompson, had made the firm some money with his idea of selling chilled watermelons off the truck docks.

After the Dawley enterprise was underway, an ice dock manager in Dallas began stocking a few food items for customers. He demonstrated the idea to Thompson, who was by then running the ice operation, and the practice was adopted at all company locations.

Thompson promoted the grocery operations by calling them Tote'm Stores and erecting Alaska-made totem poles by the docks. In 1928 he arranged for the construction of gas stations at some stores.

Insull bought out Dawley in 1930, and Thompson became president. He expanded Southland's operations even as the Depression-hurt company operated briefly under the direction of bankruptcy court (1932–34). It began a dairy, Oak Farms, to meet its needs as the largest dairy retailer in the Dallas–Fort Worth area (1936). By 1946 the company had bought other Texas ice-retail operations, changed its name to the Southland Corporation, and adopted for its stores the name 7-Eleven, a reference to its store hours.

After Thompson died in 1961, his eldest son, John, became president and opened new stores in Colorado, New Jersey, and Arizona in 1962 and in Utah, California, and Missouri in

1963. The company purchased Gristede Brothers (1968), a New York grocer; Baricini Stores (1969), a candy chain; and Hudgins Truck Rental (1971; sold in 1980).

Southland franchised the 7-Eleven format in the UK (1971) and in Japan (1973). In 1983 the company purchased Citgo, a gasoline refining and marketing business, later selling 50% of the company to Petróleos de Venezuela, a Venezuelan oil company (1986).

In 1988 John Thompson and his 2 brothers borrowed heavily to buy 70% of Southland's stock in an LBO. The company defaulted on $1.8 billion in publicly traded debt in mid-1990. Southland filed for bankruptcy protection that year; the company persuaded bondholders to restructure its debt and take 25% of the company stock, clearing the way for the purchase of 70% of Southland in 1991 by its Japanese partner, Ito-Yokado.

In 1992 the company contracted with Wal-Mart's McLane subsidiary to provide wholesale distribution services to its stores and sold to McLane 2 distribution centers and 3 food processing plants. From 1991 through 1993 the company closed about 600 underperforming 7-Elevens. In 1993 Southland realized its first annual profit since 1986.

In 1994 Southland broke off relations with the National Coalition of Associations of 7-Elevens, a franchisee group. That year, 9 7-Eleven franchisees sued the company for more than $1 billion on charges of fraud and breach of contract, claiming that Southland had not spent enough money on store maintenance and remodeling, advertising, and other services.

Southland opened 18 stores and closed 184 in 1994; the company planned to close another 150 stores in 1995.

Nasdaq symbol: SLCMC
Fiscal year ends: December 31

WHO

Chairman: Masatoshi Ito, age 70
VC: Toshifumi Suzuki, age 62
President and CEO: Clark J. Matthews II, age 58, $567,840 pay
EVP and COO: Stephen B. Krumholz, age 45, $383,980 pay
SVP Distribution and Foodservice: Rodney A. Brehm, age 47, $259,280 pay
SVP Finance: James W. Keyes, age 39
VP and Controller: Vernon P. Lotman, age 55
VP and General Counsel: Bryan F. Smith Jr., age 42
VP Human Resources: David M. Finley, age 54
Auditors: Coopers & Lybrand L.L.P.

WHERE

HQ: 2711 N. Haskell Ave., Dallas, TX 75204-2906
Phone: 214-828-7011
Fax: 214-822-7848

	1994 Owned/Franchised Stores	
	No.	% of total
California	1,196	21
Virginia	639	11
Florida	447	8
Maryland	346	6
Texas	308	5
Washington	253	5
Colorado	244	4
New York	222	4
New Jersey	203	4
Nevada	187	3
Pennsylvania	174	3
Illinois	151	3
Oregon	137	3
Other states	662	12
Canada	461	8
Total	**5,630**	**100**

WHAT

	1994 Stores – US and Canada	
	No.	% of total
Franchised	2,962	53
Company-operated	2,668	47
Total	**5,630**	**100**

	1994 Stores – US and Canada	
	No.	% of total
7-Eleven	5,541	98
Quik Mart/Super-7	51	1
High's Dairy Stores	38	1
Total	**5,630**	**100**

	1994 Sales
	% of total
Gasoline	24
Tobacco products	17
Groceries	10
Beer/wine	9
Soft drinks	9
Food service	8
Nonfoods	6
Dairy products	5
Baked goods	4
Candy	4
Customer services	2
Health/beauty aids	2
Total	**100**

KEY COMPETITORS

Albertson's	Exxon	Shell Oil
American Stores	Kroger	Sun Co.
Atlantic Richfield	Mobil	Texaco
British Petroleum	National	Thrifty Oil
Chevron	Convenience	Unocal
Circle K	Publix	Wal-Mart
Cumberland	QuikTrip	Wawa
Farms	Safeway	Winn-Dixie

HOW MUCH

	Annual Growth	1985	1986	1987	1988	1989	1990	1991	1992	1993	1994
Sales ($ mil.)	(2.7%)	—	7,783	8,076	7,950	8,275	8,348	8,010	7,426	6,814	6,760
Net income ($ mil.)	(9.3%)	—	200	(60)	(216)	(1,251)	(302)	(74)	(131)	99	92
Income as % of sales	—	—	2.6%	—	—	—	—	—	—	1.3%	1.4%
Earnings per share ($)	—	—	—	—	—	—	—	(0.22)	(0.32)	0.21	0.22
Stock price – high ($)	—	—	—	—	—	—	—	3.03	4.25	7.69	6.75
Stock price – low ($)	—	—	—	—	—	—	—	0.94	1.19	2.97	3.81
Stock price – close ($)	33.8%	—	—	—	—	—	—	1.88	3.03	6.75	4.50
P/E – high	—	—	—	—	—	—	—	—	—	37	31
P/E – low	—	—	—	—	—	—	—	—	—	14	17
Dividends per share ($)	—	—	—	—	—	—	—	0.00	0.00	0.00	0.00
Book value per share ($)	—	—	—	—	—	—	—	(2.95)	(3.22)	(3.05)	(2.82)
Employees	(9.4%)	—	67,174	65,800	50,724	48,114	45,665	42,616	35,646	32,406	30,417

1994 Year-end:
Debt ratio: 100.0%
Return on equity: —
Cash (mil.): $59
Current ratio: 0.44
Long-term debt (mil.): $2,227
No. of shares (mil.): 410
Dividends
  Yield: —
  Payout: —
Market value (mil.): $1,845

Stock Price History High/Low 1991–94

SOUTHWEST AIRLINES CO.

OVERVIEW

For several years Southwest Airlines's successful low-cost, on-time, no-frills, no-allocated seats, no-meals approach to air travel has helped the company fly high above its competitors with hefty profit gains. In contrast with the industry as a whole, which has lost billions of dollars, Southwest's lean, mean flying machine has carved out 22 consecutive years of profits and has risen to become the #8 US airline.

However, its days of flying solo may be over. USAir, Continental, United, and Delta are muscling into the low-frills, short-haul market. In particular, United's shuttle service in the West (introduced in October 1994) is taking a bite out of the company's profits. Starting with 184, United increased its daily flights to 304 by the end of the year. Continental gave

over about half of its 2,000 flights to low-fare, short-haul operations (but recently made plans to pull out of its "Continental Lite" strategy, which had cost the carrier millions of dollars and led to the exit of its CEO). Competitors have also resorted to electronic warfare. Citing Southwest's refusal to pay for service, 3 airline reservation systems partially owned by rivals bumped Southwest off their computer systems, making it more difficult for travel agents to write tickets for Southwest.

The company, which operates a fleet of 199 Boeing 737s, acquired Morris Air in 1994. The Salt Lake City–based carrier (also a Boeing 737 operator) had a strong route system in the Pacific Northwest. The acquisition gave the company more planes to counter the United shuttle incursion in the West.

WHEN

Texas businessman Rollin King and lawyer Herb Kelleher founded Air Southwest Company in 1967 as an intrastate airline, linking Dallas, Houston, and San Antonio. Braniff and Texas International sued the company, questioning whether the region needed another airline, but the Texas Supreme Court ruled in Southwest's favor. In 1971 the company (renamed Southwest Airlines) made its first scheduled flight, from Dallas Love Field to San Antonio.

Capitalizing on its home base at Love Field, Southwest adopted love as the theme of its early ad campaigns, complete with stewardesses wearing hot pants and serving love potions (drinks) and love bites (peanuts). To curb maintenance costs, the airline uses only fuel-efficient Boeing 737s. When other airlines moved to the Dallas–Fort Worth (D/FW) airport in 1974, Southwest stayed at Love Field, gaining a virtual monopoly at the airfield. This monopoly proved to be limiting, however, with adoption of the Wright Amendment in 1979. This federal law prevents airlines operating out of Love Field from providing direct service to states other than those neighboring Texas. Southwest's customers can fly from Love Field to New Mexico, Oklahoma, Arkansas, and Louisiana but must buy new tickets and board different Southwest flights to points beyond.

When Lamar Muse, Southwest's president, resigned in 1978 because of differences with King, Kelleher became president. Muse later took over his son Michael's nearly bankrupt airline, Muse Air Corporation, and in 1985 sold it to Southwest. Kelleher operated the

Houston-based airline as TranStar but liquidated it in 1987.

Regarded as something of an industry maverick, Kelleher went on to introduce advance-purchase "Fun Fares" in 1986 and a frequent-flyer program based on the number of flights rather than mileage in 1987. He often stars in Southwest's unconventional TV commercials, and, when Southwest became the official airline of Sea World (Texas) in 1988, Kelleher had a 737 painted to resemble Shamu, the park's killer whale.

Southwest established an operating base at Phoenix Sky Harbor Airport in 1990. The airline continues to add destinations, especially on the West Coast, with service to Oakland and Indianapolis (1989), Burbank and Reno (1990), Sacramento (1991), San Jose (1993), and Spokane (1994).

In 1992 Southwest assumed the leased operations of Northwest Airlines at Chicago Midway Airport and Detroit Metropolitan Airport and in 1993 initiated service to Baltimore, its first East Coast destination. The airline also won the first annual Triple Crown for the best on-time performances, best baggage handling record, and best customer satisfaction in 1992 (winning again in 1993). In 1994 the company acquired Morris Air in a stock swap.

In 1995 Southwest launched a "ticketless" travel system to trim travel agent commissions and announced that it would begin flights to Ft. Lauderdale, Orlando, and Tampa in 1996. The company is also using a new computer reservation system for automated booking of passengers.

NYSE symbol: LUV
Fiscal year ends: December 31

WHO

Chairman, President, and CEO: Herbert D. Kelleher, age 63, $567,000 pay
EVP and COO: Gary A. Barron, age 50, $322,209 pay
EVP Customers and Corporate Secretary: Colleen C. Barrett, age 50, $305,361 pay
EVP Corporate Services: John G. Denison, age 50, $300,754 pay
VP and General Counsel: James F. Parker, age 48, $240,680 pay
VP Finance and CFO: Gary C. Kelly, age 39
VP Governmental Affairs: Ron Ricks, age 45
VP Ground Operations: James C. Wimberly, age 42
VP People: Elizabeth P. Sartain, age 40
Auditors: Ernst & Young LLP

WHERE

HQ: PO Box 36611, Love Field, Dallas, TX 75235-1611
Phone: 214-904-4000
Fax: 214-904-4200
Reservations: 800-435-9792

Cities Served

Albuquerque	Houston	Orange County
Amarillo	Indianapolis	Phoenix
Austin	Kansas City	Portland
Baltimore	Las Vegas	Reno
Birmingham	Little Rock	Sacramento
Boise	Los Angeles	St. Louis
Burbank	Louisville	Salt Lake City
Chicago	Lubbock	San Antonio
Cleveland	Midland	San Diego
Columbus	Nashville	San Francisco
Corpus Christi	New Orleans	San Jose
Dallas	Oakland	Seattle
Detroit	Oklahoma City	Spokane
El Paso	Omaha	Tucson
Harlingen	Ontario	Tulsa

WHAT

	1994 Sales	
	$ mil.	% of total
Passengers	2,498	96
Freight	54	2
Other	40	2
Total	**2,592**	**100**

Services
The Company Club (frequent-flyer program based on trips rather than mileage)

1994 Flight Equipment	No.	Orders & Options
Boeing 737-30	124	66
Boeing 737-200	50	—
Boeing 737-500	25	—
Boeing 737-700	—	126
Total	**199**	**192**

1994 Statistics	No. (bil.)
Revenue passengers carried	42.7
Revenue passenger miles	21.6
Available seat miles	32.1

KEY COMPETITORS

Alaska Air
America West
AMR
Continental Airlines
Delta
Mesa Air
Midwest Express
Northwest Airlines
Reno Air
TWA
UAL
USAir
ValuJet Airlines

HOW MUCH

	9-Year Growth	1985	1986	1987	1988	1989	1990	1991	1992	1993	1994
Sales ($ mil.)	16.0%	680	769	778	860	1,058	1,237	1,379	1,803	2,297	2,592
Net income ($ mil.)	16.0%	47	50	20	58	75	51	33	97	154	179
Income as % of sales	—	7.0%	6.5%	2.6%	6.7%	7.0%	4.1%	2.4%	5.4%	6.7%	6.9%
Earnings per share ($)	15.3%	0.34	0.34	0.14	0.41	0.54	0.39	0.25	0.68	1.05	1.22
Stock price – high ($)	—	6.89	6.11	5.61	4.64	6.83	6.67	11.67	19.92	37.63	39.00
Stock price – low ($)	—	4.72	4.06	2.61	2.92	4.36	4.25	5.45	10.80	18.13	15.50
Stock price – close ($)	12.1%	5.97	4.58	2.97	4.50	5.33	5.83	11.38	19.67	37.38	16.75
P/E – high	—	20	18	40	11	13	17	47	29	36	32
P/E – low	—	14	12	19	7	8	11	22	16	17	13
Dividends per share ($)	3.7%	0.03	0.03	0.03	0.03	0.03	0.03	0.03	0.04	0.04	0.04
Book value per share ($)	11.6%	3.21	3.53	3.65	4.03	4.47	4.78	4.96	6.16	7.38	8.65
Employees	13.8%	5,271	5,819	5,765	6,467	7,760	8,620	9,778	11,397	15,175	16,818

1994 Year-end:
Debt ratio: 32.4%
Return on equity: 15.6%
Cash (mil.): $175
Current ratio: 0.60
Long-term debt (mil.): $583
No. of shares (mil.): 143
Dividends
  Yield: 0.2%
  Payout: 3.3%
Market value (mil.): $2,400

**Stock Price History
High/Low 1985–94**

STAR ENTERPRISE

OVERVIEW

Despite the cyclical nature of the oil business, Star Enterprise hopes to keep its star on the rise through joint projects with a variety of fast-food chains. Star Enterprise is a joint venture between Texaco and the state-owned Saudi Arabian Oil Company (Saudi Aramco, the world's largest crude oil producer).

With 1,400 outlets, it is the 6th largest branded gasoline retailer in the US (ranked by outlets) and #2 in market share in its operating area. Based in Houston, Star also acts as Texaco's refining and marketing arm for 8,100 independently owned Texaco-brand retail out-

lets in 26 states in the eastern and southern US and in the District of Columbia. As part of the joint venture agreement, Saudi Aramco provides crude oil for Star's 3 refineries, which produce gasoline, home heating oil, petrochemical feedstocks, and other petroleum-related products.

Star Enterprise is riding the growing trend of combining gasoline sales with branded fast-food sales. By mid-1995 the company had formed marketing alliances with Baskin-Robbins, McDonald's, and a number of other fast-food chains.

WHEN

Texaco and Saudi Aramco had been doing business together in various ventures since 1936, but they had never tried anything on the scale of the joint venture signed in London by Texaco CEO James Kinnear and Saudi oil minister Hisham Nazer in late 1988. The deal, valued at nearly $2 billion, was the largest joint venture of its kind in the US.

The agreement to create Star Enterprise sprang, in part, from Texaco's tumultuous ride following its acquisition of Getty Oil in 1984. After acquiring Getty, Texaco was sued by Pennzoil for preempting Pennzoil's bid for Getty. A Texas court ordered Texaco to pay Pennzoil $10.5 billion in 1985, the largest damage award ever. After losing an appeal, Texaco filed for bankruptcy in 1987 and eventually settled with Pennzoil for $3 billion.

In 1988 Texaco emerged from bankruptcy after announcing a reorganization. However, corporate raider Carl Icahn had begun buying up Texaco's stock in a bid to take control of the company. Icahn wanted 5 seats on Texaco's board, but he was narrowly defeated in a proxy vote after Texaco's management announced the deal with Saudi Aramco at a stockholder meeting.

Texaco got a much needed injection of cash, and Saudi Aramco got a steady US outlet for its supply of crude. The Saudis had been at odds with their OPEC partners for several years, and in late 1985 Saudi oil minister Sheikh Yamani and Saudi Aramco began increasing production, leading to an oil price crash in 1986. Nazer replaced Yamani and changed Saudi Aramco's strategy. In order to secure market share, the Saudis began signing long-term supply contracts.

The deal with Texaco gave Saudi Aramco a 50% interest in Texaco's refining and marketing operations in the East and on the Gulf

Coast — about 2/3 of Texaco's US downstream operations — including 3 refineries and its Texaco-brand stations. In return the Saudis paid $812 million cash and provided 75% of Star's initial inventory, about 30 million barrels of oil. They also agreed to a 20-year, 600,000-barrel-a-day commitment of crude. Each company named 3 representatives to Star's management, and Donald Schmude, a Texaco VP, was named CEO.

The new company officially began operation on January 1, 1989. It soon began a modernization and expansion program, acquiring 65 stations, building 30 new outlets, and remodeling another 172 during 1989.

The company continued to upgrade its retail outlets in 1990. It made plans to spend $300 million over 5 years to build approximately 300 new System 2000 stations.

In 1992 Star settled a dispute with homeowners near a tank farm it operated with 3 other companies in Fairfax, Virginia, after an estimated 100,000 to 200,000 gallons of refined products leaked from the facility. In a settlement estimated at $200 million, Star agreed to cover cleanup costs and to pay compensation to homeowners. Also in 1992 Star completed construction of a delayed coker unit, which aids in the refining of low-grade crude, at its Port Arthur, Texas, refinery.

In 1993 Texaco and Star formed a cooperative association, Star Marketers Acceptance Corporation, to provide loans to Texaco-brand marketers.

In 1994, under new CEO Seth Sharr, Star posted lower revenues and earnings due to reduced refinery margins. Also that year the company began franchising its Texaco-brand Star Mart convenience store. By mid-1995 the company had sold 30 franchises, including 16 to retailers and 2 to wholesalers.

Joint venture
Fiscal year ends: December 31

WHO

President and CEO: Seth L. Sharr
VP Finance and CFO: William J. Mathe
VP Marketing: Joseph W. Bernitt
VP Refining: Reidar O. Fauli
Treasurer: Michael V. Carlucci
General Counsel and Secretary: Clydia J. Cuykendall
Director Public and Government Affairs: Paul B. Doucette
Manager, Atlantic Region: David H. Trautmann
Manager, Gulf Region: E. V. Don Becker
Director Human Resources: Floyd Chaney
Auditors: Arthur Andersen & Co, SC; Deloitte & Touche LLP

WHERE

HQ: 12700 Northborough Dr., Houston, TX 77067-2508
Phone: 713-874-7000
Fax: 713-874-7760 (public relations)

Star operates refineries in Convent, Louisiana; Delaware City, Delaware; and Port Arthur, Texas. It sells its products in Texaco-brand stations in the eastern and southern US.

WHAT

	1994 Retail Outlets Served	
	No.	% of total
Independently owned	8,100	85
Company owned & leased	1,400	15
Total	**9,500**	**100**

	1994 Sales	
	Barrels (mil.)	% of total
Gasoline	123.4	76
Middle distillate	39.4	24
Total	**162.8**	**100**

Selected Fast-Food Joint Venture Partners
Baskin-Robbins
Burger King
Dunkin' Donuts
Manhattan Bagel
McDonald's
Subway

Refinery Products
Asphalt
Aviation fuel
Butane
Diesel fuel
Gasoline
Home heating oil
Lubricant base oils
Natural gas liquids
Petrochemical feedstocks
Propane

KEY COMPETITORS

Amoco
Ashland, Inc.
British Petroleum
Circle K
Coastal
Cumberland Farms
Dairy Mart
Diamond Shamrock
DuPont
Exxon
EZ Mart
E-Z Serve
FINA
FFP Partners
Kerr-McGee
Maverick Markets
Mobil
National Convenience
PDVSA
Phillips Petroleum
QuikTrip
Racetrac Petroleum
Shell Oil
Southland
Sun Co.
Sunshine JR.
Uni-Marts
USX–Marathon
Wawa

HOW MUCH

	Annual Growth	1985	1986	1987	1988	1989	1990	1991	1992	1993	1994
Sales ($ mil.)	(1.3%)	—	—	—	—	6,503	8,053	7,159	6,814	6,250	6,086
Assets ($ mil.)	4.5%	—	—	—	—	3,348	3,657	3,902	4,178	4,203	4,167
Partners' equity ($ mil.)	1.3%	—	—	—	—	2,169	2,362	2,475	2,291	2,395	2,318
Employees	(10.6%)	—	—	—	—	—	—	—	5,000	5,000	4,000

1994 Year-end:
Return on capital: 4.4%
Debt ratio: 27.6%

StarEnterprise

Sales
($ mil.)
1989–94

SYSCO CORPORATION

OVERVIEW

Be it frozen or fresh, served on paper plates or china, eaten in a restaurant, hospital, or hotel, there's a lot of food out there that SYSCO helped put on the table. The Houston company is the #1 food service distributor in the US, providing products and services to 245,000 dining sites outside the home. Although SYSCO's share of the market is less than 10% — the food service industry is dominated by local operators — the company is bigger than its 6 closest competitors put together.

SYSCO's market area includes the entire United States, Mexico, and the Pacific Coast region of Canada. The company distributes frozen foods, canned and dry goods, fresh meat and produce, imported specialties, paper products, and tableware to customers including hotels, schools, industrial caterers, and hospi-

tals. Its SYGMA subsidiary services 22 restaurant chains.

A variety of brand names appear on the products SYSCO distributes, including not only national name brands but also SYSCO's Imperial, Classic, and Reliance labels. The company has introduced new brand names for its ethnic food products, with Arrezzio appearing on Italian food, the Casa Solana on Mexican food, and Jade Mountain and Imperial Dynasty on Chinese food.

Other products distributed by SYSCO include restaurant and kitchen equipment and supplies, cleaning supplies, and medical and surgical supplies. SYSCO plans to expand the number of its subsidiaries distributing medical and personal care supplies. Currently, 17 SYSCO units have medical departments.

WHEN

SYSCO was founded in 1969 when John Baugh, a Houston wholesale foods distributor, convinced the owners of 8 other US wholesalers that they should combine and form a national distribution company. Joining Baugh's Zero Foods of Houston to form SYSCO were Frost-Pack Distributing (Grand Rapids, Michigan), Louisville Grocery (Louisville, Kentucky), Plantation Foods (Miami), Thomas Foods and its Justrite subsidiary (Cincinnati), Wicker (Dallas), Houston's Food Service Company (Houston), Global Frozen Foods (New York), and Texas Wholesale Grocery (Dallas). The company went public in 1970. SYSCO, which derives its name from Systems and Services Company, benefited from Baugh's recognition of the trend toward dining out in American society. Until SYSCO was formed, food distribution to restaurants, hotels, and other nongrocers was provided almost exclusively by thousands of small, independent, regional operators.

Since SYSCO's inception the company has expanded to 96 times its original size through internal growth and the acquisitions of strong local distributors. SYSCO has ensured the success of its acquisitions through buyout agreements requiring the seller to continue managing the company and earn a portion of the sale price with future profits.

In 1988, when SYSCO was already the largest food service distributor, it purchased Olewine's, a Harrisburg, Pennsylvania, distributor. It also acquired CFS Continental, the 3rd largest food distributor at the time, for $750 million. The CFS acquisition added sev-

eral warehouses and a large truck fleet and increased the company's penetration along the West Coast of the US and Canada. In 1990 SYSCO acquired the Oklahoma City–based food service distribution business of Scrivner (renamed SYSCO Food Services of Oklahoma).

In 1991 SYSCO's Houston subsidiary pleaded guilty to one count of conspiring to rig contract bids for sales to schools in southeastern Texas. SYSCO reorganized its school-bid department and added controls to prevent any recurrences.

SYSCO acquired Collin's Foodservice and Benjamin Polakoff & Son in 1992. It also acquired Philadelphia-based Perloff Brothers, which operated Tartan Foods, and created a new subsidiary, Tartan Sysco Food Services. SYSCO sold its last remaining retail business, consumer-size frozen food distributor Global Sysco, that same year.

In 1993 SYSCO acquired St. Louis–based Clark Foodservice and New Jersey's Ritter Food Corporation.

In 1994 SYSCO announced the acquisition of Woodhaven Foods, a distributor owned by ARA (now ARAMARK), one of the nation's largest cafeteria and concession operators. Also that year, SYSCO's SYGMA unit entered a distribution agreement with 71-unit Pancho's Mexican Buffet.

SYSCO's newest distribution facilities, all scheduled to open by the end of 1995, include sites in Hartford, Connecticut; in Milwaukee, Wisconsin; and on Florida's west coast. The company had profits of $252 million in 1995 on sales of $12.1 billion.

NYSE symbol: SYY
Fiscal year ends: Saturday nearest June 30

Chairman: John F. Woodhouse, age 63, $1,015,129 pay
President and CEO: Bill M. Lindig, age 57, $886,663 pay (prior to promotion)
EVP and COO; President, Foodservice Operations: Charles H. Cotros, age 57, $701,840 pay (prior to promotion)
SVP Multi-Unit Sales; CEO, SYGMA Network, Inc.: Gregory K. Marshall, age 47, $423,195 pay
SVP, CFO, and Controller: John K. Stubblefield Jr.
SVP Merchandising Services: Richard J. Schnieders
VP Employee Relations/Management Development: Michael C. Nichols
Auditors: Arthur Andersen & Co, SC

WHERE

HQ: 1390 Enclave Pkwy., Houston, TX 77077-2099
Phone: 713-584-1390
Fax: 713-584-1245

SYSCO has 106 facilities in 38 states and 2 in Canada.

State	1994 Facilities No.
California	9
New York	9
Texas	9
Ohio	7
Pennsylvania	6
Colorado	5
Tennessee	5
Maryland	4
Michigan	4
Florida	3
Georgia	3
Massachusetts	3
Other states	39
Canada	2
Total	**108**

WHAT

Customers	1994 Sales % of total
Restaurants	60
Hospitals & nursing homes	13
Schools & colleges	7
Hotels & motels	6
Other	14
Total	**100**

Products	1994 Sales % of total
Canned & dry products	25
Fresh & frozen meats	16
Poultry	9
Dairy products	8
Paper & disposable products	7
Fresh produce	6
Seafoods	6
Beverage products	3
Equipment & smallwares	3
Janitorial products	2
Medical supplies	1
Other frozen products	14
Total	**100**

KEY COMPETITORS

Alex Lee
Alliant Foodservice
AmeriServ Food
Cagle's
Gordon Food Service
Heinz
JP Foodservice
Performance Food
Rykoff-Sexton
Services Group
US Foodservice

HOW MUCH

	9-Year Growth	1985	1986	1987	1988	1989	1990	1991	1992	1993	1994
Sales ($ mil.)	17.2%	2,628	3,172	3,656	4,385	6,851	7,591	8,150	8,893	10,022	10,942
Net income ($ mil.)	17.6%	50	58	62	80	108	133	154	172	202	217
Income as % of sales	—	1.9%	1.8%	1.7%	1.8%	1.6%	1.7%	1.9%	1.9%	2.0%	2.0%
Earnings per share ($)	16.4%	0.30	0.34	0.35	0.45	0.30	0.73	0.84	0.93	1.08	1.18
Stock price – high ($)	—	5.81	8.47	10.38	9.72	16.00	19.19	23.69	27.75	31.00	29.25
Stock price – low ($)	—	3.97	5.59	5.63	6.50	9.16	12.81	15.00	20.56	22.25	21.13
Stock price – close ($)	18.5%	5.59	7.50	6.78	9.63	15.81	16.81	23.31	26.38	29.25	25.75
P/E – high	—	19	25	30	22	53	26	28	30	29	25
P/E – low	—	13	16	16	14	31	18	18	22	21	18
Dividends per share ($)	22.9%	0.05	0.06	0.07	0.08	0.09	0.10	0.12	0.17	0.26	0.32
Book value per share ($)	14.7%	1.97	2.25	2.55	3.01	3.93	4.20	4.96	5.69	6.17	6.78
Employees	12.5%	9,100	10,700	12,000	13,000	18,700	19,600	21,000	22,500	24,200	26,200

1994 Year-end:
Debt ratio: 30.7%
Return on equity: 18.2%
Cash (mil.): $87
Current ratio: 1.89
Long-term debt (mil.): $539
No. of shares (mil.): 183
Dividends
  Yield: 1.2%
  Payout: 27.1%
Market value (mil.): $4,714

Stock Price History High/Low 1985–94

TANDY CORPORATION

OVERVIEW

One of the US's leading electronics retailers, Fort Worth–based Tandy has sold off most of its computer manufacturing operations to focus on its core retail business. But not just manufacturing has fallen by the wayside; some of Tandy's other retail operations are being discontinued as well. In 1995 the company announced plans to close all of its VideoConcepts mall stores and more than half of its McDuff electronics stores. The company is concentrating on 3 retail formats: Radio Shack, Computer City, and Incredible Universe.

The newest is Incredible Universe, a chain of "gigastores" each the size of 3 football fields, which sells an array of electronics (including appliances, cameras, and computers) and software and other accessories. The stores also offer child-care facilities, fast food, live entertainment, and a recording studio. Sales at the first 9 gigastores have grown rapidly, and Tandy plans to add 8 new stores during 1995.

Tandy is also expanding Computer City. It is adding 30 stores in 1995 to the chain, which had 1994 sales of $1.2 billion, double the previous year's sales.

Tandy still gets most of its sales from its Radio Shack chain, but the balance is shifting. Radio Shack sales accounted for 58% of 1994 company revenues, down from about 66% in 1993. Analysts see Radio Shack as an important anchor to Tandy's retailing scheme since its products tend to be less price sensitive than the higher-end products at its other 2 chains.

WHEN

During the 1950s Charles Tandy expanded his family's small Fort Worth leather business (founded in 1919) into a nationwide chain of leathercraft and hobby stores. By 1960 Tandy Corporation stock was being traded on the NYSE. In the early 1960s Tandy began to expand into other retail areas, buying Leonard's, a Fort Worth department store.

In 1963 Tandy purchased Radio Shack, a nearly bankrupt electronic parts supplier with a mail-order business and 9 retail stores in the Boston area. Tandy collected part of the $800,000 owed the company and began expanding, stocking the stores with quick turnover items and putting 8–9% of sales revenue into advertising. Between 1961 and 1969 Tandy's sales grew from $16 million to $180 million, and earnings rose from $720,000 to $7.7 million, with the bulk of the growth due to the expansion of Radio Shack. Between 1968 and 1973 Tandy expanded from 172 to 2,294 stores; Radio Shack provided over 50% of Tandy's sales and 80% of earnings in 1973.

The company sold its department store operations to Dillard in 1974. The next year Tandy spun off to shareholders its leather products business as Tandy Brands and its hobby and handicraft business as Tandycrafts, focusing Tandy Corporation on the consumer electronics business. During 1976 the boom in CB radio sales pushed income up 125% as Tandy opened 1,200 stores. In 1977 it introduced the first mass-marketed personal computer, the TRS-80, which became the #1 PC on the market. In 1979, the year after Charles Tandy died, there were 5,530 McDonald's, 6,805 7-Elevens, and 7,353 Radio Shacks.

The company in 1984 introduced the Tandy 1000, the first IBM-compatible PC priced under $1,000. Since 1984 Tandy has expanded through acquisitions — Scott/McDuff and VideoConcepts in 1985, GRiD Systems in 1988, and Victor Technologies in 1990.

In 1987 Tandy spun off its foreign retail operations as InterTAN. Realizing that Radio Shack had nearly exhausted its expansion possibilities, the company focused on alternate retail formats such as GRiD Systems Centers and in 1991 opened Computer City and the Edge in Electronics. That same year Tandy announced the introduction of name-brand products into Radio Shack stores. The company also increased its manufacturing and R&D capacity and focused on such emerging technologies as digital audio recording and multimedia computing.

Tandy sold Memtek Products (magnetic tape), O'Sullivan Industries (ready-to-assemble furniture), LIKA (printed circuit boards), and its computer manufacturing and marketing operations in 1993. As part of the restructuring, Tandy scaled back 2 mall retail operations, VideoConcepts and McDuff Electronics.

In 1994 Radio Shack stores began offering repair services under the name the Repair Shop at Radio Shack. The service fixes VCRs, audio equipment, and computers that are no longer under manufacturer warranty.

The company announced plans in 1995 to sell its credit card business to SPS Services — a subsidiary of Dean Witter, Discover — for $710 million. Also in 1995 Radio Shack introduced an expanded in-store catalog for hard-to-find electronic equipment and parts.

NYSE symbol: TAN
Fiscal year ends: December 31

WHO

Chairman, President, and CEO: John V. Roach, age 56,
$1,050,028 pay
President, Radio Shack: Leonard H. Roberts, age 46,
$814,291 pay
President, Computer City: Alan C. Bush
SVP and Secretary: Herschel C. Winn, age 63,
$389,670 pay
SVP, Tandy Retail Services: Robert M. McClure, age 59,
$360,023 pay
SVP and CFO: Dwain H. Hughes, age 47
VP and General Manager, Incredible Universe: Rich
Hollander
VP and Controller: Richard L. Ramsey, age 49
VP Law and Assistant Secretary: Frederick W. Padden,
age 62
VP and Treasurer: Loren K. Jensen
VP Tax: Mark W. Barfield, age 37
VP Corporate Relations: Lou Ann Blaylock, age 56
VP Corporate Development: Ronald L. Parrish, age 52
VP Human Resources: George Berger
Auditors: Price Waterhouse LLP

WHERE

HQ: 1800 One Tandy Center, Fort Worth, TX 76102
Phone: 817-390-3700
Fax: 817-390-3500

Tandy operates or franchises more than 6,600 Radio
Shacks throughout the US; operates 69 Computer
City stores in the US, Canada, and Europe; and has 9
Incredible Universe stores in the US. The company also
operates 15 distribution centers and 128 service centers
in the US. Tandy has 9 manufacturing plants in the US
and 2 manufacturing plants in China and Taiwan.

WHAT

	1994 Retail Outlets
	No.
Radio Shack	
Company-owned	4,598
Dealer/franchise	2,005
Tandy Name Brand Retail Group	
VideoConcepts (mall stores)	219
McDuff Supercenters	71
The Edge in Electronics	16
Computer City SuperCenters	69
Incredible Universe	9
Total	**6,987**

	1994 Sales
	% of total
Consumer electronics	45
Electronic parts, accessories & specialty equipment	36
PCs, peripherals, software & accessories	12
Other	7
Total	**100**

KEY COMPETITORS

Anam Group	Future Shop	Office Depot
Barnes & Noble	Gateway 2000	Office Max
Best Buy	Good Guys	Philips
CDW Computer	InaCom	Price/Costco
Centers	Intelligent	Sears
Circuit City	Electronics	Service
CompuCom	J & R Music	Merchandise
CompUSA	Kmart	Sharper Image
Dell	Matsushita	Staples
Egghead	MicroAge	Sun Television &
ELEK-TEK	Micro Warehouse	Appliances
Entex	Montgomery	Tiger Direct
Fretter	Ward	Vanstar
Fry's Electronics	NeoStar	Wal-Mart

HOW MUCH

	9-Year Growth	1985	1986	1987	1988	1989	1990	1991	1992	1993	1994
Sales ($ mil.)	6.3%	2,841	3,036	3,452	3,794	4,181	4,500	4,562	4,680	4,103	4,944
Net income ($ mil.)	1.6%	189	198	242	316	324	290	206	184	84	218
Income as % of sales	—	6.7%	6.5%	7.0%	8.3%	7.7%	6.5%	4.5%	3.9%	2.1%	4.4%
Earnings per share ($)	3.6%	2.11	2.22	2.70	3.54	3.64	41.13	36.50	31.75	1.01	2.91
Stock price – high ($)	—	42.13	45.00	56.50	48.63	48.75	41.13	36.50	31.75	50.75	50.63
Stock price – low ($)	—	24.00	30.50	28.00	31.50	37.00	23.50	23.38	22.25	24.63	30.75
Stock price – close ($)	2.3%	40.75	42.50	33.00	41.00	39.13	29.25	28.88	29.75	49.50	50.00
P/E – high	—	20	20	21	14	13	12	14	14	50	17
P/E – low	—	11	14	10	9	10	7	9	10	24	11
Dividends per share ($)	—	0.00	0.00	0.25	0.55	0.60	0.60	0.60	0.60	0.60	0.63
Book value per share ($)	7.3%	12.00	14.57	15.38	18.10	20.13	21.78	23.56	22.17	22.22	22.66
Employees	3.0%	35,000	36,000	39,000	37,000	38,000	40,000	40,000	37,000	42,000	45,800

1994 Year-end:
Debt ratio: 19.6%
Return on equity: 15.9%
Cash (mil.): $206
Current ratio: 2.12
Long-term debt (mil.): $153
No. of shares (mil.): 58
Dividends
  Yield: 1.3%
  Payout: 21.6%
Market value (mil.): $2,913

**Stock Price History
High/Low 1985–94**

TEMPLE-INLAND INC.

OVERVIEW

Far from worshiping insularity, Temple-Inland is a rapidly expanding company with a goal to develop a strong presence in Mexico and South America. The Diboll-based holding company has major interests in paper, packaging, building products, and financial services. Temple-Inland operates 7 containerboard mills, one bleached paperboard mill, 43 corrugated box plants, 5 lumber mills, and 7 building products plants in the US. The company also operates 2 corrugated container plants in Mexico and one in Argentina. It owns or leases approximately 1.36 million acres of timberland in Louisiana and Texas and 530,000 acres in Alabama and Georgia.

Approximately 46% of the company's operating earnings come from the manufacture of building products (including gypsum items, hardboard paneling, lumber, particleboard,

and plywood). Corrugated container products account for 35% of operating earnings.

Temple-Inland also runs a number of financial institutions. Headquartered in Dallas, its Guaranty Federal Bank (with 123 branches in major Texas cities) is the 5th largest financial institution in Texas. Other financial subsidiaries include Temple-Inland Mortgage Corp., Lumbermen's Investment Corp. (real estate), and Timberline Insurance.

The recovery of pulp prices in 1993 lifted industry shipments of corrugated containers by 5.4% in 1994, exceeding the growth rate of the US economy. Although the market began to go soft in 1995, the firm is confident that containerboard and boxes will hold steady.

In late 1994 the company announced a joint venture with Massuh S.A., of Buenos Aires, to make corrugated containers in Argentina.

WHEN

The company's origins date back to 1893 when Thomas Temple, a native of Virginia who had migrated to Texarkana, purchased 7,000 acres of Texas timberland from J. C. Diboll. Temple founded the Southern Pine Lumber Co. and built his mill in the town of Diboll (107 miles north of Houston and on the H. E. & W. T. railway). In 1894 he opened his first sawmill. In 1903 the company set up its 2nd sawmill and in 1907 a hardwood mill. In 1910 Temple formed the Temple Lumber Company.

In 1934 the Temple company began using trucks in its logging operations in Diboll. That year Temple died, and his son Arthur inherited a company that was $2 billion in debt. In 1937 one of its sawmills (at Hemphill) was destroyed by fire.

In the housing boom that followed WWII, Southern Pine Lumber produced basic hardwood and pine lumber items for the construction and furniture industries. By the early 1950s, the company had moved into the new technology of converting chips, sawdust, and shavings to profitable panel products for the manufacture of fiberboard sheathing. It subsequently pioneered the early research and development of southern pine plywood manufacture and branched into the manufacture of particleboard, gypsum wallboard, and other building materials. Southern Pine Lumber and Temple merged in 1956 under the Southern Pine corporate name.

In 1962 Southern Pine moved into finance with the purchase of the controlling interest of Lumbermen's Investment Corp., of Austin.

The company changed its name to Temple Industries in 1964. By that year the company's land holdings had grown to 450,000 acres. Temple Industries expanded in the early 1970s, opening a particleboard mill in Diboll in 1971 and acquiring AFCO, a manufacturer of do-it-yourself products in 1972.

In 1973 Time Inc. acquired Temple and merged it with Eastex Pulp and Paper (formerly a joint venture with Houston Oil before Time bought Houston Oil's share in 1956). The company was renamed Temple-Eastex.

Time acquired Inland Container, a fully integrated packaging company, in 1978 for $272 million. Inland, which traces its roots back to 1918, when Herman Krannert started Anderson Box Co. in Indiana, made ventilated corrugated products for baby chicks. It had grown into a major manufacturer, providing packaging materials for the agricultural, horticultural, and poultry industries.

Time spun off the Temple and Inland operations to its shareholders as Temple-Inland in 1983. Temple-Inland expanded its financial businesses in the late 1980s, acquiring a Kansas insurance company in 1985 and 3 insolvent Texas S&Ls in 1988.

Temple-Inland appointed Clifford Grum as chairman and CEO (the first nonfamily chairman in the history of the company) in 1991, following the retirement of Arthur Temple Jr.

In 1994 the company bought Rand-Whitney Packaging for $57.5 million, and in 1995 it launched Inland-Chile, a joint venture box manufacturing plant in Chile.

NYSE symbol: TIN
Fiscal year ends: Last Saturday in December

Chairman and CEO: Clifford J. Grum, age 60,
$803,000 pay
Group VP, Building Products: Harold C. Maxwell,
age 54, $508,000 pay
Group VP; Chairman and CEO, Inland Container Corp.:
William B. Howes, age 57, $500,625 pay
**CFO; President and COO, Temple-Inland Financial
Services:** Kenneth M. Jastrow II, age 47, $450,000 pay
Group VP, Bleached Paperboard: David L. Ashcraft,
age 49, $318,000 pay
VP, General Counsel, and Secretary: M. Richard
Warner, age 43
VP and Chief Accounting Officer: David H. Dolben,
age 59
Treasurer: David W. Turpin, age 44
VP Human Resources: Herb George
Auditors: Ernst & Young LLP

WHERE

HQ: 303 S. Temple Dr., Diboll, TX 75941
Phone: 409-829-2211
Fax: 409-829-1366

Temple-Inland operates 7 containerboard mills, one
bleached paperboard mill, 43 corrugated box plants, 5
lumber mills, and 7 building products plants in the US.
The company also operates 2 corrugated container
plants in Mexico and one in Argentina.

	1994 Owned and Leased Timberland	
	Acres (thou.)	% of total
Louisiana & Texas	1,360	72
Alabama & Georgia	530	28
Total	**1,890**	**100**

WHAT

	1994 Sales	
	$ mil.	% of total
Corrugated containers	1,438	49
Financial services	631	21
Building products	549	19
Bleached paperboard	299	10
Other	21	1
Total	**2,938**	**100**

Selected Products

Corrugated Containers	Plywood
	Retail distribution
Financial Services	Rigid foam insulation
Building Products	**Bleached Paperboard**
Fiber products	Market pulp
Gypsum wallboard	Nodular pulp
Particleboard	Paperboard
Pine lumber	

Selected Subsidiaries

Guaranty Federal Bank
Inland Container Corp.
Lumbermen's Investment Corp.
Temple-Inland Forest Products Corp.
Temple-Inland Mortgage Corp.
Timberline Insurance Managers Inc.

KEY COMPETITORS

Aancor	Mead
Boise Cascade	National Gypsum
Canadian Pacific	Plum Creek Timber
Champion International	Rayonier
Fletcher Challenge	Stone Container
Georgia-Pacific	USG
International Paper	Weyerhaeuser
Jefferson Smurfit	Willamette
Louisiana-Pacific	

HOW MUCH

	9-Year Growth	1985	1986	1987	1988	1989	1990	1991	1992	1993	1994
Sales ($ mil.)	10.0%	1,243	1,329	1,610	2,099	2,124	2,401	2,507	2,713	2,736	2,938
Net income ($ mil.)	4.9%	85	81	141	199	207	233	138	147	67	131
Income as % of sales	—	6.8%	6.1%	8.8%	9.5%	9.8%	9.7%	5.5%	5.4%	2.5%	4.5%
Earnings per share ($)	5.9%	1.40	1.32	2.35	3.58	3.75	4.20	2.51	2.65	1.21	2.35
Stock price – high ($)	—	17.81	23.66	34.25	28.31	35.50	38.63	51.50	57.50	52.50	56.75
Stock price – low ($)	—	12.72	16.81	17.50	20.13	23.38	24.13	28.50	43.88	37.25	43.00
Stock price – close ($)	11.1%	17.47	22.91	24.13	23.81	34.75	31.75	51.50	51.50	50.38	45.13
P/E – high	—	13	18	15	8	10	9	21	22	43	24
P/E – low	—	9	13	7	6	6	6	11	17	31	18
Dividends per share ($)	16.4%	0.26	0.29	0.34	0.42	0.58	0.80	0.88	0.96	1.00	1.02
Book value per share ($)	9.3%	14.29	15.30	16.76	19.86	22.95	26.37	27.89	29.55	30.64	31.83
Employees	4.6%	10,000	10,700	11,600	11,000	12,000	13,700	14,500	14,500	15,000	15,000

1994 Year-end:
Debt ratio: 43.9%
Return on equity: 7.5%
Cash (mil.): $315
Current ratio: 12.77
Long-term debt (mil.): $1,398
No. of shares (mil.): 56
Dividends
  Yield: 2.3%
  Payout: 43.4%
Market value (mil.): $2,528

Stock Price History
High/Low 1985–94

TENNECO INC.

OVERVIEW

Happy trails, Tenneco. The diversified, Houston-based company announced in 1995 that it will relocate to Greenwich, Connecticut, in 1996. Tenneco's operations include natural gas pipelines, shipbuilding, automotive parts, packaging, and chemicals. The 1994 sale of 56% of Case, its suffering, Wisconsin-based farm and construction equipment manufacturer, has helped Tenneco's financial picture.

Tenneco's best-known, most profitable business is gas pipelines. In the past 10 years, as federal energy regulations have changed, Tenneco has gone from being primarily a seller of the gas its pipelines transport (which made the company subject to a maze of federal regulations and tariff restrictions) to a transporter of gas to be bought and sold by others (a business subject to less regulation, which is therefore more profitable).

Tenneco's Newport News Shipbuilding and Dry Dock Co., the US's #1 privately owned shipbuilder, once specialized in nuclear submarines. With the end of the Cold War, Newport News Shipbuilding faced a declining nuclear business; to compensate it has diversified into designing, building, repairing, and overhauling conventional ships for both domestic and foreign governments and commercial entities. Tenneco's Packaging Corporation of America subsidiary is the 5th largest supplier of corrugated containers in the US.

In 1994 chairman Michael Walsh died at age 51 from brain cancer. Also in 1994 Tenneco announced a strategy to build its value by focusing on higher-return, less-cyclical businesses, including packaging, automotive parts, and nonregulated natural gas operations, and by continuing to sell its cyclical businesses.

WHEN

Tennessee Gas and Transmission began in 1943 as a division of The Chicago Corporation, headed by Gardiner Symonds and authorized to construct a 1,265-mile pipeline between the Gulf of Mexico and West Virginia. As the US faced WWII fuel shortages, the group finished the project in a record 11 months, obtaining right-of-way from thousands of landowners and crossing 67 rivers.

After WWII, Tennessee Gas went public with Symonds as president. The company expanded its pipeline and merged its oil and gas exploration interests into Tennessee Production Company (1954), which, with Bay Petroleum (bought 1955), became Tenneco Oil (1961). Symonds entered the chemical industry by acquiring 50% of Petro-Tex Chemical (1955).

In 1963 Tennessee Gas moved its headquarters to Houston and in 1966 adopted the Tenneco name. In 1967 Tenneco bought Kern County Land Company, which owned 2.5 million acres of California farmland and mineral rights. The purchase thrust Tenneco into the farming business; by 1984 Tenneco was the US's largest grower/shipper of table grapes and 2nd largest almond processor. The Kern purchase also included 2 Racine, Wisconsin–based manufacturers: J. I. Case, known for tractors and construction digging equipment, and Walker Manufacturing, which entered the automotive field in 1912 by producing jacks.

Symonds bought Packaging Corporation of America, a maker of shipping containers, pulp, and paperboard products, in 1965. In 1968 he

acquired Newport News Shipbuilding, founded by Collis Huntington in 1886. Newport News began building submarines and nuclear-powered aircraft carriers in the 1960s.

After Symonds's death in 1971, Tenneco bought shock absorber manufacturer Monroe of Monroe, Michigan (1977), and Philadelphia Life Insurance Company (1977; sold to ICH Corporation in 1986). In 1985 Tenneco bought UK chemical company Albright & Wilson (which administered all the company's chemical operations until its sale in 1995), and Case bought International Harvester's farm equipment operations. Tenneco sold its agricultural production operations in 1987 and its oil exploration and production operations in 1988.

Restructuring in the 1990s included the sale of Tenneco's natural gas liquids business to Enron ($632 million), the sale of its pulp chemicals business to Sterling Chemicals ($202 million), the sale of a US soda ash plant to Belgium's Solvay ($500 million), and the purchase of EnTrade Corp., a gas marketer.

As the company continued to reposition its segments (Newport News Shipbuilding, for example, raised its commercial repair business from zero contracts in 1991 to 38 contracts in 1993), it came to the conclusion that Tenneco's poorly performing farm and construction equipment company, Case, no longer fit in with its long-term plans. It sold 56% of Case stock to the public in 1994. Tenneco agreed to buy Mobil's plastics division (Hefty, Baggies) for nearly $1.3 billion in 1995.

NYSE symbol: TEN
Fiscal year ends: December 31

WHO

Chairman and CEO: Dana G. Mead, age 59,
$1,778,177 pay
CEO and President, Tenneco Gas: Stephen D.
Chesebro', age 53, $647,880 pay
**President and CEO, Newport News Shipbuilding and
Dry Dock Company:** William P. Fricks
General Counsel: Theodore R. Tetzlaff, age 50,
$700,000 pay
SVP and CFO: Robert T. Blakely, age 53, $637,640 pay
SVP Strategy: Stacy S. Dick, age 38, $578,560 pay
SVP Government Relations: John J. Castellani, age 43
SVP Corporate Affairs: Arthur H. House, age 52
SVP: Peter Menikoff, age 53
SVP Human Resources: Barry R. Schuman, age 53
VP Operations: Ilene S. Gordon, age 41
VP Investor Relations: Jack Lascar, age 40
VP Financial Analysis and Planning: Mark A. McCollum
VP: Kenneth D. Allen, age 55
Auditors: Arthur Andersen & Co, SC

WHERE

HQ: Tenneco Bldg., PO Box 2511, Houston, TX
77252-2511
Phone: 713-757-2131
Fax: 713-757-1410

	1994 Sales		1994 Operating Income	
	$ mil.	% of total	$ mil.	% of total
US	9,492	78	1,165	84
European Community	1,656	14	74	5
Canada	532	4	82	6
Other regions	494	4	72	5
Total	**12,174**	**100**	**1,393**	**100**

WHAT

	1994 Sales		1994 Operating Income	
	$ mil.	% of total	$ mil.	% of total
Farm & const. equip.	3,881	32	326	24
Nat. gas pipelines	2,378	20	415	30
Packaging	2,184	18	209	15
Automotive parts	1,989	16	223	16
Shipbuilding	1,753	14	200	15
Other & adjustments	(11)	—	6	—
Total	**12,174**	**100**	**1,379**	**100**

Selected Pipeline Concerns
Channel Industries Gas Co. (50%)
East Tennessee Natural Gas Co.
Iroquois Gas Transmission Co. (13.2%)
Kern River Gas Transmission Co. (50%)
Midwestern Gas Transmission Co.
Tennessee Gas Pipeline

Manufacturing Companies
Case Corp. (farm and construction equipment, 44%)
Newport News Shipbuilding and Dry Dock Co.
Packaging Corp. of America
Tenneco Automotive
Tenneco Gas

KEY COMPETITORS

Allied Products
AlliedSignal
American Oil and Gas
American Standard
Bath Iron Works
Borg-Warner Automotive
Coastal
Columbia Gas
Eaton
General Dynamics
Hyundai
Johnson Controls
Litton Industries
Occidental
Owens-Illinois
Panhandle Eastern
Reynolds Metals
Stone Container
USX–Delhi

HOW MUCH

	9-Year Growth	1985	1986	1987	1988	1989	1990	1991	1992	1993	1994
Sales ($ mil.)	(2.4%)	15,200	14,529	14,790	13,234	14,083	14,511	13,662	13,139	13,255	12,174
Net income ($ mil.)	10.9%	172	7	(218)	822	584	561	(732)	(612)	451	437
Income as % of sales	—	1.1%	0.0%	—	6.2%	4.1%	3.9%	—	—	3.4%	3.6%
Earnings per share ($)	14.1%	0.75	(0.40)	(1.81)	5.48	4.46	4.37	(6.09)	(4.35)	2.59	2.45
Stock price – high ($)	—	45.25	43.13	62.50	51.00	64.25	71.00	52.00	46.00	55.00	58.75
Stock price – low ($)	—	36.50	34.50	36.13	38.25	46.88	40.00	27.38	31.25	39.13	37.00
Stock price – close ($)	0.7%	39.75	38.25	39.75	48.88	62.25	47.50	31.38	40.63	52.63	42.50
P/E – high	—	60	—	—	9	14	16	—	—	21	24
P/E – low	—	49	—	—	7	11	9	—	—	15	15
Dividends per share ($)	(6.6%)	2.95	3.04	3.04	3.04	3.04	3.12	2.80	1.60	1.60	1.60
Book value per share ($)	(10.1%)	40.22	30.04	25.67	24.93	26.02	27.60	22.40	9.11	15.32	15.45
Employees	(7.5%)	111,000	101,000	104,000	94,000	90,000	92,000	89,000	79,000	75,000	55,000

1994 Year-end:
Debt ratio: 58.7%
Return on equity: 16.4%
Cash (mil.): $405
Current ratio: 1.28
Long-term debt (mil.): $3,570
No. of shares (mil.): 188
Dividends
  Yield: 3.8%
  Payout: 65.3%
Market value (mil.): $7,978

**Stock Price History
High/Low 1985–94**

THE TEXAS A&M UNIVERSITY SYSTEM

OVERVIEW

There are nearly 76,000 students in the Texas A&M system, which is made up of 7 universities and 8 research and service agencies. Headquartered in College Station, the system is governed by a 9-member board of regents appointed by the governor and confirmed by the Texas Senate. The system has one of the largest endowments in the US, totaling more than $4.6 billion (including shared funds).

The largest university in the system (and one of the largest in the US) is Texas A&M in College Station. It has more than 40,000 undergraduate and graduate students on its 5,200-acre campus. The university, which includes 10 colleges, has a 2,500-member faculty, including 2 Nobel laureates, one Pulitzer Prize winner, and one recipient of the National Medal of Science. It also includes a branch campus, Texas A&M University at Galveston. Other system schools include the traditionally black Prairie View A&M and Texas A&M International, which is located on the Mexican border, in Laredo.

The system plans to add more schools. The Baylor College of Dentistry and East Texas State University are slated to join in 1996.

WHEN

The Texas Constitution of 1876 created an agricultural and mechanical college and stated that "separate schools shall be provided for the white and colored children, and impartial provisions shall be made for both." The white school, the Agricultural and Mechanical College of Texas (later Texas A&M), began instruction that year. Texas A&M was a men's school at first, and membership in its Corps of Cadets was mandatory. The Agricultural and Mechanical College of Texas for Colored Youth (later Prairie View A&M) opened its doors in 1878.

To help fund the agricultural colleges and the University of Texas, the state legislature established the Permanent University Fund in 1876 to hold more than one million acres of land in West Texas as an endowment. An additional one million acres were added in 1883.

Texas A&M and Prairie View were part of an unofficial system of agricultural and mechanical colleges. They were joined in 1917 by Arlington Training School (later Arlington State) and John Tarleton College (now Tarleton State), which was founded in 1899 with an endowment left by the school's namesake.

In 1923 the Santa Rita, a well on university lands in West Texas, struck oil. As the oil flowed, so did the money into the University of Texas (UT) and Texas A&M systems' coffers. Under the provisions of the constitution, UT got 2/3 of the income and A&M got 1/3.

The Texas A&M College System was officially established in 1948, and it included Texas A&M, Prairie View A&M, Tarleton State, and Arlington State (now the University of Texas at Arlington; it dropped out in 1965). In 1963 it changed its name to the Texas A&M University System.

In 1962 Texas A&M University at Galveston was created as the Texas Maritime Academy, although it traced its roots back to a school of seamanship and navigation founded in 1931. In 1963 Texas A&M went coeducational, and in 1965 Corps of Cadets membership became voluntary. Texas A&M's enrollment began a dramatic increase, from about 8,000 in 1963 to more than 35,000 by the mid-1980s.

In 1989, 3 South Texas universities joined the system: Texas A&I University, Corpus Christi State, and Laredo State University. Texas A&I was founded in 1925 as South Texas State Teachers College. It soon diversified its offerings and became Texas College of Arts and Industries (changed to Texas A&I University in 1967, then to Texas A&M University-Kingsville in 1993). Corpus Christi State (renamed Texas A&M University-Corpus Christi in 1993) was founded as a private Baptist college in 1947. It became a state-supported public college in 1971. Laredo State University (renamed Texas A&M International in 1993) was founded as Texas A&I at Laredo in 1969 and adopted its current name in 1977.

In 1990 West Texas State College became the 7th member of the system. It was founded in 1910 and reached university status in 1963. It changed its name to West Texas A&M University in 1993.

In 1993 the system was rocked when an anonymous letter was sent to every member of the board of regents except its chairman, Ross Margraves; the letter accused Margraves of using school business for his own profit. Margraves resigned in 1994 and was replaced by rancher/college dropout Mary Nan West.

Also in 1994 Texas A&M broke ground on the George Bush Presidential Library, scheduled for completion in 1997.

A 1995 audit of the system sharply criticized it for overpayment on some projects, mismanagement of employees, and duplication of administration systems.

Public university
Fiscal year ends: August 31

Chairman Board of Regents: Mary Nan West, age 69
VC Board of Regents: Raul B. Fernandez
Chancellor: Barry B. Thompson
Vice Chancellor for Finance and Operations: Richard Lindsay
Vice Chancellor for Academic Affairs: David A. Sanchez
Vice Chancellor for State and Public Affairs: James B. Bond
Vice Chancellor and General Counsel: Mary Beth Kurz
President, Texas A&M University: Ray M. Bowen
President, Prairie View A&M University: Julius W. Becton Jr.
President, Tarleton State University: Dennis P. McCabe
President, Texas A&M International University: Leo Sayavedra
President, Texas A&M University-Corpus Christi: Robert R. Furgason
President, Texas A&M University-Kingsville: Manuel L. Ibáñez
Interim President, West Texas A&M University: Russell Long
VP Human Resources: Patti Courer
Auditors: Texas State Auditor

WHERE

HQ: John B. Connally Bldg., College Station, TX 77843-1118
Phone: 409-845-2531
Fax: 409-862-2679

Universities
Prairie View A&M University (Prairie View)
Tarleton State University (Stephenville)
Texas A&M International University (Laredo)
Texas A&M University (College Station)
    Texas A&M University at Galveston (branch campus)
Texas A&M University-Corpus Christi
Texas A&M University-Kingsville
West Texas A&M University (Canyon)

WHAT

	1994 Revenues	
	$ mil.	% of total
Government appropriations	527	41
Gifts, grants & contracts	306	23
Tuition & fees	150	12
Auxiliary enterprises	149	12
University Fund income	79	6
Endowment & investment income	20	2
Sales, services & other	56	4
Total	**1,287**	**100**

	1995 Preliminary Enrollment
	No.
Texas A&M University (including Texas A&M-Galveston)	43,031
West Texas A&M	6,630
Tarleton State	6,533
Texas A&M-Kingsville	6,134
Prairie View A&M	5,999
Texas A&M-Corpus Christi	5,560
Texas A&M International	2,512
Total	**76,399**

Research and Service Agencies
The Texas Agricultural Experiment Station
The Texas Agricultural Extension Service
The Texas Animal Damage Control Service
The Texas Engineering Experiment Station
The Texas Engineering Extension Service
The Texas Forest Service
The Texas Transportation Institute
The Texas Veterinary Medical Diagnostic Laboratory

KEY COMPETITORS

Baylor	Texas Tech
Rice	University of Arizona
Sam Houston State	University of California
Southern Methodist	University of Houston
Southwest Texas State	University of North Texas
Southwestern University	University of Texas

HOW MUCH

	9-Year Growth	1985	1986	1987	1988	1989	1990	1991	1992	1993	1994
Revenues ($ mil.)	7.8%	652	689	666	769	804	1,079	1,073	1,172	1,212	1,287
Enrollment	5.6%	46,473	45,513	46,229	50,180	51,212	69,596	70,782	71,400	73,884	75,573
Endowment market value ($ mil.)[1]	6.5%	2,613	3,183	3,472	3,319	3,844	3,668	4,063	4,302	4,639	4,616
Employees	2.3%	13,425	13,286	13,436	13,557	14,076	14,802	15,228	15,670	15,966	16,367

Revenues ($ mil.)
1985–94

[1]Includes Texas A&M system endowment and Permanent University Fund

TEXAS INSTRUMENTS INCORPORATED

OVERVIEW

Texas Instruments (TI) dazzled technology fans in mid-1995 when it unveiled DMD. The Dallas-based company's patented "digital mirror device" gives big-screen TVs, computer monitors, and other display panels a super-clear picture.

One of the world's top makers of computer chips, TI is riding the industry's boom — income was up nearly 50% in 1994. The company's chip menu includes DSPs (digital signal processors, used in computer sound cards and cellular phones) and DRAMs (dynamic random-access memory chips). TI also makes computers, defense electronics, personal productivity products such as calculators and printers, and electrical control devices.

TI's marketing failures and defense cutbacks (in 1994 the US government accounted for 10% of revenues, down from 12% in 1993) prompted a recent company restructuring.

DMD is just one of many recent advances developed by TI, which has been known for thinking up new gizmos (the company spends about 7% of revenues on R&D) but not for getting them to consumers. Notebook computers, one area where TI has fallen short, are now the focus of a renewed marketing effort. The company has several joint ventures, including a new Dallas plant (with Hitachi) and 2 Asian fabs (with Acer and Kobe Steel).

In 1995 Northern California chip makers Cypress Semiconductor, LSI Logic, and VLSI Technology were ordered to pay $51.8 million to TI for infringement of a patented process for encasing chips in plastic. The award was overturned, and TI plans to appeal.

WHEN

"Doc" Karcher and Eugene McDermott founded Geophysical Service Inc. (GSI) in Newark, New Jersey, in 1930. The company specialized in reflective seismology, a new technology used to explore for oil and gas deposits. In 1934 GSI moved its headquarters to Dallas.

GSI started making defense electronics during WWII, when it made submarine detectors for the US Navy, and established a defense division in 1946. The company changed its name to Texas Instruments in 1951 and was listed on the NYSE in 1953.

TI started manufacturing transistors in 1952 after buying a license from Western Electric. TI invested about $2 million in an effort to reduce the price of the germanium transistor, which expanded the market for its uses and made possible the pocket transistor radio (1954). TI produced the first commercial silicon transistor in 1954, and TI engineer Jack Kilby (with Intel founder Bob Noyce) invented the integrated circuit in 1958. By 1959 TI's semiconductor manufacturing division accounted for half of its total sales.

TI's technological know-how led to other firsts in microelectronics, including terrain-following airborne radar (1958), forward-looking infrared (FLIR) systems (1964), hand-held calculators (1967), single-chip microcomputers (1971), and the LISP (list processing language) chip, a 32-bit microcomputer for artificial intelligence applications (1987).

TI moved from defense and semiconductors into consumer products in the 1970s with calculators, digital watches, and home computers. Although TI developed the basic technologies for these products, its inability to follow through in the face of low-cost foreign competition led it to lose money and then abandon its digital watch and PC businesses. Attempts to meet competitors' prices, as well as plunging semiconductor prices, led to TI's first annual loss in 1983.

TI's Kilby patent for the integrated circuit (named after the coinventor of the IC) was upheld in Japan in 1989, and all major Japanese electronics firms except Fujitsu pay royalties to TI.

In 1991 TI sold its remaining interest in GSI to Halliburton; Hewlett-Packard bought its industrial controls business (1991) and multiuser minicomputer business (1992). In 1991 TI signed a licensing pact with chip maker Cyrix for its design of a clone of Intel's 486. TI introduced the TI486 in 1992.

In tough times TI leveraged its DRAM know-how in a number of strategic alliances that include a joint venture (26%) with Canon, Hewlett-Packard, and the Singapore Economic Development Board to make 4-megabit DRAMs (TECH, 1991) and an agreement with Hitachi to research and develop 256-megabit DRAM chips (1993).

The company posted record profits and sales in 1994 thanks in large part to a strong performance from its semiconductor business. That same year TI and Hitachi announced plans to form a joint venture and build a $500 million DRAM chip plant in Richardson, Texas.

In 1995 the company sold its line of educational toys, including Speak & Spell and Speak & Math, to Tiger Electronics.

NYSE symbol: TXN
Fiscal year ends: December 31

WHO

Chairman, President, and CEO: Jerry R. Junkins,
age 57, $1,927,800 pay
VC: William P. Weber, age 54, $995,000 pay
VC: William B. Mitchell, age 59, $859,100 pay
EVP; President, Semiconductor Group: Thomas J.
Engibous, age 42, $906,000 pay
EVP: William F. Hayes, age 51, $831,350 pay
**EVP; President, Defense Systems and Electronics
Group:** Gary D. Clubb, age 48
SVP, Treasurer, and CFO: William A. Aylesworth,
age 52
SVP, Secretary, and General Counsel: Richard J.
Agnich, age 51
VP; President, Materials and Controls Group: Nicholas
K. Brookes, age 47
VP: Elwin L. Skiles Jr., age 53
VP and Corporate Controller: Marvin M. Lane Jr., age 60
VP Human Resources: Charles F. Nielson, age 57
Auditors: Ernst & Young LLP

WHERE

HQ: 13500 N. Central Expwy., PO Box 655474, Dallas,
TX 75265
Phone: 214-995-2551
Fax: 214-995-4360

Texas Instruments has manufacturing operations in 18
countries.

	1994 Sales		1994 Pretax Income	
	$ mil.	% of total	$ mil.	% of total
US	5,943	58	1,018	82
East Asia	2,729	26	(12)	—
Europe	1,574	15	219	18
Other regions	69	1	5	0
Adjustments	—	—	(188)	—
Total	**10,315**	**100**	**1,042**	**100**

WHAT

	1994 Sales		1994 Pretax Income	
	$ mil.	% of total	$ mil.	% of total
Components	6,787	66	1,101	82
Defense electronics	1,710	17	172	13
Digital products	1,661	16	62	5
Metallurgical matls.	152	1	(8)	—
Adjustments	5	—	(285)	—
Total	**10,315**	**100**	**1,042**	**100**

Selected Products
Audio decoders
Avionics and missile guidance and control systems
Digital mirror devices (DMD)
Digital signal processors (DSP)
Dynamic random-access memory (DRAM) chips
Electrical and electronic control devices
Electronic connectors
microLaser Pro E printers
Multimedia video processors
Navigation systems
Notebook computers
Radar systems
Speech recognition products
Thermal Vision infrared imaging systems

KEY COMPETITORS

AMD	Harris Corp.	Motorola
Apple	Hewlett-Packard	National
AST	Hitachi	Semiconductor
Canon	Honeywell	NEC
Casio	Hyundai	Oki
Compaq	IBM	Raytheon
Cypress	Intel	Rockwell
Semiconductor	Kurzweil	Samsung
EG&G	Applied	Sharp
Emerson	Intelligence	Siemens
Fujitsu	LG Group	Thomson SA
Gateway 2000	LSI Logic	Thorn EMI
General Dynamics	Micron	Toshiba
General Electric	Technology	Zilog

HOW MUCH

	9-Year Growth	1985	1986	1987	1988	1989	1990	1991	1992	1993	1994
Sales ($ mil.)	8.6%	4,925	4,974	5,595	6,295	6,522	6,567	6,784	7,440	8,523	10,315
Net income ($ mil.)	—	(119)	40	257	366	292	(39)	(409)	247	476	691
Income as % of sales	—	—	0.8%	4.6%	5.8%	4.5%	—	—	3.3%	5.6%	6.7%
Earnings per share ($)	—	(1.59)	0.38	2.96	4.05	3.04	(0.92)	(5.40)	2.50	5.07	7.27
Stock price – high ($)	—	43.88	49.38	80.25	60.00	46.75	44.00	47.63	52.25	84.25	89.50
Stock price – low ($)	—	28.72	34.22	36.25	34.50	28.13	22.50	26.00	30.00	45.75	61.00
Stock price – close ($)	8.8%	35.13	39.34	55.75	41.00	35.88	38.00	30.75	46.63	63.50	74.88
P/E – high	—	—	—	27	15	15	—	—	21	17	12
P/E – low	—	—	—	12	9	9	—	—	12	9	8
Dividends per share ($)	3.7%	0.67	0.67	0.69	0.72	0.72	0.72	0.72	0.72	0.72	0.93
Book value per share ($)	6.3%	18.89	22.49	21.95	21.36	24.10	22.46	19.36	20.92	25.49	32.79
Employees	(3.5%)	77,872	77,270	77,984	75,685	73,854	70,318	62,939	60,577	59,048	56,333

1994 Year-end:
Debt ratio: 21.2%
Return on equity: 25.8%
Cash (mil.): $1,290
Current ratio: 1.83
Long-term debt (mil.): $808
No. of shares (mil.): 93
Dividends
  Yield: 1.2%
  Payout: 12.8%
Market value (mil.): $6,940

**Stock Price History
High/Low 1985–94**

TEXAS UTILITIES COMPANY

OVERVIEW

Dallas-based Texas Utilities is one of the largest electric utilities in the US. Through its principal subsidiary, Texas Utilities Electric Company (TU Electric), it provides electric service to about 5.7 million people, about 1/3 of the state's population. TU Electric's service area covers 372 cities and towns (including the Dallas–Fort Worth metroplex) in north-central, eastern, and western Texas.

Other TU subsidiaries support TU Electric by providing the lignite coal (Texas Utilities Mining Company) and natural gas and oil (Texas Utilities Fuel Company) for the company's generating plants. TU Fuel Company owns a 50% interest in a 395-mile natural gas pipeline linking the Dallas–Fort Worth area to West Texas producing fields, and Chaco Energy owns coal reserves totaling some 120 million recoverable tons.

Increased competition in the power industry has hurt Texas Utilities. The company has lost about 380 megawatts of wholesale business to competitors, equal to about 4% of TU's revenues. It has focused on improving efficiency in order to compete more effectively. TU is also moving into new areas. In 1995 the company paid $200 million for a 20% stake in the Texas operations of PCS PrimeCo, a wireless telecommunications firm created by Bell Atlantic, U S West, and NYNEX.

WHEN

The first electric power company in North Texas was founded in Dallas in 1883. Another was built in 1885 in Fort Worth. From these and other small power plants grew 3 companies to serve the north-central, western, and eastern regions of the state: Texas Power and Light (1912), Dallas Power and Light (1917), and Texas Electric Service Company (1929). By 1932 a network of transmission lines connecting these 3 utilities was virtually complete. Texas Utilities Company was formed in 1945 as a holding company to enable the 3 utilities to raise capital and obtain construction financing at lower cost.

Beginning in the 1940s TU moved away from strict dependence on natural gas, which was cheap and abundant, and began to lease large lignite coal reserves. In 1952 it formed Industrial Generating Company to mine lignite and operate an early coal-fired generating plant. It pioneered new lignite coal–burning technology during the 1960s, building larger boilers than had ever been used in the US. The first of 9 large lignite plants went into use in 1971, and TU began construction of the Comanche Peak nuclear plant, 45 miles southwest of Fort Worth, in 1974.

In 1984 Dallas Power and Light, Texas Electric Service, Texas Power and Light, and Texas Utilities Generating Company were combined as Texas Utilities Electric. The mining company was renamed Texas Utilities Mining.

In 1985 the Nuclear Regulatory Commission suspended licensing of the Comanche Peak nuclear plant, citing both design and construction faults. Further negotiations with the NRC resulted in the granting of a license to operate the plant at 5% of capacity in 1990, followed by a full-power license in the spring of that year. In the interim TU lost its 3 construction partners over the issue of multibillion-dollar cost overruns and bought their interests for $984.5 million.

In 1990 Santa Fe Pacific Corporation agreed to settle an antitrust suit brought by TU in 1981 over a 1977 lease agreement granting TU the right to mine about 228 million tons of coal owned by Santa Fe. TU won substantial royalty and lease agreement concessions from Santa Fe in a new agreement, running from 1990 through 2017.

In 1991 the Public Utilities Commission of Texas (PUC) authorized a 10.2% rate increase (worth about $442 million in revenues) but disallowed $1.4 billion in costs related to the construction of its Comanche Peak nuclear facility and the buyout of a former minority interest in the project.

In 1993 Texas Utilities acquired Southwestern Electric Service Company for approximately $65 million in stock and cash. That same year TU Electric received a low-power license for Unit 2 at Comanche Peak. Also in 1993 Texas Utilities' profits suffered a power outage after the PUC disallowed $250 million in costs related to construction of TU's Comanche Peak nuclear plant and approved only an 8.7% rate increase instead of the 15.3% rate increase TU had requested. As a result, in 1994 Texas Utilities failed to raise its dividend for the first time since 1948.

In 1994 TU bought Atlantic Richfield's I. M. Pei–designed office tower in Dallas for $29 million; critics claimed the price was unusually low because TU is one of Atlantic Richfield's major customers.

In 1995 Erle Nye succeeded Jerry Farrington (who remains chairman) as CEO.

NYSE symbol: TXU
Fiscal year ends: December 31

WHO

Chairman: Jerry S. Farrington, age 60, $804,167 pay
President and CEO: Erle Nye, age 57, $618,750 pay
(prior to promotion)
EVP, TU Services: Michael D. Spence, $302,000 pay
EVP, TU Electric: W. M. Taylor, $289,333 pay
VP and Principal Financial Officer: H. Jarrell Gibbs,
age 57, $285,167 pay
Controller and Principal Accounting Officer: H. Dan
Farell
Treasurer and Assistant Secretary: Cathryn C. Hulen
Secretary and Assistant Treasurer: Peter B. Tinkham
VP Personnel: Pitt Pittman
Auditors: Deloitte & Touche LLP

WHERE

HQ: Energy Plaza, 1601 Bryan St., Dallas, TX 75201
Phone: 214-812-4600
Fax: 214-812-4651

Generating Facilities

Oil and Gas

Collin	Rivercrest
Decordova	Stryker Creek
Eagle Mountain	Tradinghouse
Graham	Trinidad
Handley	Valley
Lake Creek	
Lake Hubbard	**Lignite**
Main	Big Brown
Morgan Creek	Martin Lake
Mountain Creek	Monticello
North Main	Sandow
Northlake	
Parkdale	**Nuclear**
Permian Basin	Comanche Peak

WHAT

	1994 Sales	
	$ mil.	% of total
Residential	2,490	43
Commercial	1,707	29
Industrial	987	17
Government & municipal	400	7
Other electric utilities	216	4
Adjustments	(136)	—
Total	**5,664**	**100**

	1994 Fuel Sources
	% of total
Lignite	37
Oil & gas	34
Nuclear	16
Purchased power	13
Total	**100**

Subsidiaries
Basic Resources Inc. (resource development and related
technology and services)
Chaco Energy Co. (coal production, sale, and delivery)
Southwestern Electric Service Co. (SESCO, electric
utility serving customers in eastern and central Texas)
Texas Utilities Electric Co. (TU Electric, electric utility
serving customers in north-central, eastern, and
western Texas)
Texas Utilities Fuel Co. (natural gas pipeline; acquires,
stores, and delivers gas fuel)
Texas Utilities Mining Co. (surface mining for lignite)
Texas Utilities Properties Inc. (property ownership,
leasing, and management)
Texas Utilities Services Inc. (accounting and
administrative services)

KEY COMPETITORS

Entergy
Houston Industries
Southwestern Public Service

HOW MUCH

	9-Year Growth	1985	1986	1987	1988	1989	1990	1991	1992	1993	1994
Sales ($ mil.)	3.5%	4,170	3,932	4,083	4,154	4,321	4,543	4,893	4,908	5,435	5,664
Net income ($ mil.)	(0.9%)	588	627	680	643	779	851	(410)	619	369	543
Income as % of sales	—	14.1%	15.9%	16.7%	15.5%	18.0%	18.7%	—	12.6%	6.8%	9.6%
Earnings per share ($)	(6.4%)	4.35	4.45	4.55	4.00	4.44	4.40	(1.98)	2.88	1.66	2.40
Stock price – high ($)	—	31.88	37.50	36.63	30.63	37.63	39.00	43.00	43.75	49.75	43.13
Stock price – low ($)	—	25.13	29.50	25.50	24.63	27.75	32.00	34.13	37.00	41.63	29.63
Stock price – close ($)	0.8%	29.88	31.50	27.00	28.13	35.13	36.63	41.75	42.50	43.25	32.00
P/E – high	—	7	8	8	8	9	9	—	15	30	18
P/E – low	—	6	7	6	6	6	7	—	13	25	12
Dividends per share ($)	2.4%	2.52	2.68	2.80	2.88	2.92	2.96	3.00	3.04	3.08	3.08
Book value per share ($)	(0.3%)	29.46	31.24	33.02	33.38	34.56	34.66	29.82	30.33	29.29	28.74
Employees	(4.6%)	16,528	16,927	16,086	15,669	15,248	15,216	15,262	10,687	10,859	10,798

1994 Year-end:
Debt ratio: 51.9%
Return on equity: 8.3%
Cash (mil.): $8
Current ratio: 0.48
Long-term debt (mil.): $7,888
No. of shares (mil.): 226
Dividends
  Yield: 9.6%
  Payout: 128.3%
Market value (mil.): $7,227

Stock Price History
High/Low 1985–94

TRINITY INDUSTRIES, INC.

OVERVIEW

For Trinity Industries, 3's a charm. A diversified manufacturer of various heavy-metal products, the Dallas-based company cornered the market for liquefied petroleum gas (LPG) storage tanks in the 1950s and 1960s. Then, when the market for railroad freight cars slumped in the 1980s, Trinity snapped up failing competitors so that it controlled more than half of the production capacity when the fleet had to be replaced in the 1990s. More recently, the former steel company has bought up half of the US's barge-building capacity in the expectation that the nation's aging fleet of barges will need to be replaced soon. "If you're in a replacement business, you just have to let time work for you," says chairman Ray Wallace.

Trinity has 6 basic business segments: railcars, marine products, construction products,

pressurized and nonpressurized containers, metal components, and leasing. The company manufactures railroad tank and hopper cars (44% of 1995 profits); tugboats, barges, and military service vessels (15%); and construction products used in building public facilities, highways, and bridges (17%). Other products include large storage containers and fittings, forgings, and container heads. Trinity also leases railcars to customers.

Wallace is betting that the next big replacement market will be the country's aging bridges and highways. The company has been buying construction-related businesses, such as Transit Mix Concrete and Materials, since 1991. One of the largest concrete companies in southeastern Texas, Transit Mix is headed by key Texas legislator Mark Stiles. Wallace owns 3.1% of the company's stock.

WHEN

Trinity Industries was the product of a 1958 merger of Trinity Steel, a manufacturer of petroleum industry metal products that had been founded in 1933, and Dallas Tank Co. In 1966 the company adopted its current name. The new company was headed from the start by Ray Wallace, who had been with Trinity Steel since the 1940s.

During the 1960s publicly owned Trinity Industries grew rapidly. The company acquired related tank, welding, and steel companies and quickly became the leading manufacturer of metal storage containers for liquefied petroleum gas. During this period the company also applied its expertise to containers for another rapidly growing industry, fertilizer, and made custom products for the oil and chemical industries. Other products included railroad hopper bodies and tanks.

During the 1970s Trinity diversified into manufacturing various seagoing vessels, buying Equitable Equipment and its Louisiana shipyards in 1972. In 1973 the company bought Houston-based Mosher Steel, which made steel beams and framing products. By the mid-1970s Trinity was producing highway guardrails and other products associated with road construction. In 1977 Trinity expanded its manufacturing of railcar parts to building the entire car and created a subsidiary to lease them under long-term contracts.

By the early 1980s the company was a leading producer of railcars. But a change in federal tax laws and a glut of railcars caused

demand to plummet; in 1985 Trinity had its first loss in 27 years.

While competitors left the industry, Wallace used proceeds from Trinity's profitable operations to quietly buy those businesses, including Pullman Standard, once the US's top freight car manufacturer. Other purchases were Greenville Steel Car (railcars, 1986), Ortner Freight (coal cars, 1987), and Standard Forgings (locomotive axles, 1987). Trinity tripled its manufacturing capacity. During this time the company also was expanding its marine division with such acquisitions as Halter Marine (1983), Moss Point Marine (military and service vessels, 1987), and Bethlehem Steel's manufacturing plant and marine facilities in Beaumont, Texas (1989).

When railroad companies started to replace their railcars, Trinity's revenues surged past $1 billion; in 1990, 52% of the company's sales were from railcar production. Also that year Trinity bought Beaird Industries, a maker of railcars and other metal containers.

In 1993 the company announced a venture with Hilton Hotels and New Orleans Paddlewheels to build a 2,400-passenger riverboat casino, *Queen of New Orleans*. Trinity also expanded its construction products line with the purchase of Syro Steel (fabricated steel products, 1992) and the Texas and Louisiana operations of LaFarge (concrete, 1994). In 1995 the company expanded into Mexico by acquiring Grupo TATSA, a manufacturer and distributor of fabricated steel products.

NYSE symbol: TRN
Fiscal year ends: March 31

WHO

Chairman, President, and CEO: W. Ray Wallace, age 72, $3,000,000 pay
SVP and CFO: K. W. Lewis, age 56, $572,000 pay
SVP: Ralph A. Banks Jr., age 71
SVP: Richard G. Brown, age 71
Group VP; President, Railcars: Timothy R. Wallace, age 41, $643,041 pay
Group VP; President, Marine: John Dane III, age 44, $381,017 pay
Group VP; Chairman, Construction Products and Metal Components: John T. Sanford, age 43, $375,111 pay
Group VP; President, Construction Products: Mark Stiles, age 46
VP Human Resources: Jack Cunningham
Auditors: Ernst & Young LLP

WHERE

HQ: 2525 Stemmons Fwy., Dallas, TX 75207-2401
Phone: 214-631-4420
Fax: 214-689-0501

WHAT

	1995 Sales		1995 Operating Profit	
	$ mil.	% of total	$ mil.	% of total
Railcars	1,187	50	88	44
Marine products	370	16	30	15
Construction products	355	15	36	17
Containers	170	7	10	5
Leasing	157	7	24	12
Metal components	109	5	15	7
Adjustments	(33)	—	(45)	—
Total	**2,315**	**100**	**158**	**100**

Business Segments and Selected Products

Railcars
Gondola cars	Miscellaneous freight cars
Hopper cars	Tank cars
Intermodal cars	

Marine Products
Crew boats	Oceanographic
Excursion boats	research ships
Ferries	Riverboat casinos
Fishing boats	Tugboats
Military boats	Yachts

Construction Products
Airport conveyor systems	Highway/railway bridges
Construction aggregate	Power plants
Highway guardrails	Ready-mix concrete
Highway safety products	

Containers
Heat transfer equipment	Pressure and nonpressure
Heavy pressure vessels	storage containers

Leasing (railcars)

Metal components
Container heads	Weld fittings

Selected Subsidiaries
Flo-Bend, Inc.
Gulf Coast Fabrication, Inc.
Platzer Shipyard, Inc.
Stearns Airport Equipment Co., Inc.
Syntechnics, Inc.
Transit Mix Concrete & Materials Co.
Trinity Industries Leasing Co.
Trinity Marine Caruthersville, Inc.

KEY COMPETITORS

ABC Rail Products	Ingram	Metallurg
CBI Industries	Itel	Morrison
Commercial	Johnston America	Knudsen
Intertech	L. B. Foster	PLM Intl.
GATX	Martin Marietta	TTX
Greenbriar	Materials	Vulcan Materials

HOW MUCH

	9-Year Growth	1986	1987	1988	1989	1990	1991	1992	1993	1994	1995
Sales ($ mil.)	20.4%	434	491	633	1,001	1,310	1,263	1,192	1,540	1,785	2,315
Net income ($ mil.)	66.6%	1	6	13	30	38	30	22	45	68	89
Income as % of sales	—	0.2%	1.2%	2.1%	3.0%	2.9%	2.4%	1.9%	2.9%	3.8%	3.8%
Earnings per share ($)	61.2%	0.03	0.23	0.49	1.07	1.34	0.95	0.69	1.27	1.69	2.20
Stock price – high ($)	—	11.42	13.34	23.01	25.26	30.68	21.84	21.09	26.51	44.13	47.38
Stock price – low ($)	—	8.34	8.84	9.50	15.51	19.09	10.34	12.17	17.09	24.76	30.38
Stock price – close ($)	13.4%	10.17	11.09	17.34	22.68	20.01	12.17	17.59	26.01	43.13	31.50
P/E – high	—	—	58	47	24	23	23	31	21	26	22
P/E – low	—	—	38	19	15	14	11	18	14	15	14
Dividends per share ($)	8.0%	0.34	0.33	0.33	0.34	0.43	0.53	0.53	0.53	0.61	0.68
Book value per share ($)	9.9%	6.82	6.73	8.33	8.40	9.79	10.74	10.92	12.96	14.37	15.95
Employees	37.9%	5,400	5,700	6,800	9,560	9,420	9,800	10,500	12,600	14,700	16,500

1995 Year-end:
Debt ratio: 41.9%
Return on equity: 14.7%
Cash (mil.): $15
Current ratio: 1.43
Long-term debt (mil.): $243
No. of shares (mil.): 40
Dividends
 Yield: 2.2%
 Payout: 30.9%
Market value (mil.): $1,266

Stock Price History High/Low 1986–95

THE UNIVERSITY OF TEXAS SYSTEM

OVERVIEW

The University of Texas (UT) System, with more than 152,000 students at 15 campuses, is the 2nd largest state university system in the US (after the University of California). The system is governed by a 9-member board of regents, members of which are appointed by the governor of Texas in staggered 6-year terms.

The system trails only Harvard in the size of its endowment, the main component of which was traditionally the income earned on invested oil and mineral royalties from over 2.1 million acres of land in West Texas. Asset managers have worked hard to reduce its dependence on oil through diverse investments.

Because UT has been one of the richest university systems, it has been able to boast of being one of the least expensive for in-state students (ranking 48th out of 50 for in-state undergraduate tuition costs and dead last for graduate). Accordingly, tuition accounts for only 7% of revenues (with federal, state, and local tax support accounting for about half).

The system excels in many fields and has been able to attract scholars and researchers of international distinction who, in turn, attract a cosmopolitan student body at several of its campuses. In particular, the faculty at the system's flagship Austin campus and its medical schools in Dallas and Houston have garnered numerous honors (the system has produced 4 Nobel laureates in 10 years).

UT's alumni list includes Walter Cronkite, Lady Bird Johnson, Bill Moyers, Nobel laureate E. Donnall Thomas, and former Secretary of State James Baker, all of whom are graduates of the Austin campus.

WHEN

The Texas Declaration of Independence of 1836 admonished Mexico for having failed to establish a public education system in Texas territory. Attempts to start a state-sponsored university were stymied until after Texas achieved US statehood and fought the Civil War. In 1876 a new constitution provided for the establishment of a university, but it was not until 1883 that the university was opened (at Austin, with a medical school to be sited at Galveston, according to the wishes of Texas voters in a 1881 referendum). In that year, 8 professors began teaching 218 students in 2 curricula: academic and law.

The school's first building opened in 1884, and in 1891 the university's medical school opened at Galveston. By 1894 UT had 534 students and a football team. In 1905 the College of Education opened, followed by the Graduate School (1910) and the College of Business Administration (1924), all located in Austin. The university added its first academic branch campus when the Texas State School of Mines and Metallurgy (opened in 1914 in El Paso) became part of the system in 1919.

UT's future was secured in 1923 when oil was found on the West Texas desert lands that had been set aside by the state legislature for educational support. The income from oil production, as well as the proceeds of surface-use leases, became the Permanent University Fund (PUF), from which only interest and earnings on the revenues could be used (2/3 by UT and 1/3 by Texas A&M University). By 1926 UT's oil royalties were over $4 million, twice as much as UT's state funding ($1.8 million). The university continued to grow thanks to the PUF, which had topped $100 million by 1940.

In the 1940s and 1950s, the system (officially organized in 1950), added a medical center in Dallas, as well as graduate schools of library science and social work and the School of Architecture, all in Austin. In 1946 Heman Sweatt was denied admission to the law school because he was black, which began a fight that ended with a Supreme Court order that UT admit him in 1950. UT hired its first black professor in 1964. Two years later a gunman named Charles Whitman shot 47 people from the Austin administration tower, killing 16, before he was killed by a policeman.

The 1960s through the 1980s were a time of geographic expansion for the system as it absorbed other institutions (Arlington College, 1965, founded in 1895; the Dallas campus, 1969, founded in 1961 as a private research facility; Pan American, 1989, founded in 1927; the academic campus at Brownsville [originally a branch of Pan American], 1989, founded in 1973). It also started new campuses (UT Permian Basin, with an emphasis on petroleum research, and UT San Antonio, 1969; UT Tyler, 1979). In addition, it expanded its network of medical centers.

One of the system's priorities is to prepare its students for the increasingly international (and Hispanic) world of research and business, particularly after the implementation of NAFTA. In 1995 a new campus was begun in San Antonio that will be more accessible to minority students. The system also renewed its dedication to affirmative action programs.

Public university
Fiscal year ends: August 31

Chairman Board of Regents: Bernard Rapoport
Chancellor: William H. Cunningham
Executive Vice Chancellor for Business Affairs (HR): R. D. Burck
Executive Vice Chancellor for Academic Affairs: James P. Duncan
Executive Vice Chancellor for Health Affairs: Charles B. Mullins
Vice Chancellor and General Counsel: Ray Farabee
Vice Chancellor for Asset Management: Thomas G. Ricks
Vice Chancellor for Development and External Relations: Shirley B. Perry
Auditors: Texas State Auditor

WHERE

HQ: 601 Colorado St., Austin, TX 78701-2982
Phone: 512-499-4201
Fax: 512-499-4215

Campuses	1994 Students No.	% of total	1994 Faculty No.	% of total
Arlington	23,280	15	1,246	10
Austin	47,957	31	2,994	23
Brownsville	7,462	5	358	3
Dallas	8,487	6	400	3
El Paso	17,188	11	835	7
Pan American (Edinburg)	13,754	9	652	5
Permian Basin (Odessa)	2,320	2	131	1
San Antonio	17,579	11	766	6
Tyler	3,987	3	264	2
Dallas (med.)	1,700	1	1,186	9
Galveston (med.)	2,327	2	782	6
Houston (med.)	3,183	2	1,736	14
San Antonio (med.)	2,790	2	1,253	10
Tyler (med.)	0	0	93	1
Total	**152,014**	**100**	**12,696**	**100**

WHAT

	1994 Revenues $ mil.	% of total
State appropriations (taxes)	1,310	33
Federal, state & local grants	647	16
Hospital revenues	626	16
Professional fees	433	11
Tuition	290	7
Private gifts & grants	216	5
Auxiliary enterprises sales	153	4
Fund & endowment income	134	3
Other	221	5
Total	**4,030**	**100**

Affiliated Institutions
Archer M. Huntington Art Gallery (Austin)
Harry Ransom Humanities Research Center (Austin)
Institute of Texan Cultures (San Antonio)
J. J. Pickle Research Campus (Austin)
LBJ Library and Museum (Austin)
LBJ School of Public Affairs (Austin)
Marine Science Institute (Port Aransas)
McDonald Observatory (Fort Davis)
M. D. Anderson Cancer Center/Science Park (Bastrop)
Montopolis Research Center (Austin)
Robotics institute (Fort Worth)
Sam Rayburn Library (Bonham)
Texas Center for Writers (Austin)
Texas Memorial Museum (Austin)
UT Brownsville/wetlands research facility
Winedale Historical Center (Fayette County)

KEY COMPETITORS

Baylor	Texas A&M
Rice	Texas Tech
Sam Houston State	University of Arizona
Southern Methodist	University of California
Southwest Texas State	University of Houston
Southwestern University	University of North Texas

HOW MUCH

	Annual Growth	1985	1986	1987	1988	1989	1990	1991	1992	1993	1994
Revenues ($ mil.)	8.4%	1,952	2,026	2,104	2,329	2,522	2,895	3,074	3,433	3,744	4,030
Net income ($ mil.)	8.0%	99	19	37	52	72	172	102	204	103	198
Endowment ($ mil.)[1]	8.2%	2,707	3,092	3,476	3,681	3,971	4,225	4,387	4,692	5,217	5,518
Enrollment	2.3%	—	126,429	129,646	136,190	140,136	143,344	145,675	153,393	151,824	152,014
Faculty	2.9%	—	10,071	10,335	10,830	11,196	11,395	11,310	12,406	12,657	12,696

Revenues ($ mil.) 1985–94

[1] Includes UT system and Permanent University Fund

USAA

OVERVIEW

San Antonio–based USAA is the stealth bomber of the insurance and financial industry. The company started out providing services only to active or retired military personnel (its property/casualty insurance and buying services are still open only to people affiliated with the military). But USAA has developed an avid following among civilians for its other insurance, annuity, and investment products and has won high respect among professionals in the industry for its stability and value.

In addition to military officers, USAA membership includes Secret Service and FBI agents and other selected government officials and their families. The company has more than 2.5 million members, including over 90% of active-duty US military officers.

In addition to auto and homeowners insurance and investments, the company provides health insurance, credit cards, a travel agency, and a buying service that allows members to buy discount merchandise. USAA also owns 86% of San Antonio amusement park Fiesta Texas, which it developed.

USAA has no field agents, finding its members instead through direct marketing and the military grapevine. In 1994 it began advertising to generate new contacts, particularly for investment products. The company's data processing functions are highly sophisticated and are often upgraded to provide better service.

In 1995 USAA was considering setting up a mutual fund service to allow account holders to move between its own and other funds without incurring transaction fees.

WHEN

In 1922 a group of US Army officers gathered in a San Antonio hotel and formed their own automobile insurance association. The reason? As military officers they often moved from one post to another, and they had a hard time getting insurance because they were considered "transient." So the 26 officers who met that day decided to insure each other. Led by Major William Garrison, who became the company's first president, they formed the United States Army Automobile Insurance Association.

In 1924, when navy and marine corps officers were allowed to join, the company changed its name to United Services Automobile Association. By the mid-1950s the company had more than 200,000 members.

During the 1960s the company added to its insurance lines when it formed USAA Life Insurance Company (1963) and USAA Casualty Insurance Company (1968).

In 1969 Robert McDermott, a retired air force brigadier general and a former dean of the Air Force Academy, became president. He cut employment through attrition (USAA has never had a layoff), established education and training seminars for employees, and invested heavily in computers and telecommunications. A new computer system cut automobile policy processing time from 13 days to 3 days.

McDermott also added new products and services, such as mutual funds, real estate investments, and banking services. Under McDermott, USAA's membership grew from 653,000 in 1969 to over 2.5 million in 1993.

In 1974 USAA began to move into its huge new headquarters facilities on a 286-acre campus featuring subsidized cafeterias, 2 walk-in medical clinics, and 2 physical fitness centers.

During the 1970s, as part of McDermott's goal to make USAA a completely paperless company, USAA switched most of its business from mail to toll-free telephone, becoming one of the insurance industry's first companies to use 800 numbers.

In the early 1980s the company introduced USAA Buying Services, allowing members to buy merchandise at a discount. In 1985 it opened the USAA Federal Savings Bank next door to its headquarters. In the late 1980s USAA began installing an optical storage system, automating some customer service operations.

McDermott retired in 1993 and was succeeded by Robert Herres, a former vice-chairman of the Joint Chiefs of Staff. USAA continues to add new services. In 1994 USAA Federal Savings Bank began developing a home banking system, providing members with information and services over advanced screen telephones provided by IBM.

In 1994 winter storms and the Northridge earthquake in California cost USAA more than $250 million in claims. The crash of the bond market was another blow.

The company has also suffered disappointment in its real estate investments. In 1995 USAA announced that it would henceforth concentrate on previously developed properties in geographically diverse areas. It sought to restructure its interest in Fiesta Texas, a theme park in San Antonio that it had helped develop.

Mutual company
Fiscal year ends: December 31

WHO

Chairman and CEO: Robert T. Herres
VC; President, USAA Capital Corporation: Hansford T. Johnson
EVP Information Services: M. Staser Holcomb
SVP, CFO, and Controller: Josue Robles Jr.
SVP Corporate Communications: John R. Cook
SVP and General Counsel: William McCrae
SVP Human Resources: William B. Tracy
President, Property and Casualty Insurance Group: Wilson C. Cooney
President, USAA Life Insurance Co.: Edwin L. Rosane
President, USAA Investment Management Co.: Michael J. C. Roth
President, USAA Real Estate Co. and La Cantera Development Co.: Edward B. Kelley
President, USAA Buying Services, Inc.: Bobby W. Presley
Acting President, USAA Federal Savings Bank: Mark Wright
Auditors: KPMG Peat Marwick LLP

WHERE

HQ: 9800 Fredericksburg Rd., USAA Bldg., San Antonio, TX 78288
Phone: 210-498-2211
Fax: 210-498-9940

USAA provides services worldwide.

Regional Offices

Colorado Springs, CO	Reston, VA
Frankfurt, Germany	Sacramento, CA
London, England	Seattle, WA
Norfolk, VA	Tampa, FL

WHAT

	1994 Sales	
	$ mil.	% of total
Premiums	4,564	74
Net investment income	757	12
Other	860	14
Total	**6,181**	**100**

	1994 Assets	
	$ mil.	% of total
Cash & equivalents	501	3
Investments	12,025	61
Net bank loans	4,037	21
Premiums receivable	660	3
Other	2,325	12
Total	**19,548**	**100**

Selected Products and Services
Auto insurance
Brokerage services
Buying services
Car rental discounts
Credit card services
Fiesta Texas (amusement park; 86%)
Life, health, and homeowners insurance
Mutual funds and other investments
Pension and retirement services
Travel services
USAA Floral Service
USAA Parklane West (health care facility)
USAA Road & Travel Plan
USAA Towers (retirement community)
USAA/Sprint Long-Distance Program

KEY COMPETITORS

20th Century Industries	ITT Hartford
AAA	John Hancock
AARP	Kemper Corp.
Aetna	Liberty Mutual
Allstate	MassMutual
American Express	MetLife
American Financial	Mutual of Omaha
American General	Nationwide Insurance
Anheuser Busch	New York Life
Berkshire Hathaway	Northwestern Mutual
Charles Schwab	Pacific Mutual Life
Chubb	Paine Webber
CIGNA	Prudential
CNA Financial	Six Flags
Dean Witter, Discover	State Farm
Equitable	T. Rowe Price
FMR	Transamerica
FTD, Inc.	Travelers
GEICO	USF&G
Guardian Life Insurance	

HOW MUCH

	9-Year Growth	1985	1986	1987	1988	1989	1990	1991	1992	1993	1994
Assets ($ mil.)	18.9%	4,121	5,740	7,168	8,866	10,562	12,258	14,520	16,235	18,494	19,548
Net income ($ mil.)	11.8%	207	294	482	430	424	321	413	140	676	564
Income as % of assets	—	5.0%	5.1%	6.7%	4.8%	4.0%	2.6%	2.8%	0.9%	3.7%	2.9%
Employees	7.6%	7,896	8,355	9,274	11,226	12,515	13,884	14,222	14,667	15,905	15,233

1994 Year-end:
Equity as % of assets: 20.8%
Return on equity: 13.6%
Sales (mil.): $6,181

Net Income
($ mil.)
1985–94

USAA®

Selected Texas Companies

ADAMS RESOURCES & ENERGY, INC.

OVERVIEW

Adams Resources & Energy and its subsidiaries engage in oil and gas exploration and production and the marketing of crude oil and petroleum products. Another business line, petroleum products and liquid chemicals trucking, helps balance the company's revenue sources, because falling oil prices lead to increased petrochemical production and higher chemical transport revenues.

The company conducts most of its gas and oil exploration activities in Louisiana, Oklahoma, and Texas. Adams owns net interests amounting to 23.4% in 209 oil and natural gas wells, primarily in Oklahoma and Texas. K. S. "Bud" Adams Jr., who owns the Houston Oilers football team and is a well-known collector of Western art, owns about 50% of Adams Resources.

Adams founded the Ada Oil Company in 1947 to explore for and produce oil and gas. These operations, with some real estate holdings, formed the core of what became Adams Resources when the company went public in 1974. An investment in coal in Illinois and Kentucky led to $65 million in losses in 1981 and the closure of those operations. Adams prospered during the oil boom (prices reached over $30 per barrel in the early 1980s) but suffered when prices crashed in 1986. In the 1990s the company made a strong comeback. In 1992 it bought Gulfmark Energy I Ltd., a crude oil trading company that specializes in oil transport and the marketing of specialty grades of crude.

In 1994 intrastate trucking was deregulated, so Adams faces new competition in Texas, which accounts for 40% of its trucking sales. The company also expanded its exploration and drilling operations, but these activities are vulnerable to market swings, and in 1995 Adams cut back on exploration, waiting for prices to rise again.

WHO

Chairman, President, and CEO: K. S. Adams Jr., age 72, $132,406 pay
VP Land Transportation; President, Service Transport Co.: Claude H. Lewis, age 51, $163,511 pay
VP Oil and Gas; President, Adams Resources Exploration Corp.: William R. Sharp, age 70, $108,705 pay
VP Finance and Treasurer: Richard B. Abshire, age 42, $103,022 pay
President, Ada Oil Co.: Juanita G. Simmons, age 41
Secretary: David B. Hurst, age 41
Director Human Resources: Jay Grimes
Auditors: Arthur Andersen & Co, SC

WHERE

HQ: 6910 Fannin St., Houston, TX 77030
Phone: 713-797-9966   **Fax:** 713-795-4495

WHAT

	1994 Sales	
	$ mil.	% of total
Marketing	610.9	96
Transportation	20.5	3
Exploration & production	3.6	1
Total	**635.0**	**100**

Primary subsidiaries
Ada Crude Oil Co. (marketing)
GulfMark Energy, Inc. (marketing)
Service Transport Co.

KEY COMPETITORS

Abraxas Petroleum	MESA Inc.
Amoco	Mitchell Energy
Anadarko Petroleum	& Development
Apache	Mobil
Arch Petroleum	Phillips Petroleum
Bass Enterprises	Royal Dutch/Shell
Cabot Oil & Gas	Santa Fe Energy
Chevron	Tejas Gas
Enron Oil & Gas	Tenneco
Exxon	Texaco
Gulf Oil	Unocal
Howell Corp.	Wainoco Oil

HOW MUCH

AMEX symbol: AE FY ends: December 31	5-Year Growth	1989	1990	1991	1992	1993	1994
Sales ($ mil.)	47.9%	89.7	110.0	119.8	550.0	695.4	635.0
Net income ($ mil.)	13.0%	1.6	1.8	1.8	0.8	1.5	3.0
Income as % of sales	—	1.8%	1.6%	1.5%	0.1%	0.2%	0.5%
Earnings per share ($)	10.4%	0.44	0.46	0.45	0.18	0.35	0.72
Stock price – high ($)	—	4.25	5.00	4.00	6.50	6.13	10.75
Stock price – low ($)	—	2.75	1.75	2.25	1.88	4.00	4.44
Stock price – close ($)	24.9%	3.25	2.75	3.50	5.13	4.50	9.88
P/E – high	—	10	11	9	36	18	15
P/E – low	—	6	4	5	10	11	6
Dividends per share ($)	—	0.00	0.00	0.00	0.00	0.00	0.03
Book value per share ($)	39.3%	0.60	1.07	1.77	2.12	2.47	3.17
Employees	10.2%	232	268	291	309	322	377

1994 Year-end:
Debt ratio: 42.8%
Return on equity: 25.6%
Cash (mil.): $2.7
Current ratio: 1.08
Long-term debt (mil.): $9.3
No. of shares (mil.): 4.2
Dividends
  Yield: 0.1%
  Payout: 4.2%
Market value (mil.): $41.3
R&D as % of sales: —
Advertising as % of sales: —

BENCHMARK ELECTRONICS, INC.

OVERVIEW

Benchmark is setting the standard for assembling printed circuit boards. It produces relatively small quantities of high-quality, complex printed circuit boards for medical equipment, communications devices, testing instruments, business and industrial computers, and other industrial equipment. As manufacturers increase the electronic content of their products, they are outsourcing more work to contract firms such as Benchmark, which can produce boards more cheaply than can in-house operations. Benchmark is dependent on a small range of industrial clients for its income and does not mass-produce circuit boards for PCs or other consumer products. In 1994 Sequent Computer accounted for 49% of total revenues, and Benchmark's top 5 customers for 67%.

Benchmark specializes in surface-mount technology, an automated process allowing for a high density of components to be placed directly on both sides of a circuit board. It also offers older, pin-through-hole printed circuit board assembly technology.

The board maker started operating in 1979 and was incorporated in 1981 as a wholly owned subsidiary of Texas medical implant maker Intermedics, which pioneered the use of surface-mount technology in cardiac pacemakers. In 1986 Intermedics sold 90% of its stock to Electronic Investors Corp. (EIC), a company formed by Intermedics executives Donald Nigbor, Steven Barton, and Cary Fu. In 1988 the 3 merged EIC with Benchmark and sold 60% of the company to a private technical services firm, Mason & Hangar. In 1990 the company completed an IPO. Mason & Hangar currently owns 22% of Benchmark.

In 1994 Benchmark moved its headquarters from Clute, Texas, to a larger plant in Angleton, Texas. In 1995 Sequent began sourcing from a 2nd company, putting increased pressure on Benchmark's sales.

WHO

President and CEO: Donald E. Nigbor, age 47, $197,115 pay
EVP, Secretary, and Treasurer: Cary T. Fu, age 46, $197,115 pay
EVP: Steven A. Barton, age 46
Manager Engineering: Ted Hirsch
Assistant Treasurer: Lenora A. Gurton
Manager Personnel: Gwyn Holden
Auditors: KPMG Peat Marwick LLP

WHERE

HQ: 3000 Technology Dr., Angleton, TX 77515
Phone: 409-849-6550   **Fax:** 409-848-5269

WHAT

	1994 Sales	
	$ mil.	% of total
Sequent Computer	48.2	49
Other customers	50.0	51
Total	**98.2**	**100**

Selected Services
Component purchase
Computer-integrated manufacturing (CIM)
Just-in-time (JIT) deliveries
OEM consultation
Post-assembly testing
Printed circuit board surface-mount technology (SMT) assembly
Project coordination
Prototype through turnkey development programs

KEY COMPETITORS

ACT Manufacturing	Merix
Advance Circuits	Micron Technology
Altron	M-Wave
Avex Electronics	PCI Ltd.
Circuit Systems	Pycon
Comptronix	Quad Systems
DDL Electronics	Sanmina
DOVatron	SCI Systems
Group Technologies	Sigma Circuits
HADCO	SigmaTron
IEC Electronics	Solectron
Jabil Circuit	Zycon

HOW MUCH

AMEX symbol: BHE FY ends: December 31	Annual Growth	1989	1990	1991	1992	1993	1994
Sales ($ mil.)	40.2%	18.1	21.3	33.3	50.6	75.9	98.2
Net income ($ mil.)	33.3%	1.4	2.0	2.1	3.1	4.5	5.8
Income as % of sales	—	7.6%	9.4%	6.3%	6.2%	5.9%	5.9%
Earnings per share ($)	16.8%	0.65	0.76	0.66	0.83	1.10	1.41
Stock price – high ($)	—	—	8.75	12.25	17.75	23.88	28.00
Stock price – low ($)	—	—	3.63	4.63	10.38	15.00	22.50
Stock price – close ($)	48.2%	—	5.00	12.00	16.38	23.88	24.13
P/E – high	—	—	12	19	21	22	20
P/E – low	—	—	5	7	13	14	16
Dividends per share ($)	—	—	0.00	0.00	0.00	0.00	0.00
Book value per share ($)	22.8%	—	4.40	5.10	7.42	8.57	10.01
Employees	21.0%	—	205	307	302	380	439

1994 Year-end:
Debt ratio: 0.0%
Return on equity: 15.5%
Cash (mil.): $8.4
Current ratio: 5.07
Long-term debt (mil.): $0.0
No. of shares (mil.): 4.0
Dividends
  Yield: —
  Payout: —
Market value (mil.): $96.7
R&D as % of sales: —
Advertising as % of sales: —

BMC SOFTWARE, INC.

OVERVIEW

Like the computer industry, BMC Software continues to evolve. While the Houston-based company's core business remains database software for IBM mainframes, BMC has recently introduced open systems data management products to keep up with the migration to client/server computing. The company markets more than 60 software tools and utilities for mainframe and network computing. Software licenses accounted for 59% of its 1995 revenues, while maintenance (product support and upgrades) accounted for 41%.

BMC was launched in 1979 by Scott Boulett, John Moores, and Dan Cloer (whose last initials gave the company its name). Its first product was the 3270 SuperOptimizer, a utility that dramatically improved terminal input/output operations. BMC, which went public in 1988, originally geared its products to corporations and institutions with large, sophisticated database systems. The company still sells its products primarily by phone, gambling that its liberal free-trial program will end in a sale; 50% of the time it does. As it moves into open systems computing, BMC is developing new marketing strategies, including strategic partnerships with OEMs and joint marketing agreements with computer manufacturers.

BMC's 1994 purchase of PATROL Software added UNIX-based open systems products to BMC's line and marked its extension beyond mainframes. PATROL earned $15 million that year.

BMC continues to develop software products for both mainframes and open systems. In 1995 the company released Basics/DB, a line of economical database utilities for mainframes. That same year BMC unveiled its MetaSUITE family of data management products for open systems. Three more products (MetaCHANGE, MetaDESK, and Meta-MANAGE) are due by April 1996.

WHO

Chairman, President, and CEO: Max P. Watson Jr., age 49, $752,360 pay
EVP and COO: Douglas J. Erwin, age 42, $600,000 pay
SVP Research and Development: James E. Juracek, age 49, $430,936 pay
SVP North American Sales: Richard P. Gardner, age 41, $412,109 pay
VP, General Counsel, and Secretary: M. Brinkley Morse, age 37, $320,970 pay
Treasurer: Stephen B. Solcher, age 34
Director Human Resources: Johnnie Horn
Auditors: Arthur Andersen & Co, SC

WHERE

HQ: 2101 CityWest Blvd., Houston, TX 77042-2827
Phone: 713-918-8800   **Fax:** 713-918-1307

	1995 Sales		1995 Operating Income	
	$ mil.	% of total	$ mil.	% of total
North America	209.5	61	28.0	26
Europe	113.8	33	75.0	69
Other regions	21.7	6	5.6	5
Total	**345.0**	**100**	**108.6**	**100**

WHAT

	1995 Sales
	% of total
IMS Database Utilities	38
MasterPlan for DB2	33
IMS/TM Enhancements	9
Network Performance	8
Other	12
Total	**100**

KEY COMPETITORS

American Software	Oracle
Apertus	PLATINUM technology
Computer Associates	SAP
Compuware	Software AG
Dun & Bradstreet	Sybase
Hewlett-Packard	System Software Associates
IBM	Walker Interactive

HOW MUCH

Nasdaq symbol: BMCS FY ends: March 31	5-Year Growth	1990	1991	1992	1993	1994	1995	1995 Year-end: Debt ratio: 0.0%
Sales ($ mil.)	30.0%	93.0	139.5	188.7	238.5	288.5	345.0	Return on equity: 27.8%
Net income ($ mil.)	30.7%	20.3	31.4	48.6	65.4	56.5	77.5	Cash (mil.): $39.5
Income as % of sales	—	21.8%	22.5%	25.8%	27.4%	19.6%	22.5%	Current ratio: 1.24
Earnings per share ($)	29.3%	0.42	0.63	0.94	1.25	1.08	1.52	Long-term debt (mil): $0.0
Stock price – high ($)[1]	—	10.09	15.13	37.38	39.50	42.06	35.50	No. of shares (mil.): 50.5
Stock price – low ($)[1]	—	4.55	8.88	13.50	18.63	19.38	20.13	Dividends
Stock price – close ($)[1]	23.0%	10.09	15.00	33.00	36.25	24.00	28.44	Yield: —
P/E – high	—	24	24	40	32	39	23	Payout: —
P/E – low	—	11	14	14	15	18	13	Market value (mil.): $1,436.2
Dividends per share ($)	—	0.00	0.00	0.00	0.00	0.00	0.00	R&D as % of sales: 16.1%
Book value per share ($)	36.9%	1.26	2.06	2.91	4.26	4.86	6.06	Advertising as % of sales: —
Employees	22.8%	424	593	782	909	987	1,185	

[1] Stock prices are for the prior calendar year.

THE BOMBAY COMPANY, INC.

OVERVIEW

Its name evokes images of coastal India, but the Bombay Company is headquartered in north Texas. In 1995 the Fort Worth–based company operated 432 stores featuring 18th- and 19th-century reproductions. It has helped revolutionize the retail furniture industry, selling fashionable products at reasonable prices. About 95% of the company's sales come from its private-label products. CEO Robert Nourse and his wife, EVP Alexandra, own 3.6% of the company's stock.

In 1979 Nourse bought the Canadian rights from the original Bombay Company, a New Orleans mail-order house founded by Brad Harper, for $1 plus 4% in royalties. Most important, the deal gave Nourse access to supply channels Harper had developed in Asia. Nourse realized the potential but wanted to move away from mail order. He viewed malls as the best way to market the concept. Alexandra began with the company writing newspaper ads for the first store in Toronto. The 2 were married in 1980. Texas-based Tandy Brands (men's accessories) bought the US company in 1980 and the Canadian operations in 1981; Nourse became head of both operations in 1984. In 1991 the accessories business was spun off as Tandy Brands Accessories (now Tandy Brands, Inc.), and the company renamed itself the Bombay Company, Inc.

Bombay gave to the furniture industry what it had always lacked: instant gratification. Purchases could be carried out of the store assembled or quickly put together at home. Bombay avoids stocking any pieces that might sit in the store for a prolonged period of time. The merchandise must move quickly for the high-rent mall stores to remain profitable.

In 1995, citing disappointing sales and escalating losses, the company announced plans to close its 62 mall-based Alex & Ivy country furniture retail stores.

WHO

President and CEO: Robert E. M. Nourse, age 56, $989,297 pay
EVP Marketing; President, BBA Direct: Alexandra M. T. Nourse, age 51, $698,006 pay
EVP, Treasurer, and CFO: James E. Herlihy, age 51, $500,445 pay
VP Real Estate: Stephen L. King, age 44, $331,291 pay
VP, Secretary, and General Counsel: Michael J. Veitenheimer, age 38
VP Human Resources: William S. Goodlatte, age 51
Auditors: Price Waterhouse LLP

WHERE

HQ: 550 Bailey Ave., Ste. 700, Fort Worth, TX 76107
Phone: 817-347-8200   **Fax:** 817-332-7066

	Stores	
	No.	% of total
South	126	28
Northeast	110	25
Midwest	90	20
West	70	16
Canada	51	11
Total	**447**	**100**

WHAT

	Sales	
		% of total
Furniture		45
Wall decor		18
Wood & metal accessories		18
Lamps, decorative accessories & other		19
Total		**100**

KEY COMPETITORS

Berkshire Hathaway	IKEA	Rhodes
Dayton Hudson	INTERCO	Roberds
Dillard	J. C. Penney	Sears
Ethan Allen	Levitz	Service
Euromarket Designs	Masco	Merchandise
Hanover Direct	May	Waban
Haverty Furniture	Mercantile Stores	Williams-
Home Express	Pier 1	Sonoma

HOW MUCH

NYSE symbol: BBA FY ends: Sat. nearest Jan. 31	5-Year Growth[1]	1990	1991	1992	1993	1994	1995[1]
Sales ($ mil.)	16.7%	111.7	139.3	176.0	231.7	317.5	241.5
Net income ($ mil.)	—	8.2	6.6	9.6	8.2	22.9	(14.7)
Income as % of sales	—	7.3%	4.7%	5.5%	3.5%	7.2%	—
Earnings per share ($)	—	0.26	0.21	0.29	0.23	0.60	(0.39)
Stock price – high ($)[2]	—	5.45	5.50	5.29	16.24	32.93	32.75
Stock price – low ($)[2]	—	2.17	1.91	1.93	4.45	12.68	8.75
Stock price – close ($)[2]	34.4%	3.91	2.28	4.92	16.24	30.00	10.00
P/E – high	—	21	26	18	71	55	—
P/E – low	—	8	9	7	19	21	—
Dividends per share ($)	—	0.00	0.00	0.00	0.00	0.00	0.00
Book value per share ($)	16.4%	1.72	1.51	1.84	3.24	4.04	3.68
Employees	21.7%	1,500	1,900	2,100	2,900	4,200	4,000

1995 Year-end:
Debt ratio: 0.0%
Return on equity: —
Cash (mil.): $30.7
Current ratio: 2.54
Long-term debt (mil.): $0.0
No. of shares (mil.): 36.7
Dividends
  Yield: —
  Payout: —
Market value (mil.): $366.5
R&D as % of sales: —
Advertising as % of sales: —

[1]Growth rates based on 7-month fiscal year for 1995 [2] Stock prices are for the prior calendar year.

BRINKER INTERNATIONAL, INC.

OVERVIEW

Brinker International is one of the largest casual-dining companies in the US, operating 5 chain restaurants: its flagship Chili's Grill and Bar, Grady's American Grill, Romano's Macaroni Grill, On the Border, and Spageddies.

Founded in Dallas in 1975 by Larry Lavine, by the early 1980s Chili's had become one of the Southwest's most popular "gourmet hamburger" chains. Norman Brinker, who pioneered the so-called "casual dining" segment with Steak and Ale in the 1960s, left Pillsbury and bought control of Chili's in 1983. In 1984 the company went public. Chili's grew from 23 restaurants in 1983 to over 360 in 1994, as Brinker and his management team aggressively recruited joint venture and franchise partners. They also expanded the menu to include items such as fajitas, staking the company's growth on aging baby boomers, who were looking for something a step up from fast food. In 1989 Chili's Inc. bought Romano's Macaroni Grill and the Regas Grill (renamed Grady's), and the company changed its name to Brinker International in 1991.

The company's strategy has been to offer tasty meals for less than $15, drinks included, and to do it with élan. With the casual-dining segment increasingly glutted, Brinker began hedging his bets, developing multiple concepts. In 1993 Brinker introduced Spageddies, a modestly priced Italian restaurant aimed at families, and opened 62 restaurants. In 1994 the company began testing Cozymel's, featuring the cuisine of Mexico's Yucatán peninsula, and acquired the $50 million, 21-unit On the Border Mexican-food chain in a $32 million stock swap.

In 1995 Brinker retired as CEO (he remains chairman) and was succeeded by Ron McDougall. That same year the company topped sales of $1.04 billion, with net income of $72.7 million.

WHO

Chairman: Norman E. Brinker, age 63, $1,365,727 pay
President and CEO: Ronald A. McDougall, age 52, $1,096,766 pay (prior to promotion)
COO: Creed L. Ford III, age 41, $619,096 pay (prior to promotion)
EVP and CFO: Debra L. Smithart-Weitzman, age 40, $418,500 pay
EVP, General Counsel, and Secretary: Roger F. Thomson, age 45
Chief Administrative Officer: F. Lane Cardwell Jr.
SVP Operations, Chili's Grill & Bar: Douglas H. Brooks
VP Human Resources: John Roberts
Auditors: KPMG Peat Marwick LLP

WHERE

HQ: 6820 LBJ Fwy., Dallas, TX 75240
Phone: 214-980-9917   **Fax:** 214-770-9593

WHAT

	Restaurants
	No.
Chili's (company owned)	277
Chili's (franchised/venture)	83
Romano's Macaroni Grill	35
Grady's	34
On the Border	21
Spageddies	6
Other	2
Total	**458**

Restaurant Formats
Chili's Grill & Bar (hamburgers, fajitas, chicken, seafood, sandwiches, salads)
Grady's American Grill (seafood, prime rib, steaks, pasta, salads, sandwiches)
On the Border (Mexican food)
Romano's Macaroni Grill (family-style Italian food)
Spageddies (modestly priced Italian food for families)

KEY COMPETITORS

Apple South
Applebee's
Bertucci's
Carlson
Cracker Barrel

Darden Restaurants
Family Restaurants
Landry's Seafood
Lone Star Steakhouse
Metromedia

Outback
Steakhouse
Pappas
Restaurants
Taco Cabana

HOW MUCH

NYSE symbol: EAT FY ends: Last Wed. in June	5-Year Growth	1989	1990	1991	1992	1993	1994	1994 Year-end: Debt ratio: 1.5%
Sales ($ mil.)	25.3%	284.7	347.1	426.8	519.3	652.9	878.5	Return on equity: 16.4%
Net income ($ mil.)	34.5%	14.0	18.1	26.1	35.7	48.9	61.6	Cash (mil.): $3.6
Income as % of sales	—	4.9%	5.2%	6.1%	6.9%	7.5%	7.0%	Current ratio: 0.46
Earnings per share ($)	26.1%	0.26	0.33	0.40	0.51	0.69	0.83	Long-term debt (mil.): $5.7
Stock price – high ($)	—	6.70	7.89	16.91	19.02	30.85	33.68	No. of shares (mil.): 71.0
Stock price – low ($)	—	4.09	5.05	6.06	13.29	18.24	15.00	Dividends
Stock price – close ($)	22.7%	6.51	6.85	16.68	18.30	30.68	18.13	Yield: —
P/E – high	—	26	24	42	37	45	41	Payout: —
P/E – low	—	16	15	15	26	26	18	Market value (mil.): $1,287.8
Dividends per share ($)	—	0.00	0.00	0.00	0.00	0.00	0.00	R&D as % of sales: —
Book value per share ($)	30.0%	1.58	2.30	3.25	3.91	4.88	5.87	Advertising as % of sales: —
Employees	22.1%	14,000	15,000	20,000	28,000	29,000	38,000	

CAMERON ASHLEY INC.

OVERVIEW

While supplying building materials to the residential market, Cameron Ashley continues to build its own business. With its industry consolidating, the company has set its sights on becoming a national distributor of roofing, millwork, aluminum, insulation, and other building products; it added 29 branch locations in fiscal 1994 and now has more than 80 branches serving markets in 35 states and in parts of Canada and Mexico. The company's goal is to better serve the major building product manufacturers and mass merchandisers. CGW Southeast Partners, an investment firm, owns 62.9% of the company's stock.

Cameron Ashley was created when CGW acquired the separate companies Cameron and Ashley in 1991. Wm. Cameron & Co. was founded in 1867 in Missouri and moved its headquarters to Waco, Texas, a year later. It was acquired by CertainTeed Products in 1954, which separated its operations into 2 divisions, distribution (Cameron Wholesale) and millwork manufacturing. During the 1980s Cameron's business slowed, and in 1991 CertainTeed (now controlled by Saint-Gobain) sold it to CGW and a management group led by Cameron CEO Ron Ross. Ashley Aluminum was founded in 1966 and acquired by Talquin Building Products in 1985. In 1991 CGW and a management group led by Talquin president Walter Muratori bought the company, which continued to expand geographically through acquisitions and the opening of new branches. Cameron Ashley went public in 1994. That same year it bought Massachusetts-based Bird Corporation's distribution business for $23 million.

In 1995 Cameron Ashley bought Albuquerque Door Co. in New Mexico and Star, a California holding company with operations including P/C Supply in Utah and Westar Building Materials in Oregon.

WHO

Chairman: Ronald R. Ross, age 42, $289,277 pay
President: Walter J. Muratori, age 51, $308,750 pay
VP: C. Steven Gaffney, age 46, $207,500 pay
VP and Chief Accounting Officer: John H. Bradberry, age 44, $141,535 pay (prior to promotion)
VP and CFO: Dixon McElwee, age 48
VP Human Resources: Thomas R. Miller, age 45
Auditors: Deloitte & Touche LLP

WHERE

HQ: 11100 Plano Rd., Dallas, TX 75238
Phone: 214-340-1996   **Fax:** 214-342-6177

WHAT

	1994 Sales	
	$ mil.	% of total
Roofing	85.9	29
Pool & patio enclosures	59.2	20
Insulation	38.5	13
Millwork	32.6	11
Industrial metals	17.8	6
Steel	11.9	4
Wood	11.9	4
Other building products	38.5	13
Total	**296.3**	**100**

Distributed Products
Industrial metals (aluminum & stainless steel products)
Insulation
Millwork (doors, moldings, shutters, stair parts, windows)
Pool and patio enclosure products (awnings, gutters, handrails, roof panels)
Roofing products (asphalt, coatings, shingles, vents)
Steel products (corrugated metal, fencing, nails, rebar)
Wood products (lumber, paneling, shelving, siding)
Other building products (ceiling tiles, fireplaces)

KEY COMPETITORS

Allied Building Products	Grossman's	Servistar
BMC West	Hechinger	Strober
Foxworth- Galbraith	Hughes Supply	Weyerhaeuser
Georgia-Pacific	Lowe's	Wickes Lumber
	Moore-Handley	Wolohan Lumber
	North Pacific	

HOW MUCH

Nasdaq symbol: CMSH FY ends: October 31	Annual Growth	1989	1990	1991	1992	1993	1994
Sales ($ mil.)	30.0%	—	—	134.8	147.2	224.0	296.3
Net income ($ mil.)	—	—	—	(1.6)	3.0	5.7	8.7
Income as % of sales	—	—	—	—	2.1%	2.6%	2.9%
Earnings per share ($)	44.6%	—	—	—	0.67	1.14	1.40
Stock price - high ($)	—	—	—	—	—	12.50	18.75
Stock price - low ($)	—	—	—	—	—	10.13	9.00
Stock price - close ($)	27.2%	—	—	—	—	11.50	14.63
P/E -high	—	—	—	—	—	11	13
P/E- low	—	—	—	—	—	9	6
Dividends per share ($)	—	—	—	—	—	0.00	0.00
Book value per share ($)	119.2%	—	—	—	—	3.07	6.73
Employees	59.2%	—	—	—	—	723	1,151

1994 Year-end:
Debt ratio: 46.1%
Return on equity: 30.4%
Cash (mil.): $0.4
Current ratio: 2.17
Long-term debt (mil.): $36.6
No. of shares (mil.): 6.5
Dividends
  Yield: —
  Payout: —
Market value (mil.): $94.5
R&D as % of sales: —
Advertising as % of sales: —

CASH AMERICA INTERNATIONAL, INC.

OVERVIEW

Fort Worth–based Cash America, the world's largest pawn company, is moving up in the world. No longer simply a chain of pawnshops, the company is setting its sights on becoming the one-stop financial services headquarters for the cash economy. In 1994 Cash America invested in Mr. Payroll Corp. and began setting up check cashing and money-order kiosks in some stores. The company is also the only international pawn company, having bought UK-based Harvey & Thompson, Ltd., in 1992 and Sweden's Svensk Pantbelåning in 1994.

The company was founded by Jack Daugherty, who as a student hocked his guitar to finance dates. After quitting school, in 1970 he opened a pawnshop. It was so successful that he used the proceeds to invest in oil, but when the oil business began a downturn he returned to the pawn business, incorporating Cash America in 1984. The company went public in 1987. At first Cash America expanded through acquisitions. More recently it has concentrated on new openings, but the company still buys promising stores.

Cash America brought economies of scale and efficiency to the pawn business and addressed pawnshops' traditional image problem by catering to bargain shoppers with its Cash America VIP Program, which offers discounts to frequent shoppers. About 70% of its US loans and 90% of its UK loans are redeemed (the latter rate is a result of UK laws that specify that only jewelry and precious metals may be pawned and therefore ensure that pawnshop patrons are more affluent than those in the US).

After a slight slowdown in income growth in 1993 related to the consolidation of its UK acquisition, Cash America recovered and continued its upward curve, entering Alabama and Missouri in 1994. In 1995 the company added another 16 US stores in the first quarter alone.

WHO

Chairman and CEO: Jack R. Daugherty, age 47, $396,000 pay
President and COO: Daniel R. Feehan, age 44, $328,500 pay
EVP Administration (HR): Robert Brockman
VP Marketing and Merchandise: Gregory W. Trees, age 51, $150,000 pay
VP Finance and Treasurer: Thomas A. Bessant, Jr., age 36
VP, Secretary, and General Counsel: Hugh A. Simpson, age 35
Auditors: Coopers & Lybrand L.L.P.

WHERE

HQ: 1600 W. 7th St., Fort Worth, TX 76102-2599
Phone: 817-335-1100 **Fax:** 817-335-1119

	1994 Stores	
	No.	% of total
Texas	145	41
Florida	44	12
Georgia	21	6
Tennessee	20	6
Oklahoma	17	5
Other US	65	18
UK	33	9
Sweden	10	3
Total	**355**	**100**

WHAT

	1994 Sales	
	$ mil.	% of total
Sales	156.2	60
Pawn service charges	105.9	40
Total	**262.1**	**100**

KEY COMPETITORS

EZCORP
First Cash
Security Finance
World Acceptance

HOW MUCH

NYSE symbol: PWN FY ends: December 31	5-Year Growth	1989	1990	1991	1992	1993	1994	1994 Year-end: Debt ratio: 39.5%
Sales ($ mil.)	24.7%	87.0	115.6	138.0	185.4	224.7	262.1	Return on equity: 8.9%
Net income ($ mil.)	17.2%	7.0	8.7	10.5	13.0	13.8	15.5	Cash (mil.): $4.8
Income as % of sales	—	8.0%	7.5%	7.6%	7.0%	6.1%	5.9%	Current ratio: 9.01
Earnings per share ($)	12.8%	0.29	0.36	0.43	0.45	0.48	0.53	Long-term debt (mil.): $119.8
Stock price – high ($)	—	7.55	10.25	9.81	12.88	11.00	10.13	No. of shares (mil.): 28.4
Stock price – low ($)	—	3.21	5.75	6.00	7.25	6.38	7.50	Dividends
Stock price – close ($)	5.5%	7.55	7.56	9.63	10.88	9.38	9.88	Yield: 0.5%
P/E – high	—	26	29	23	29	23	19	Payout: 9.4%
P/E – low	—	11	16	14	16	13	14	Market value (mil.): $280.6
Dividends per share ($)	4.6%	0.04	0.03	0.04	0.05	0.05	0.05	R&D as % of sales: —
Book value per share ($)	13.2%	3.47	3.79	4.21	5.46	5.87	6.46	Advertising as % of sales: —
Employees	25.2%	805	1,000	1,300	1,700	1,530	2,475	

CELLSTAR CORPORATION

OVERVIEW

CellStar is one of the leading non–telephone company wholesale distributors of cellular phones in the US and a leading retailer of mobile phones. It distributes cellular telephones made by Ericsson, NEC, Nokia, and Motorola to retailers, carriers, exporters, and dealers in the US and abroad. CellStar retails cellular phones and accessories through kiosks in more than 100 Sam's Clubs and also operates stand-alone retail stores in the US and Latin America. Founder and CEO Alan Goldfield owns 51.5% of the company, and auto electronics distributor Audiovox owns 21%.

Goldfield founded a record store, National Tape and Record Center, in Dallas in 1969; when the business floundered he began selling car stereos. He soon moved into distribution, supplying stereos and other auto accessories to car dealers and other installers. In 1981 he entered a joint venture with Audiovox to distribute that company's car accessory products in New Mexico, Oklahoma, and Texas. In 1984, when Audiovox began offering Toshiba cellular phones, Goldfield followed suit. But by the late 1980s Audiovox began to run into inventory problems, so Goldfield added Motorola products. He moved into retail in 1988 when he signed a deal to put kiosks in Sam's Clubs.

As the popularity of cellular phones took off, so did the company's fortunes. It has also been helped by a close relationship with Motorola. While the US market has been hot, Goldfield sees even more potential overseas because of the lack of phone lines in less-developed countries. CellStar moved into Mexico in 1991 and expanded into Brazil, Chile, Venezuela, and Hong Kong in 1993. That same year the company changed its name to CellStar and went public.

CellStar began shipping phones to China in 1994 and signed distribution deals in India, the Philippines, Singapore, and South Africa in 1995.

WHO

Chairman, President, and CEO: Alan H. Goldfield, age 51, $800,000 pay
President and COO: Terry S. Parker
EVP, CFO, and Treasurer: Kenneth W. Sanders, age 37
VP South American Operations: Daniel T. Bogar, age 35, $240,000 pay
VP Mexican Operations and Asia-Pacific Region: Timothy L. Maretti, age 41, $240,000 pay
VP Wholesale Sales: Michael S. Hedge, age 38, $183,000 pay
VP Retail Sales: Kenneth E. Kerby, age 49, $161,740 pay
VP, General Counsel, and Secretary: Elaine Flud Rodriguez, age 38
Director Human Resources: Barbara O'Neal
Auditors: KPMG Peat Marwick LLP

WHERE

HQ: 1730 Briercroft Dr., Carrollton, TX 75006
Phone: 214-323-0600   **Fax:** 214-994-1516

	1994 Sales	
	$ mil.	% of total
US	398.1	77
Mexico	69.0	13
South America	51.3	10
Total	**518.4**	**100**

WHAT

	1994 Sales
	% of total
Product sales	86
Activation income	12
Residual income	2
Total	**100**

KEY COMPETITORS

Advanced Cellular	BT	Office Depot
Allied Distributing	Cellular	Pacific Telesis
Ameritech	Wholesalers	Pana Pacific
AT&T	Circuit City	Pep Boys
Bell Atlantic	GTE	Tandy
BellSouth	Hello Direct	U S WEST
Best Buy	NYNEX	Wholesale Cellular

HOW MUCH

Nasdaq symbol: CLST FY ends: November 30	Annual Growth	1989	1990	1991	1992	1993	1994
Sales ($ mil.)	71.8%	34.7	69.8	112.6	181.0	275.4	518.4
Net income ($ mil.)	—	—	(0.3)	(0.3)	(0.0)	7.9	16.2
Income as % of sales	—	—	—	—	—	2.9%	3.1%
Earnings per share ($)	—	—	(0.02)	(0.02)	0.00	0.58	0.88
Stock price – high ($)	—	—	—	—	—	17.50	23.25
Stock price – low ($)	—	—	—	—	—	12.00	9.13
Stock price – close ($)	35.1%	—	—	—	—	16.75	22.63
P/E – high	—	—	—	—	—	30	26
P/E – low	—	—	—	—	—	21	10
Dividends per share ($)	—	—	—	—	—	0.00	0.00
Book value per share ($)	619.4%	—	—	—	—	0.57	4.13
Employees	78.6%	—	—	—	—	700	1,250

1994 Year-end:
Debt ratio: 17.1%
Return on equity: 38.5%
Cash (mil.): $14.0
Current ratio: 1.60
Long-term debt (mil.): $3.1
No. of shares (mil.): 18.6
Dividends
  Yield: —
  Payout: —
Market value (mil.): $419.9
R&D as % of sales: —
Advertising as % of sales: —

CLEAR CHANNEL COMMUNICATIONS

OVERVIEW

San Antonio–based Clear Channel Communications is a Texas-size, diversified media company with hefty stakes in radio and TV, mainly in Sunbelt states. In 1995 the company owned 31 radio stations (13 AM, 18 FM) and 9 TV stations (8 Fox affiliates) in midsize markets as well as in major markets such as Houston, Miami, and New Orleans. Most were acquired since 1992, and half are concentrated in Texas, Florida, and Oklahoma. The company has sales and advertising agreements with additional radio and TV stations. It also operates 4 radio networks that provide sports coverage (Clear Channel Sports) and news and agricultural information (Kentucky News Network, Oklahoma News Network, and Virginia News Network). Chief stockholders include founder and CEO Lowry Mays (22%) and B. J. "Red" McCombs (17%).

The company was founded in 1972 when Mays, an investment banker, teamed up with local car dealer McCombs to buy a struggling FM radio station (2 of Mays's clients had backed out of the purchase). Mays revived the station within a year and then bought others. The company's name came from the 1975 purchase of a "clear channel" station that was part of the nation's emergency broadcast network.

In 1984 Clear Channel went public and continued to buy ailing stations at favorable terms. The company diversified with the 1988 purchase of a TV station. Clear Channel sold some of its smaller radio stations to merge in 1994 with Metroplex Communications and keep its holdings at the level authorized by the FCC. In 1995 it bought a 50% stake in the Australian Radio Network (Australia's #2 radio network); a CBS network affiliate in Harrisburg, Pennsylvania (pending FCC approval); and 80% of 2 Houston radio stations. With a $350 million credit line, the company intends to buy other media properties.

WHO

President and CEO: L. Lowry Mays, age 59, $1,227,396 pay
President, Clear Channel TV: J. Daniel Sullivan, age 43, $346,647 pay
Regional VP: James D. Smith, age 46, $168,645 pay
SVP Operations: Mark P. Mays, age 31
VP, Controller, and Director Human Resources: Herbert W. Hill Jr.
Auditors: Ernst & Young LLP

WHERE

HQ: Clear Channel Communications, Inc., 200 Concord Plaza, Ste. 600, San Antonio, TX 78216
Phone: 210-822-2828   **Fax:** 210-822-2299

WHAT

	1994 Sales		1994 Operating Income	
	$ mil.	% of total	$ mil.	% of total
Radio	94.1	47	19.4	40
Television	79.0	39	28.6	60
Total	**173.1**	**100**	**48.0**	**100**

	1995 Holdings	
	Radio stations	TV stations
Texas	7	—
Florida	6	1
Oklahoma	5	1
Virginia	4	—
Connecticut	3	—
Kentucky	2	—
Louisiana	2	—
Ohio	2	—
Alabama	—	1
Arizona	—	1
Arkansas	—	1
Kansas	—	1
Minnesota	—	1
New York	—	1
Tennessee	—	1
Total	**31**	**9**

KEY COMPETITORS

A. H. Belo	Chris-Craft	Washington Post
BHC Comm.	Infinity Broadcasting	

HOW MUCH

NYSE symbol: CCU FY ends: December 31	5-Year Growth	1989	1990	1991	1992	1993	1994
Sales ($ mil.)	30.5%	47.5	60.3	64.1	82.2	118.2	173.1
Net income ($ mil.)	—	(0.4)	(0.3)	1.1	4.3	9.1	22.0
Income as % of sales	—	—	—	1.7%	5.2%	8.0%	12.7%
Earnings per share ($)	—	(0.03)	(0.03)	0.09	0.29	0.59	1.27
Stock price – high ($)	—	5.59	6.14	7.94	14.48	36.90	52.00
Stock price – low ($)	—	3.42	3.88	5.38	6.91	12.96	31.40
Stock price – close ($)	59.3%	4.95	5.44	7.23	13.04	36.80	50.75
P/E – high	—	—	—	88	50	63	41
P/E – low	—	—	—	60	24	22	25
Dividends per share ($)	(100.0%)	1.02	0.00	0.00	0.00	0.00	0.00
Book value per share ($)	104.9%	0.21	0.24	1.73	2.10	5.79	7.58
Employees	17.2%	700	764	800	1,150	1,354	1,549

1994 Year-end:
Debt ratio: 65%
Return on equity: 19.2%
Cash (mil.): $6.8
Current ratio: 1.95
Long-term debt (mil.): $238.2
No. of shares (mil.): 17.2
Dividends
  Yield: —
  Payout: —
Market value (mil.): $874.2
R&D as % of sales: —
Advertising as % of sales: —

COMPUADD COMPUTER CORPORATION

OVERVIEW

Niche work if you can get it. Austin-based CompuAdd is no slacker, having bounced back from Chapter 11 bankruptcy reorganization with an aggressive strategy of selling niche-market products such as cash register systems and notebooks. CompuAdd designs, markets, sells, and supports its own line of computers and workstations. It also markets and supports a broad range of related hardware, software, and accessories manufactured by 3rd parties.

CompuAdd pioneered the computer mail-order business. With $100,000 gained by dabbling in real estate, Bill Hayden, a former Texas Instruments engineer, started CompuAdd by selling computer add-on equipment (hence the company name) in 1982. In 1983 Hayden opened a retail outlet in Austin, Texas. In 1986 the company began offering IBM clones made in Taiwan. Three years later CompuAdd introduced its own line of computers and launched a major retail expansion. CompuAdd became a major player in the electronic point-of-sale (POS) terminal market in 1991 when Sears signed a $53 million deal with CompuAdd; Sears installed 28,000 CompuAdd POS units in its stores across the US.

But Hayden overreached himself. The #11 computer maker in 1992 declared bankruptcy in 1993 when its aggressive expansion into the retail computer market was hammered by rampant price cutting by larger competitors and computer superstores. After suffering huge losses, CompuAdd quit the retail business.

The leaner CompuAdd that emerged from reorganization in 1993 has only 250 staff members, down from over 1,500 in 1990. In addition, Hayden resigned to pursue other interests. New CEO Rick Krause (who has been with the company since 1989) is pushing the niche-market strategy and the company's superior after-sales support. In 1994 a private investment company, Dimeling, Schrieber & Park, took over ownership of CompuAdd.

In 1995 the firm launched 2 new notebook computers, the CompuAdd P90 Colorscan and the CompuAdd P90 Colorpro, both incorporating 90MHz Pentium processors. In addition, closely held Power Computing signed up CompuAdd to produce the first official clones of Apple Power Macintosh computers.

WHO

CEO: Rick Krause, age 42
VP Sales and Marketing: Jerry Mixon
VP Finance (CFO): Walter Kluchki
Director Business and Product Development: Joe Guevremont
Director Manufacturing: Michael Grimm
Director Logistics and Service: Billy Lowe
Director Human Resources: Jeanne Nelson
Auditors: KPMG Peat Marwick LLP

WHERE

HQ: 12317 Technology Blvd., Austin, TX 78727
Phone: 512-250-1489 **Fax:** 512-331-2776

WHAT

Products
Apple Power Macintosh clones
Cash registers
Color notebooks
Desktop systems
Input devices and diskettes
Low-profile sytems
Modems
Multimedia
Network servers
Notebook systems and accessories
Printers and accessories
Software
Storage devices
Tower and minitower PCs
Video

KEY COMPETITORS

Acer
Advanced Logic Research
Apple
AST
AT&T
Canon
Compaq
DEC
Dell
Gateway 2000
Hewlett-Packard
IBM
Machines Bull
Micron Technology
Olivetti
Packard Bell
Random Access
Sony
Toshiba
Unisys

HOW MUCH

Private company FY ends: December 31	5-Year Growth	1989	1990	1991	1992	1993	1994
Sales ($ mil.)	(21.4%)	400.0	516.0	513.6	524.4	233.4	120.0
Employees	(28.0%)	1,290	1,560	1,370	1,300	1,300	250

CompuAdd®
Customer driven. by design.™

CONSOLIDATED GRAPHICS, INC.

OVERVIEW

Houston-based Consolidated Graphics (COGI), one of the fastest-growing printing companies in the US, is actually a network of 10 printing companies serving 5 metropolitan markets. By operating as part of COGI, the company's print houses can exploit the buying power and management depth of a large firm while offering customers local service. COGI companies together boast 27 sheet-fed and 5 web presses and offer a full menu of complementary services, from electronic prepress to distribution.

COGI was founded in 1985 by CPA Joe Davis, a veteran of both Price Waterhouse and Houston's Arthur Andersen office, where he had become a partner at age 33. Davis left Arthur Andersen in 1979 to become VP of finance and administration at International Paper. He left that firm and purchased his first printing company, Western Lithographic, in 1985. Since then Davis has concentrated on acquiring established small to medium-sized printers (those with annual sales between $2 million and $15 million) that have a reputation for quality and a strong customer base. All of the print shops in the COGI family specialize in printing recurring materials such as financial, promotional, and sales pieces. In 1993 COGI bought Gulf Printing, one of Houston's largest printers, from SBC Communications. COGI went public in 1994. Davis owns about 32% of the company.

Davis continues selectively acquiring local printers. In 1994 COGI entered the Dallas market with the purchase of the Jarvis Press. It also added 2 Denver-area companies — Gritz-Ritter Graphics and Frederic Printing.

In 1995 COGI bought the assets of 88-year-old Brandt & Lawson, a Houston-based printer, and merged them into Gulf Printing. That same year COGI entered 2 new markets with the acquisitions of Heritage Graphics (Phoenix) and Clear Visions (San Antonio).

WHO

President and CEO: Joe R. Davis, age 52, $228,000 pay
President, Chas. P. Young Co.: Scott L. Fordham, age 36, $166,000 pay
President, Gulf Printing: W. Mark Rand, age 36, $125,000 pay
VP Finance and Administration, CFO, and Chief Accounting Officer: Mary K. Collins, age 38, $115,000 pay
VP Human Resources: Janet Swikard
Auditors: Arthur Andersen & Co, SC

WHERE

HQ: 2210 W. Dallas St., Houston, TX 77019
Phone: 713-529-4200   **Fax:** 713-525-4305

WHAT

	1995 Sales % of total
Commercial printing	96
Financial printing	4
Total	**100**

Selected Services

Distribution	Packaging
Electronic prepress	Printing
Finishing, folding, and binding	Warehousing

Subsidiaries
Chas. P. Young Co. (Houston)
Clear Visions (San Antonio)
Frederic Printing Co. (Denver)
Gritz-Ritter Graphics, Inc. (Boulder)
Grover/Houston Litho Co. (Houston)
Gulf Printing Co. (Houston)
Heritage Graphics (Phoenix)
The Jarvis Press, Inc. (Dallas)
Tewell Warren Printing Co. (Denver)
Western Lithographic Co. (Houston)

KEY COMPETITORS

Banta	R. R. Donnelley	Quebecor
Bowne	Hart Graphics	World Color Press
Courier	Quad/Graphics	

HOW MUCH

Nasdaq symbol: COGI FY ends: March 31	Annual Growth	1990	1991	1992	1993	1994	1995	1995 Year-end:
Sales ($ mil.)	35.7%	12.4	14.9	20.5	28.9	48.6	57.2	Debt ratio: 20.7%
Net income ($ mil.)	46.9%	0.7	0.9	0.8	2.1	3.0	4.5	Return on equity: 19.0%
Income as % of sales	—	5.3%	6.3%	3.8%	7.2%	6.1%	7.8%	Cash (mil.): $1.7
Earnings per share ($)	35.1%	0.20	0.34	0.39	0.72	0.90	0.90	Current ratio: 2.32
Stock price – high ($)[1]	—	—	—	—	—	—	22.50	Long-term debt (mil.): $8.8
Stock price – low ($)[1]	—	—	—	—	—	—	9.75	No. of shares (mil.): 5.5
Stock price – close ($)[1]	—	—	—	—	—	—	11.25	Dividends
P/E – high	—	—	—	—	—	—	25	Yield: —
P/E – low	—	—	—	—	—	—	11	Payout: —
Dividends per share ($)	—	—	—	—	—	—	0.00	Market value (mil.): $61.5
Book value per share ($)	—	—	—	—	—	—	6.98	R&D as % of sales: —
Employees	48.1%	—	—	—	—	474	702	Advertising as % of sales: —

[1] Stock prices are for the prior calendar year.

THE CONTINUUM COMPANY, INC.

OVERVIEW

Continuum is the world's leading supplier of software and services to the insurance industry. It provides proprietary software for processing insurance claims (including its Colossus program, which provides an objective, data-based method of assessing pain and suffering damages for personal injury claims) and data processing outsourcing services. Outsourcing accounts for over 90% of sales; it consists of services that range from the installation and operation of data processing departments to the outright purchase of a client's data operations and the hiring of its data processing staff. The company provides its goods and services worldwide.

Continuum was established in 1968 as Tracor Computing Corp., a spinoff of the conglomerate Tracor. When one of the spinoff's main stockholders went belly-up in the 1980s, a group called Continuum Holdings, which included both Continuum's current chairman and CEO, acquired 52% of the company's shares. Since 1987, when it was named the Continuum Company, the firm has made several major acquisitions. Its purchase of Computations Holdings in 1990 gave the company a presence in Australia and northern Europe, as well as an entry into the property and casualty insurance software market (including the Colossus software.)

In 1993 Continuum bought Paxus Corporation of Australia, which expanded its European and Pacific Rim customer base. Its purchase of US-based Vantage Computer Systems gave Continuum access to new outsourcing revenues and to VANTAGE-ONE, a relational database system. The costs of these acquisitions took Continuum into the red in 1994.

In 1995 Continuum concluded a $45 million outsourcing contract with Allianz Life Insurance of North America.

WHO

Chairman: Ronald C. Carroll, age 60, $345,833 pay
President and CEO: W. Michael Long, age 42, $618,750 pay
EVP: Robert S. Maltempo, age 54, $375,000 pay
EVP: Neil R. Cullimore, age 51, $308,333 pay
SVP: Piers G. D. Fox, age 50, $268,106 pay
SVP: Michael W. Brinsford, age 45
VP, Secretary, Treasurer, and CFO: John L. Westermann III, age 49
Managing Director, Continuum Australia Ltd.: Philip H. Small, age 45
Manager Human Resource Development: Deborah Stafford
Auditors: Ernst & Young LLP

WHERE

HQ: 9500 Arboretum Blvd., Austin, TX 78759-6399
Phone: 512-345-5700 **Fax:** 512-338-7041

	1995 Sales	
	$ mil.	% of total
US	141.8	44
Asia/Pacific	106.9	33
Europe	71.2	22
Canada & other regions	3.6	1
Total	**323.5**	**100**

WHAT

	1995 Sales	
	$ mil.	% of total
Service revenues	301.8	93
Software licensing	21.1	7
Interest income	0.6	—
Total	**323.5**	**100**

Selected Products
Life insurance software products
Property and casualty insurance software products

KEY COMPETITORS

Agency Mgmt. Services	IBM
Computer Sciences	Policy Mgmt. Systems
EDS	Unisys

HOW MUCH

NYSE symbol: CNU FY ends: March 31	5-Year Growth	1990	1991	1992	1993	1994	1995
Sales ($ mil.)	32.2%	80.1	112.7	125.9	122.9	242.9	323.5
Net income ($ mil.)	36.6%	5.5	8.9	8.6	6.4	(29.8)	26.2
Income as % of sales	—	6.9%	7.9%	6.8%	5.2%	—	8.1%
Earnings per share ($)	16.6%	0.64	0.93	0.81	0.60	(1.79)	1.38
Stock price – high ($)[1]	—	12.56	21.50	19.88	25.75	25.75	30.50
Stock price – low ($)[1]	—	6.19	9.13	10.13	12.25	14.50	18.00
Stock price – close ($)[1]	21.4%	11.56	14.13	12.25	25.75	19.25	30.50
P/E – high	—	20	23	25	43	—	22
P/E – low	—	10	10	13	20	—	13
Dividends per share ($)	—	0.00	0.00	0.00	0.00	0.00	0.00
Book value per share ($)	11.2%	2.53	4.11	4.85	5.44	2.68	4.30
Employees	30.0%	807	1,150	1,080	1,109	2,519	3,000

[1] Stock prices are for the prior calendar year.

1995 Year-end:
Debt ratio: 7.7%
Return on equity: 39.4%
Cash (mil.): $44.5
Current ratio: 1.81
Long-term debt (mil.): $6.0
No. of shares (mil.): 19.1
Dividends
  Yield: —
  Payout: —
Market value (mil.): $583.4
R&D as % of sales: 31.7%
Advertising as % of sales: —

CYRIX CORPORATION

OVERVIEW

While the semiconductor market has plenty of competitors, Cyrix CEO Jerry Rogers has his eye on the giant in the contest, Intel. Rogers's goal is to reach a 20% (up from about 3%) share of the microprocessor market by 1997 by taking market share away from Intel with Cyrix's newest microprocessor, the M1.

Rogers founded Cyrix in 1988 with a former Texas Instruments buddy, Tom Brightman. The company's first product was a coprocessor designed to relieve a PC's main processor of performing large math equations, thereby improving overall computer performance. From conception to initial shipments, the entire design process took only 14 months. With the revenues generated by the math coprocessor, Cyrix turned to the $10 billion main microprocessor market. Within 18 months a 6-engineer design team had developed a 486-compatible chip, a feat which had required hundreds of engineers and more than 4 years of work at Intel. Intel responded by filing a patent infringement suit, which Cyrix has largely fended off so far. Cyrix went public in 1993.

Cyrix grew by competing on the basis of price and performance while emphasizing a fast design cycle with extensive simulations and compatibility verifications. By "going fabless" (not fabricating its own chips), the company can concentrate on design and marketing. By entering joint ventures with Intel licensees such as Texas Instruments and SGS-Thompson, Cyrix has also obtained protection from lawsuits by Intel for patent infringement.

In 1994 Cyrix tied up a major deal with IBM to produce jointly the M1 chip to outperform Intel's Pentium chip. However, the M1's release date was delayed until late 1995 because of manufacturing problems. In 1995 Cyrix introduced the Cyrix 5x86, a chip with performance and price features that bridge the gap between 486-class and Pentium-class chips.

WHO

Chairman: Harvey B. Cash, age 56
President and CEO: Gerald D. "Jerry" Rogers, age 51, $239,447 pay
SVP Sales: James N. Chapman, age 45, $222,099 pay
VP Product Marketing: Stephen L. Domenik, age 43, $174,726 pay
SVP Engineering: Kevin C. McDonough, age 45, $172,991 pay
VP Business and Technology Development: Thomas B. Brightman, age 40, $169,275 pay
VP, General Counsel, and Secretary: Russell N. Fairbanks Jr., age 51
Controller, Treasurer, and Chief Accounting Officer (CFO): Timothy W. Kinnear, age 31
Director Human Resources: Margaret Quinn
Auditors: Ernst & Young LLP

WHERE

HQ: 2703 N. Central Expwy., Richardson, TX 75080
Phone: 214-968-8387   **Fax:** 214-699-9857

	1994 Sales		1994 Operating Income	
	$ mil.	% of total	$ mil.	% of total
US	169.4	69	52.8	95
Europe	76.7	31	2.0	4
Asia/Pacific	—	—	0.8	1
Adjustments	—	—	0.2	—
Total	**246.1**	**100**	**55.8**	**100**

WHAT

Selected Products

Math Coprocessors	Microprocessors
FasMath 387DX Coprocessor	Cx486DRx^2
FasMath 387SX Coprocessor	Cyrix 5x86
	Cyrix M1

KEY COMPETITORS

AMD	IBM	NexGen
Apple	Intel	Sun Microsystems
Chips and Technologies	Motorola	Texas Instruments

HOW MUCH

Nasdaq symbol: CYRX FY ends: Sun. nearest Dec. 31	Annual Growth	1989	1990	1991	1992	1993	1994	1994 Year-end: Debt ratio: 15.3%
Sales ($ mil.)	76.8%	0.0	25.2	55.3	72.9	125.1	246.1	Return on equity: 35.8%
Net income ($ mil.)	—	(2.9)	9.8	12.7	8.4	19.6	37.6	Cash (mil.): $59.2
Income as % of sales	—	—	39.1%	23.0%	11.5%	15.7%	15.3%	Current ratio: 2.53
Earnings per share ($)	—	(0.87)	0.70	0.78	0.49	1.06	1.88	Long-term debt (mil.): $18.3
Stock price – high ($)	—	—	—	—	—	40.50	47.50	No. of shares (mil.): 18.8
Stock price – low ($)	—	—	—	—	—	19.30	18.50	Dividends
Stock price – close ($)	(3.1%)	—	—	—	—	20.25	19.63	Yield: —
P/E – high	—	—	—	—	—	38	25	Payout:—
P/E – low	—	—	—	—	—	18	10	Market value (mil.): $368.1
Dividends per share ($)	—	—	—	—	—	0.00	0.00	R&D as % of sales: 10.1%
Book value per share ($)	46.4%	—	—	—	—	4.58	6.70	Advertising as % of sales: —
Employees	83.1%	15	70	125	140	229	309	

DALLAS SEMICONDUCTOR

OVERVIEW

Dallas Semiconductor designs and manufactures specialty chips for computers. Its 14 product families include chips that enhance the security of systems (I.D. chips and software authorizations), provide safety backup for computers (battery backup and chargers), and that improve or extend the capacity of computers (system extensions). Dallas Semiconductor makes most of its own products, rather than farming them out to contractors in the US or abroad, and sells primarily to distributors and OEMs through its own sales force.

The company was formed in 1984 by a group of hardy survivors of Mostek, a Dallas-based chip maker that foundered in the early 1980s in part because it offered too few products to too small a base of clients. The Mostek survivors included founding chairman C. V. Prothro and Chao C. Mai. Learning from Mostek's mistakes, Dallas Semiconductors' management has sought targeted niche products with a wide variety of uses and users. It now offers more than 190 basic products to more than 8,000 customers worldwide. The company went public in 1987.

The company's technical edges include the combination of lithium cells with its chips, which give them added life, and using direct laser writing to program the chips, which provides a higher level of precision.

Dallas Semiconductor has done well, with increased sales and profits annually, despite the volatile nature of the chip business, which is characterized by intense competition, periodic materials shortages, price erosion, and constant technological change. The company has negotiated these pitfalls by staying ahead of the market's twists and turns and by making the necessary investments to keep up with technology.

Chairman Prothro owns about 10% of the company, with other members of the founding group owning about 6%.

WHO

Chairman, President, and CEO: C. V. Prothro, $957,811 pay
SVP: Chao C. Mai, $451,898 pay
VP Marketing and Product Development: Michael L. Bolan, $3423,459 pay
VP Finance: Alan P. Hale
VP Computer Products: F. A. Scherpenberg, $287,124 pay
VP Sales: John A. Mattis, $241,043 pay
Director Personnel: Gay Vencill
Auditors: Ernst & Young LLP

WHERE

HQ: Dallas Semiconductor Corporation, 4401 S. Beltwood Pkwy., Dallas, TX 75244-3292
Phone: 214-450-0400   **Fax:** 214-450-3748

WHAT

Automatic identification chips
Integrated Battery backup and battery chargers
Intelligent sockets
Microcontrollers
Multiport Memory
Nonvolatile RAM
Silicon timed circuits
Software authorization chips
System extension
Telecommunications chips
Timekeeping chips
User-insertable memory

KEY COMPETITORS

Advance Circuits
AMD
Atmel
Brooktree
Chips and Technologies
Intergrated Device Technology
Intel
Linear Technology
Microchip Technology
Motorola
National Semiconductor
Siliconix
Texas Instruments

HOW MUCH

NYSE symbol: DS FY ends: Sun. nearest Dec. 31	5-Year Growth	1989	1990	1991	1992	1993	1994
Sales ($ mil.)	17.2%	82.2	100.0	103.8	120.2	156.9	181.4
Net income ($ mil.)	21.8%	11.1	13.9	14.7	18.6	25.6	29.7
Income as % of sales	—	13.5%	13.8%	14.2%	15.5%	21.2%	16.4%
Earnings per share ($)	—	0.45	0.56	0.58	0.71	0.95	1.09
Stock price – high ($)	—	8.63	9.63	12.38	14.50	19.00	20.13
Stock price – low ($)	—	6.00	4.13	5.38	7.00	11.75	13.38
Stock price – close ($)	21.1%	6.38	6.13	7.88	13.38	15.50	16.63
P/E – high	—	19	17	21	20	20	18
P/E – low	—	13	7	9	10	12	12
Dividends per share ($)	—	0.00	0.00	0.00	0.00	0.00	0.00
Book value per share ($)	16.7%	3.54	4.08	4.69	5.47	6.53	7.66
Employees	6.9%	588	701	662	696	748	821

1994 Year-end:
Debt ratio: 0.0%
Return on equity: 16.5%
Cash (mil.): $17.5
Current ratio: 3.50
Long-term debt (mil.): $0.0
No. of shares (mil.): 25.4
Dividends
  Yield: —
  Payout: —
Market value (mil.): $422.6
R&D as % of sales: 12.5%
Advertising as % of sales: —

DAL-TILE INTERNATIONAL INC.

OVERVIEW

Dal-Tile doesn't mind being walked on. The Dallas-based company is one of the world's largest producers of ceramic tile. Dal-Tile makes its bathroom, counter, floor, and wall tiles at facilities in the US and Mexico. The company sells its products at over 200 North American sales centers as well as through leading retailers such as Color Tile and the Home Depot. Customers include architects, builders, and home owners as well as hotels, restaurants, and shopping centers.

Dal-Tile was founded as the Dallas Ceramic Company in 1947 by Robert Brittingham. During the 1950s the company opened its plant in Monterrey, Mexico, and acquired talc mining rights in West Texas (talc is a main ingredient in its wall tile). The company became Dal-Tile in 1980. In 1987 Brittingham and company president John LoMonaco were charged with illegally dumping lead-contaminated waste at Seagoville, near Dallas. AEA Investors (a group of retired corporate chief executives) acquired Dal-Tile in 1990 for $650 million; Brittingham received about $345 million. Under AEA Investors, Dal-Tile stopped using lead-based materials. In 1993 Brittingham and LoMonaco were found guilty of 16 felony violations related to the 1987 waste dumping charges. The pair was fined $6 million and ordered to perform community service supervising a lead abatement program. They paid another $6 million to build an ecology center for Dallas-area schoolchildren. Also in 1993 AEA Investors member Charles Pilliod became chairman and CEO of Dal-Tile, replacing Bill Cox, who had been CEO for 34 years. Pilliod is a former US ambassador to Mexico and a former chairman of Goodyear. AEA Investors owns 49% of Dal-Tile. In 1994 Howard Bull, a fomer executive with Baker Hughes and York International, assumed the role of CEO; Pilliod remained chairman.

In 1995 Armstrong World Industries agreed to merge its American Olean unit, which manufactures glazed and unglazed ceramic tile, with Dal-Tile. Armstrong will become a significant shareholder in Dal-Tile, with AEA Investors the controlling shareholder. Also in 1995 Dal-Tile planned to build a 20-million-square-foot production facility in El Paso.

WHO

Chairman: Charles J. Pilliod Jr., age 76, $182,692 pay
President and CEO: Howard I. Bull, age 54, $609,615 pay
VP; President, Ceramica and Materiales: Harold L. Turk, age 66, $767,500 pay
VP; EVP Marketing, Dal-Tile Corp.: Harold G. Turk, age 48, $396,250 pay
VP, CFO, and Treasurer: Carlos E. Sala, age 35, $344,000 pay
VP; EVP Sales, Dal-Tile Corp.: William J. Coppola, age 44, $240,000 pay
VP and COO: Barry J. Kulpa, age 46
VP Human Resources: Steve L. Blake
Auditors: Ernst & Young LLP

WHERE

HQ: 7834 Hawn Fwy., PO Box 17130, Dallas, TX 75217
Phone: 214-398-1411   Fax: 214-309-4140

	1994 Sales		1994 Operating Income	
	$ mil.	% of total	$ mil.	% of total
US	452.9	89	52.5	76
Mexico	48.6	10	16.3	24
Other countries	4.8	1	(0.5)	—
Total	**506.3**	**100**	**68.3**	**100**

WHAT

Selected Brand Names
Dal-Duraflor
Dal-Expressions
Dal-Monte-Floor
Dal-Monte-Permatones
Dal-Monte-Wall
Dal-Pavers
Dal-Tile

Selected Subsidiaries
Cerámica Regiomontana SA de CV (Mexico)
Dal-Minerals Corp.
Dal-Tile Corp.
Dal-Tile of Canada
Materiales Cerámicos SA de CV (Mexico)
R&M Supplies

KEY COMPETITORS

American	General Felt	Mohawk Industries
Biltrite	Image Industries	Premark
Congoleum	Integrated Floor	ProGroup
Fieldcrest	Sources	Shaw Industries
Cannon	Interface	Triangle Pacific

HOW MUCH

Private company FY ends: December 31	Annual Growth	1989	1990	1991	1992	1993	1994	1994 Year-end: Debt ratio: 100.0%
Sales ($ mil.)	8.5%	336.9	360.0	357.6	398.0	440.6	506.3	Return on equity: —
Net income ($ mil.)	(25.5%)	30.0	1.9	(9.3)	0.0	(267.7)	6.9	Cash (mil.): $13.0
Income as % of sales	—	8.9%	0.5%	—	—	—	1.4%	Current ratio: 1.18
Employees	15.8%	—	3,500	3,500	3,500	5,900	6,300	Long-term debt (mil.): $489.4

DATA RACE, INC.

OVERVIEW

DATA RACE is trying to get back up to speed. The San Antonio–based company manufactures data/fax modems for portable computers, but it stumbled in 1994 after it lost 2 of its biggest customers, Dell and Tandy. It continues to make custom and private-label modems for OEM customers, including IBM, Texas Instruments, and Xerox, but it is working to strengthen its other product line: multiplexers, which can connect a company's branch offices via a single phone line by integrating voice, fax, and data. Chairman Herbert Hensley owns 5% of DATA RACE.

The company was founded in 1983 by a group of executives from computer maker Datapoint International. In 1985 it introduced its first product, a high-speed modem called Race, that beat competitors such as Hayes Microproducts to market by nearly 2 years. DATA RACE focused on the high end of the market, making custom modems for OEMs. In the mid- and late-1980s it also began to diversify into multiplexers and other telecommunications products. In 1990 it began making modems for the notebook computer market. DATA RACE went public in 1992.

Looking for new markets, DATA RACE released a line of data/fax modems and ethernet LAN adapters for sale to dealers and resellers in 1993. However, after a year of disappointing sales, it dropped the line in 1994. The company was also hurt by the growing popularity of PCMCIA-standard modems (credit card–sized devices that can be easily installed into a notebook computer), which cut into its sales of custom, internal modems and made price competition fierce.

The company rebounded in fiscal 1995, posting a small profit on sales of $30 million, thanks to a major contract with IBM to provide fax modems for its ThinkPad notebook computers.

WHO

Chairman: Herbert T. Hensley, age 55
President and CEO: W. B. Barker, age 47
SVP Operations: Walter D. Warren, age 58, $120,313 pay
VP and Chief Technical Officer: Leven E. Staples, age 52, $116,711 pay
VP Sales: Gerard Goebeler, age 43, $95,206 pay
VP Finance and Administration and CFO: Gregory Skalla
VP Marketing: Jeffrey Gabura, age 41
Director Human Resources: Greg Williamson
Auditors: KPMG Peat Marwick LLP

WHERE

HQ: 11550 IH-10 West, Ste. 395, San Antonio, TX 78230
Phone: 210-558-1900   **Fax:** 210-558-1929

WHAT

	1994 Sales	
	$ mil.	% of total
Data/fax products	11.6	52
Network products	10.8	48
Adjustments	0.7	—
Total	**23.1**	**100**

Products

Data/fax Products
PCMCIA modems
PCMCIA Type II Ethernet LAN adapters

Network Products
DATA RACE MACHnet (Ethernet bridge)
MACH DS plus (multiplexer)
NETRACER (router)

KEY COMPETITORS

Angia Communications	IBM
Apex Data	Intel
Ascend Communications	MICOM
AT&T	Motorola
Boca Research	Multi-Tech Systems
Global Village	Penril DataComm Networks
GVC Technologies	U.S. Robotics
Hayes Microcomputer	Zoom Telephonics

HOW MUCH

Nasdaq symbol: RACE FY ends: June 30	Annual Growth	1989	1990	1991	1992	1993	1994
Sales ($ mil.)	41.3%	4.1	4.7	7.7	21.7	43.9	23.1
Net income ($ mil.)	—	0.1	0.1	0.3	2.3	4.9	(15.5)
Income as % of sales	—	3.1%	2.0%	4.1%	10.8%	11.2%	—
Earnings per share ($)	—	0.05	0.03	0.10	0.70	1.12	(3.47)
Stock price – high ($)	—	—	—	—	27.50	30.75	11.00
Stock price – low ($)	—	—	—	—	14.25	6.50	3.50
Stock price – close ($)	(60.6%)	—	—	—	23.75	9.00	3.69
P/E – high	—	—	—	—	39	27	—
P/E – low	—	—	—	—	20	6	—
Dividends per share ($)	—	—	—	—	0.00	0.00	0.00
Book value per share ($)	(1.0%)	—	—	—	3.55	7.03	3.48
Employees	35.5%	35	110	150	150	258	160

1994 Year-end:
Debt ratio: 0.1%
Return on equity: —
Cash (mil.): $5.2
Current ratio: 4.23
Long-term debt (mil.): $0.0
No. of shares (mil.): 4.5
Dividends
  Yield: —
  Payout: —
Market value (mil.): $16.6
R&D as % of sales: 13.6%
Advertising as % of sales: —

DESTEC ENERGY, INC.

OVERVIEW

Destec is striving to build a new head of steam after being short-circuited by expired sales agreements and the Texas legislature. The Houston-based firm is a leading independent power producer with interests in 17 US cogeneration plants. The facilities produce electricity (sold wholesale to utilities) and steam (sold to industrial customers). Destec also uses a proprietary coal gasification process to produce an alternative fuel for power generation facilities (syngas). Dow Chemical owns 76.5% of Destec's stock.

Destec was formed as a subsidiary of Dow in 1989. It took over Dow's cogeneration and syngas technologies, developed to take advantage of the Public Utilities Regulatory Policies Act of 1978, which encouraged independent producers to enter the electric power business. Destec acquired power developer PSE, Inc., in late 1989, and in 1991 Dow spun off Destec in a public offering. The new company took advantage of Dow's deep pockets to vertically integrate its operations (unique among independents) and expand rapidly. From 1988 to 1994 sales grew tenfold.

However, in 1994 and 1995 the firm's power agreements with Houston Lighting & Power and Texas Utilities expired. In a flash Destec lost accounts that made up nearly 1/3 of its revenue — and had an extra 700 megawatts of electricity with few prospective customers. The firm failed to persuade the 1995 legislature to allow independent producers to sell directly to retail customers. These setbacks and generally slow domestic market growth forced the company to change its strategy. Destec de-emphasized its vertical integration and moved aggressively into the international arena. While some of Destec's competitors have a more substantial position overseas, analysts expect Dow (which has 80 plants in 28 countries) to initially provide Destec with a reservoir of foreign customers.

WHO

Chairman: Robert McFedries, age 64
President and CEO: Charles F. Goff, age 54, $623,058 pay
EVP and COO: Keys A. Curry Jr., age 59, $519,439 pay
SVP, CFO, and Treasurer: Enrique M. Larroucau, age 52, $379,388 pay
VP Human Resources, Communications, and Quality: Gerald Crone
Auditors: Deloitte & Touche LLP

WHERE

HQ: 2500 CityWest Blvd., Ste. 150, Houston, TX 77042
Phone: 713-735-4000   **Fax:** 713-735-4201

WHAT

	1994 Sales	
	$ mil.	% of total
Engineering & operations	358.4	49
Power, steam & syngas	317.6	44
Development	27.5	4
Energy resources	23.2	3
Total	**726.7**	**100**

Selected Projects in Operation
Badger Creek CoGen (Bakersfield, CA)
Black Mountain (Las Vegas, NV)
Chalk Cliff CoGen (Taft, CA)
CoGen Lyondell (Houston, TX)
CoGen Power (Port Arthur, TX)
Commonwealth Atlantic (Chesapeake, VA)
Corona CoGen (Corona, CA)
Double "C" CoGen (Bakersfield, CA)
High Sierra CoGen (Bakersfield, CA)
Kern Front CoGen (Bakersfield, CA)
Louisiana Gasification Technology (Plaquemine, LA)
McKittrick CoGen (Bakersfield, CA)
Oyster Creek CoGen (Freeport, TX)
San Joaquin CoGen (Stockton, CA)

KEY COMPETITORS

AES	General Electric	Pacific Gas and
California Energy	Houston Industries	Electric
Duke Power	Indeck Energy	SCEcorp
FPL	Pacific Enterprises	Sithe Energies

HOW MUCH

NYSE symbol: ENG FY ends: December 31	Annual Growth	1989	1990	1991	1992	1993	1994
Sales ($ mil.)	36.6%	152.7	412.3	437.0	507.6	673.8	726.7
Net income ($ mil.)	25.2%	35.9	70.3	81.5	87.5	103.1	110.5
Income as % of sales	—	23.5%	17.1%	18.6%	17.2%	15.3%	15.2%
Earnings per share ($)	18.1%	0.80	1.56	1.39	1.41	1.67	1.84
Stock price – high ($)	—	—	—	18.63	22.75	19.25	15.63
Stock price – low ($)	—	—	—	15.00	13.00	13.50	9.00
Stock price – close ($)	(19.3%)	—	—	19.75	16.13	14.38	10.38
P/E – high	—	—	—	13	16	12	8
P/E – low	—	—	—	11	9	8	5
Dividends per share ($)	—	—	—	0.00	0.00	0.00	0.00
Book value per share ($)	18.5%	—	—	7.61	9.20	10.81	12.65
Employees	8.4%	—	436	568	606	667	603

1994 Year-end:
Debt ratio: 4.7%
Return on equity: 15.7%
Cash (mil.): $354.1
Current ratio: 3.94
Long-term debt (mil.): $37.1
No. of shares (mil.): 58.9
Dividends
  Yield: —
  Payout: —
Market value (mil.): $610.9
R&D as % of sales: —
Advertising as % of sales: —

D.R. HORTON, INC.

OVERVIEW

Home building is a family affair for D.R. Horton of Arlington — president Donald Horton's brother Terrill and uncle Leon (Richard L.) are company VPs. D.R. Horton, which sold 2,360 houses in 1994, builds homes in 19 states. The company develops tracts of "customizable" homes (options include raised ceilings, whirlpool baths, and marble hallways) that sell for an average of $160,000. A key Horton strategy is to develop a limited number of homes in a tract before market fluctuations leave it stranded with unsold properties.

Arkansas native Donald Horton was selling homes for a builder in Fort Worth when he hit upon a strategy for increasing sales — add options to a basic floor plan. In 1978 Horton borrowed $33,000 to build his first home, added a bay window for an additional charge, and sold the home for $44,000. Since then Horton has continued to hone his strategy (the company now offers 10 customizable floor plans) and has weathered the housing market's boom-bust cycles. In 1987 the company began expanding, first into Phoenix, then Atlanta and Orlando (1988), North Carolina (1989), Houston (1990), Washington, DC (1991), and Chicago, Cincinnati, and South Florida (1992). D.R. Horton went public in 1992. Donald Horton owns 30.5% of his namesake company; Terrill Horton owns 25.5%.

D.R. Horton expanded into Austin, San Diego, Los Angeles, and Salt Lake City in 1993. The following year the company entered the Kansas City, Las Vegas, and Minneapolis markets. Also in 1994 D.R. Horton bought Joe Miller Homes of Minneapolis/St. Paul.

Denver and Birmingham, Alabama, became the 21st and 22nd markets in D.R. Horton's expansion program in 1995. That same year the company acquired Regency Development, a home builder in Birmingham, and the assets of Arappco Homes, a North Carolina builder.

WHO

Chairman and President: Donald R. Horton, age 44, $342,457 pay
EVP, Treasurer, and CFO: David J. Keller, age 46, $262,500 pay
EVP: Richard Beckwitt, age 35, $225,000 pay
VP Dallas/Fort Worth East Division: Richard L. Horton, age 51
VP Dallas/Fort Worth North Division: Terrill J. Horton, age 46
VP Eastern Region: Scott J. Stone, age 43
Manager Human Resources: Mary Ledbetter
Auditors: Ernst & Young LLP

WHERE

HQ: 1901 Ascension Blvd., Ste. 100, Arlington, TX 76006
Phone: 817-856-8200   **Fax:** 817-856-8249

	1994 Sales	
	$ mil.	% of total
Southwest	139.4	35
Mid-Atlantic	121.8	31
Midwest	54.0	14
Southeast	53.4	14
West	24.6	6
Other regions	0.1	—
Total	**393.3**	**100**

WHAT

Selected Services
Architectural design
Construction
Home Sales
Lot development

KEY COMPETITORS

Centex	Koll Real Estate
Continental Homes	Lewis Homes Management
David Weekley Homes	Neumann Homes
Del Webb	Oriole Homes
Devcon Construction	Pulte
H. G. Hill	Ryland
Hovnanian Residential	U.S. Home
Kaufman and Broad	Village Homes

HOW MUCH

Nasdaq symbol: DRHI FY ends: September 30	Annual Growth	1989	1990	1991	1992	1993	1994
Sales ($ mil.)	36.8%	82.2	94.0	124.1	182.6	190.1	393.3
Net income ($ mil.)	40.7%	3.2	5.1	5.8	9.2	8.8	17.7
Income as % of sales	—	3.9%	5.4%	4.7%	5.0%	4.7%	4.5%
Earnings per share ($)	21.0%	—	0.33	0.42	0.42	0.35	0.70
Stock price – high ($)	—	—	—	—	6.63	11.13	12.20
Stock price – low ($)	—	—	—	—	4.13	5.59	5.81
Stock price – close ($)	2.2%	—	—	—	5.73	10.69	5.98
P/E – high	—	—	—	—	16	31	17
P/E – low	—	—	—	—	10	16	8
Dividends per share ($)	—	—	—	—	0.00	0.00	0.00
Book value per share ($)	18.3%	—	—	—	2.44	2.68	3.41
Employees	41.4%	—	—	—	—	326	461

1994 Year-end:
Debt ratio: 56.2%
Return on equity: 23.5%
Cash (mil.): $8.5
Current ratio: —
Long-term debt (mil.): $8.2
No. of shares (mil.): 24.8
Dividends
 Yield: —
 Payout: —
Market value (mil.): $148.5
R&D as % of sales: —
Advertising as % of sales: —

DRYPERS CORPORATION

OVERVIEW

Drypers's major competitors have dampened its prospects in the disposable diaper market. Procter & Gamble and Kimberly-Clark, which together have 65% of the market, are fighting to regain lost market share from private-label and smaller brands like Drypers with an aggressive price and promotion war. Houston-based Drypers, which rapidly earned 5.5% of the US's $4 billion market, has seen its financial resources dwindle. Without additional financing the company may be forced to seek a buyer or file for bankruptcy protection.

In 1984 college friends David Pitassi and Walter Klemp, along with a 3rd friend, founded Vancouver, Washington–based diaper maker VMG. When rapid growth strained relations between founders and investors, the 2 were ousted by VMG's limited partners (the 3rd friend stayed on). Pitassi and Klemp moved to Houston, forming Veragon Corp. They drafted P&G veteran Terry Tognietti as operations chief and shipped the first Drypers in 1988. Veragon changed its name to Drypers in 1991. In 1992 Drypers purchased 2 regional diaper makers, UltraCare Products, which sells in the Midwest and Northeast, and VMG (the same company that Pitassi and Klemp founded), which distributes in the Northwest . VMG president Raymond Chambers joined the Drypers management team.

Drypers claimed its niche by creating value-priced diapers and training pants and concentrating on making its products profitable for grocers. By 1993 sales had grown over 49,000%, earning Drypers the #1 spot on *Inc.* magazine's list of fastest-growing private companies. Drypers went public in 1994. Pitassi owns 5.9%, Klemp 5.9%, and Tognietti 4.8%. In 1994 Drypers combined its 4 regional diaper brands — Baby's Choice, Cozies, Drypers, and Wee-Fits — under the Drypers name.

In 1995 Drypers consolidated its diaper production into its Ohio and Washington plants.

WHO

Chairman and Co-CEO: Walter V. Klemp, age 35, $230,000 pay
Co-CEO; President, Drypers North America: Terry A. Tognietti, age 38, $230,000 pay
Co-CEO; President, Drypers International: Raymond M. Chambers, age 39, $230,000 pay
CFO: T. Jack Gainer, age 33
VP; COO, Drypers International: Joe D. Tanner, age 48
Special Advisor: David M. Pitassi, $230,000 pay
Office Manager (HR): Joan Cunningham
Auditors: Arthur Andersen & Co, SC

WHERE

HQ: 1415 West Loop North, Houston, TX 77055
Phone: 713-682-6848   **Fax:** 713-682-3104

Drypers operates manufacturing facilities in Ohio, Texas, and Washington in the US and in Puerto Rico and Argentina.

WHAT

	1994 Sales
	% of total
US	87
International	13
Total	**100**

Brand Names
Comfees (price-value diapers)
Drypers premium diapers
Drypers premoistened wipes
Drypers Training Pants (disposables)

Private-label Diapers sold under the labels of major retailers

KEY COMPETITORS

Diplomat
DSG
Kimberly-Clark
Paragon Trade Brands
Pope & Talbot
Procter & Gamble
Sandoz

HOW MUCH

Nasdaq symbol: DYPR FY ends: December 31	Annual Growth	1989	1990	1991	1992	1993	1994
Sales ($ mil.)	63.4%	14.9	25.8	35.1	77.7	156.1	173.6
Net income ($ mil.)	33.2%	0.7	0.6	(1.0)	(4.8)	(0.3)	3.1
Income as % of sales	—	5.0%	2.5%	—	—	—	1.8%
Earnings per share ($)	—	—	—	—	(3.0)	(0.10)	0.50
Stock price - high ($)	—	—	—	—	—	—	16.00
Stock price - low ($)	—	—	—	—	—	—	9.50
Stock price - close ($)	—	—	—	—	—	—	12.50
P/E - high	—	—	—	—	—	—	32
P/E - low	—	—	—	—	—	—	19
Dividends per share ($)	—	—	—	—	—	—	0.00
Book value per share ($)	—	—	—	—	—	—	8.66
Employees	90.6%	—	—	110	461	450	762

1994 Year-end:
Debt ratio: 48.5%
Return on equity: 5.6%
Cash (mil.): $1.5
Current ratio: 1.79
Long-term debt (mil.): $46.6
No. of shares (mil.): 6.6
Dividends
  Yield: —
  Payout: —
Market value (mil.): $81.9
R&D as % of sales: —
Advertising as % of sales: —

DSC COMMUNICATIONS

OVERVIEW

With the global explosion in telecommunications, DSC Communications is dialing for dollars, pounds, and yen. Its hardware and software products allow telecommunications providers to transmit more information at faster speeds and to send data, video, and voice transmissions. Motorola, MCI, and Ameritech together accounted for 46% of DSC's 1994 revenues; sales to international customers accounted for 9.4%.

DSC was founded in 1976 and originally focused on the digital switch market but with little success. The company went public in 1980 and hired CEO James Donald the next year. Donald convinced DSC to produce tandem switches (which work with local switches to route multiple calls) for the newly deregulated long-distance market. In 1982 MCI became DSC's first customer. Growth slowed in the mid-1980s when demand for tandem switches went flat, but DSC found new customers in the international arena. In the early 1990s a worldwide recession caused sales to falter; then Motorola, one of the company's largest customers, began to diversify away from DSC's products. Amid rumors of bankruptcy, Donald drastically reduced payroll and inventories. By 1992 DSC was once again profitable.

In 1994 DSC and General Instrument, a supplier of cable TV equipment, began developing a fiber optic cable system that offers video, phone, and data services. That same year DSC acquired NKT Elektronik, a Danish maker of optical transmission equipment, and established its Broadband Products Division to develop technology for interactive networks.

In 1995 DSC debuted its iMPAX 5000 asynchronous transfer mode (ATM) access and switching products (ATM is a standard for network-based interactive and multimedia transmissions). DSC also signed new contracts in Chile, Korea, Mexico, Moldova, and Sweden.

WHO

Chairman, President, and CEO: James L. Donald, age 63, $1,490,864 pay
SVP and CFO: Gerald F. Montry, age 56, $739,092 pay
SVP: Michael R. Bernique, age 51, $515,400 pay
Group VP: Allen R. Adams, age 45, $561,300 pay
Group VP: Hensley E. West, age 50, $538,390 pay
VP, Secretary, and General Counsel: George B. Brunt
VP Human Resources: John O'Loughlin
Auditors: Ernst & Young LLP

WHERE

HQ: DSC Communications Corporation, 1000 Coit Rd., Plano, TX 75075
Phone: 214-519-3000   Fax: 214-519-4122

WHAT

	1994 Sales
	% of total
Switching & Intelligent Network	52
Access	27
Transmission	17
Other	4
Total	**100**

Selected Products

Access products (equipment that connects the telephone company office to the customer's premises)
Broadband products (Asynchronous Transfer Mode [ATM] products for advanced networking features)
Optical transmission equipment (fiber optic transmission and network management products)
Switching and intelligent network products (systems that connect and route calls through a network)
Transmission products (digital cross-connect equipment for voice and data transmissions at very high speeds)

KEY COMPETITORS

Adage	Ericsson	Northern Telecom
ADC Telecom.	EXECUTONE	QUALCOMM
ADTRAN	Fujitsu	Rockwell
Alcatel Alsthom	General	Symmetricom
Ascom Timeplex	DataComm	Telco Systems
AT&T	Harris Corp.	Tellabs
BroadBand	Norstan	

HOW MUCH

Nasdaq symbol: DIGI FY ends: December 31	5-Year Growth	1989	1990	1991	1992	1993	1994
Sales ($ mil.)	18.5%	429.7	519.3	461.5	536.3	730.8	1,003.1
Net income ($ mil.)	37.3%	33.3	20.1	(108.3)	11.6	81.7	162.6
Income as % of sales	—	7.8%	3.9%	—	2.2%	11.2%	16.2%
Earnings per share ($)	28.6%	0.40	0.23	(1.31)	0.12	0.77	1.39
Stock price – high ($)	—	4.28	4.19	2.44	5.75	18.28	18.94
Stock price – low ($)	—	1.69	1.09	0.91	0.91	5.22	8.94
Stock price – close ($)	37.7%	3.63	1.72	0.97	5.50	15.38	17.94
P/E – high	—	11	18	—	48	24	14
P/E – low	—	4	5	—	8	7	6
Dividends per share ($)	—	0.00	0.00	0.00	0.00	0.00	0.00
Book value per share ($)	18.9%	3.16	3.43	2.10	2.30	5.61	7.50
Employees	10.3%	3,317	4,043	3,262	3,301	4,041	5,414

1994 Year-end:
Debt ratio: 8.8%
Return on equity: 22.1%
Cash (mil.): $271.3
Current ratio: 2.14
Long-term debt (mil.): $25.3
No. of shares (mil.): 113.5
Dividends
 Yield: —
 Payout: —
Market value (mil.): $2,036.4
R&D as % of sales: 8.6%
Advertising as % of sales: —

ENCORE WIRE CORPORATION

OVERVIEW

Encore Wire, a low-cost manufacturer of copper electrical building wire and cable, offers the wire industry's fast-food equivalent. The McKinney-based company was founded on the belief that there existed a need for a wire manufacturer that could produce inexpensive residential wire and respond quickly to customer demands through the maintenance of an inventory. The company supplies wire for the interior wiring of homes, and it began manufacturing commercial wire in 1994, following completion of a major plant expansion. Encore sells primarily to wholesale electrical distributors through representatives across the US, though the company also does limited direct marketing.

Encore was founded in 1989 by wire and cable industry veterans Vincent Rego and Donald Spurgin after their previous company, Capital Wire, was bought out by Penn Central in 1988. Encore rolled through the home-building recession of the early 1990s, even gathering market share as it went. The company went public in 1992. Proceeds from the offering bought additional manufacturing equipment and paid off debt.

Encore believes its highly automated manufacturing facility is its key to success and has expanded its plant 4 times since its inception. The company's manufacturing method differs from traditional batch processing of wire in that it reduces the need for materials handling — in other words, labor. Hourly employees receive incentive-based pay.

Rumors of a possible takeover in the 2nd quarter of 1995 sent Encore's stock prices soaring, though company officials refused to comment on the reports. Encore was selected by the *Dallas Morning News* in May 1995 as one of the metroplex's 10 "Fast-Track" firms — companies with record sales and profit growth and high stock returns.

WHO

Chairman: Vincent A. Rego, age 71, $120,000 pay
President and CEO: Donald M. Spurgin, age 57, $120,000 pay
VP Finance, Treasurer, and Secretary: Scott D. Weaver, age 36
VP Operations: David K. Smith, age 35
VP Engineering: Phillip J. Johnson, age 35
VP Sales and Marketing: Daniel L. Jones, age 31
VP Credit and Assistant Secretary: Shirley A. Wright, age 53
Director Human Resources: Gina Vogt
Auditors: Ernst & Young LLP

WHERE

HQ: 1410 Millwood Rd., McKinney, TX 75069
Phone: 214-562-9473   **Fax:** 214-542-4744

WHAT

Commercial Wire
THHN Cable (feeder, circuit, and branch wiring in commercial and industrial buildings)

Residential Wire
NM Cable (nonmetallic sheathed cable used as interior wiring in homes, apartments, and manufactured housing)
UF Cable (underground feeder cable for outside lighting and other applications remote from buildings)

KEY COMPETITORS

AFC Cable
Belden
Cable Design Technologies
Communication Cable
Essex Group
Insteel
Keystone Consolidated
MMI Products
Okonite
Southwire
VTX Electronics
Wassall

HOW MUCH

Nasdaq symbol: WIRE FY ends: December 31	Annual Growth	1989	1990	1991	1992	1993	1994
Sales ($ mil.)	84.0%	—	10.7	31.3	63.1	74.0	122.7
Net income ($ mil.)	—	—	(0.6)	2.0	3.3	2.6	6.7
Income as % of sales	—	—	—	6.3%	5.3%	3.6%	5.4%
Earnings per share ($)	—	—	(0.49)	0.50	0.64	0.45	0.98
Stock price – high ($)	—	—	—	—	13.25	11.75	20.75
Stock price – low ($)	—	—	—	—	8.13	6.50	10.75
Stock price – close ($)	29.7%	—	—	—	10.25	11.25	17.25
P/E – high	—	—	—	—	21	26	21
P/E – low	—	—	—	—	13	14	11
Dividends per share ($)	—	—	—	—	0.00	0.00	0.00
Book value per share ($)	33.6%	—	—	—	3.29	3.59	5.87
Employees	40.2%	13	`25	35	85	120	167

1994 Year-end:
Debt ratio: 28.9%
Return on equity: 21.6%
Cash (mil.): $1.3
Current ratio: 3.1
Long-term debt (mil.): $16.9
No. of shares (mil.): 7.1
Dividends
  Yield: —
  Payout: —
Market value (mil.): $122.1
R&D as % of sales: —
Advertising as % of sales: —

EZCORP, INC.

OVERVIEW

Things haven't been easy for EZCORP lately. Its EZ Pawn chain, the US's 2nd largest pawn-shop chain (after Cash America), has been suffering from the effects of too much growth and an attempt to move too heavily into retail jewelry sales. Since mid-1994 the Austin-based company has undergone a complete change in management that will help it make the transition from entrepreneurial exuberance to corporate caution. Many new positions were created and filled by executives with extensive sales experience. MS Pawn, a limited partnership owned by Phillip Cohen of New York, owns 34% of the company's stock; founder Courtland Logue Jr. (ousted as chairman in 1995) owns 8%.

Logue opened the first EZ Pawn in Austin in 1974. By 1989 there were 16 stores. Bankrolled by private investors, Logue, an admirer of Wal-Mart's Sam Walton, began expanding nationally. EZCORP went public in 1991. Along with the growth came problems. In response EZCORP began tightening loan valuation standards, beefing up internal audit procedures to decrease shrinkage, setting up a centralized jewelry center to refurbish forfeited collateral, and buying more new jewelry to expand its retail sales. In September 1994 the company held a massive inventory reduction sale that contributed to the year's plummeting earnings. Other expenses resulted from new store openings and management turnover.

EZCORP combats the traditional poor image of pawnshops by maintaining a mainstream retail ambience in its stores and stressing its role as a source of consumer credit and as a specialty retailer of pre-owned jewelry, tools, electronics, and firearms.

EZCORP added more than 20 stores in fiscal 1995, but the effects of the restructuring continued to depress financial results.

WHO

Chairman: Sterling B. Brinkley, age 43
President and CEO: Vincent A. Lambiase, age 54
SVP and CFO: Daniel N. Tonissen, age 44
VP and Chief Marketing Officer: Mark A. Stuart
VP Human Resources: John Woodward
Controller: Pamela C. Berger
Auditors: Ernst & Young LLP

WHERE

HQ: 1901 Capital Pkwy., Austin, TX 78746
Phone: 512-314-3400   **Fax:** 512-314-3404

	1994 Stores	
	No.	% of total
Texas	158	60
Colorado	23	9
Indiana	19	7
Alabama	17	7
Mississippi	12	5
Georgia	11	4
Oklahoma	9	3
Tennessee	8	3
Louisiana	4	2
Arkansas	1	0
Total	**262**	**100**

WHAT

	1994 Sales	
	$ mil.	% of total
Sales	104.8	62
Pawn service charges	63.1	38
Total	**167.9**	**100**

KEY COMPETITORS

Cash America
First Cash
Security Finance
World Acceptance

HOW MUCH

Nasdaq symbol: EZPW FY ends: September 30	Annual Growth	1989	1990[1]	1991	1992	1993	1994
Sales ($ mil.)	72.1%	11.1	11.7	23.8	51.2	108.6	167.9
Net income ($ mil.)	58.5%	0.2	0.1	1.1	2.9	6.1	1.8
Income as % of sales	—	1.6%	0.6%	4.6%	5.7%	5.6%	1.1%
Earnings per share ($)	—	(0.15)	(0.01)	0.21	0.32	0.56	0.15
Stock price – high ($)	—	—	—	16.00	25.50	28.00	17.50
Stock price – low ($)	—	—	—	9.00	9.75	10.25	9.50
Stock price – close ($)	(10.4%)	—	—	14.25	25.00	15.50	10.25
P/E – high	—	—	—	76	80	50	117
P/E – low	—	—	—	43	30	18	63
Dividends per share ($)	—	—	—	0.00	0.00	0.00	0.00
Book value per share ($)	27.5%	—	—	5.04	7.15	10.36	10.45
Employees	55.1%	—	—	421	919	1,404	1,572

[1] 9-month fiscal year

1994 Year-end:
Debt ratio: 22.9%
Return on equity: 1.4%
Cash (mil.): $6.3
Current ratio: 9.81
Long-term debt (mil.): $36.8
No. of shares (mil.): 12.0
Dividends
   Yield: —
   Payout: —
Market value (mil.): $122.7
R&D as % of sales: —
Advertising as % of sales: —

FARAH INCORPORATED

OVERVIEW

Richard Allender wears the pants at Farah Incorporated, manufacturer of men's and boys' dress and casual wear. Since taking over as CEO of the El Paso–based company in 1989 (following years of disastrous despotic direction by Willie Farah, son of the company's founder), he has fired thousands, streamlined manufacturing operations, and wooed back dissatisfied customers with a new line of 100% cotton, No Wrinkle pants. In 1993 Farah reported its first profit in 7 years. By 1994, the same year the company introduced its Savane Friday Wear brand in response to more relaxed office dress codes, sales had increased another 35%.

Farah was founded in 1920 by Lebanese immigrants Mansour and Hana Farah. Mansour died in 1937, and sons Willie and Jimmy took over. Jimmy died in 1964, 3 years before the company went public.

By 1970 Farah had become El Paso's largest non-government employer, but a 1971 strike by Farah workers led to a nationwide boycott of the company's products. An untimely decision to invest in double knits further crippled the company with excess inventory, and infighting among family management added to the trouble. In 1976, with a loss of $24 million, Farah's board of directors ousted Willie Farah. Furious, Willie contested the move and was reinstated in 1978. Profits returned briefly, but in 1989, amid rising losses and rabid animosity, Willie resigned as CEO; he was stripped of his chairman title in 1990 (though not without a fight).

Farah reported a loss for the first half of 1995 due in part to the start-up of new finishing plants in Mexico and Costa Rica. However, private-label sales to retailers like the County Seat and Wal-Mart are expected to double, and Farah is optimistic about its new "Soft Wash" line of wrinkle-resistant garments.

WHO

Chairman, President, and CEO: Richard C. Allender, age 49, $464,850 pay
President, Farah U.S.A.: Michael R. Mitchell, age 41, $294,078 pay
EVP, CFO, Secretary, and Treasurer: James C. Swaim, age 42, $251,930 pay
EVP Operations, Farah U.S.A.: Jackie L. Boatman, age 36, $207,525 pay
SVP Merchandising, Farah U.S.A.: Gary J. Kernaghan
SVP Operations, Farah U.S.A.: Franz A. Maccarrone
SVP Private Label, Farah U.S.A.: Edward P. Srsic Jr.
SVP, Farah International: Helmut H. Meinel
President, Value Slacks: Donald G. Carney
Director Human Resources: David Gallardo
Auditors: Arthur Andersen & Co., SC

WHERE

HQ: 8889 Gateway West, El Paso, TX 79925-6584
Phone: 915-593-4444   **Fax:** 915-593-4203

Farah Inc. includes Farah U.S.A.., Farah International (Australia, Asia, and Europe), and Value Slacks (US and Puerto Rico).

WHAT

Primary Labels
Farah/Farah Clothing Co. (men's dress slacks and suit separates in blended fibers and men's 100% cotton casual slacks)
John Henry (high-fashion dress slacks and suit separates in blended fabrics)
Savane (men's and boys' 100% cotton, wrinkle-resistant casual clothing)
Savane Friday Wear (combed-cotton casual separates)

KEY COMPETITORS

Bugle Boy	Hampton Industries	Phillips-Van
Calvin Klein	Hartmarx	Heusen
ChiPants	J. Crew	Polo/Ralph
Delta Woodside	Lands' End	Lauren
Industries	Levi Strauss	Spiegel
Esprit de Corp.	Liz Claiborne	Supreme
The Gap	Nautica Ent.	Intl.
Guess?	Oxford Industries	VF Corp.
Haggar		

HOW MUCH

NYSE symbol: FRA FY ends: November 4	5-Year Growth	1989	1990	1991	1992	1993	1994
Sales ($ mil.)	0.3%	239.0	139.6	151.2	152.0	180.1	242.8
Net income ($ mil.)	—	(11.6)	(6.6)	(5.5)	(9.6)	0.1	10.8
Income as % of sales	—	—	—	—	—	0.1%	4.4%
Earnings per share ($)	—	(1.86)	(1.06)	(0.93)	(1.52)	0.02	1.16
Stock price – high ($)	—	12.63	8.00	8.88	8.13	12.00	21.88
Stock price – low ($)	—	5.25	2.38	2.38	4.25	6.13	6.33
Stock price – close ($)	0.7%	6.75	2.75	6.25	7.13	11.25	7.00
P/E – high	—	—	—	—	—	—	19
P/E – low	—	—	—	—	—	—	6
Dividends per share ($)	—	0.00	0.00	0.00	0.00	0.00	0.00
Book value per share ($)	(3.0%)	9.95	8.72	7.70	5.40	5.44	8.53
Employees	7.9%	5,200	4,300	4,600	5,150	5,300	6,000

1994 Year-end:
Debt ratio: 22.0%
Return on equity: 16.7%
Cash (mil.): $2.4
Current ratio: 2.19
Long-term debt (mil.): $5.2
No. of shares (mil.): 10.1
Dividends
  Yield: —
  Payout: —
Market value (mil.): $70.6
R&D as % of sales: —
Advertising as % of sales: —

FOSSIL, INC.

OVERVIEW

If you've got the money, Fossil has the time. The company is one of the leading makers of midpriced fashion watches. Like rivals Anne Klein, Guess?, and Swatch, Fossil targets middle- and upper-income consumers in their teens, 20s, and 30s. Fossil's funky timepieces, with a retro '50s look, have proven to be a timely addition to the fashion fray, and the company's sales continue to tick higher.

College dropout Tom Kartsotis founded the Dallas-based import-export company, originally called Overseas Products International, in 1984. He was only 24, and Swatch was *the* hot fashion accessory. Kosta Kartsotis, Tom's brother and a department store executive, had told Tom about high profits from Asian imports. With Lynne Stafford (now Tom's wife) as designer, the company gave its Asian-made FOSSIL watches a retro image, and sales took off. In 1988 Kosta joined the firm to woo department stores. Between 1987 and 1989 sales rose from $2 million to $20 million. In 1990 a less expensive brand of watches, RELIC, was created for stores such as JCPenney and Sears. Tom Kartsotis renamed the company in 1992 and took it public in 1993. He owns 40.5% of Fossil, and Kosta owns 18.8%.

To mitigate the risks of fashion's fickleness, Fossil broadened its line of products, selling small leather goods such as handbags, wallets, and belts under the FOSSIL name. It also introduced a series of collectors' watches, starting with a Nolan Ryan edition that included an autographed baseball. In addition Fossil licenses images from DC Comics and others and makes private-label watches for companies including PepsiCo and Snapple.

In 1995 Fossil signed a deal with Viacom to design and sell a limited number of *Star Trek* collectors watches. Also that year the company announced plans to launch a line of sunglasses and a line of sport watches.

WHO

Chairman and CEO: Tom Kartsotis, age 35, $262,500 pay
President and COO: Kosta N. Kartsotis, age 42, $255,000 pay
EVP: Michael W. Barnes, age 34, $207,219 pay
EVP: Richard H. Gundy, age 52, $179,611 pay
SVP and CFO: Randy S. Kercho, age 38
SVP Product Development: Lynne M. Kartsotis, age 34
VP, General Counsel, and Secretary: T. R. Tunnell
Director Human Resources: Shane Winkles
Auditors: Deloitte & Touche LLP

WHERE

HQ: 2280 N. Greenville Ave., Richardson, TX 75082
Phone: 214-234-2525   **Fax:** 214-348-1366

	1994 Sales
	% of total
US	76
Other countries	24
Total	**100**

Manufacturing Locations

Brazil	South Korea
China	Taiwan
Hong Kong (principal site)	Turkey
Italy	US Virgin Islands
Japan	

WHAT

Products	Major Retail Outlets
FOSSIL watch straps	Dayton Hudson
FOSSIL watches	Dillard's
Handbags	JCPenney
Private-label/licensed products	Macy's
RELIC watches	Montgomery Ward
Small leather goods	Nordstrom
and belts	Sears
Sunglasses	Service Merchandise

KEY COMPETITORS

Anne Klein	Forschner Group	North American
Bausch & Lomb	Guess	Watch
Benrus Watch	Loews	Seiko
Casio	LVMH	SMH
		Timex

HOW MUCH

Nasdaq symbol: FOSL FY ends: December 31	Annual Growth	1989	1990	1991	1992	1993	1994	1994 Year-end:
Sales ($ mil.)	51.4%	20.3	32.5	57.1	73.8	105.1	161.9	Debt ratio: 20.4%
Net income ($ mil.)	50.3%	2.0	3.1	6.9	7.1	11.5	15.3	Return on equity: 37.5%
Income as % of sales	—	9.8%	9.5%	12.0%	9.5%	10.9%	9.5%	Cash (mil.): $2.3
Earnings per share ($)	36.2%	—	—	—	0.62	0.91	1.15	Current ratio: 2.65
Stock price – high ($)	—	—	—	—	—	21.00	29.50	Long-term debt (mil.): $4.8
Stock price – low ($)	—	—	—	—	—	7.50	12.25	No. of shares (mil.): 13.2
Stock price – close ($)	(30.9%)	—	—	—	—	19.00	13.13	Dividends
P/E – high	—	—	—	—	—	23	26	Yield: —
P/E – low	—	—	—	—	—	8	11	Payout: —
Dividends per share ($)	—	—	—	—	—	0.00	0.00	Market value (mil.): $172.8
Book value per share ($)	47.7%	—	—	—	—	2.52	3.72	R&D as % of sales: —
Employees	51.3%	70	97	130	234	370	555	Advertising as % of sales: —

HAGGAR CORPORATION

OVERVIEW

Haggar is turning casual clothing into serious business. Although the Dallas-based company is the leading maker of men's dress slacks (with 20% of the $1.6 billion market), the booming casual clothing market helped raise its bottom line in 1994. Haggar sells its clothing through major department stores nationwide (J. C. Penney is its largest customer). The company's Horizon Group sells lower-priced brands, such as the Reed St. James label, through mass market retailers (e.g., Wal-Mart). Haggar also makes private-label clothing. The Haggar family owns about 25% of the company's stock.

J. M. Haggar Sr., an immigrant from Lebanon, started Haggar Corp. near Dallas in 1926 as a regional clothing maker. In the late 1940s Haggar coined the word "slacks" to describe pants worn during the slack time between work and play. The company was a big promoter of permanent-press pants in the 1960s. In the 1980s the company, then under the direction of J. M. Haggar Jr., used electronic inventory systems to improve distribution and reduce costs.

In 1990 Joseph Haggar III took over his father's job as head of the company, just as the popularity of Levi's Dockers was shrinking the dress pants market. With market research showing that ironing or dry cleaning was a hassle for cotton pants wearers, Haggar responded with Wrinkle-free cotton pants in 1992. It went public that same year. Riding the fashion trend of natural fibers and casual clothing, Haggar made cotton products which rose in just 2 years to 30% of 1994 net sales.

In 1995 the company continued its efforts to fill in fashion gaps by diversifying its product lines with Wrinkle-free cotton shirts and a new line of boys' apparel. It is also expanding its distribution channels by opening Haggar retail stores located in outlet mall centers.

WHO

Chairman and CEO: J. M. Haggar III, age 43, $852,304 pay
President and COO: Frank D. Bracken, age 54, $633,554 pay
EVP, CFO, Secretary, and Treasurer: Ralph A. Beattie, age 46, $444,821 pay
SVP Marketing: Alan Burks
SVP; General Manager, The Horizon Group: J. Milton Hickman Jr.
SVP Administration: Billy Langston
SVP International Operations: David Perdue
SVP Management Information Systems: Thomas A. Sample
VP Human Resources: George Greer
General Counsel: Marc Joseph
Auditors: Arthur Andersen & Co, SC

WHERE

HQ: 6113 Lemmon Ave., Dallas, TX 75209
Phone: 214-352-8481   **Fax:** 214-956-4367

WHAT

	1994 Sales % of total
Haggar label	83
Horizon Group	13
Private & specialty labels	4
Total	**100**

Clothing

Pants	Sport coats
Shirts	Suits
Shorts	

KEY COMPETITORS

Bugle Boy	Hartmarx	Phillips-Van
Calvin Klein	J. Crew	Heusen
Delta Woodside	Jordache	Polo/Ralph
Industries	Lands' End	Lauren
Esprit de Corp.	Levi Strauss	Spiegel
Farah	Liz Claiborne	Supreme Intl.
The Gap	Nautica Enterprises	VF Corp.
Guess?	Oxford Industries	

HOW MUCH

Nasdaq symbol: HGGR FY ends: September 30	Annual Growth	1989	1990	1991	1992	1993	1994
Sales ($ mil.)	9.6%	310.2	292.2	354.5	380.8	394.1	491.2
Net income ($ mil.)	66.6%	2.0	(10.9)	4.5	11.3	15.0	25.7
Income as % of sales	—	0.7%	—	1.3%	3.0%	3.8%	5.2%
Earnings per share ($)	53.2%	0.35	(1.93)	0.80	1.95	1.88	2.95
Stock price – high ($)	—	—	—	—	21.50	25.50	40.50
Stock price – low ($)	—	—	—	—	18.25	15.50	20.50
Stock price – close ($)	9.7%	—	—	—	21.00	25.50	25.25
P/E – high	—	—	—	—	11	14	14
P/E – low	—	—	—	—	9	8	7
Dividends per share ($)	—	—	—	—	0.00	0.10	0.20
Book value per share ($)	27.6%	—	—	—	11.37	15.70	18.51
Employees	(1.8%)	7,000	—	—	5,100	6,100	6,400

1994 Year-end:
Debt ratio: 9.5%
Return on equity: 17.6%
Cash (mil.): $2.6
Current ratio: 2.55
Long-term debt (mil.): $15.0
No. of shares (mil.): 8.5
Dividends
  Yield: 0.8%
  Payout: 6.8%
Market value (mil.): $215.6
R&D as % of sales: —
Advertising as % of sales: 5.3%

HARTE-HANKS COMMUNICATIONS, INC.

OVERVIEW

San Antonio–based Harte-Hanks is a diversified communications company whose 4 core areas (newspapers, direct marketing, "shoppers," and TV/radio) are scattered over 14 states, Canada, and the UK. The company's top revenue generators are its shoppers, weekly advertising publications delivered to households in a particular area; these are concentrated in Dallas, Miami, and Northern and Southern California. Harte-Hanks also has nationwide direct-marketing operations that offer a wide range of specialized services. In Texas it has 7 community newspapers in the Dallas/Fort Worth area, 4 daily newspapers, and a TV and radio station in San Antonio.

Harte-Hanks was founded by Houston Harte Sr. and Bernard Hanks in the early 1920s as a newspaper company. It went public in 1972, and over the next 12 years the company diversified and expanded outside Texas. In 1984, 5 executives took the company private again in one of the first LBOs in the media business, but the deal added $700 million in debt. In 1986 Harte-Hanks consolidated its operations to reduce its debt and focus on fewer, larger markets; by 1988 it had sold off half of its holdings and bought others in California, Dallas, and Boston. In 1993 the company went public again. Principal stockholders include brothers Houston Jr. (23.7%) and Edward Harte (11.4%) and Abilene newspaper publisher Andrew Shelton (16.7%). Company officers and directors own 61% of company stock.

Harte-Hanks is shopping for acquisitions, especially direct-marketing publications. The company recently acquired Select Marketing (marketing services to the high-tech industry, 1994) and Steinert & Associates (advertising and direct-marketing communications, 1995). Fourteen suburban Boston newspapers, whose acquisition caused a hefty loss in 1993, were sold in 1995.

WHO

Chairman: Houston H. Harte Jr., age 68
President and CEO: Larry Franklin, age 52, $1,105,000 pay
SVP Direct Marketing: Richard M. Hochhauser, age 50, $504,900 pay
SVP Shoppers: Harry J. Buckel, age 51, $462,840 pay
SVP Legal and Secretary: Donald R. Crews, age 51, $459,000 pay
SVP Finance and CFO: Richard L. Ritchie, age 48, $430,100 pay
Auditors: KPMG Peat Marwick LLP

WHERE

HQ: 200 Concord Plaza Dr., San Antonio, TX 78216
Phone: 210-829-9000   **Fax:** 210-829-9403

WHAT

	1994 Sales		1994 Operating Income	
	$ mil.	% of total	$ mil.	% of total
Shoppers	176.5	34	17.7	25
Direct marketing	167.7	33	19.4	26
Newspapers	140.8	27	26.4	36
TV & radio	28.6	6	8.9	13
Other	—	—	(8.4)	—
Total	**513.6**	**100**	**64.0**	**100**

Selected Major Media

Shoppers (free weekly advertising publications)

Newspapers
Abilene Reporter-News (42,653 daily circulation)
Corpus Christi Caller-Times (67,322 daily circulation)
San Angelo Standard-Times (32,594 daily circulation)
Wichita Falls Times Record News (39,385 daily circulation)

Radio and Television
KENS-TV and KENS-AM, San Antonio

KEY COMPETITORS

Acxiom	Gannett	R.R. Donnelley
A. H. Belo	Hearst	Times Mirror
Catalina Marketing	Knight-Ridder	Tribune
Dimark	New York Times	Washington Post

HOW MUCH

NYSE: HHS FY ends: December 31	Annual Growth	1989	1990	1991	1992	1993	1994
Sales ($ mil.)	4.8%	—	426.3	416.2	423.3	463.5	513.6
Net income ($ mil.)	—	—	(18.3)	(7.0)	2.3	(52.9)	23.8
Income as % of sales	—	—	—	—	0.6%	—	4.6%
Earnings per share ($)	—	—	(1.37)	(0.57)	0.19	(4.05)	1.20
Stock price – high ($)	—	—	—	—	—	19.50	21.63
Stock price – low ($)	—	—	—	—	—	15.13	17.63
Stock price – close ($)	0.0%	—	—	—	—	19.50	19.50
P/E – high	—	—	—	—	—	—	18
P/E – low	—	—	—	—	—	—	15
Dividends per share ($)	—	—	—	—	—	0.00	0.00
Book value per share ($)	26.9%	—	—	—	—	4.63	5.87
Employees	1.2%	—	—	—	5,825	6,150	6,225

1994 Year-end:
Debt ratio: 73.2%
Return on equity: 24.9%
Cash (mil.): $4.4
Current ratio: 1.48
Long-term debt (mil.): $292.9
No. of shares (mil.): 18.3
Dividends
 Yield: —
 Payout: —
Market value (mil.): $357.7
R&D as % of sales: —
Advertising as % of sales: —

HERITAGE MEDIA CORPORATION

OVERVIEW

Dallas-based Heritage Media generates revenues from advertisers on its 5 television stations and 15 radio stations, but its real marketing power comes from its ACTMEDIA subsidiary, the world's largest provider of in-store marketing products and services. Its point-of-sale blitz includes ads on shopping carts and shelves, samples services, and the ACTMEDIA-developed Instant Coupon Machine (a shelf-mounted coupon dispenser), and it is aurally complemented by ACTRADIO, the #1 in-store radio network. Chairman Jim Hoak owns 6% of Heritage Media stock.

Heritage Media was formed in 1987 when Tele-Communications, Inc., bought Heritage Communications, Inc. (HCI), for its cable systems. Investors led by HCI managers (including Hoak and Heritage CEO David Walthall) created Heritage Media as a spin-off for HCI's 13 TV and radio stations; in 1988 the company went public. In January 1989 Heritage bought 78% of ACTMEDIA, and 6 months later it merged with ACTMEDIA, which became its subsidiary. Heritage moved into Canada in 1990 with the purchase of Something Else Marketing (now ACTMEDIA Canada). In 1992 ACTMEDIA Europe bought the Netherlands's Media Meervoud. In 1994 Heritage Media acquired in-store marketing companies in Australia and New Zealand, in addition to Infonet, ACTMEDIA's primary competitor in Canada.

Heritage Media finally turned a major profit in 1994 as it reduced interest expenses and benefited from increased spending by advertisers. Strong growth for its high-margin Instant Coupon Machine and high radio ratings in St. Louis added significantly to the bottom line.

In 1995 Heritage Media bought Powerforce Services, an in-store merchandising group that allows product manufacturers to outsource display building and shelf resetting. Also in 1995 the company sold its television station serving Sioux Falls, South Dakota.

WHO

Chairman: James M. Hoak, age 51, $360,000 pay
President and CEO: David N. Walthall, age 49, $577,000 pay
EVP; President, ACTMEDIA, Inc.: Wayne W. LoCurto, age 51, $430,400 pay
EVP; President, Television Group: James J. Robinette, age 61, $346,500 pay
EVP; President, Radio Group: Paul W. Fiddick, age 45, $298,550 pay
VP Finance: Douglas N. Woodrum, age 37
Manager Human Resources: Amy Kruckemeyer
Auditors: KPMG Peat Marwick LLP

WHERE

HQ: 13355 Noel Rd., Ste. 1500, Dallas, TX 75240
Phone: 214-702-7380　　　**Fax:** 214-702-7382

WHAT

	1994 Sales	
	$ mil.	% of total
In-store marketing	230.1	72
Television	46.7	15
Radio	40.8	13
Total	**317.6**	**100**

In-Store Marketing	Radio
ACTMEDIA Australia/	KCFX (FM), Kansas City, MO
New Zealand	KIHT (FM), St. Louis
ACTMEDIA Canada	KKSN (AM/FM), Portland, OR
ACTMEDIA Europe	KRPM (AM/FM), Seattle
ACTMEDIA, Inc.	WBBF (AM), Rochester, NY
	WBEE (FM), Rochester, NY
Television	WEMP (AM), Milwaukee
KEVN-TV, Rapid City, SD	WEZW (FM), Milwaukee
KOKH-TV, Oklahoma City	WIL (FM), St. Louis
WCHS-TV, Charleston, WV	WKLX (FM) Rochester, NY
WEAR-TV, Pensacola, FL	WMYX (FM), Milwaukee
WNNE-TV, Hanover, NH	WOFX (FM), Cincinnati
(satellite of WPTZ-TV)	WRTH (AM), St. Louis
WPTZ-TV, Plattsburgh, NY	

KEY COMPETITORS

Advanced	Cox	Information
Promotion	E.W. Scripps	Resources
ADVO	Gannett	LIN Broadcasting
Catalina Marketing	General Electric	Viacom
CBS	Hearst	Walt Disney

HOW MUCH

AMEX symbol: HTG FY ends: December 31	5-Year Growth	1989	1990	1991	1992	1993	1994
Sales ($ mil.)	14.0%	165.0	203.9	222.4	250.9	291.2	317.6
Net income ($ mil.)	—	(30.0)	(25.0)	(20.4)	(25.5)	(4.8)	22.3
Income as % of sales	—	—	—	—	—	—	7.0%
Earnings per share ($)	—	(4.13)	(2.72)	(1.97)	(1.76)	(0.29)	0.15
Stock price – high ($)	—	23.00	22.50	20.00	15.50	19.88	27.63
Stock price – low ($)	—	10.00	10.50	9.50	5.63	8.38	15.75
Stock price – close ($)	16.5%	12.50	13.50	14.00	8.63	19.88	26.88
P/E – high	—	—	—	—	—	—	184
P/E – low	—	—	—	—	—	—	105
Dividends per share ($)	—	0.00	0.00	0.00	0.00	0.00	0.00
Book value per share ($)	(9.2%)	8.25	5.84	4.02	4.40	4.31	5.10
Employees	11.7%	14,100	14,200	14,200	15,300	16,300	24,500

1994 Year-end:
Debt ratio: 79.8%
Return on equity: 27.9%
Cash (mil.): $4.3
Current ratio: 0.86
Long-term debt (mil.): $339.7
No. of shares (mil.): 17.5
Dividends
　Yield: —
　Payout: —
Market value (mil.): $470.7
R&D as % of sales: —
Advertising as % of sales: —

ID SOFTWARE, INC.

OVERVIEW

id Software spells doom for computer gamesters, and they love it. *Doom* is the title of id's adventure game phenomenon in which players shoot it out with digitally created demons in an ultra-fast 3-D environment. id uses an innovative try-before-you-buy marketing strategy, releasing a fully featured portion of a game as shareware (available on the Internet, via major on-line services, or from id's bulletin board). Gamesters can try the teaser for free and, if satisfied, order the full game from id or buy it through retail outlets.

Friends John Carmack, Adrian Carmack (no relation), and John Romero worked together as programmers at Softdisk Publishing in Shreveport, Louisiana. With a 4th friend, Tom Hall, they created the first *Commander Keen* game, *Invasion of the Vorticons* (starring child genius Billy Blaze), and released it as shareware in late 1990. One month later the quartet launched id Software, named for Freud's psychic seat of pleasure. (Hall has since left to pursue other interests.) Late in 1991 the 2nd in the *Commander Keen* series, *Goodbye, Galaxy!*, debuted. The release of *Wolfenstein 3-D* followed in 1992. The game's 3-D graphics, recognized by the Computer Gaming World Hall of Fame, raised the standard for the entire industry. By 1995 over 250,000 copies of *Wolfenstein 3-D* had been sold via retail.

Doom, one of gamedom's hottest titles and the first product released on id's own label, debuted in December 1993. An estimated 100 million players downloaded the shareware version, with 1 in 10 paying for the more advanced version. *Doom II: Hell on Earth* shipped straight to retail in 1994 with 500,000 copies (worth $25 million) presold. Now PocketBooks is publishing a book series based on *Doom,* an interactive television tie-in is being negotiated, and Ivan Reitman (*Ghostbusters*) will produce *Doom: The Movie.* GT Interactive Software markets and distributes the company's products. *Quake,* a multiplayer 3-D game with a client/server engine, is the next id game slated for release.

id's current focus is the ways computer games are played. The company is continuing to expand its games' multiplayer capabilities and has licensed *Doom* to an interactive arcade developer, Austin Virtual Gaming.

WHO

"Biz Guy": Jay Wilbur, age 38
Lead Programmer: John Carmack, age 23
Programmer and Game Designer: John Romero, age 26
Computer Artist: Adrian Carmack, age 27
Computer Artist: Kevin Cloud
Quality Control and Tech Support: Shawn Green

WHERE

HQ: Town East Tower, 18601 LBJ Fwy., Ste. 615, Mesquite, TX 75150
Phone: 214-613-3589   **Fax:** 214-686-9288

WHAT

Selected Products
Commander Keen series
  Commander Keen: Aliens Ate My Babysitter
  Commander Keen: Goodbye, Galaxy!
  Commander Keen: Invasion of the Vorticons
Doom
Doom II: Hell on Earth
Heretic
Heretic II
Spear of Destiny
Wolfenstein 3-D

KEY COMPETITORS

3DO	Interplay Productions
7th Level	Knowledge Adventure
Absolute Entertainment	Lucasfilm
Acclaim Entertainment	PF. Magic
Activision	Maxis
All-Pro Products	Microsoft
Blockbuster	News Corp.
Brøderbund	Nintendo
Catapult Entertainment	Rocket Science Games
Crystal Dynamics	Sierra On-Line
Cyan	Simutronics
Davidson & Associates	Spectrum HoloByte
Digital Pictures	T-HQ
Electronic Arts	Time Warner
Gametek	Trilobyte

HOW MUCH

Private company FY ends: December 31	Annual Growth	1989	1990	1991	1992	1993	1994
Estimated sales ($ mil.)	260.0%	—	—	—	1.0	3.0	13.0
Employees	49.4%	—	—	3	5	6	10

KANEB SERVICES, INC.

OVERVIEW

When an oil refinery springs a leak, Richardson-based Kaneb Services often gets the call. The company's Furmanite division specializes in sealing high-pressure leaks without shutting down the plant, which can be costly. The division also provides other repair and maintenance services to chemical plants, pipelines, and power generation companies. Another Kaneb division, Kaneb Pipe Line Partners, operates a 2,075-mile petroleum pipeline that runs from Kansas to North Dakota.

Kaneb Services was founded in 1953 and built its first pipeline between Kansas and Nebraska. As the pipeline grew through the Midwest, so did Kaneb's interests in other operations, which included offshore drilling, coal production, and savings and loans. When CEO John Barnes joined the company in 1986, it was $574 million in debt. Barnes sold all of Kaneb's energy-related business except the pipeline company, restructured Kaneb's debt, and in 1989 sold 1/3 of the pipeline company to the public for $100 million, forming the Kaneb Pipe Line Partners, L.P.

Kaneb bought Furmanite in 1991. Furmanite was founded in the early 1920s by Clay Furman, who developed methods of sealing steam leaks; since then it has expanded its services into industrial markets worldwide.

In 1993 Kaneb bought Support Terminal Services, one of the largest petroleum and specialty liquids storage companies in the US. That year it also acquired Kraftwerks-und Anlagenbau, an engineering firm that was sold as part of the East German privatization plan. However, Kraftwerks was returned to the Germans in 1994 when Kaneb concluded that it could not make the company profitable.

In 1995 Kaneb purchased the 550-mile Wyco pipeline, giving the company a presence in the Rocky Mountain area. Also that year Kaneb sold some of its pipeline partnership units to reduce its debt load by $53 million.

WHO

Chairman, President, and CEO: John R. Barnes, age 50, $313,296 pay
SVP: Edward D. Doherty II, age 59, $220,417 pay
SVP: Jere M. Denton, age 48, $217,417 pay
SVP: Frank E. Sheeder, age 52, $122,051 pay
VP, Treasurer, and Secretary: Howard C. Wadsworth, age 50, $175,833 pay
Controller: Tony M. Regan, age 35
Director Human Resources: William Kettler
Auditors: Price Waterhouse LLP

WHERE

HQ: 2435 N. Central Expwy., Richardson, TX 75080
Phone: 214-699-4000   **Fax:** 214-699-4025

	1994 Sales	
	$ mil.	% of total
US	124.7	60
Continental Europe	43.2	21
UK	36.3	17
Other regions	4.5	2
Total	**208.7**	**100**

WHAT

	1994 Sales	
	$ mil.	% of total
Industrial services	118.2	56
Pipeline & terminaling	78.7	38
Other	11.8	6
Total	**208.7**	**100**

Industrial Services
Bolting
Fugitive emissions testing
Maintenance outsourcing
On-line leak sealing
On-site machining
Valve testing and repair

Pipeline and Terminaling
Loading
Storage
Transportation

KEY COMPETITORS

Adams Resources	Halliburton	Panhandle Eastern
Bechtel	Matrix Service	Serv-Tech
Coastal	McDermott	Tenneco
Columbia Gas	Newflo	Turner Industries
Enron Corp.	Occidental	

HOW MUCH

NYSE symbol: KAB FY ends: December 31	5-Year Growth	1989	1990	1991	1992	1993	1994
Sales ($ mil.)	41.0%	37.5	40.9	135.0	176.7	198.5	208.7
Net income ($ mil.)	—	(4.5)	(13.2)	(22.2)	(4.7)	14.7	0.5
Income as % of sales	—	—	—	—	—	7.4%	0.3%
Earnings per share ($)	—	(0.14)	(0.42)	(0.70)	(0.19)	0.46	0.02
Stock price – high ($)	—	6.50	6.25	7.25	5.00	3.75	4.13
Stock price – low ($)	—	2.13	3.13	3.63	2.75	2.63	1.88
Stock price – close ($)	(15.7%)	5.00	3.63	4.25	3.25	2.88	2.13
P/E – high	—	—	—	—	—	8	—
P/E – low	—	—	—	—	—	6	—
Dividends per share ($)	—	0.00	0.00	0.00	0.00	0.00	0.00
Book value per share ($)	(20.1%)	0.40	0.31	(0.25)	(0.43)	0.03	0.13
Employees	53.3%	252	423	1,722	2,026	2,115	2,134

1994 Year-end:
Debt ratio: 89.7%
Return on equity: 18.5%
Cash (mil.): $10.5
Current ratio: 0.53
Long-term debt (mil.): $103.4
No. of shares (mil.): 36.4
Dividends
  Yield: —
  Payout: —
Market value (mil.): $77.4
R&D as % of sales: —
Advertising as % of sales: —

KENT ELECTRONICS CORPORATION

OVERVIEW

Kent Electronics is well connected. The distributor supplies connectors and other specialty parts to manufacturers in 3 fast-growing industries: computers, medical equipment, and telecommunications. It has 2 subsidiaries: K*TEC Electronics, a contract manufacturer of interconnect assemblies and battery power packs, and Kent Datacomm, a distributor of premise wiring products for LANS and internal communication systems.

Kent was founded in 1973 by chairman Morrie Abramson and James Corporron (now retired) when they bought the consumer parts division of their employer, Sterling Electronics. Kent first focused on radio and TV parts, but as prices of new radios and TVs dropped, so did the demand for repairs. Kent switched to selling parts to the oil and gas industry. In 1982, 80% of Kent's business came from the oil industry, so when oil prices took a nosedive that year the company shifted its focus again. Kent began narrowing its product line (to connectors) while broadening its customer base. It also diversified into manufacturing, starting K*TEC in 1983. Kent went public in 1986. Its 1992 acquisition of distributor Shelly-Ragon boosted sales by 2/3 and added 15 branches.

Kent is riding the boom in outsourcing by electronics manufacturers (Apple, Dell, and Compaq are Kent customers). The company's cautious acquisition strategy, its double duty as a distributor and a manufacturer, and its advanced order fulfillment system (over 99% of orders are shipped within 24 hours) have earned the company a leadership position in its niche market. In 1994 Kent's sales jumped 31%, its 9th consecutive annual increase.

In 1995 Kent doubled its manufacturing capacity with a new 250,000-square-foot plant in Texas. Also in 1995 K*TEC gained a foothold in the automobile market with a manufacturing contract for auto parts.

WHO

Chairman, CEO, and President: Morrie K. Abramson, age 60, $1,047,579 pay
EVP Manufacturing Services; President, K*TEC Electronics: Randy J. Corporron, age 38, $779,659 pay
VP; EVP, K*TEC Electronics: Rodney J. Corporron, age 38, $646,713 pay
EVP Operations–Distribution: Mark A. Zerbe, age 34, $198,263 pay
EVP Sales–Distribution: Larry D. Olson, age 38
VP, Treasurer, and Secretary (Principal Financial Officer): Stephen J. Chapko, age 41
Manager Human Resources: Pam Huffman
Auditors: Grant Thornton LLP

WHERE

HQ: 7433 Harwin Dr., Houston, TX 77036-2015
Phone: 713-780-7770   **Fax:** 713-978-5892

WHAT

	1995 Sales
	% of total
Distribution	62
Manufacturing	38
Total	**100**

Distribution	Manufacturing (K*TEC)
Capacitors	Cable assemblies
Connectors	Custom battery power
Electromechanical parts	packs
Receptacles	Subassemblies
Resistors	Wiring harnesses
Sockets	
Premise wiring products	
(Kent Datacomm)	

KEY COMPETITORS

Anthem Electronics	Marshall	Sanmina
Arrow Electronics	Industries	SCI Systems
Avnet	PC Service Source	Solectron
Bell Industries	Pioneer-Standard	Sterling
Bell Microproducts	Electronics	Electronics
Comptronix	Premier	TTI
Graybar Electric	Industrial	Western Micro
IBM	Richardson	Technology
Jaco Electronics	Electronics	Wyle Electronics

HOW MUCH

NYSE symbol: KNT FY ends: Sat. nearest Mar. 31	5-Year Growth	1990	1991	1992	1993	1994	1995
Sales ($ mil.)	39.8%	47.5	71.0	94.7	154.7	192.9	253.5
Net income ($ mil.)	35.3%	3.0	3.8	5.8	7.7	9.5	13.4
Income as % of sales	—	6.2%	5.3%	6.1%	5.0%	4.9%	5.3%
Earnings per share ($)	20.2%	0.53	0.63	0.69	0.80	0.96	1.32
Stock price – high ($)[1]	—	6.25	9.92	13.58	17.25	19.17	27.00
Stock price – low ($)[1]	—	3.75	4.83	7.17	11.33	13.33	17.67
Stock price – close ($)[1]	36.5%	5.58	8.08	13.50	16.92	19.00	26.42
P/E – high	—	12	16	20	22	20	20
P/E – low	—	7	8	10	14	14	13
Dividends per share ($)	—	0.00	0.00	0.00	0.00	0.00	0.00
Book value per share ($)	22.0%	4.10	4.76	7.60	8.49	9.55	11.10
Employees	23.4%	334	368	612	669	808	957

1995 Year-end:
Debt ratio: 0.3%
Return on equity: 13.3%
Cash (mil.): $21.3
Current ratio: 3.67
Long-term debt (mil.): $0.3
No. of shares (mil.): 9.8
Dividends
  Yield: —
  Payout: —
Market value (mil.): $259.0
R&D as % of sales: —
Advertising as % of sales: —

[1] Stock prices are for the prior calendar year.

KEYSTONE INTERNATIONAL, INC.

OVERVIEW

The keystone of Keystone's business is valves. The Houston-based company designs and produces specialized industrial valves and systems used to control the flow of gases, liquids, and solids in operations ranging from water treatment to processing of chemicals and petroleum to production of food and beverage products. It has 28 manufacturing plants in 13 countries. International revenues accounted for 57% of 1994 total sales.

Keystone was founded in 1947 as the Keystone Tool Company. Its founder, C. K. Stillwagon, designed and patented the "butterfly valve," which was used primarily by the oil industry. During an oil slump in the early 1950s, the company went several months without a major sale, prompting Stillwagon to diversify the company. In 1968 he sold his stake to Systems Engineering and Manufacturing. The company expanded to 5 continents, and in 1986 it merged with Anderson, Greenwood & Co. and bought Yarway Corp., thus acquiring 2 of the world's leading flow control companies. Keystone bought Kunkle Industries and Valvtron Industries in 1991. Keystone's former chairman Floyd Cailloux owns 13.2% of the company.

In 1992 Keystone expanded its Mexican operations with the purchase of a 2nd plant in Guadalajara, and it acquired a valve repair business to boost service on the Texas Gulf Coast. Also that year it opened sales offices in Beijing and Shanghai. In 1993 a Keystone subsidiary was awarded a multimillion-dollar, 3-year contract to provide safety relief valves and parts to Exxon. That same year Keystone acquired Morin, a maker of steel actuators, and Richards Ball Valve (Australia). To save costs, in 1994 it closed a valve plant in Fort Wayne, Indiana.

Cooper Industries veteran Nishan Teshoian took over as chairman and CEO in 1995.

WHO

Chairman, President, and CEO: Nishan Teshoian, age 54
EVP: Arthur L. French, age 54, $332,100 pay
VP and CFO: Mark E. Baldwin, $165,700 pay
Secretary: Donna D. Moore
Controller: Gordon Beittenmiller
Director Human Resources: Kathy Ruf
Auditors: Arthur Andersen & Co, SC

WHERE

HQ: 9600 W. Gulf Bank Dr., Houston, TX 77040
Phone: 713-466-1176   **Fax:** 713-937-5453

	1994 Sales	
	$ mil.	% of total
US	228.2	43
Europe, Middle East & Africa	145.4	27
Asia/Pacific	123.8	23
Other Americas	37.7	7
Total	**535.1**	**100**

WHAT

	1994 Sales
	% of total
Industrial valves	40
Safety & environmental products	23
Keystone Controls (power actuators)	19
Specialty products	12
Keystone Vanessa & Valvtron (rotary & ball valves)	6
Total	**100**

Selected Products
Ball valves
Butterfly valves
Electric actuators
Safety relief valves
Steam traps

KEY COMPETITORS

Baker Hughes	Emerson	ITT Industries
Cooper Cameron	General Signal	Mark IV
Cooper Industries	Graco	Roper Industries
Dana	IDEX	Teledyne
Dresser	Ingersoll-Rand	Watts Industries

HOW MUCH

NYSE symbol: KII FY ends: December 31	5-Year Growth	1989	1990	1991	1992	1993	1994
Sales ($ mil.)	7.3%	375.7	446.2	520.5	528.4	516.1	535.1
Net income ($ mil.)	1.9%	36.2	44.0	22.8	45.5	39.1	33.0
Income as % of sales	—	9.6%	9.9%	4.4%	8.6%	7.6%	6.2%
Earnings per share ($)	2.7%	1.08	1.31	0.66	1.22	1.12	0.94
Stock price – high ($)	—	21.25	29.75	35.38	30.38	29.13	29.50
Stock price – low ($)	—	14.50	18.88	23.50	21.38	23.00	16.75
Stock price – close ($)	(4.1%)	21.25	25.25	28.50	25.13	27.38	17.25
P/E – high	—	20	23	54	25	26	31
P/E – low	—	13	14	36	18	21	18
Dividends per share ($)	5.7%	0.56	0.60	0.64	0.68	0.72	0.74
Book value per share ($)	6.4%	5.94	6.89	7.11	7.23	7.70	8.11
Employees	4.9%	3,300	3,500	4,100	4,100	4,200	4,200

1994 Year-end:
Debt ratio: 21.7%
Return on equity: 11.8%
Cash (mil.): $18.7
Current ratio: 2.46
Long-term debt (mil.): $60.5
No. of shares (mil.): 35.3
Dividends
  Yield: 4.3%
  Payout: 78.7%
Market value (mil.): $609.0
R&D as % of sales: —
Advertising as % of sales: —

KIRBY CORPORATION

OVERVIEW

If you're on the waterfront, Kirby can give you curbside service. The Houston-based company has the nation's largest fleet of tank barges providing transportation on the US's inland waterways and coasts for chemical and petroleum companies. Its ocean-going tankers and barges carry petroleum and dry cargos to and from the Gulf of Mexico and ports around the world. Kirby also owns subsidiaries engaged in marine and rail diesel repair and property and casualty insurance.

Kirby Petroleum entered the marine transportation business in 1968 with the purchase of Dixie Carriers, an inland barge business started in 1948 by the family of current Kirby chairman George Peterkin. In 1969 the Kirby Exploration Company was incorporated as a subsidiary; it owned Dixie Carriers and began the Puerto Rican insurance business in 1972. The subsidiary went public in 1976, and in 1982 it entered the diesel repair business by acquiring Marine Systems.

In 1988 Kirby exited the oil and gas industries to focus on marine transportation. To reflect the change it was renamed Kirby Corporation in 1990. Because of overbuilding in the 1970s, Kirby was able to snap up several shipping companies at bargain prices (including Brent Towing in 1989 and Sabine Towing in 1992), expanding the fleet from 71 vessels in 1988 to more than 400 by 1993. By then shipping markets had firmed and Kirby was positioned to benefit from rising freight rates.

Weakness in the offshore markets for petroleum products hurt profits in 1994, but the company has continued growing, creating Rail Systems, a diesel repair and parts service for locomotives, and buying Dow Chemical's marine assets for $24 million that same year.

In 1995 J. H. Pyne was promoted to CEO, replacing longtime leader Peterkin, who became chairman.

WHO

Chairman: George A. Peterkin Jr., age 68, $339,360 pay
President and CEO: J. H. Pyne, age 47, $239,360 pay
SVP Finance and Treasurer: Brian K. Harrington, age 48, $167,360 pay
VP; President, Dixie Marine: Ronald C. Dansby, age 55, $176,360 pay
VP; EVP, Dixie Carriers: Steven M. Bradshaw, age 46, $141,360 pay
VP Human Resources: Jack M. Sims, age 52
Auditors: KPMG Peat Marwick LLP

WHERE

HQ: 1775 St. James Place, Ste. 300, Houston, TX 77056-3453
Phone: 713-629-9370   **Fax:** 713-964-2200

WHAT

	1994 Sales	
	$ mil.	% of total
Transportation	311.1	72
Insurance premiums	65.8	15
Diesel repair	45.3	10
Other	10.9	3
Total	**433.1**	**100**

	1994 Vessels	
	No.	% of total
Inland tank barges	505	76
Boats	139	21
Offshore tank ships	9	1
Offshore dry cargo barges	6	1
Offshore break-bulk ships	3	1
Offshore tank barges	2	0
Total	**664**	**100**

KEY COMPETITORS

Adams Resources
Crowley Maritime
CSX
General Steamship
Hollywood Marine
Ingram
Maritrans

HOW MUCH

AMEX symbol: KEX FY ends: December 31	5-Year Growth	1989	1990	1991	1992	1993	1994
Sales ($ mil.)	25.1%	141.3	175.8	189.0	269.5	378.4	433.1
Net income ($ mil.)	7.7%	11.5	15.4	13.3	13.6	22.8	16.7
Income as % of sales	—	8.1%	8.8%	7.0%	5.0%	6.0%	3.8%
Earnings per share ($)	8.3%	0.39	0.60	0.61	0.60	0.86	0.58
Stock price – high ($)	—	11.13	16.13	15.50	22.00	23.38	23.38
Stock price – low ($)	—	6.13	7.00	10.00	11.38	15.50	15.50
Stock price – close ($)	20.6%	7.75	12.13	13.13	21.38	19.75	19.75
P/E – high	—	29	27	25	37	27	40
P/E – low	—	16	12	16	19	18	27
Dividends per share ($)	—	0.00	0.00	0.00	0.00	0.00	0.00
Book value per share ($)	15.3%	3.87	4.48	5.14	5.43	7.51	7.88
Employees	19.6%	940	950	1,450	1,875	2,050	2,300

1994 Year-end:
Debt ratio: 41.7%
Return on equity: 7.7%
Cash (mil.): $7.4
Current ratio: 1.43
Long-term debt (mil.): $148.5
No. of shares (mil.): 28.3
Dividends
  Yield: —
  Payout: —
Market value (mil.): $559.2
R&D as % of sales: —
Advertising as % of sales: —

KITTY HAWK, INC.

OVERVIEW

Displaying a lot of the right stuff, Kitty Hawk is a privately owned Dallas/Fort Worth–based airline that provides air cargo services on a time-sensitive basis through charter management of 3rd-party carriers (73.7% of sales) and through its own charter cargo airline (26.3%). Its major customer for several years has been General Motors (GM), which accounted for 63% of the company's revenues in 1994. Other major users of its just-in-time and outsourcing services include the US Postal Service and Roadway Global Air. The company's air cargo charter management business arranged over 16,700 on-demand charters in 1994 for more than 550 customers in a wide range of industries, including the automotive, computer, mail and bulk package delivery, and oil field service and equipment businesses.

In 1980 Tom Christopher founded Christopher Charters (later changed to Kitty Hawk, Inc.), which arranged on-demand air charters using 3rd-party air cargo carriers. It acquired Kitty Hawk Airways, a small-aircraft, independent, on-demand air cargo carrier, in 1985. From the mid-1980s until 1990 the company used its own aircraft to fly on-demand charters for GM assembly plants and suppliers. After GM decided to outsource its charter management function in 1990, Kitty Hawk beat out competitors to become GM's primary air cargo charter manager. It secured an extension of its GM contract through May 1997.

Kitty Hawk currently operates through 2 wholly owned subsidiaries, Kitty Hawk Aircargo and Kitty Hawk Charters. The cargo operator grew rapidly in the 1990s, with revenues jumping from $16.4 million in 1990 to $107.7 million in 1994. Further expansion is focused on bringing in 5 more Boeing 727 jets and integrating them profitably into Kitty Hawk's largely small-plane fleet.

As the company is dependent on just 2 customers for 73% of its sales, Kitty Hawk is keen both to retain existing customers and to generate new clients as it expands its operations.

The company issued a prospectus in 1994, but Christopher put Kitty Hawk's IPO on indefinite hold in 1995.

WHO

Chairman and CEO: M. Tom Christopher, age 47, $632,000 pay
President and COO: Tilmon J. Reeves, age 54, $326,000 pay
SVP Finance, CFO, and Secretary: Richard R. Wadsworth, age 47, $206,000 pay
VP Human Resources: Lena Knowlton
Auditors: Ernst & Young LLP

WHERE

HQ: 1515 W. 20th St., PO Box 612787, Dallas/Fort Worth International Airport, TX 75261
Phone: 214-456-2200   **Fax:** 214-456-2210

WHAT

	1994 Sales	
	No.	% of total
General Motors	67.9	63
US Postal Service	11.2	10
Roadway Global Air	6.0	6
Other customers	22.6	21
Total	**107.7**	**100**

	1994 Aircraft	
	No.	% of total
Convair 600	6	38
Convair 640	4	25
DC-9-15F	3	19
Boeing 727-200	2	12
Beechcraft 58	1	6
Total	**16**	**100**

Selected Services
Air cargo charter
Air cargo charter management

KEY COMPETITORS

Air Express
AirTran
AMR
Celadon
Consolidated Freightways
Delta
DHL Worldwide Express
Express One International
FedEx
Grand Aire Express
Harper Group
Pittston Services
UAL
UPS

HOW MUCH

Private company FY ends: August 31	Annual Growth	1989	1990	1991	1992	1993	1994	1994 Year-end:
Sales ($ mil.)	60.1%	—	16.4	33.4	52.7	65.8	107.7	Debt ratio: 42.2%
Net income ($ mil.)	120.1%	—	0.2	0.8	1.0	4.1	5.3	Return on equity: 53.0%
Income as % of sales	—	—	1.4%	2.5%	1.9%	6.2%	4.9%	Cash (mil.): $4.8
Employees	79.3%	—	23	39	63	99	204	Current ratio: 1.25

1994 Year-end:
Debt ratio: 42.2%
Return on equity: 53.0%
Cash (mil.): $4.8
Current ratio: 1.25
R&D as % of sales: —

LA QUINTA INNS, INC.

OVERVIEW

San Antonio–based La Quinta operates a chain of more than 200 motels located primarily in Texas, Florida, and California. The company is one of the US's leading operators in the mid-priced lodging market, targeting cost-conscious business travelers by offering rooms comparable to those at a full-service hotel without such amenities as in-house restaurants, cocktail lounges, or room service.

La Quinta (Spanish for "the country place") was founded by Sam Barshop and his brother, Phil, who built their first 2 hotels in San Antonio for the HemisFair in 1968. Seeing a growing market in the Sunbelt for limited-service motels, they began adding outlets through partnerships and franchising. La Quinta went public in 1973. Wanting more control over the chain, La Quinta stopped franchising in 1977. (It now has 2 licensed inns).

The company continued to grow during the late 1970s and early 1980s, focusing particularly on salesmen who traveled by car by offering lower-priced rooms with few perks. To increase market share and name recognition, the company clustered its motels, building in and around existing markets. To fund growth, La Quinta formed joint ventures with financial institutions, primarily insurance companies. However, by the late 1980s the economy in the Southwest was in decline, and La Quinta's growth slowed. In 1991 millionaires Sid and Lee Bass and adviser Thomas Taylor joined with 2 other dissident shareholder groups to take majority ownership of the company. Barshop resigned as CEO in 1991 (he remained chairman until 1994). He was replaced by Gary Mead, who began to refurbish most of the company's hotels.

In 1994 La Quinta signed a deal with several Mexican investors to build 22 hotels in Mexico. However, the decline of the peso led the company to delay its Mexican expansion in 1995.

WHO

Chairman: Thomas M. Taylor, age 52
President and CEO: Gary L. Mead, age 47, $600,000 pay
SVP Finance and CFO: Michael A. Depatie, age 38, $288,000 pay
SVP Accounting and Administration: William C. Hammett Jr., age 48, $288,000 pay
SVP Development: Steven T. Schultz, age 48, $263,000 pay
SVP Operations: Thomas W. Higgins, age 47, $252,000 pay
SVP Marketing: Stephen B. Hickey
VP General Counsel and Secretary: John F. Schmutz
VP Human Resources: Robert T. Foley
Auditors: KPMG Peat Marwick LLP

WHERE

HQ: Weston Centre, 112 E. Pecan St., PO Box 2636, San Antonio, TX 78299-2636
Phone: 210-302-6000   **Fax:** 210-302-6191

	1994 Inns
	No.
Texas	88
Florida	20
California	15
Louisiana	12
Georgia	10
Other states	83
Total	**228**

WHAT

	1994 Sales	
	$ mil.	% of total
Room revenue	340.2	93
Other inn revenue	13.1	4
Restaurant rental & other	7.7	2
Management services	1.2	1
Total	**362.2**	**100**

KEY COMPETITORS

Accor	Manor Care	Red Lion
Bass	Marriott	Red Roof Inns
Best Western	International	ShoLodge
Hospitality Franchise	Promus	

HOW MUCH

NYSE symbol: LQI FY ends: December 31	5-Year Growth	1989	1990	1991	1992	1993	1994
Sales ($ mil.)	23.4%	126.6	226.5	242.5	255.8	271.9	362.2
Net income ($ mil.)	46.5%	5.6	2.2	1.4	(7.8)	19.4	37.8
Income as % of sales	—	4.4%	1.0%	0.6%	—	7.1%	10.4%
Earnings per share ($)	43.1%	0.13	0.05	0.03	(0.17)	0.41	0.78
Stock price – high ($)	—	5.49	5.30	4.60	6.16	15.96	25.88
Stock price – low ($)	—	3.86	3.34	2.97	4.23	5.97	12.79
Stock price – close ($)	34.3%	4.90	3.52	4.30	5.93	15.68	21.38
P/E – high	—	42	106	153	—	39	33
P/E – low	—	30	67	99	—	15	16
Dividends per share ($)	—	0.00	0.00	0.01	0.00	0.02	0.08
Book value per share ($)	7.9%	2.79	2.92	2.92	2.75	3.27	4.08
Employees	(0.6%)	6,400	6,300	5,900	6,000	6,100	5,800

1994 Year-end:
Debt ratio: 72.1%
Return on equity: 22.3%
Cash (mil.): $2.6
Current ratio: 0.33
Long-term debt (mil.): $448.3
No. of shares (mil.): 46.4
Dividends
  Yield: 0.4%
  Payout: 10.3%
Market value (mil.): $992.0
R&D as % of sales: —
Advertising as % of sales: —

LANDMARK GRAPHICS CORPORATION

Landmark Graphics designs and sells leading-edge geoscience and engineering software to the oil and gas industry. Its programs transform seismic, well-log, and other data into 3D computer pictures of underground formations, which help geologists and engineers decide if, and where, to drill. A pioneer in computer imaging, Houston-based Landmark also configures IBM, Sun, and Silicon Graphics workstations with its software and sells them to clients; other services include consulting, training, and maintenance. Customers include most of the world's largest oil and gas companies. At $171.2 million, revenues in 1995 were nearly 30% higher than in 1994. Major stockholders include Landmark VP Rutt Bridges (14%) and Merrill Lynch (9.4%).

Landmark was founded in 1982 by 2 former Exxon executives, John Mouton and Anson Hildebrand, and geophysics consultant Roice Nelson. The company concentrated on developing user-friendly software for geophysicists, who make the decisions to drill; its first software program was introduced in 1984. Despite a lull in the industry, Landmark was immediately successful and became the leading producer of computer-aided exploration (CAEX) software by the late 1980s. The company went public in 1988.

Landmark has grown by acquiring other companies for their technology. But competition from such oil service giants as Schlumberger and Halliburton, plus industry cutbacks, caused Landmark to post a loss in 1992. Also that year former Schlumberger executive Robert Peebler became CEO, and the company restructured; Landmark quickly rebounded. The company is continuing to widen its product offerings through acquisitions, which in 1995 included software developer GeoGraphix, seismic-data concern Munro Garrett, and DRD Corporation's Wellplan software.

President, CEO, and COO: Robert P. Peebler, age 47, $241,000 pay
EVP: James A. Downing II, age 54, $157,340 pay
VP; President, Advance Geophysical Corp.: Rutt Bridges, age 43
VP; General Manager, The Americas Operations: Larry J. White, age 46, $177,262 pay
VP Sales Development, Landmark Integrated Solutions: Lewis M. Fluke, age 46, $149,463 pay
VP Finance and CFO: William H. Seippel, age 37
VP Human Resources: Daniel L. Casaccia, age 45
Auditors: Price Waterhouse LLP

HQ: 15150 Memorial Dr., Houston, TX 77079-4304
Phone: 713-560-1000   **Fax:** 713-560-1379

	1994 Sales	
	$ mil.	% of total
US	62.3	47
Europe, Africa & Middle East	38.2	29
Pacific Rim	15.6	12
Canada	5.9	4
Latin America & other regions	10.3	8
Total	**132.3**	**100**

	1994 Sales	
	$ mil.	% of total
Software	63.3	48
Services	37.9	29
Hardware	31.1	23
Total	**132.3**	**100**

Selected Subsidiaries and Divisions
Advance Geophysical Corp. (seismic processing)
Geocomputing Technologies and Services (outsourcing)
Zycor Inc. (geologic products)

Digicon (TX)	Litton	Synopsys
Halliburton	Oceaneering Intl.	ViewLogic
Input/Output	Schlumberger	Zycad
Intergraph	Structural Dynamics Research	

Nasdaq symbol: LMRK FY ends: June 30	5-Year Growth	1989	1990	1991	1992	1993	1994	1994 Year-end: Debt ratio: 8.5%
Sales ($ mil.)	26.2%	41.4	68.7	89.9	81.9	87.6	132.3	Return on equity: 5.0%
Net income ($ mil.)	2.8%	4.8	7.4	9.8	(7.2)	5.2	5.5	Cash (mil.): $73.7
Income as % of sales	—	11.6%	10.8%	10.9%	—	5.9%	4.2%	Current ratio: 4.95
Earnings per share ($)	(16.4%)	0.66	0.74	0.94	(0.67)	0.49	0.27	Long-term debt (mil.): $12.0
Stock price – high ($)	—	23.25	23.75	26.00	25.25	26.75	35.25	No. of shares (mil.): 15.9
Stock price – low ($)	—	9.25	12.75	13.00	8.00	12.75	16.00	Dividends
Stock price – close ($)	0.9%	17.25	14.25	22.25	13.63	18.50	18.00	Yield: —
P/E – high	—	35	32	28	—	55	131	Payout: —
P/E – low	—	14	17	14	—	26	59	Market value (mil.): $285.4
Dividends per share ($)	—	0.00	0.00	0.00	0.00	0.00	0.00	R&D as % of sales: 12.5%
Book value per share ($)	15.6%	4.30	6.34	7.46	6.76	7.34	8.87	Advertising as % of sales: —
Employees	23.0%	218	327	499	542	510	613	

LANDRY'S SEAFOOD RESTAURANTS, INC.

OVERVIEW

Landry's continues to reel in big sales. The company, which operates more than 30 seafood restaurants primarily in the southern US, is one of the nation's fastest-growing casual-dining chains. It operates midpriced Landry's Seafood Houses and more upscale Willie G's eateries, which feature colorful Cajun/Gulf Coast decor and are usually located in high-profile sites — in resort areas, near convention and entertainment centers, and along waterfronts. Landry's recently introduced a new seafood concept, Joe's Crab Shack, a less formal, family-style seafood restaurant.

The first Landry's Seafood House opened in Houston in 1980 and the first Willie G's a year later. They drew the attention of Houston real estate developer Tilman Fertitta, who saw seafood restaurants as an undertapped market. Fertitta's father had owned a seafood restaurant in Galveston, and Fertitta had experience with his own company, Evangeline Restaurants. In 1986 Fertitta (then in his 20s) acquired an interest in the Landry's chain. In 1988 he bought the remaining interest and took the helm. The company went public in 1993. Fertitta is a hands-on CEO, developing the 1940s wharfside look and guiding management, accounting, and training programs. He now owns 28% of the company and is also a minority owner of the NBA's Houston Rockets.

With Darden Restaurants' Red Lobster the sole seafood casual-dining competition throughout its market, and with Cajun-style cuisine maintaining its popularity, Landry's is well positioned for growth. Its unique restaurant design, large portions, and moderately priced meals have helped to attract crowds wherever it has opened a new restaurant.

In 1994 the company expanded into Arizona, Colorado, and Oklahoma. Fertitta plans to continue to add restaurants, with a goal of 38 by the end of 1995.

WHO

President and CEO: Tilman J. Fertitta, age 37, $548,084 pay
EVP and COO: E. A. Jaksa Jr., age 47, $248,077 pay
VP Administration, Secretary, and General Counsel: Steven L. Scheinthal, age 33, $168,694 pay
VP Finance and CFO: Paul S. West, age 36, $158,851 pay
Human Resources Director: Rex E. Lee
Auditors: Arthur Andersen & Co, SC

WHERE

HQ: 1400 Post Oak Blvd., Ste. 1010, Houston, TX 77056
Phone: 713-850-1010   **Fax:** 713-623-4702

	1994 Restaurants
	No.
Texas	17
Colorado	2
Florida	2
Louisiana	2
Arkansas	1
Arizona	1
Mississippi	1
Oklahoma	1
Tennessee	1
Total	**28**

WHAT

Selected Menu Items
Crab and lump crabmeat
Crawfish
Flounder
Lobster
Oysters
Red snapper
Shrimp

KEY COMPETITORS

Applebee's
Bayport Restaurant
Brinker
Carlson
Chart House
Darden Restaurants
Family Restaurants
Lone Star Steakhouse
Metromedia
Morrison Restaurants
Outback Steakhouse
Pappas Restaurants
Restaurant Co.

HOW MUCH

Nasdaq symbol: LDRY FY ends: December 31	Annual Growth	1989	1990	1991	1992	1993	1994
Sales ($ mil.)	39.4%	11.9	15.4	19.5	22.4	34.2	62.5
Net income ($ mil.)	—	(2.2)	0.1	1.7	3.4	3.8	5.7
Income as % of sales	—	—	0.5%	8.7%	15.2%	11.2%	9.1%
Earnings per share ($)	24.0%	—	—	—	0.52	0.56	0.80
Stock price – high ($)	—	—	—	—	—	24.25	30.75
Stock price – low ($)	—	—	—	—	—	13.00	17.25
Stock price – close ($)	18.2%	—	—	—	—	24.00	28.38
P/E – high	—	—	—	—	—	43	38
P/E – low	—	—	—	—	—	23	22
Dividends per share ($)	—	—	—	—	—	0.00	0.00
Book value per share ($)	163.8%	—	—	—	—	3.18	8.38
Employees	54.3%	—	—	—	1,050	1,323	2,500

1994 Year-end:
Debt ratio: 1.6%
Return on equity: 14.1%
Cash (mil.): $19.5
Current ratio: 2.84
Long-term debt (mil.): $0.7
No. of shares (mil.): 7.4
Dividends
   Yield: —
   Payout: —
Market value (mil.): $209.8
R&D as % of sales: —
Advertising as % of sales: 2.0%

LUBY'S CAFETERIAS, INC.

OVERVIEW

Combining healthy menus with healthy sales, San Antonio–based Luby's Cafeterias operates a chain of more than 170 restaurants in Arizona, Arkansas, Florida, Kansas, Louisiana, Mississippi, Missouri, New Mexico, Oklahoma, Tennessee, and Texas. About half of Luby's units are in shopping malls and the remainder are free-standing. Each seats around 300 people. Luby's serves a wide range of lunch and dinner foods cafeteria-style.

Harry Luby opened his first New England Dairy Lunch cafeteria-style restaurant in 1911 in Springfield, Missouri. Over the next 15 years, Luby started other restaurants in Louisiana, Missouri, Oklahoma, and Texas. Harry retired in 1927, and later son Bob launched the first Luby's Cafeteria, in Dallas. After WWII Bob Luby teamed up with his cousin Charles Johnston to launch a cafeteria chain. They won a contract for the Veterans Administration's cafeteria at Dallas's Love Field in 1946 and opened a cafeteria in downtown San Antonio in 1947. The company expanded across Texas over the next 15 years. Luby's opened its first New Mexico restaurant in 1966 and went public in 1973. In 1981 it exceeded $100 million in sales for the first time. In 1991 tragedy struck when a gunman killed 23 diners at a Luby's in Killeen, Texas.

One secret to Luby's success has been the profit-sharing basis of its cafeteria management. Managers receive no base salaries. Instead, each gets 20–25% of a location's operating profits. The company also serves the growing takeout market; takeout orders accounted for 9% of 1994 sales.

The 1995 devaluation of the Mexican peso slowed cross-border traffic and hurt sales in about 10% of Luby's restaurants. Luby's launched a media campaign on Spanish-speaking radio and TV stations on the border to lure back customers.

WHO

Chairman: John B. Lahourcade, age 70, $225,000 pay
President and CEO: Ralph Erben, age 63, $478,500 pay
EVP and CFO: John E. Curtis Jr., age 47, $299,000 pay (prior to promotion)
EVP Operations: William E. Robson, age 53, $299,000 pay (prior to promotion)
VP Operations: Clyde C. Hays III, age 43
VP Operations: Jimmy W. Woliver, age 57
VP Real Estate: John A. Finch
VP Construction: Dick M. Jennison
Auditors: Ernst & Young LLP

WHERE

HQ: 2211 Northeast Loop 410, PO Box 33069, San Antonio, TX 78265-3069
Phone: 210-654-9000   **Fax:** 210-654-3211

	1994 Luby's Cafeterias	
	No.	% of total
Houston	25	15
San Antonio	18	10
Dallas	8	5
Austin	6	3
El Paso	6	3
Fort Worth	6	3
Other locations	108	61
Total	**177**	**100**

WHAT

	1994 Sales
	% of total
Customers under 65	81
Customers over 65	19
Total	**100**

KEY COMPETITORS

Apple South
Applebee's
Bob Evans
Buffets
Cracker Barrel
Family Restaurants
Flagstar

Furr's/Bishop's Cafeterias
IHOP
Metromedia
Morrison Restaurants
Restaurant Co.
Taco Cabana
Wyatt Cafeterias

HOW MUCH

NYSE symbol: LUB FY ends: August 31	5-Year Growth	1989	1990	1991	1992	1993	1994	1994 Year-end: Debt ratio: 7.4%
Sales ($ mil.)	6.6%	283.3	311.1	328.2	346.6	367.8	390.7	Return on equity: 16.7%
Net income ($ mil.)	5.1%	29.5	32.1	32.3	32.6	35.5	37.8	Cash (mil.): $10.9
Income as % of sales	—	10.4%	10.3%	9.9%	9.4%	9.7%	9.7%	Current ratio: 0.32
Earnings per share ($)	6.1%	1.08	1.17	1.18	1.19	1.31	1.45	Long-term debt (mil.): $0.0
Stock price – high ($)	—	19.82	21.25	20.75	23.50	25.88	24.63	No. of shares (mil.): 25.1
Stock price – low ($)	—	15.42	15.58	12.00	14.00	19.75	21.63	Dividends
Stock price – close ($)	4.5%	17.92	18.00	14.38	22.25	22.50	22.38	Yield: 2.8%
P/E – high	—	18	18	18	20	20	17	Payout: 42.8%
P/E – low	—	14	13	10	12	15	15	Market value (mil.): $562.0
Dividends per share ($)	9.7%	0.39	0.44	0.47	0.51	0.56	0.62	R&D as % of sales: —
Book value per share ($)	7.4%	5.94	6.68	7.40	8.01	8.78	8.50	Advertising as % of sales: 1.7%
Employees	4.8%	8,000	8,600	9,000	9,200	9,600	10,100	

MAXXIM MEDICAL, INC.

OVERVIEW

Sterile Design leads the way at MAXXIM Medical. MAXXIM, which specializes in selling surgical and medical procedural supplies, sterile drapes and clothing, and physical therapy equipment, has grown steadily since its acquisition of Johnson & Johnson's Sterile Design subsidiary (custom surgical trays) in 1993. Sterile Design now accounts for half of the company's total sales. MAXXIM's 3 other divisions are Argon Medical (specialty medical products), Boundary Healthcare (surgical clothes), and Henley Healthcare (physical therapy products).

Henley International (which became MAXXIM in 1993) was started in 1976, when Ernest Henley, a chemical engineering professor, sought a way to ease his son's tennis elbow. The result was Fluidotherapy, which used ground corncobs to apply heat and pressure to the affected joint. Henley patented the process and looked for backers. He found Kenneth Davidson, director of business development for Intermedics, which invested $500,000 and installed Davidson on the board. Besides making its own products, Henley grew by buying other firms (including Neromedics, an Intermedics unit). In 1986 Davidson became chairman, president, and CEO, and Ernest Henley continued his academic career.

Henley went public in 1990 and expanded into specialty medical equipment and trays of disposable products for individual medical procedures (1991), sterile textiles (1992), and customized trays (1993). Under the leadership of its somewhat unorthodox CEO (Davidson has a drooping mustache and shoulder-length hair and is the lead singer and guitarist of the company's rock band), MAXXIM has acquired 13 companies in 8 years.

It bought Southwest Medical Packaging (custom trays) in 1994 and gained a foothold in Europe with the 1995 purchase of Medica, a Dutch medical supply and catheter firm.

WHO

Chairman, President, and CEO: Kenneth W. Davidson, age 47, $260,000 pay
EVP, COO, and Treasurer: Peter M. Graham, age 48, $135,769 pay
President, Sterile Design: Jack F. Cahill, $135,000 pay
VP; Group VP, Argon Medical and Henley Healthcare: David L. Lamont, age 48, $121,769 pay
VP; President, Boundary Healthcare: Henry T. DeHart, age 48, $120,000 pay
VP and Corporate Controller: Alan S. Blazei
Manager Human Resources: Donna Hustis
Auditors: KPMG Peat Marwick LLP

WHERE

HQ: 104 Industrial Blvd., Sugar Land, TX 77478
Phone: 713-240-5588   **Fax:** 713-240-2577

WHAT

	1994 Sales	
	$ mil.	% of total
Sterile Design	95.2	50
Argon Medical	41.6	22
Boundary Healthcare	35.2	18
Henley Healthcare	19.4	10
Total	**191.4**	**100**

Operating Groups and Selected Products

Sterile Design	Needles
Customized procedural trays	Preassembled procedural trays
Preassembled procedural trays	**Boundary Healthcare**
	Sterile surgical clothing
Argon Medical	Surgical draping systems
Catheters	
Guidewires	**Henley Healthcare**
Introducers	Physical therapy products

KEY COMPETITORS

Arrow International   C. R. Bard
Ballard Medical   Johnson & Johnson
Baxter   Ni-Med
Becton, Dickinson   Staodyn
Boston Scientific   Superior
CONMED   Orthopedic

HOW MUCH

NYSE symbol: MAM FY ends: October 31	Annual Growth	1989	1990	1991	1992	1993	1994
Sales ($ mil.)	61.9%	17.2	27.1	45.3	74.5	129.7	191.4
Net income ($ mil.)	61.5%	0.7	1.2	1.6	3.5	5.5	7.7
Income as % of sales	—	4.1%	4.4%	3.5%	4.7%	4.2%	4.0%
Earnings per share ($)	18.9%	0.42	0.48	0.57	0.75	0.94	1.00
Stock price – high ($)	—	—	8.50	17.63	24.25	20.63	20.50
Stock price – low ($)	—	—	4.00	4.38	11.50	12.25	10.38
Stock price – close ($)	32.2%	—	4.75	17.50	13.88	20.00	14.50
P/E – high	—	—	18	31	32	22	21
P/E – low	—	—	8	8	15	13	10
Dividends per share ($)	—	—	0.00	0.00	0.00	0.00	0.00
Book value per share ($)	33.4%	—	4.37	5.05	10.73	11.57	13.85
Employees	49.9%	215	365	800	1,800	2,282	1,626

1994 Year-end:
Debt ratio: 20.8%
Return on equity: 8.6%
Cash (mil.): $31.9
Current ratio: 4.47
Long-term debt (mil.): $28.8
No. of shares (mil.): 8.1
Dividends
 Yield: —
 Payout: —
Market value (mil.): $116.8
R&D as % of sales: 1.2%
Advertising as % of sales: —

MEMOREX TELEX N.V.

OVERVIEW

Manufacturing is out and service is in at Memorex Telex. Led by CEO Marcelo Gumucio, the company is reinventing itself, transforming from a computer and peripherals manufacturer into a systems integrator. Memorex Telex emerged from bankruptcy in 1994, and since then it has focused on providing networking and storage integration services with partners including Novell, Intel, and Shiva. It also sells servers, tape drives, and other peripherals. Although it has a Dutch holding company, Memorex Telex's worldwide headquarters are in Irving.

Founded in 1961 by Laurence Spitters, an executive with audiotape maker Ampex, Memorex made computer tape and audiotape (known for the slogan, "Is it live? Or is it Memorex?"). In the late 1960s it began making disk drives for IBM mainframes and other large computer systems. In the early 1970s Memorex made an ill-fated attempt to enter the mainframe market, which it abandoned in 1973. By the mid-1970s, with competition in the tape drive business heating up, Memorex began to lose ground. In 1978 it made a failed bid for Storage Technology, which had passed it in the market for IBM-compatible tape drives. In 1981 it sold its audiotape business to Tandy. (The Memorex brand name has since been licensed to BASF in Europe.) That same year the company was acquired by Burroughs (now Unisys). In 1986 several European managers of Memorex acquired the company in an LBO. Memorex adopted its present name after buying computer terminal maker Telex in 1988.

By 1992 the company was struggling with a US recession and stiff competition and filed for bankruptcy. It hired Gumucio, former head of Cray Research, as CEO in 1992. However, Memorex Telex continued to post losses because of a European recession and a slow recovery in the US, and it filed for bankruptcy again in early 1994.

As part of its new strategy, the company has eliminated its manufacturing operations, cut its work force, and streamlined its sales organization. In fiscal 1995 its sales dipped and it posted a loss as network and storage revenues fell and margins on its products and services tightened.

WHO

Chairman, President, and CEO: Marcelo A. Gumucio, age 57, $1,220,000 pay
VC: David J. Faulkner, age 55, $520,000 pay
SVP Finance and Administration (HR): Rudolph G. Morin, age 58, $390,000 pay
VP Worldwide Marketing: Brad Sowers
VP North American Sales: George Bennett
Auditors: Ernst & Young LLP

WHERE

HQ: 545 E. John Carpenter Fwy., Irving, TX 75062
Phone: 214-444-3500　　**Fax:** 214-444-3501

	1995 Sales	
	$ mil.	% of total
US	438.6	48
Europe	352.7	39
Other regions	118.5	13
Total	**909.8**	**100**

WHAT

	1995 Sales
	% of total
Networks	48
Services	39
Storage	11
Other	2
Total	**100**

Networks
Connectivity products
Desktop products
Servers

Services
Hardware maintenance and support
Network design, implementation, management, diagnostics, support, and training

Storage
Automated tape libraries
Multiplatform disk and tape cartridge subsystems

KEY COMPETITORS

BDM Intl.
Cap Gemini
Computer Sciences
Control Data Systems
DEC
EDS
Harris Corp.
Hewlett-Packard
Hitachi
IBM
ICL
Perot Systems
SHL Systemhouse
Storage Technology
Systems & Computer Technology
Unisys
Wang

HOW MUCH

Nasdaq symbol: MEMXY FY ends: March 31	Annual Growth	1990	1991	1992	1993	1994	1995
Sales ($ mil.)	(14.4%)	1,983.4	1,869.9	1,499.1	1,326.4	1,015.6	909.8
Net income ($ mil.)	—	(76.0)	(270.8)	104.3	(395.8)	227.0	(108.0)
Income as % of sales	—	—	—	7.0%	—	22.4%	—
Employees	(14.2%)	9,700	—	—	—	5,200	4,500

1995 Year-end:
Debt ratio: 100.0%
Return on equity: —
Cash (mil.): $36.9
Long-term debt (mil.): $87.4
R&D as % of sales: 1.7%

THE MEN'S WEARHOUSE, INC.

OVERVIEW

CEO George Zimmer "guarantees" a lot in his folksy television ads. Not only does he pledge that his suits will be priced lower than competitors', but he even promises the men who purchase clothes at the Men's Wearhouse a totally painless shopping experience.

Founded as a single Houston store in 1973 when Zimmer was only 23, the Men's Wearhouse today outfits men at 250 stores in 26 states, offering tailored business attire (with free alteration and pressing for the life of the garment) at about 20–30% below traditional department and specialty store prices. Fashion-trained sales reps ease the task of pairing shoes, ties, and outerwear with the store's core inventory of gray suits, khaki slacks, and navy sport coats.

The Men's Wearhouse went public in 1992. The Zimmer family controls about 42% of company shares, and EVP Richard Goldman owns another 11%.

Benefiting from department store downsizing of tailored clothing departments, the Men's Wearhouse has experienced its most significant growth in the past 5 years. To ensure continuation of this trend, the company has turned its attention to 2 new markets: Big & Tall apparel and the booming "business casual" market. Although most Men's Wearhouse locations have traditionally carried Big & Tall wear, the company is expanding its selection to become the only national, off-price Big & Tall retailer. Business casual clothing, introduced in response to more relaxed office dress codes, is expected to boost the company's accessories business but not replace its traditional stock.

Ever aiming to reach its goal of 500–600 stores in the US, the Men's Wearhouse planned to open some 50 in 1995, about half in new markets, bringing the total to 300 by the year's end.

WHO

Chairman, President, and CEO: George Zimmer, age 46, $420,000 pay
COO, CFO, and Treasurer: David H. Edwab, age 40, $452,298 pay
EVP: Richard E. Goldman, age 44, $336,000 pay
SVP Merchandising: James E. Zimmer, age 43, $324,000 pay
SVP Real Estate: Robert E. Zimmer, age 71, $199,000 pay
SVP Planning and Systems and Chief Information Officer: Harry M. Levy, age 46
VP Administration (HR): Julie Maciag
Auditors: Deloitte & Touche LLP

WHERE

HQ: 5803 Glenmont Dr., Houston, TX 77081
Phone: 713-295-7200   **Fax:** 713-664-1957

	1995 Stores
	No.
California	73
Texas	44
Florida	17
Michigan	17
Georgia	11
Washington	11
Colorado	8
Minnesota	7
Other states	62
Total	**250**

WHAT

	1995 Sales
	% of total
Tailored clothing	77
Accessories & other	23
Total	**100**

KEY COMPETITORS

Dayton Hudson	Jos. A. Bank	Ross Stores
Dillard	Marks and Spencer	Sears
Edison Brothers	May	S&K Famous
Federated	Melville	Brands
Gottschalks	Montgomery Ward	Syms
J. C. Penney	Nordstrom	Today's Man

HOW MUCH

Nasdaq symbol: SUIT FY ends: Sat. nearest Jan. 31	Annual Growth	1990	1991	1992	1993	1994	1995
Sales ($ mil.)	31.7%	80.2	105.4	133.4	170.0	240.4	317.1
Net income ($ mil.)	32.7%	2.9	3.4	4.2	5.9	8.7	12.1
Income as % of sales	—	3.7%	3.2%	3.1%	3.5%	3.6%	3.8%
Earnings per share ($)	24.3%	0.32	0.36	0.43	0.53	0.72	0.95
Stock price – high ($)[1]	—	—	—	—	11.84	32.75	34.75
Stock price – low ($)[1]	—	—	—	—	5.67	10.67	15.75
Stock price – close ($)[1]	40.9%	—	—	—	11.34	32.63	22.50
P/E – high	—	—	—	—	22	45	37
P/E – low	—	—	—	—	11	15	17
Dividends per share ($)	—	—	—	—	0.00	0.00	0.00
Book value per share ($)	39.2%	—	—	—	3.47	4.79	6.71
Employees	35.7%	—	—	1,277	1,766	2,545	3,190

1995 Year-end:
Debt ratio: 22.9%
Return on equity: 17.0%
Cash (mil.): $1.2
Current ratio: 2.45
Long-term debt (mil.): $24.6
No. of shares (mil.): 12.7
Dividends
  Yield: —
  Payout: —
Market value (mil.): $284.8
R&D as % of sales: —
Advertising as % of sales: 7.3%

[1] Stock prices are for the prior calendar year.

MESA INC.

OVERVIEW

MESA, owned by flamboyant businessman T. Boone Pickens, is one of the largest independent natural gas producers in the US. In 1994 the Irving-based company produced over 82 billion cubic feet of natural gas and 546 million barrels of oil. Most of MESA's reserves are in Kansas's Hugoton Field and the Texas Panhandle. The company is also the US's #5 producer of helium gas, a natural gas byproduct.

In 1956 Pickens left his job as a geologist at Phillips Petroleum and with $2,500 started Petroleum Exploration Inc. In 1964 Petroleum Exploration and Pickens's Canadian subsidiary, Altair Oil and Gas, merged as MESA and went public. MESA's 1986 acquisition of Pioneer Corp. gave the company its West Texas field. In 1988 it bought Tenneco holdings that included 1/4 of the Hugoton Field. MESA was the base for Pickens's frequent raids on bigger petroleum companies, including Cities Services (1982) and Unocal (1985). With gas prices declining in the early 1990s, MESA began selling assets and restructuring its $600 million debt. The company raised $93 million from a public offering in 1994. Late that year Pickens put the Hugoton Field up for sale, saying he wanted MESA to refocus on exploration and development. Pickens owns 7.5% of the company.

As gas stockpiles increase, the result of recent warm winters, MESA's profits are being squeezed by gas supplies from Canada and the Gulf of Mexico. In response, MESA is attempting to pump up the market for natural gas. In 1994 the company opened its first MESA natural gas station, in Phoenix.

A group of dissident shareholders (including oil investor Marvin Davis and Montana businessman Dennis Washington and led by former MESA executive David Batchelder) is challenging Pickens's autonomy. In response to shareholder pressure, in mid-1995 MESA began seeking a potential buyer or merger partner.

WHO

Chairman and CEO: T. Boone Pickens, age 66, $850,000 pay
President and COO: Paul W. Cain, age 56, $550,020 pay
VP Exploration and Production: Dennis E. Fagerstone, age 46, $299,980 pay
VP Public Affairs: Andrew J. Littlefair, age 34, $215,980 pay
VP and CFO: Stephen K. Gardner, age 35
Controller: William D. Ballew, age 36, $161,230 pay
Manager Employee Relations: Paul M. Cashion
Auditors: Arthur Andersen & Co, SC

WHERE

HQ: 5205 N. O'Connor Blvd., Ste. 1400, Irving, TX 75039-3746
Phone: 214-444-9001   **Fax:** 214-402-7023

Selected Properties

Fields
Gulf Coast (offshore, Louisiana and Texas)
Hugoton Field (Kansas)
Rocky Mountain area (primarily in North Dakota and Wyoming)
West Panhandle Field (Texas)

Processing Plants
Fain Plant (Texas)
Satanta Plant (Kansas)

WHAT

Selected Products

Helium	Natural gas liquids
Natural gas	Oil

KEY COMPETITORS

Amerada Hess	KCS Energy	Quaker State
Amoco	Kerr-McGee	Royal Dutch/Shell
Anadarko	Koch	Texaco
' Petroleum	Mobil	TransTexas Gas
Atlantic Richfield	NGC	Unocal
Chevron	Occidental	USX-Delhi
Exxon	Panhandle	Williams Cos.
Flying J	Eastern	Zapata
Hunt Oil	Phillips	
Imperial Oil	Petroleum	

HOW MUCH

NYSE symbol: MXP FY ends: December 31	5-Year Growth	1989	1990	1991	1992	1993	1994	1994 Year-end: Debt ratio: 90.8%
Sales ($ mil.)	(6.9%)	326.9	329.6	249.5	237.1	222.2	228.7	Return on equity: —
Net income ($ mil.)	—	(60.4)	(200.3)	(79.2)	(89.2)	(102.4)	(83.4)	Cash (mil.): $162.5
Income as % of sales	—	—	—	—	—	—	—	Current ratio: 2.30
Earnings per share ($)	—	(1.56)	(5.19)	(2.05)	(2.31)	(2.61)	(1.42)	Long-term debt (mil.): $1,192.8
Stock price – high ($)	—	13.50	8.13	3.50	13.38	8.13	8.50	No. of shares (mil.): 64.1
Stock price – low ($)	—	6.88	2.00	1.00	2.50	3.50	3.63	Dividends
Stock price – close ($)	(10.5%)	8.50	3.00	1.38	4.63	5.63	4.88	Yield: —
P/E – high	—	—	—	—	—	—	—	Payout: —
P/E – low	—	—	—	—	—	—	—	Market value (mil.): $312.2
Dividends per share ($)	(100.0%)	6.80	0.85	0.00	0.00	0.00	0.00	R&D as % of sales: —
Book value per share ($)	—	(0.20)	(10.61)	7.09	4.78	2.41	1.94	Advertising as % of sales: —
Employees	(9.2%)	648	537	351	382	383	399	

MICHAELS STORES, INC.

OVERVIEW

You don't have to be Michelangelo to shop at Michaels Stores. The Irving-based company will provide the supplies for your creation whether you want to spend 4 years painting on the ceiling or an afternoon sewing sequins on a sweatshirt. Michaels is the nation's largest specialty retailer of arts, crafts, and decorative items, operating more than 460 stores in 41 states, Puerto Rico, and Canada. It sells a range of products, from picture frames to paint-by-number kits to party supplies.

Michaels was founded in Colorado in 1962 by Michael Dupey. By 1983 Dupey had a chain of 11 stores, located primarily in Texas. That year brothers Sam and Charles Wyly, who co-founded Dallas-based Sterling Software in 1981, acquired the company from Dupey (who has since founded rival MJ Designs). The Wyly family now owns about 21% of the company. After going public in 1984, Michaels began a series of acquisitions. By 1989 the company had 122 stores. That year Robert Bass's Acadia Partners made a hostile bid for the company. Michaels fended off the bid but had to take a $5 million charge in the process. To improve profitability, the company restructured its operations and centralized merchandising and advertising.

Acquisitions have continued to play a key role in the company's growth. In 1994 the company paid about $88 million for the 101-store Leewards Creative Crafts chain, which gave Michaels a major presence in the Northeast. The company is adding higher-margin products, such as wedding accessories, to its merchandise mix, and it is experimenting with new store sizes, such as smaller stores for markets with fewer than 100,000 people.

In 1995 Michaels acquired California framing and art supply chain Aaron Brothers. It plans to continue operating the 71-unit chain under the Aaron Brothers name.

WHO

Chairman and CEO: Sam Wyly, age 60, $434,875 pay
VC: Charles J. Wyly Jr., age 61, $217,438 pay
President and COO: Douglas B. Sullivan, age 44, $271,924 pay (prior to promotion)
EVP and CFO: R. Don Morris, age 55, $321,154 pay
EVP: David E. Bolen, age 43
EVP and Chief Merchandising Officer: Robert H. Rudman, age 44
VP, General Counsel, and Secretary: Mark V. Beasley
VP Personnel: Donald C. Toby
Auditors: Ernst & Young LLP

WHERE

HQ: 5931 Campus Circle Dr., Las Colinas Business Park, Irving, TX 75063
Phone: 214-714-7000   **Fax:** 214-714-7155

WHAT

	1995 Sales % of total
Silk & dried flowers & plants	22
General craft materials & wearable art	20
Hobby, party, needlecraft & ribbon	19
Picture framing	15
Seasonal & promotional items	14
Fine art materials	10
Total	**100**

Stores
Aaron Brothers (specialty framing and art supply stores in Arizona, California, and Nevada)
Michaels (arts and crafts stores in 41 states and Puerto Rico)

KEY COMPETITORS

Amber's Stores
Ben Franklin Retail
Garden Ridge
General Host
General Housewares
Kmart

MJ Designs
National Picture & Frame
Old America Stores
Rag Shops
Wal-Mart

HOW MUCH

Nasdaq symbol: MIKE FY ends: Sun. nearest Jan 31	5-Year Growth	1990	1991	1992	1993	1994	1995
Sales ($ mil.)	28.0%	289.8	362.0	410.9	493.2	619.7	994.6
Net income ($ mil.)	—	0.0	5.9	10.7	20.4	26.3	35.6
Income as % of sales	—	0.0%	1.6%	2.6%	4.1%	4.2%	3.6%
Earnings per share ($)	—	0.00	0.57	0.87	1.21	1.52	1.76
Stock price – high ($)[1]	—	10.25	6.50	17.13	34.00	39.00	46.50
Stock price – low ($)[1]	—	4.88	2.88	3.63	16.00	25.25	29.50
Stock price – close ($)[1]	46.6%	5.13	3.75	16.50	34.00	35.75	34.75
P/E – high	—	—	11	20	28	26	26
P/E – low	—	—	5	4	13	17	17
Dividends per share ($)	—	0.00	0.00	0.00	0.00	0.00	0.00
Book value per share ($)	32.3%	4.11	4.73	8.39	9.43	11.10	16.67
Employees	29.2%	4,840	5,310	5,310	10,040	20,000	17,440

1995 Year-end:
Debt ratio: 28.0%
Return on equity: 13.2%
Cash (mil.): $1.9
Current ratio: 2.25
Long-term debt (mil.): $138.1
No. of shares (mil.): 21.4
Dividends
  Yield: —
  Payout: —
Market value (mil.): $742.1
R&D as % of sales: —
Advertising as % of sales: —

[1] Stock prices are for the prior calendar year.

NABORS INDUSTRIES, INC.

OVERVIEW

This company has neighbors everywhere. Nabors Industries is the world's largest drilling contractor for land-based oil and gas projects, and it operates worldwide in almost every major oil, gas, and geothermal drilling market. It also provides engineering, logistics, and management services. Director Martin Whitman owns 5.2% of the company.

Nabors is the successor to Anglo Industries (later Anglo Energy), a drilling company founded in 1978. Anglo's fortunes took a nosedive, along with worldwide oil prices, in the mid-1980s, and the company filed for bankruptcy in 1984. Whitman's investment firm bought most of Anglo's bank debt and, following a reorganization, sold its shares to Equity Strategies, which Whitman manages. Anglo Energy became Nabors Industries in 1989.

The company has grown by acquiring overseas operations and by moving many of its rigs from the continental US to drilling hot spots like Yemen and Venezuela. Nabors has also been helped by its contracts on Alaska's North Slope, where, because of the harsh conditions, it earns 8 to 10 times more than when drilling in the contiguous US.

Although overseas sales account for over 1/3 of total revenues, Nabors is pursuing a strategy of buying up drilling companies in the continental US. In 1993 Nabors acquired W. R. Grace's US land drilling operations for $32 million, boosting its number of domestic deep-drilling rigs to more than 100. In 1994 the company acquired 16 US land rigs from Mitchell Energy & Development for approximately $10 million. In that year the company acquired Sundowner Offshore Services, a leading provider of well servicing and work-over services, through a tax-free merger.

In 1995 Nabors completed a $20 million acquisition of Delta Drilling, boosting its drilling rig fleet by 30.

WHO

Chairman and CEO: Eugene M. Isenberg, age 65, $1,000,000 pay
VC: Richard A. Stratton, age 48, $360,000 pay
President and COO: Anthony G. Petrello, age 40, $695,000 pay
VP and General Counsel: Michael W. Dundy, age 52, $154,440 pay
VP Administration (HR): Daniel McLachlin, age 57
Controller: Bruce P. Koch, age 35, $112,500 pay
Auditors: Coopers & Lybrand L.L.P.

WHERE

HQ: 515 W. Greens Rd., Ste. 1200, Houston, TX 77067
Phone: 713-874-0035   **Fax:** 713-872-5205

	1994 Sales		1994 Operating Income	
	$ mil.	% of total	$ mil.	% of total
Lower 48 states				
& Canada	198.0	47	20.1	42
Alaska	72.4	17	12.4	26
UK	52.0	12	5.7	12
Other regions	100.2	24	9.2	20
Adjustments	—	—	(11.3)	—
Total	**422.6**	**100**	**36.1**	**100**

WHAT

	1994 Rig Fleet	
	No.	% of total
Land rigs	249	87
Offshore rigs	37	13
Total	**286**	**100**

Selected Services
Construction
Design engineering
Drilling
Environmental services
Logistics
Maintenance
Oil field management
Transportation

KEY COMPETITORS

Ashland, Inc.
Baker Hughes
BJ Services
Camco
Dresser
Fluor
Halliburton
Kaneb Services
Matrix Service
McDermott
Noble Drilling
Petrolite
Schlumberger
Weatherford
Western Atlas

HOW MUCH

AMEX symbol: NBR FY ends: September 30	5-Year Growth	1989	1990	1991	1992	1993	1994
Sales ($ mil.)	41.5%	74.5	139.0	240.1	286.3	352.0	422.6
Net income ($ mil.)	(33.8%)	5.5	14.6	27.1	33.8	34.3	0.7
Income as % of sales	—	7.4%	10.5%	11.3%	11.8%	9.7%	0.2%
Earnings per share ($)	(39.2%)	0.12	0.27	0.44	0.52	0.50	0.01
Stock price – high ($)	—	4.00	7.25	8.13	8.13	11.00	7.88
Stock price – low ($)	—	1.50	3.25	4.00	5.50	6.13	5.75
Stock price – close ($)	13.2%	3.50	5.63	6.25	6.50	8.13	6.50
P/E – high	—	33	27	19	16	22	—
P/E – low	—	13	12	9	11	12	—
Dividends per share ($)	—	0.00	0.00	0.00	0.00	0.00	0.00
Book value per share ($)	30.6%	1.02	1.92	2.52	3.15	3.84	3.88
Employees	48.4%	672	2,298	2,949	3,168	5,700	4,833

1994 Year-end:
Debt ratio: 19.9%
Return on equity: 0.3%
Cash (mil.): $22.4
Current ratio: 2.10
Long-term debt (mil.): $57.5
No. of shares (mil.): 71.3
Dividends
  Yield: —
  Payout: —
Market value (mil.): $463.5
R&D as % of sales: —
Advertising as % of sales: —

NCI BUILDING SYSTEMS, INC.

OVERVIEW

NCI Building Systems has put the pedal to the metal. It is the 5th largest US manufacturer of metal structures, and its growth has been accelerated by the popularity of metal buildings. NCI designs, manufactures, and markets metal building systems, components, and roofing systems to commercial, agricultural, industrial, and community service users. The company sells its products directly to building contractors and resellers and markets them through a network of authorized builders.

While the building market is sensitive to economic conditions, demand for NCI's prefabricated metal buildings has remained strong as companies seek quickly built factory space. Metal building systems are used primarily for low-rise, nonresidential structures of up to 150,000 square feet (such as banks, schools, and factories). Metal buildings have low construction and materials costs, have short construction time, and require low maintenance.

CEO Johnie Schulte began his career in the mid-1950s, when he landed a job punching and shearing metal building components in Houston for $1.15 an hour. In 1984 he founded NCI. The enterprise made only metal building components until 1987, when it began making metal building systems. That year NCI had sales of about $2 million. The company went public in 1992, and the next year NCI's sales were more than $130 million. NCI is expanding beyond the Texas market to midwestern, south central, southeastern, and coastal states.

The company's business strategy has been to keep cost structure low, add satellite plants, develop its authorized builder organization, and acquire other makers of metal building systems and components.

In 1994 NCI bought Ellis Building Components, a metal building maker based in Tallapoosa, Georgia, for $4.9 million. In 1995 it launched a venture to make steel-frame homes.

WHO

Chairman: C. A. Rundell Jr., age 63, $172,750 pay
President and CEO: Johnie Schulte Jr., age 59, $337,917 pay
EVP: Leonard F. George, age 42, $286,250 pay
VP and CFO: Robert J. Medlock, age 55, $181,291 pay
VP Sales; President, A&S Building Systems, Inc.: Alvan E. Richey Jr., age 59, $151,084 pay
VP and Secretary: Donnie R. Humphries, age 45
VP: Frederick D. Koetting, age 36
General Counsel: Ernest O. Ross
Director Human Resources: Karen Rosales
Auditors: Ernst & Young LLP

WHERE

HQ: 7301 Fairview St., Houston, TX 77041
Phone: 713-466-7788   **Fax:** 713-466-3194

Manufacturing and Office Sites
Caryville, TN (manufacturing)
Houston, TX (offices and 2 manufacturing sites)
Jackson, MS (manufacturing)
Mattoon, IL (manufacturing)
Tallapoosa, GA (manufacturing)

WHAT

	1994 Sales	
	$ mil.	% of total
Metal building systems	126.7	76
Components	41.1	24
Total	**167.8**	**100**

Brand Names	Selected Products
A&S Building Systems	Metal building components
All American Systems	Metal building systems
Architectural Roof Systems	Roofing systems
Metallic Buildings	
Mid-West Metallic	
Mid-West Steel Buildings	
NCI	
Steel Systems	

KEY COMPETITORS

American Buildings   Robertson-Ceco
Butler Manufacturing   United Dominion Industries

HOW MUCH

Nasdaq symbol: BLDG FY ends: October 31	Annual Growth	1989	1990	1991	1992	1993	1994
Sales ($ mil.)	33.1%	40.1	57.6	66.3	79.0	134.5	167.8
Net income ($ mil.)	38.2%	2.0	2.6	2.9	3.6	6.3	10.3
Income as % of sales	—	—	5.1%	4.5%	4.3%	4.6%	4.7%	6.1%
Earnings per share ($)	22.7%	0.55	0.61	0.69	0.67	0.96	1.53
Stock price – high ($)	—	—	—	—	9.17	20.50	20.75
Stock price – low ($)	—	—	—	—	5.34	8.63	15.00
Stock price – close ($)	38.4%	—	—	—	9.00	16.75	17.25
P/E – high	—	—	—	—	14	21	14
P/E – low	—	—	—	—	8	9	10
Dividends per share ($)	—	—	—	—	0.00	0.00	0.00
Book value per share ($)	34.7%	—	—	—	3.54	4.65	6.42
Employees	59.5%	—	—	—	481	907	1,224

1994 Year-end:
Debt ratio: 1.0%
Return on equity: 30.0%
Cash (mil.): $6.3
Current ratio: 1.77
Long-term debt (mil.): $0.3
No. of shares (mil.): 6.2
Dividends
  Yield: —
  Payout: —
Market value (mil.): $106.5
R&D as % of sales: —
Advertising as % of sales: —

NEOSTAR RETAIL GROUP, INC.

OVERVIEW

The supernova of software retailing, NeoStar Retail Group was created in 1994 through the merger of Software Etc. and Babbage's. The Dallas-based company is the #1 consumer software retailer in the US, operating more than 700 Babbage's, Software Etc., and Supr Software stores, primarily in malls. About 40 of the company's stores are located within or next to a Barnes & Noble or B. Dalton bookstore. Leonard Riggio (head of Barnes & Noble) and Dutch retailer Vendex (a major Barnes & Noble shareholder) own 13.2% and 14.4% of NeoStar, respectively.

Software Etc. began as a division of B. Dalton Bookseller in 1984. Riggio and Vendex acquired B. Dalton in 1986, and in 1987 they established Software Etc. as a separate entity that went public in 1992. Babbage's, named for 19th-century mathematician Charles Babbage (considered the father of the computer), was founded by James McCurry and Gary Kusin, former Harvard Business schoolmates, in 1983. When the pair's ambitious expansion plan ran short of capital, Kusin's family friend H. Ross Perot stepped in to help. He put up $3 million initially and advised the team to proceed a little more cautiously. Babbage's went public in 1988.

Both companies focused on mall retailing, but each had its own niche: Babbage's concentrated on game software, while Software Etc. sold a broader variety of PC software. Both saw growth spurred by the rising popularity of Nintendo and Sega game systems and by falling PC prices. The 2 merged in an effort to stave off growing competition from big retail chains like Best Buy and Wal-Mart, which had begun adding more software.

The company is looking to add more stores outside malls. It planned to open 40–60 mall stores and 50–60 units in Barnes & Noble superstores in 1995.

WHO

Chairman and CEO: James B. McCurry, age 46, $275,000 pay
President and COO: Daniel A. DeMatteo, age 47, $265,000 pay
CFO, Secretary, and Treasurer: Opal P. Ferraro, age 40, $160,000 pay
VP Software Etc. Stores: Stanley A. Hirschman, age 47, $145,600 pay
VP Babbage's Stores: Mary P. Evans, age 35
VP Personnel: Michael A. Ivanich, age 43
Auditors: Ernst & Young LLP

WHERE

HQ: 10741 King William Dr., Dallas, TX 75220
Phone: 214-401-9000   **Fax:** 214-401-9002

	1995 Stores
	No.
Midwest	187
West	172
Northeast	147
Southeast	131
Southwest	67
Canada & Puerto Rico	6
Total	**710**

WHAT

	1995 Sales
	% of total
Video game systems & software	40
PC entertainment & educational software	27
PC productivity software	15
PC supplies & accessories	13
Computer books & magazines	5
Total	**100**

KEY COMPETITORS

Best Buy	Kmart	Staples
Borders	Micro Warehouse	Stream
Circuit City	Office Depot	International
CompUSA	OfficeMax	Tandy
Egghead	Software	Toys "R" Us
Fry's Electronics	Spectrum	Wal-Mart

HOW MUCH

Nasdaq symbol: NEOS FY ends: Sat. nearest Jan. 31	Annual Growth	1990[1]	1991[1]	1992[1]	1993[1]	1994[1]	1995
Sales ($ mil.)	37.0%	104.3	117.5	151.9	203.4	247.0	503.7
Net income ($ mil.)	—	(16.0)	(8.5)	1.6	5.7	5.7	(4.6)
Income as % of sales	—	—	—	1.1%	2.8%	2.3%	—
Earnings per share ($)	—	—	(2.10)	0.15	0.83	0.72	(0.31)
Stock price – high ($)[2]	—	—	—	—	19.00	23.25	10.50
Stock price – low ($)[2]	—	—	—	—	7.13	8.88	9.50
Stock price – close ($)[2]	(24.5%)	—	—	—	18.00	9.88	10.25
P/E – high	—	—	—	—	23	32	—
P/E – low	—	—	—	—	9	12	—
Dividends per share ($)	—	—	—	—	0.00	0.00	0.00
Book value per share ($)	88.6%	—	—	—	1.56	3.99	5.55
Employees	27.9%	1,800	1,825	2,025	2,280	2,953	6,150

1995 Year-end:
Debt ratio: 19.7%
Return on equity: —
Cash (mil.): $19.6
Current ratio: 1.27
Long-term debt (mil.): $16.0
No. of shares (mil.): 14.7
Dividends
  Yield: —
  Payout: —
Market value (mil.): $150.9
R&D as % of sales: —
Advertising as % of sales: —

[1] Software Etc. [2] Stock prices are for the prior calendar year.

NETWORTH, INC.

OVERVIEW

NetWorth is enjoying all the hubbub over computer networks. The company is a leading manufacturer of hubs, the small boxes where computer network cables converge. Its "intelligent" hubs allow network managers to monitor and manipulate the network's electronic traffic. NetWorth makes stackable hubs and modular, chassis-based hubs. The products are used for small networks as well as for large LANs. Its products support Novell's NetWare, the #1 operating system for client/server computing. UB Networks (a subsidiary of Tandem) accounted for 36.9% of NetWorth's 1994 sales; wholesalers Ingram Micro and Tech Data together accounted for 33.6%.

Irving, Texas–based NetWorth was founded in 1985 by CEO John McHale and Gabriel Pugliese. McHale had been a lead engineer with Texas Instruments and a design engineer with Interphase, a maker of peripheral controllers. Pugliese had been quality control manager at Interphase. NetWorth introduced products that used existing telephone wiring to connect computers into a network (rather than requiring dedicated wiring to be installed). The company added networking software to its product line in 1990 and went public in 1992. UB Networks owns 16.5% of NetWorth, McHale owns 9.8%, and Pugliese (now retired) and his family own 5.9%.

NetWorth expanded its manufacturing facility in 1994, adding a production line for board assemblies that incorporates state-of-the-art surface mount technology. That same year the company added IBM as an OEM customer.

In 1995 NetWorth acquired Network Resources Corp. (NRC), a developer of Ethernet switching and routing technologies. The company ended fiscal 1995 with $55.5 million in revenues, up 14% from 1994. However, NetWorth lost nearly $24 million because of the NRC acquisition and R&D write-offs.

WHO

Chairman, President, and CEO: John F. McHale, age 38, $168,750 pay
EVP Sales and Marketing: William E. Steele Jr.
General Manager, Internal Networking Division: Craig M. Scott, age 42, $154,996 pay
CFO and Secretary: Paul S. Zito, age 39, $132,500 pay
VP Operations: Nancy E. H. Miracle, age 43, $113,727 pay
VP Engineering: K. Arlan Harris, age 38
Director Human Resources and Facilities
  Administration: Cecilia Gannon
Auditors: KPMG Peat Marwick LLP

WHERE

HQ: 8404 Esters Blvd., Irving, TX 75063
Phone: 214-929-1700   **Fax:** 214-929-1720

	1994 Sales % of total
US	70
Other countries	30
Total	**100**

WHAT

	1994 Sales % of total
Stackable hubs	54
Other products	46
Total	**100**

Selected Products

Hardware	Software
Modular chassis-based hubs	HubView for NMS
Network adapter cards	HubView for Windows
Remote PowerRouter	
Stackable hubs	
Unmanaged hubs	

KEY COMPETITORS

3Com	AT&T	DEC
Accton	Bay Networks	D-Link
Asante	Cabletron	Novell

HOW MUCH

Nasdaq symbol: NWTH FY ends: June 30	Annual Growth	1989	1990	1991	1992	1993	1994	1994 Year-end:
Sales ($ mil.)	90.8%	—	3.7	9.4	17.1	29.8	48.6	Debt ratio: 54.9%
Net income ($ mil.)	74.3%	—	0.2	0.8	1.2	0.7	1.9	Return on equity: 6.8% Cash (mil.): $19.5
Income as % of sales	—	—	5.5%	8.7%	7.2%	2.3%	3.8%	Current ratio: 5.66
Earnings per share ($)	42.4%	—	0.09	0.32	0.37	0.14	0.37	Long-term debt (mil.): $22.1 No. of shares (mil.): 3.7
Stock price – high ($)	—	—	—	—	39.50	37.75	15.50	Dividends
Stock price – low ($)	—	—	—	—	28.50	7.25	7.25	Yield: —
Stock price – close ($)	(51.5%)	—	—	—	37.75	10.25	8.88	Payout: —
P/E – high	—	—	—	—	107	270	42	Market value (mil.): $33.1
P/E – low	—	—	—	—	77	52	20	R&D as % of sales: 5.7%
Dividends per share ($)	—	—	—	—	0.00	0.00	0.00	Advertising as % of sales: 3.7%
Book value per share ($)	36.0%	—	—	—	2.65	6.96	4.91	
Employees	—	—	—	—	—	—	161	

PAGING NETWORK, INC.

OVERVIEW

That beeping sound could mean a medical emergency, the close of a big sales contract, or a mother trying to find her child. Plano, Texas–based PageNet helps get the attention of its more than 5.4 million pager subscribers (ranking the company #1 in US marketshare). PageNet's spectrum of services over its one-way wireless digital network includes local, regional, and nationwide paging by tone and both numeric and alphanumeric display. Images and text files can also be transmitted to specially equipped laptop computers. PageNet's strategy reaches beyond simply underpricing or buying up its highly fragmented competition; the company plans to lure more nationwide subscribers, begin offering advanced 2-way digital wireless communication services (such as a pocket answering machine), and move into the global arena.

PageNet was founded in 1981 by George Perrin after he left his position as president of Zip-Call, the #1 paging company in New England. In 1982 and 1983 the company started acquiring paging operations; sales then grew at an annual rate of 40% for 8 years. In 1991 the company went public. By 1993 PageNet had operations nationwide; in that year it acquired 2 nationwide paging frequencies that together reach 90% of the US population.

In 1994 PageNet won 3 narrowband personal communications services frequencies (more than any other company) in the FCC's airwaves auction. The following year the firm began building a nationwide digital wireless network that will start commercial operation in 1996 (providing digitized voice and 2-way data messaging services). Also in 1995 PageNet bought Page Florida, International Paging, and 2 subsidiaries of PageAmerica. That same year president and CEO Terry Scott announced he would resign effective October 1995.

WHO

Chairman: George M. Perrin, age 49
President and CEO: Terry L. Scott, age 44, $513,167 pay
SVP Finance and Administration, CFO, and Treasurer: Barry A. Fromberg, age 39, $256,270 pay
President, Paging Network — Northeastern Region, Inc.: John R. Mixon, age 44, $193,550 pay
VP New Business Development: Douglas R. Ritter, age 36, $193,647 pay
VP Systems and Technology: Alain C. Briancon, age 34
VP Corporate Development: Michael A. DiMarco, age 36
VP Regulatory Affairs: David P. Gamble, age 44
VP Investor and Public Relations: Mary V. Haynes, age 47
VP Information Systems and Chief Information Officer: Ross W. Holman, age 43
President, Paging Network International, Inc.: Read D. McNamara, age 47
VP Human Resources: Levy H. Curry, age 46
Auditors: Ernst & Young LLP

WHERE

HQ: 4965 Preston Park Blvd., Ste. 600, Plano, TX 75093
Phone: 214-985-4100   **Fax:** 214-985-6711

WHAT

Wireless Services
Alphanumeric display
Digital transmission of images and data to computer laptops or palmtops via PCMCIA receiver cards
Digitized voice messaging service (VoiceNow)
Numeric display
Personalized/automated answering services
Tone-only
Tone-plus-voice
Two-way data messaging

KEY COMPETITORS

A+ Communications	BellSouth
AirTouch	Metrocall
American Paging	MobileMedia
Ameritech	Telephone & Data Systems
Arch Communications	USA Mobile
AT&T	Communications

HOW MUCH

Nasdaq symbol: PAGE FY ends: December 31	Annual Growth	1989	1990	1991	1992	1993	1994
Sales ($ mil.)	44.5%	77.8	111.2	153.2	221.9	311.4	489.7
Net income ($ mil.)	—	(13.6)	(0.8)	(9.3)	(21.6)	(20.0)	(18.0)
Income as % of sales	—	—	—	—	—	—	—
Earnings per share ($)	—	(0.34)	(0.02)	(0.22)	(0.43)	(0.40)	(0.35)
Stock price – high ($)	—	—	—	14.33	21.00	34.50	34.25
Stock price – low ($)	—	—	—	10.75	10.58	17.33	20.75
Stock price – close ($)	35.0%	—	—	13.83	20.17	30.50	34.00
P/E – high	—	—	—	—	—	—	—
P/E – low	—	—	—	—	—	—	—
Dividends per share ($)	—	—	—	0.00	0.00	0.00	0.00
Book value per share ($)	—	—	—	0.33	(0.10)	(0.46)	(0.79)
Employees	33.6%	—	—	1,675	—	3,150	3,997

1994 Year-end:
Debt ratio: 100.0%
Return on equity: —
Cash (mil.): $2.5
Current ratio: 0.16
Long-term debt (mil.): $504.0
No. of shares (mil.): 50.7
Dividends
　Yield: —
　Payout: —
Market value (mil.): $1,723.9
R&D as % of sales: —
Advertising as % of sales: —

PARKER & PARSLEY PETROLEUM

OVERVIEW

Parker & Parsley Petroleum is pumped. The company is one of the largest independent oil and gas companies in the US. In 1994 its 5,800 operating wells produced a daily average of more than 33,275 barrels of oil and 218 million cubic feet of natural gas. The company also owns an interest in 10 natural gas processing plants. Parker & Parsley's primary reserves are located in West Texas's Permian Basin. It also has operations in Australia (11% of proved reserves) and onshore along the Gulf Coast. The company's customers include Mobil Oil and Phibro Energy.

Midland-based Parker & Parsley began in 1962 as a partnership between geologist Howard Parker and reservoir engineer Joe Parsley. In 1977 the company began drilling wells in the productive Spraberry Field near Midland. The company was bought by Southmark Corp., a Dallas real estate and financial services firm, in 1984. Scott Scheffield became president the following year. Parker & Parsley had prospered by sticking to its West Texas neighborhood, but under new ownership the company moved into other areas. In 1989 management purchased the company from Southmark. Parker & Parsley went public in 1991. That year it bought 600 oil and gas wells from Mobil Corp. and the reserves of Damson Oil (the equivalent of over 20 million barrels). In 1993 the company acquired 35 oil and gas partnerships from Prudential Securities.

Parker & Parsley's 1994 income was slashed by exploration costs, depressed prices, and its purchases of Bridge Oil Ltd., an Australian oil and gas developer, and PG&E's oil and gas properties. In 1995 Parker & Parsley announced it would slow its rate of acquisitions and begin concentrating on developing its primary properties. With natural gas prices still depressed in early 1995, the company abandoned its plan to acquire Tulsa-based Tide West Oil Company.

WHO

Chairman, President, and CEO: Scott D. Scheffield, age 42, $549,087 pay
EVP: Timothy M. Dunn, age 39, $366,058 pay
EVP Exploration: Robert J. Castor, age 62, $297,175 pay
EVP Operations: James D. Moring, age 59, $297,175 pay
SVP Finance, CFO, and Treasurer: Steven L. Beal
VP Administration Risk Management (HR): Larry Paulsen
Auditors: KMPG Peat Marwick LLP

WHERE

HQ: Parker & Parsley Petroleum Company, 303 W. Wall, Ste. 101, Midland, TX 79701
Phone: 915-683-4768   **Fax:** 915-571-5063

Parker & Parsley Petroleum's main reserves are located in the Permian Basin of West Texas. It also has operations in Australia, onshore along the Gulf Coast in Louisiana and Texas, and in the mid-continental US (Colorado, Kansas, Montana, Oklahoma, and Wyoming).

	1994 Production	
	Oil (mil. barrels)	Gas (mil. cubic feet)
US	11.3	75.1
Other countries	0.9	4.6
Total	**12.2**	**79.7**

WHAT

	1994 Sales	
	$ mil.	% of total
Oil & gas	337.6	68
Gas marketing	103.0	21
Natural gas processing	39.1	8
Other	16.5	3
Total	**496.2**	**100**

KEY COMPETITORS

Anadarko	Castle Energy	Noble Affiliates
Apache	Enron	Santa Fe Energy
Broken Hill	EOTT Energy	Sun Energy
Burlington	Mitchell Energy	Tide West Oil
Resources	NGC	Vastar Resources

HOW MUCH

NYSE symbol: PDP FY ends: December 31	Annual Growth	1989	1990	1991	1992	1993	1994
Sales ($ mil.)	48.6%	68.4	68.0	147.3	208.4	341.8	496.2
Net income ($ mil.)	—	12.2	10.2	15.4	27.1	31.4	(14.0)
Income as % of sales	—	17.9%	15.1%	10.5%	13.0%	9.2%	—
Earnings per share ($)	—	—	0.83	0.77	1.05	1.13	(0.47)
Stock price – high ($)	—	—	—	14.25	15.75	35.88	28.25
Stock price – low ($)	—	—	—	8.50	11.38	13.63	19.13
Stock price – close ($)	19.9%	—	—	11.88	13.75	24.75	20.50
P/E – high	—	—	—	19	15	32	—
P/E – low	—	—	—	11	11	12	—
Dividends per share ($)	26.0%	—	—	0.05	0.10	0.10	0.10
Book value per share ($)	15.8%	—	—	9.40	10.84	12.49	14.59
Employees	31.1%	—	340	641	674	771	1,004

1994 Year-end:
Debt ratio: 58.3%
Return on equity: —
Cash (mil.): $39.9
Current ratio: 1.36
Long-term debt (mil.): $708.8
No. of shares (mil.): 34.9
Dividends
  Yield: 0.5%
  Payout: —
Market value (mil.): $715.9
R&D as % of sales: —
Advertising as % of sales: —

PEROT SYSTEMS CORPORATION

OVERVIEW

Ross Perot needed a project. He'd sold Electronic Data Systems (EDS, founded in 1962) to General Motors for $2.6 billion in 1984. So the feisty entrepreneur started Perot Systems Corp., an EDS-in-miniature. Perot Systems provides technology services to a small roster of international clients, including the UK's largest bank, Barclays, and over 100,000 end users at NationsBank. The company's services include development and integration of office automation, software, and telecommunications systems.

Perot Systems was founded in 1988 as a systems integration service. When it added outsourcing (overseeing a client's computer operations), the company quickly signed up $1.2 billion worth of new business. But just as quickly, business floundered. Some clients said Perot Systems had promised more than it could deliver. Then Ross Perot alienated Mexicans with anti-NAFTA rhetoric just as his company was working on deals with Volkswagen de Mexico and Multibanco Mercantil Probursa. Former Perot aide Mort Meyerson, who had been a senior executive at EDS and a consultant to Dell, took over the company's reins in 1992. Meyerson is leading the company away from computer outsourcing to higher-margin consulting services.

In 1994 Perot Systems acquired the Custom Development Division of Platinum Software Corp., a developer of LAN and client/server financial software for corporate clients. Perot gained rights to use Platinum's *SeQueL to Platinum* software for custom software development.

In 1995 Perot Systems's Troy, Michigan–based outsourcing unit became the first information technology services provider to receive ISO 9001 certification for computer facilities management. That same year the company named MCI its preferred telecommunications provider. Under a 5-year agreement, the 2 companies will jointly develop a certification lab to test new telecommunications products.

A Perot family trust owns about 40% of the company. In 1995 Perot Systems agreed to sell a 24.9% stake to Swiss Bank Corporation in exchange for a contract expected to nearly double the company's revenues. Perot Systems is considering going public in 1997.

WHO

Chairman and CEO: Morton H. Meyerson
President and COO: James A. Cannavino, age 51
CFO: John Bonesh
Chief, Office of Technology: Bill Harmon
General Counsel: Peter Altabes
Director Human Resources: Carol Barnett

WHERE

HQ: 12377 Merit Dr., Ste. 1100, Dallas, TX 75251
Phone: 214-383-5600   **Fax:** 214-383-5827

WHAT

Selected Clients
Barclays Bank (UK)
Cadillac Plastic and Chemical Company
East Midlands Electricity (UK)
Europcar (France)
Kelsey-Hayes
NationsBank
Robert Plan Corp.
Tenet Healthcare
University of Texas Southwestern Medical Center
Vishay Intertechnology
Volkswagen of America

Selected Services
Application performance tuning
Business reengineering
Change management
Executive information/decision support systems
Office automation
Software development and maintenance
Systems integration
Technology consulting
Telecommunications engineering and operations
Virtual prototyping
Workflow and imaging systems

KEY COMPETITORS

Andersen Consulting
Arthur D. Little
Booz, Allen
Cambridge Technology
Cap Gemini Sogeti
Computer Sciences
Coopers & Lybrand
DEC
Deloitte & Touche
EDS
IBM
MCI
Technology Solutions

HOW MUCH

Private company FY ends: December 31	Annual Growth	1989	1990	1991	1992	1993	1994
Estimated sales ($ mil.)	52.6%	—	—	90.0	247.0	280.0	320.0
Employees	43.0%	—	—	800	1,500	—	2,300

PIER 1 IMPORTS, INC.

OVERVIEW

Fort Worth–based Pier 1 sticks out as North America's #1 home furnishings retailer. It sells a range of imported items including furniture, dining and kitchen products, and accessories. In 1995 it operated 600 stores in 46 states, Canada, and Puerto Rico, selling over 5,000 items imported from more than 44 countries. Pier 1 also has joint ventures in Mexico (with Sears) and in the UK. Seven centers in California, Georgia, Illinois, Maryland, Ohio, Texas, and Quebec form Pier 1's North American distribution system.

The company was set up by Charles Tandy and Luther Henderson in the early 1960s, when they invested in a San Mateo, California, rattan furniture outlet called Cost Plus. Tandy moved the company's headquarters to Fort Worth in 1962. A strong US dollar encouraged management to import a variety of household and decorative items from Asia to expand the range of goods offered, mainly to the college student market. Tandy moved on to found Radio Shack while Henderson led an LBO of Pier 1 in 1966. By 1969, when Pier 1 went public, the chain had grown to 42 stores. Under the leadership of Clark Johnson, Pier 1 grew from 250 stores in the mid-1980s to more than 600 in 1995; sales surged from $204 million in 1986 to $712 million in 1995.

Over the years, Pier 1 has managed to upgrade its products and broaden its appeal to match the changing tastes of North American consumers. In place of the exotic but inexpensive Asian-made knickknacks of the 1970s, it brought in high-quality functional and decorative furniture and clothing items. It also increased its store size and upgraded its formats.

In 1995 the company opened 42 new stores. That year Pier 1 launched its first nationwide advertising campaign, featuring local shoppers extolling the company's virtues.

WHO

Chairman and CEO: Clark A. Johnson, age 64, $1,220,000 pay
President and COO: Marvin J. Girouard, age 55, $722,000 pay
EVP and CFO: Robert G. Herndon, age 61, $462,500 pay
SVP Legal Affairs and Secretary: J. Rodney Lawrence, age 49, $211,500 pay
SVP Marketing: Phil E. Schneider, age 43
SVP Merchandising: Jay R. Jacobs, age 40
SVP Stores: Charles H. Turner, age 38
SVP Human Resources: E. Mitchell Weatherly, age 47
Auditors: Price Waterhouse LLP

WHERE

HQ: 301 Commerce St., Ste. 600, Fort Worth, TX 76102
Phone: 817-878-8000   **Fax:** 817-878-7883

	1995 Stores	
	No.	% of total
California	80	13
Texas	51	8
Florida	41	7
Illinois	33	5
Other locations	423	67
Total	**628**	**100**

WHAT

	1995 Sales
	% of total
Furniture	28
Decorative home furnishings	26
Dining & kitchen goods	15
Textiles	13
Clothing, jewelry & fashion accessories	9
Other	9
Total	**100**

KEY COMPETITORS

Bed Bath & Beyond	Hanover Direct	Lechters
Blair	Home Express	Solo Serv
Bombay Co.	IKEA	Spiegel
Euromarket Designs	Lands' End	Williams-Sonoma

HOW MUCH

NYSE symbol: PIR FY ends: Sat. nearest Feb. 28	9-Year Growth	1990	1991	1992	1993	1994	1995
Sales ($ mil.)	6.6%	516.6	562.7	586.7	629.2	685.4	712.0
Net income ($ mil.)	(0.4%)	25.4	6.3	26.3	23.0	5.9	24.9
Income as % of sales	—	4.9%	1.1%	4.5%	3.7%	0.9%	3.5%
Earnings per share ($)	(1.2%)	0.67	0.17	0.71	0.62	0.16	0.63
Stock price – high ($)[1]	—	12.92	11.89	9.36	12.50	12.50	10.13
Stock price – low ($)[1]	—	8.61	2.52	3.97	6.31	7.86	6.78
Stock price – close ($)[1]	(1.3%)	9.41	4.42	7.14	11.91	9.28	8.81
P/E – high	—	19	70	13	20	78	16
P/E – low	—	13	15	6	10	49	11
Dividends per share ($)	(1.7%)	0.12	0.15	0.00	0.07	0.10	0.11
Book value per share ($)	4.4%	4.82	4.28	4.82	5.33	5.35	5.98
Employees	2.9%	7,500	8,300	7,600	7,500	7,850	8,671

1995 Year-end:
Debt ratio: 41.1%
Return on equity: 11.7%
Cash (mil.): $54.2
Current ratio: 4.15
Long-term debt (mil.): $154.4
No. of shares (mil.): 37.7
Dividends
  Yield: 1.2%
  Payout: 17.5%
Market value (mil.): $331.9
R&D as % of sales: —
Advertising as % of sales: —

[1] Stock prices are for the prior calendar year.

PILGRIM'S PRIDE CORPORATION

OVERVIEW

Pilgrim's is making steady progress. The company posted record sales in 1994 and profits that were up by 48% over the previous year. Pittsburg, Texas–based Pilgrim's Pride has vertically integrated operations that consist of the breeding, hatching, raising, processing, and marketing of poultry. The company is the #5 producer of chicken products in the US and is #2 in Mexico. The firm's US production and distribution facilities are located in Arizona, Arkansas, Oklahoma, and Texas. The company provides an extensive range of fresh and processed chickens for the retail and food service industries. Pilgrim's Pride is 65.3% owned by Lonnie "Bo" Pilgrim. His nephew Lindy "Buddy" Pilgrim is president and COO.

The company was formed in 1946 as a partnership between Aubrey Pilgrim and his brother Bo to run a retail feed store. It grew internally and through the acquisitions of farming operations and chicken processors. Aubrey died in 1966, and the company was incorporated as Pilgrim's Industries in 1968. Beginning in 1983, Bo began promoting his company through an award-winning TV ad that featured him pitching his chickens while wearing a pilgrim's hat. The advertising campaign gave a strong lift to the company's profile and to its sales. In 1985 the company's name was changed to Pilgrim's Pride Corp. The firm was listed on the NYSE in 1986.

In 1988 Pilgrim's Pride expanded into Mexico through the acquisitions of 4 vertically integrated poultry production operations for approximately $15.1 million. By 1994 Mexican operations accounted for 20% of total revenues and 30% of total employees.

Despite Mexico's recent economic instability, Pilgrim's Pride is committed to expansion there. In 1995 it acquired Union de Queretaro, a group of 5 chicken operations serving Mexico City, for $32 million.

WHO

Chairman and CEO: Lonnie "Bo" Pilgrim, age 66, $929,950 pay
VC, CFO, Secretary, and Treasurer: Clifford E. Butler, age 52, $496,009 pay
President and COO: Lindy M. "Buddy" Pilgrim, age 40, $644,814 pay
EVP Operations: Robert L. Hendrix, age 58, $395,461 pay
President, Mexican Operations: David Van Hoose, age 52, $334,040 pay
SVP Sales and Marketing, Retail and Fresh Products: Terry Berkenbile, age 44
SVP and Corporate Controller: Richard A. Cogdill, age 34
SVP Human Resources: Ray Gameson, age 46
Auditors: Ernst & Young LLP

WHERE

HQ: 110 S. Texas, Pittsburg, TX 75686-0093
Phone: 903-855-1000   **Fax:** 903-856-7505

	1994 Sales	
	$ mil.	% of total
US	733.9	80
Mexico	188.7	20
Adjustments	0.7	—
Total	**923.3**	**100**

WHAT

	1994 Sales
	% of total
Prepared food service foods	32
Fresh food service chicken	24
Prepackaged chicken	20
Bulk-packaged chicken	14
Prepared consumer foods	10
Total	**100**

KEY COMPETITORS

Cagle's	Golden Poultry	Sanderson Farms
ConAgra	Hudson Foods	Tyson Foods
Foster Poultry	IBP	WLR Foods
Gold Kist	Perdue	

HOW MUCH

NYSE symbol: CHX FY ends: Sat. nearest Sept. 30	5-Year Growth	1989	1990	1991	1992	1993	1994	1994 Year-end: Debt ratio: 49.3%
Sales ($ mil.)	6.9%	661.1	720.6	786.7	819.6	887.8	923.3	Return on equity: 21.1%
Net income ($ mil.)	8.9%	20.3	15.6	21.3	(29.7)	21.0	31.1	Cash (mil.): $11.2
Income as % of sales	—	3.1%	2.2%	2.7%	—	2.4%	3.4%	Current ratio: 2.34
Earnings per share ($)	4.7%	0.90	0.69	0.54	(1.24)	0.76	1.13	Long-term debt (mil.): $152.6
Stock price – high ($)	—	11.25	8.75	8.75	8.13	9.50	10.50	No. of shares (mil.): 27.6
Stock price – low ($)	—	5.75	4.88	5.25	5.00	6.25	6.38	Dividends
Stock price – close ($)	7.2%	6.88	5.50	6.50	6.13	6.88	9.75	Yield: 0.6%
P/E – high	—	13	13	16	—	13	9	Payout: 5.3%
P/E – low	—	6	7	10	—	8	6	Market value (mil.): $269.0
Dividends per share ($)	0.0%	0.06	0.06	0.06	0.06	0.03	0.06	R&D as % of sales: —
Book value per share ($)	8.7%	3.86	4.49	4.97	4.06	4.80	5.86	Advertising as % of sales: —
Employees	5.7%	7,800	10,000	10,300	10,300	10,700	10,300	

RAILTEX, INC.

OVERVIEW

When is a railroad not a railroad? When it is RailTex, the US's leading operator of short-haul railroads. This was the 1994 ICC ruling that allowed the San Antonio–based company to complete the bitterly contested purchase of the about-to-be abandoned Central Vermont Railway without honoring CVR's labor contracts (opponents had sought full-pay severance for 6 years for employees fired).

RailTex buys feeder lines that are too expensive for the big railroads to run and serves towns, factories, and commodities producers that the majors have forgotten. In the process, it uses far fewer, far less specialized employees at below-union wages to run the lines.

RailTex was founded in 1977 by Bruce Flohr (who owns 7.7% of the company), a former executive with Southern Pacific Railroad and former deputy of the Federal Railroad Administration. RailTex bought rock-hopper cars and leased them to users. After the company took over a San Diego railroad in 1984, Flohr turned the unprofitable line around with strict cost controls and aggressive marketing to drum up new customers. By 1989 sales from RailTex's 9 rail lines had overtaken leasing revenues, and Flohr sold the cars to buy railroads. When RailTex went public in late 1993 it had 23 lines in the US, Mexico, and Canada.

The company's growth has been fueled by deregulation that let large railroads sell feeder lines and let short-haul operators buy them. When RailTex buys a railroad, it sends in a "Go Team" to cut staff, install new management, and beef up marketing. RailTex cross-trains its staff to fill a number of roles. The company keeps its geographic, cargo, and client bases diverse and maintains good relations with the major railroads into which it feeds cargo.

In 1995 the Canadian government deregulated its railroads, paving the way for easier access by RailTex and similar companies.

WHO

Chairman and CEO: Bruce M. Flohr, age 55, $290,440 pay
President and COO: Henry M. Chidgey, age 45
EVP and Chief Engineer: Chris Dodge
VP Line Analysis: Dave P. Valentine, $179,730 pay
VP Finance and CFO: Laura D. Davies, $142,875 pay
VP Acquisitions: Daniel T. McShane, $130,975 pay
Director Human Resources: Susan Mustacchio
Auditors: Arthur Andersen & Co, SC

WHERE

HQ: 4040 Broadway, Ste. 200, San Antonio, TX 78209
Phone: 210-841-7600   **Fax:** 210-841-7629

Selected States and Canadian Provinces Served

Alabama	Missouri	Texas
California	North Carolina	Utah
Kansas	Nova Scotia	Vermont
Michigan	Ontario	Virginia

WHAT

	1994 Sales	
	$ mil.	% of total
Interline traffic	52.2	70
Local traffic	9.6	13
Bridge traffic	0.4	1
Nonfreight sales	12.3	16
Total	**74.5**	**100**

	1994 Sales by Cargo	
	$ mil.	% of total
Coal	16.1	22
Ores, minerals & stone	8.7	12
Food, lumber & forest products	7.4	10
Chemicals	8.0	11
Other freight	22.0	29
Nonfreight	12.3	16
Total	**74.5**	**100**

KEY COMPETITORS

American Freightways	Heartland Express	Wisconsin Central Trans.
Arkansas Best	Southeast Shortline	Yellow Corp.
Carolina Freight	Union Pacific	

HOW MUCH

Nasdaq symbol: RTEX FY ends: December 31	Annual Growth	1989	1990	1991	1992	1993	1994
Sales ($ mil.)	35.1%	16.6	21.4	27.6	39.3	59.8	74.5
Net income ($ mil.)	17.9%	3.0	1.6	1.8	2.7	3.6	6.9
Income as % of sales	—	18.2%	7.3%	6.5%	6.9%	6.1%	9.2%
Earnings per share ($)	3.2%	0.75	0.38	0.39	0.52	0.64	0.88
Stock price – high ($)	—	—	—	—	—	28.25	31.50
Stock price – low ($)	—	—	—	—	—	19.75	15.63
Stock price – close ($)	(14.4%)	—	—	—	—	27.75	23.75
P/E – high	—	—	—	—	—	44	36
P/E – low	—	—	—	—	—	31	18
Dividends per share ($)	—	—	—	—	—	0.00	0.00
Book value per share ($)	10.2%	—	—	—	—	9.18	10.11
Employees	41.2%	116	155	212	277	466	652

1994 Year-end:
Debt ratio: 32.4%
Return on equity: 10.0%
Cash (mil.): $2.2
Current ratio: 1.01
Long-term debt (mil.): $28.9
No. of shares (mil.): 7.2
Dividends
  Yield: —
  Payout: —
Market value (mil.): $170.0
R&D as % of sales: —
Advertising as % of sales: —

RENTERS CHOICE, INC.

OVERVIEW

Renters Choice is one of the largest rent-to-own chains in the US. The Dallas-based company operates more than 100 outlets in 17 states and Puerto Rico. Renters Choice's products include home electronics, appliances, furniture, and accessories rented to customers on a weekly or monthly basis. Customers take ownership of the products if they rent for a predetermined period (usually 18 months or more). However, rentals average about 2 months and only about 20% of the company's customers actually buy its products. Founder and CEO Ernest Talley and president Mark Speese own 31.3% and 15.8% of the company, respectively.

Talley is recognized as a pioneer in the rent-to-own industry. He started one of the first rent-to-own chains, called Mr. T's, in Wichita, Kansas, in 1963. He sold the chain to Remco (now Rent-A-Center, a subsidiary of the UK's Thorn EMI) in 1974. Talley left the rent-to-own business to work in commercial real estate in Dallas. In 1987 Talley and his son Michael started Talley Leasing to rent appliances to apartment complex owners. Talley reentered the rent-to-own business with the acquisition of Vista Rent To Own, a chain of 22 stores in New Jersey and Puerto Rico, in 1989.

After the purchase Talley focused on improving the marginally profitable chain's operations by upgrading merchandise, increasing selection, installing computer systems, and improving store management. Following the changes, revenues-per-store increased 15% a year for 5 years. In 1993 the company acquired DEF, a chain of 84 rent-to-own stores, and began upgrading the chain's outlets in the same way it improved the Vista stores. Also in 1993 the company changed its name to Renters Choice.

Renters Choice went public in 1995. The company plans to continue to seek out underperforming chains in the highly fragmented industry. It acquired Texarkana, Texas–based Crown Leasing, which operates a chain of 72 rent-to-own stores in 18 states, for about $20 million in early 1995. Also in 1995 the company named David Glasgow as its 3rd CFO in 3 months.

WHO

Chairman and CEO: J. Ernest Talley, age 60, $60,000 pay
President and COO: Mark E. Speese, age 37, $159,668 pay
Regional VP: L. Dowell Arnette, age 47, $165,531 pay
Regional VP: Christopher R. Dement, age 33
Regional VP: John R. Dixon Jr., age 42
Regional VP: Michael C. Talley, age 29
Secretary and Treasurer (CFO): David M. Glasgow
Manager Human Resources: Robert D. Davis
Auditors: Grant Thornton LLP

WHERE

HQ: 2720 N. Stemmons Fwy., Ste. 300, Dallas, TX 75207
Phone: 214-638-6633   **Fax:** 214-638-7711

	1994 Stores
	% of total
Ohio	23
New York	14
Michigan	13
Georgia	10
New Jersey	10
Tennessee	8
Other states	30
Puerto Rico	8
Total	**116**

WHAT

	1994 Sales	
	$ mil.	% of total
Rentals & fees	70.6	95
Merchandise sales	3.5	5
Other	0.3	0
Total	**74.4**	**100**

	1994 Sales
	% of total
Consumer electronics	40
Appliances	35
Furniture	24
Accessories	1
Total	**100**

KEY COMPETITORS

Aaron Rents	Circuit City	RTO/Rentronics
Advantage Cos.	Color Tyme	Sears
Best Buy	Globe Furniture	Tandy
Central Rents	Levitz	Thorn EMI
Champion Rent-	Magic Rentals	U-Can-Rent
to-Own	Rent America	Wal-Mart

HOW MUCH

Nasdaq symbol: RCII FY ends: December 31	Annual Growth	1989	1990	1991	1992	1993	1994	**1994 Year-end:** Debt ratio: 71.6%
Sales ($ mil.)	46.2%	11.1	11.8	15.8	20.3	53.2	74.4	Return on equity: 59.2%
Net income ($ mil.)	—	(1.4)	(0.6)	1.8	4.1	1.3	4.0	Cash (mil.): $1.4
Income as % of sales	—	—	—	11.5%	20.0%	2.5%	5.4%	Long-term debt (mil.): $17.1
Employees	(0.6%)	—	—	—	—	672	668	

SEMATECH, INC.

OVERVIEW

A research consortium cosponsored by the Department of Defense and several US semiconductor manufacturers, SEMATECH (for SEmiconductor MAnufacturing TECHnology) is credited by many with helping US semiconductor makers pass Japanese manufacturers in market share. US makers hold about 45% of the world's semiconductor market, compared with about 41% for the Japanese. The consortium's mission is to improve semiconductor manufacturing techniques by funding research into areas such as lithography and materials processing.

In 1986, when Secretary of Defense Caspar Weinberger learned that half the chips in an F-16's fire-control radar came from Japan, he wanted to find a way to improve US technology. Enter the Semiconductor Industry Association, a group of leading US semiconductor makers. They were being left in the vapor trail of Japanese companies riding on new technologies and improved manufacturing techniques. The directors of the association, led by Robert Noyce (co-inventor of the semiconductor), founded SEMATECH in 1987 with $100 million per year for 5 years from the DOD's Defense Advanced Research Projects Agency and with another $100 million per year from 14 member companies.

While SEMATECH made technological advances, there were complaints that it benefited only the largest companies and that larger members dominated the agenda; in 1991 Micron Technology and LSI Logic, the 2 smallest members, dropped out. In 1992 the US passed Japan in worldwide semiconductor market share. That same year SEMATECH's government funding was extended, although it was lowered to $90 million a year.

Since the US has regained its market leadership, SEMATECH's goals have changed. It now focuses on research that might be too risky for one company. In 1995 a US House-Senate conference committee recommended slashing SEMATECH's government funding to $39 million for fiscal 1996. A House committee, supposedly in a jab at Austin Congressman Lloyd Doggett, had voted to kill the funding entirely. SEMATECH had already volunteered to phase out its federal backing by 1998.

WHO

President and CEO: Bill Spencer
COO: Jim Owens
Chief Administrative Officer: Frank Squires
Chief Strategy Officer: Sam Harrell
CFO: Dan Damon
General Counsel: Bif Falstad
Director Human Resources: Mike Foster
Auditors: General Accounting Office

WHERE

HQ: 2706 Montopolis Dr., Austin, TX 78741-6499
Phone: 512-356-3500 **Fax:** 512-356-3083

SEMATECH Centers of Excellence (Research Centers)
Boston University
Carnegie Mellon University (Pennsylvania)
Cornell University (New York)
Massachusetts Institute of Technology
North Carolina State University
Rensselaer Polytechnic Institute (New York)
Sandia National Laboratories (Arizona, New Mexico)
Stanford University (California)
State University of New York – Albany
Texas A&M University
University of Arizona
University of California at Berkeley
University of New Mexico
The University of Texas at Austin
University of Wisconsin/Madison

WHAT

	1994 Budget
	% of total
Interconnect systems	15
Manufacturing methods	13
Lithography	12
Strategy/New thrusts	9
Materials & bulk processes	9
CIM/Manufacturing systems	8
Contamination-free manufacturing	6
SEMATECH Centers of Excellence	5
Modeling & statistical methods	4
Total quality management	2
Future factory expansion	2
Electrical characterization	2
Other	13
Total	**100**

Consortium Members

AMD	Motorola
AT&T	National Semiconductor
DEC	Rockwell International
Hewlett-Packard	Texas Instruments
IBM	United States Department
Intel	of Defense

HOW MUCH

Research consortium FY ends: December 31	5-Year Growth	1989	1990	1991	1992	1993	1994
Annual budget ($ mil.)	(2.1%)	200.0	200.0	200.0	200.0	200.0	180.0
Patents awarded	—	0	0	6	12	11	17
Employees	8.7%	555	701	729	723	742	841

SERV-TECH, INC.

OVERVIEW

Serv-Tech is whom oil companies turn to when they need maintenance and clean-up work on their plants and refineries. Its customers include the 10 largest oil companies in the US. Serv-Tech's biggest revenue generator is turnaround management services (which involve shutting down an operating unit to complete the maintenance work). Serv-Tech, through its SECO and EPC subsidiaries, also provides electrical and instrumentation installation services as well as engineering, procurement, and construction services for a wide range of industries (including power and pulp). Serv-Tech's Environmental Services and Performance Chemicals business provides cleaning services and specialty chemicals.

Serv-Tech was founded in 1978 (with Richard Krajicek as its chairman) to provide hydroblasting and chemical cleaning services. In 1985 it developed a new cleaning system, called Fast Clean, for heat exchangers used in petroleum refining. The process proved to be faster and required less manpower than conventional hydroblasting methods. Serv-Tech added other turnaround services in the late 1980s and went public in 1989. It bought electrical and instrumentation contractor SECO Industries in 1991.

With its growth spurred by the Fast Clean system, Serv-Tech concentrated on expanding its services, and in 1992 it acquired engineering firm Talbert & Associates. The company has also expanded internationally. In 1992 it formed Serv-Tech Europe in a joint venture with Thyssen. In 1994 it acquired Hartney Industrial Services, which installs and maintains heat-resistant and corrosion-resistant materials. A decision to write off unprofitable lines in 1994 led the company to take a $12.2 million special charge and post a loss.

In 1995 Krajicek (who holds 12.5% of stock) retired as chairman. Director Robert Cresci replaced him.

WHO

Chairman: Robert J. Cresci, age 51
President and CEO: Richard L. Daerr, age 50, $103,030 pay
SVP, Serv-Tech EPC, Inc.: Larry A. Talbert
President, SECO Industries: Frank L. Calandro, $174,160 pay
SVP Finance and Administration: David P. Tusa
VP, General Counsel, and Corporate Secretary: Frank A. Perrone
Manager Human Resources: Joyce Currie
Auditors: Coopers & Lybrand L.L.P.

WHERE

HQ: 5200 Cedar Crest Blvd., Houston, TX 77087
Phone: 713-644-9974 **Fax:** 713-644-0731

WHAT

	1994 Sales	
	$ mil.	% of total
Serv-Tech Services	121.4	67
SECO	45.5	25
Serv-Tech EPC (engineering, procurement & construction)	13.3	7
Corporate and other	0.9	1
Total	**181.1**	**100**

Serv-Tech Services	Serv-Tech EPC
Heat exchanger services	(Engineering, Procurement,
Planning and management services	and Construction) Construction
Specialty pipe welding	Drafting
Tower and vessel maintenance	Estimating services Procurement

SECO Industries, Inc.	Environmental Services and
(Electrical and	Performance Chemicals
Instrumentation	Specialty chemicals
Contracting Services)	Tank cleaning

KEY COMPETITORS

Allwaste	GZA GeoEnvironmental	Newpark
Baker Hughes	Halliburton	Resources
C. H. Heist	Kaneb	Ogden
Dresser	Matrix Service	
Fluor	Nabors Industries	

HOW MUCH

Nasdaq symbol: STEC FY ends: December 31	5-Year Growth	1989	1990	1991	1992	1993	1994
Sales ($ mil.)	41.8%	31.6	42.4	88.3	148.0	162.0	181.1
Net income ($ mil.)	—	3.0	3.3	3.1	5.6	2.9	(8.8)
Income as % of sales	—	9.4%	7.8%	3.5%	3.8%	1.8%	—
Earnings per share ($)	—	0.80	0.75	0.59	0.97	0.50	(1.44)
Stock price – high ($)	—	20.00	18.00	21.75	15.75	11.75	12.75
Stock price – low ($)	—	10.50	11.75	9.25	6.00	6.13	5.88
Stock price – close ($)	(14.5%)	14.25	12.75	11.25	10.50	9.25	6.50
P/E – high	—	25	24	37	16	24	—
P/E – low	—	13	16	16	6	12	—
Dividends per share ($)	—	0.00	0.00	0.00	0.00	0.00	0.00
Book value per share ($)	11.4%	4.53	5.32	8.00	8.84	9.28	7.77
Employees	69.1%	100	147	1,041	817	1,016	1,383

1994 Year-end:
Debt ratio: 22.9%
Return on equity: —
Cash (mil.): $1.9
Current ratio: 1.82
Long-term debt (mil.): $15.0
No. of shares (mil.): 6.5
Dividends
Yield: —
Payout: —
Market value (mil.): $42.3
R&D as % of sales: —
Advertising as % of sales: —

SNYDER OIL CORPORATION

OVERVIEW

Snyder Oil develops and acquires oil and gas properties and has about 5,300 wells in 15 states (mostly in the Rocky Mountain region) and the Gulf of Mexico. The company, based in Fort Worth, also gathers, transports, processes, and markets natural gas. Snyder is exploiting properties it acquired cheaply during the bust years. The company's reserves are concentrated in 5 major producing areas in Colorado, Wyoming, and Texas. Cofounders John Snyder and Tom Edelman own 6.1% and 5.0% of the company's stock, respectively.

The 2 started the company in 1978 to explore for oil in the Rocky Mountains. In one of the first master limited partnerships, the company became the managing partner of Snyder Oil Properties in 1982; it began to acquire acreage, finding bargains within a troubled industry while ignoring exploration and most drilling activities. Yet when the first drop in oil prices came in 1983, Snyder found itself out on a limb. It cut back its operations and regained its financial footing by 1986, the year the oil bust began. Snyder's earlier troubles proved to be a blessing in disguise as the company found itself one of the few independents with cash. Overall Snyder has spent more than $650 million on more than 100 acquisitions, but since 1990 development drilling has been the company's primary focus.

As part of a new breed of postbust oil companies, Snyder has restructured itself into business units and has placed responsibility and resources in the hands of unit managers.

Snyder is expanding internationally through government-sponsored joint ventures. In 1993 it formed Permtex, a joint venture with a Russian oil company, to develop 4 fields in the Volga-Urals Basin east of Moscow. In 1995 it took on an Indonesian partner (PT BIP Energimas) for a joint venture project in Mongolia that will explore for crude oil with the intention of selling it to a Chinese firm.

WHO

Chairman and CEO: John C. Snyder, age 53, $363,324 pay
President: Thomas J. Edelman, age 44, $338,320 pay
EVP: John A. Fanning, age 55, $257,492 pay
VP International: Edward T. Story, age 51, $250,833 pay
VP Rocky Mountains: Charles A. Brown, age 48, $177,833 pay
VP Finance: James H. Shonsey, age 43
VP, General Counsel, and Secretary: Peter E. Lorenzen, age 45
Auditors: Arthur Andersen & Co, SC

WHERE

HQ: 777 Main St., Ste. 2500, Fort Worth, TX 76102-5328
Phone: 817-338-4043   **Fax:** 817-882-5992

	1994 Wells	
	No.	% of total
Wattenberg (Colorado)	1,627	31
Northern Wyoming	1,042	20
Western Slope (Colorado & Utah)	231	4
Green River (Southern Wyoming)	170	3
Giddings (Texas)	114	2
Other	2,085	40
Total	**5,269**	**100**

WHAT

	1994 Sales	
	$ mil.	% of total
Oil & gas sales	137.9	52
Gas processing, transportation & marketing	107.2	41
Other	17.2	7
Total	**262.3**	**100**

KEY COMPETITORS

Ashland, Inc.	Mobil	Petrofina
British Petroleum	Occidental	Phillips Petroleum
Chevron	Oryx	Repsol
Elf Aquitaine	Panhandle	Royal Dutch/Shell
Exxon	Eastern	Sun Co.
Imperial Oil	Pennzoil	Texaco

HOW MUCH

NYSE symbol: SNY FY ends: December 31	Annual Growth	1989	1990	1991	1992	1993	1994
Sales ($ mil.)	35.2%	58.0	79.2	86.8	116.0	229.9	262.3
Net income ($ mil.)	33.7%	2.9	7.5	8.8	16.9	27.6	12.4
Income as % of sales	—	5.0%	9.5%	10.1%	14.6%	12.0%	4.7%
Earnings per share ($)	(8.6%)	0.11	0.36	0.37	0.53	0.80	0.07
Stock price – high ($)	—	—	9.50	8.50	10.50	23.00	21.38
Stock price – low ($)	—	—	4.75	4.75	5.88	10.00	13.88
Stock price – close ($)	27.5%	—	5.63	6.75	10.00	17.75	14.88
P/E – high	—	—	26	23	20	29	—
P/E – low	—	—	13	13	11	13	—
Dividends per share ($)	20.1%	—	0.12	0.20	0.25	0.22	0.25
Book value per share ($)	16.2%	—	4.98	7.64	8.06	12.78	9.07
Employees	27.3%	—	175	265	289	327	460

1994 Year-end:
Debt ratio: 133.2%
Return on equity: 4.3%
Cash (mil.): $21.7
Current ratio: 1.01
Long-term debt (mil.): $318.5
No. of shares (mil.): 30.2
Dividends
   Yield: 1.7%
   Payout: —
Market value (mil.): $449.5
R&D as % of sales: —
Advertising as % of sales: —

SOFTWARE SPECTRUM, INC.

OVERVIEW

With an inventory of about 2,200 business software titles, and services that include consulting, application development, training, and technical support, Software Spectrum provides a rainbow of products and services to its customers. The Garland-based company is one of the largest resellers of microcomputer business software in the US, selling primarily to large companies through its direct sales force. It reaches small and medium-sized businesses through telemarketing. CEO Judy Sims and her husband, Richard, who is president, together own 10.8% of the company.

Frank Tindle (a director who owns 5.8% of the company) and the Simses, all CPAs, founded Software Spectrum in 1983 as the Software Store, a computer software retail operation located in a Dallas shopping center. When customers failed to come to her, Judy Sims started calling on local businesses, including Ross Perot's Electronic Data Systems. She landed the EDS account and soon added GTE, Mobil, and others. By concentrating on *FORTUNE* 500 companies and other major corporations that had large numbers of PCs, Software Spectrum leveraged its sales efforts, expanding later to smaller businesses. The company adopted its present name in 1991, just prior to going public.

Software Spectrum benefited from the downsizing of computers and the growing complexity of software products, which had led more businesses to use PCs and to seek out help with the newest business software. By developing close relationships with software publishers such as Microsoft and Lotus, Software Spectrum established itself as an informed source for inexpensive software.

With demand for business software growing around the world, Software Spectrum is expanding overseas. In 1995 it announced plans to move into the Asia/Pacific market.

WHO

Chairman and CEO: Judy O. Sims, age 42, $360,000 pay
President: Richard G. Sims, age 41, $316,000 pay
VP Sales: Roger J. King, age 42, $231,499 pay
VP Operations: Keith R. Coogan, age 43, $198,273 pay
VP and Chief Information Officer: Robert B. Mercer, age 43, $176,000 pay
VP Finance, Secretary, and Treasurer: Deborah A. Nugent, age 41
Director Human Resources: Sue Zurber
Auditors: Grant Thornton LLP

WHERE

HQ: 2140 Merritt Dr., Garland, TX 75041
Phone: 214-840-6600 **Fax:** 214-864-7878

WHAT

	1995 Sales
	% of total
Microsoft products	39
Lotus products	13
Other products & services	48
Total	**100**

Selected Products and Services
Assurance Process software management
Consulting
DIAMOND electronic software order system
Disk duplication
Hardware, peripheral products, and accessories
  (modems, printers, expansion cards)
Seminars
Software and software upgrades
Software evaluation library
Technical support

KEY COMPETITORS

Best Buy	Fry's	Random Access
Circuit City	Electronics	Sears
CompuCom	Ingram	Staples
CompUSA	Micro Warehouse	Stream
DEC	NeoStar	International
Egghead	Office Depot	Tandy
ELEK-TEK	OfficeMax	Tiger Direct

HOW MUCH

Nasdaq symbol: SSPE FY ends: March 31	Annual Growth	1990	1991	1992	1993	1994	1995
Sales ($ mil.)	31.8%	88.6	118.5	158.9	219.5	283.1	352.1
Net income ($ mil.)	49.0%	1.2	1.9	3.8	6.3	7.0	8.8
Income as % of sales	—	1.4%	1.6%	2.4%	2.9%	2.5%	2.5%
Earnings per share ($)	27.4%	0.62	0.89	1.28	1.70	1.66	2.08
Stock price – high ($)[1]	—	—	—	17.75	29.25	30.75	23.50
Stock price – low ($)[1]	—	—	—	9.50	14.75	20.00	9.25
Stock price – close ($)[1]	(5.0%)	—	—	17.50	22.75	22.00	15.00
P/E – high	—	—	—	14	17	19	11
P/E – low	—	—	—	7	9	12	4
Dividends per share ($)	—	—	—	0.00	0.00	0.00	0.00
Book value per share ($)	29.3%	—	3.25	7.24	12.03	13.72	15.64
Employees	28.8%	188	201	303	388	514	667

[1] Stock prices are for the prior calendar year.

1995 Year-end:
Debt ratio: 0.0%
Return on equity: 14.3%
Cash (mil.): $26.3
Current ratio: 2.01
Long-term debt (mil.): $0.0
No. of shares (mil.): 4.2
Dividends
  Yield: —
  Payout: —
Market value (mil.): $63.1
R&D as % of sales: —
Advertising as % of sales: —

STERLING INFORMATION GROUP

OVERVIEW

Sterling Information has polished its list of services and is shining brightly. The Austin-based company is a privately held provider of technology business solutions, including strategies developed for the semiconductor industry. Its services include project evaluation; software analysis, development, and support; and systems installation. In 1995 the company added management consulting, software product development, and training.

Sterling was founded in 1985 as Chip Wolfe & Associates. Wolfe had worked as a programmer at DataPoint Research & Development. With work stalled by a hostile takeover, Wolfe invested $3,000 in a computer and set up his own business in his living room. Soon he was hired to create a computerized order-entry program for a nascent local company called Dell Computers. The programmer cleared $30,000 his first year. In 1986 Wolfe hired Dan Thibodeau, a software developer who had worked for Digital Research. Three years later the company became Sterling Information Group. In 1991 the company won a contract to develop a customer service database for Fisher Controls International.

In 1993 Sterling made *Inc.* magazine's list of the 500 fastest-growing companies. In 1994 it was included in *Upside* magazine's list of the US's 140 fastest-growing private technology companies. That same year the company reported record revenues.

Sterling seems to like its business close to home; many of its major clients are in the "Silicon Hills" of central Texas. But with Austin continuing to attract major high-tech corporations (AMD, IBM, and Motorola have facilities there), a "home-grown" attitude shouldn't limit the company's growth.

In 1995 Sterling formed strategic provider relationships with 3 major software vendors, becoming a Lotus Business Partner, a Microsoft Solution Provider, and a Powersoft Power-Channel Partner. That same year the company announced Sterling Silverware, an outsourcing service for software product development. Also in 1995 Sterling was listed among the National Technology Fast 500, a ranking of the fastest-growing US technology companies sponsored by the Association of Technology Business Councils.

WHO

CEO: Chip Wolfe
President: Michael Haney
VP and Ombudsman: Dan Thibodeau
VP Business Development: Alan Godfrey
VP Software Consulting (CTO): Darrell Hanshaw
Director Team Resources (HR): Leslie Martinich

WHERE

HQ: 515 Capital of Texas Hwy. South, Ste. 100, Austin, TX 78746-0197
Phone: 512-327-0090
Fax: 512-327-0197

WHAT

Selected Products
Electrical-defect device mapping system (UNIX-based system that detects defects during testing of IC wafers)
Five-year technology plan (analyzes a client's business process to develop a business plan, including time requirements and resource recommendations)
Market research questionnaire (diskette-based interactive research package available for Macintosh and Windows)
Paperless integrated manufacturing system (PIMS; online, SQL-based system for manufacturers, including order definition, maintenance, tracking, and record-keeping)
Sterling Silverware (software development outsourcing service)

Selected Services
Business operations assessment
Business planning and strategy
Management consulting
Professional development courses
Software product development
Specialized applications training
Start-up assistance
Technology review

Selected Clients

Adidas	Johnson & Johnson
AMD	Lotus
Apple	3M
AT&T	Motorola
Chevron	Radian
Control Data	Whole Foods
GoldStar	

KEY COMPETITORS

American Management	Computer Sciences	IDG
Arthur Andersen	DEC	Perot Systems
Arthur Little	EDS	SAS Institute
Cap Gemini	IBM	SHL Systemhouse

HOW MUCH

Private company FY ends: December 31	Annual Growth	1989	1990	1991	1992	1993	1994
Sales ($ mil.)	39.5%	—	—	—	1.9	3.2	3.7
Employees	100.0%	—	—	—	—	30	60

STERLING
INFORMATION
GROUP INC.

STERLING SOFTWARE, INC.

OVERVIEW

Sterling Software is one of the 10 largest software companies in the world because of its early and continuing dominance in EDI (electronic data interchange). EDI speeds transaction times and reduces paperwork by allowing computer-to-computer transmission of documents between businesses. Other business lines include applications and systems management. Sterling serves more than 40,000 customers worldwide through 75 offices.

Sam Wyly, Charles Wyly, Phillip Moore, and Sterling Williams (who inspired the company name) — all former executives with University Computing — founded Sterling in 1981 and took it public 2 years later. Following a strategy of high growth through acquisitions, the company acquired, among other companies, Informatics General (software, 1985), Knowledge Systems Concepts (professional engineering services to the US military, 1992), and National Systems (banking EDI products, 1992). The Wyly family controls about 17% of the company's stock.

In 1993 charges related to Sterling's 22nd acquisition — Systems Center, a systems software developer — plunged the company into the red. But the acquisitions program continued in 1994 with the addition of the troubled KnowledgeWare (it took about 6 shares of KnowledgeWare to get one share of Sterling stock). Although there are numerous suits against KnowledgeWare, which was headed by football great Fran Tarkenton, an indemnity fund was set aside. The company also bought American Business Computer, maker of UNIX-based EDI software.

As it has grown, Sterling has used its acquisitions to form the core of new divisions. The KnowledgeWare acquisition allowed the company to reorganize into 5 groups: Systems Management, Electronic Commerce, Federal Systems, Applications Management, and International.

WHO

Chairman: Sam Wyly, age 60, $1,170,000 pay
VC: Charles J. Wyly, Jr., age 61, $585,000 pay
President and CEO: Sterling L. Williams, age 51, $1,050,000 pay
EVP Business Development: Werner L. Frank, age 65, $525,001 pay
EVP: Warner C. Blow, age 57, $561,614 pay
EVP Technology: Phillip A. Moore, age 52
EVP and CFO: George H. Ellis, age 45
EVP, General Counsel, and Secretary: Jeannette P. Meier, age 47
Auditors: Ernst & Young LLP

WHERE

HQ: 8080 N. Central Expwy., Ste. 1100, Dallas, TX 75206
Phone: 214-891-8600   **Fax:** 214-739-0535

	1994 Sales		1994 Operating Income	
	$ mil.	% of total	$ mil.	% of total
US	341.9	72	97.7	84
Europe	77.6	16	11.0	9
Pacific	26.5	6	3.0	3
Canada & Latin America	18.8	4	4.8	4
Other regions	8.6	2	(21.0)	—
Total	**473.4**	**100**	**95.5**	**100**

WHAT

	1994 Sales	
	$ mil.	% of total
Products	178.2	38
Services	161.4	34
Product support	133.8	28
Total	**473.4**	**100**

KEY COMPETITORS

ARI Network	IBM
BMC Software	Microsoft
BT Financial	System Software
Computer Associates	Associates
EDI Inc.	TCI International
General Electric	

HOW MUCH

NYSE symbol: SSW FY ends: September 30	5-Year Growth	1989	1990	1991	1992	1993	1994
Sales ($ mil.)	21.3%	180.2	200.2	224.4	259.3	411.8	473.4
Net income ($ mil.)	46.5%	8.6	10.5	12.7	13.8	(33.4)	58.1
Income as % of sales	—	4.8%	5.3%	5.6%	5.3%	—	12.3%
Earnings per share ($)	25.9%	0.73	0.90	1.05	1.19	(2.00)	2.31
Stock price – high ($)	—	9.38	11.00	24.88	25.25	33.63	36.88
Stock price – low ($)	—	5.00	5.50	7.38	13.75	17.63	25.00
Stock price – close ($)	32.1%	9.13	8.50	24.63	21.00	28.38	36.75
P/E – high	—	13	12	24	21	—	16
P/E – low	—	7	6	7	12	—	11
Dividends per share ($)	—	0.00	0.00	0.00	0.00	0.00	0.00
Book value per share ($)	(6.3%)	11.83	13.31	14.50	10.14	5.47	8.54
Employees	10.8%	1,800	1,900	2,000	2,150	2,800	3,000

1994 Year-end:
Debt ratio: 41.2%
Return on equity: 42.6%
Cash (mil.): $143.7
Current ratio: 1.73
Long-term debt (mil.): $115.9
No. of shares (mil.): 20.6
Dividends
  Yield: —
  Payout: —
Market value (mil.): $756.5
R&D as % of sales: 7.0%
Advertising as % of sales: —

TACO CABANA, INC.

OVERVIEW

San Antonio–based Taco Cabana wants to be the Big Enchilada of Tex-Mex. Its chain of more than 130 Mexican patio cafes, including about 20 franchised units, serves up fajitas, enchiladas, tacos, and margaritas, as well as salads and breakfast foods. Most are located in Texas, but the company provides its spicy fare in locations from California to Minnesota.

Felix Stehling (who owns 5.5% of the company) founded his first Taco Cabana in 1978 in San Antonio. He needed a parking lot for his nightclub, so he bought the property across the street. To make the property pay for itself, he opened a taco stand. The stand became a 24-hour restaurant for security reasons; thieves stole all of its patio furniture after it closed the first night. From the beginning Stehling focused on providing quality food, made from scratch, for low prices. With sales booming, Stehling hired Richard Cervera, an executive at San Antonio–based Fuddruckers but a devotee of Taco Cabana (he ate there up to 6 times a week) who had inquired about franchise possibilities. Cervera became EVP in 1987 and president in 1989. Taco Cabana continued to flourish, so much so that it attracted imitators. In 1992 Taco Cabana won a Supreme Court decision awarding it $3.7 million in damages from copycat chain Two Pesos. Taco Cabana then acquired the 31-unit chain. Also in 1992 Taco Cabana went public.

Taco Cabana prospered by finding its niche. It provides food that competes with most sit-down Tex-Mex restaurants but prices and fast service that compete with fast-food outlets.

Stehling stepped down as chairman in 1994. He was succeeded by Cervera. In 1995 Cervera left the company to become president of the House of Blues restaurant chain, although he remains chairman. COO Stephen Clark became CEO. The company planned to open more than 15 restaurants in 1995.

WHO

Chairman: Richard Cervera, age 38
President and CEO: Stephen Clark, age 42
SVP and General Counsel: James A. Eliasberg, age 37, $135,000 pay
SVP Operations: Louis Smallwood, age 39, $130,000 pay
VP Finance, CFO, Secretary, and Treasurer: David G. Lloyd, age 31
VP Marketing: Greg Cotter, age 42
VP Human Resources: Linda Wishard
Auditors: Deloitte & Touche LLP

WHERE

HQ: 262 Losoya, Ste. 330, San Antonio, TX 78205
Phone: 210-231-8226   **Fax:** 210-227-0436

	1994 Restaurants
	No.
Houston	38
San Antonio	28
Austin	13
Dallas/Fort Worth	11
Denver	6
El Paso	5
Other Texas cities	16
Other cities	15
Total	**132**

WHAT

	1994 Sales	
	$ mil.	% of total
Restaurant sales	124.9	98
Franchise fees & royalty income	2.4	2
Total	**127.3**	**100**

KEY COMPETITORS

Apple South	Darden	Ninfa's
Applebee's	Restaurants	Pancho's Mexican
Brinker	El Chico	Buffet
Cracker Barrel	Restaurants	Pappas Restaurants
Cucos	Foodmaker	PepsiCo
Dairy Queen	Morrison	Restaurant
DAKA	Restaurants	Enterprises

HOW MUCH

Nasdaq symbol: TACO FY ends: Sun. nearest Dec. 31	Annual Growth	1989	1990	1991	1992	1993	1994
Sales ($ mil.)	34.3%	29.1	32.4	33.5	59.2	96.9	127.3
Net income ($ mil.)	103.0%	0.2	1.3	3.9	3.2	7.1	8.5
Income as % of sales	—	0.8%	4.1%	11.7%	5.4%	7.3%	6.7%
Earnings per share ($)	61.5%	0.05	0.28	0.79	0.40	0.55	0.55
Stock price – high ($)	—	—	—	—	14.17	22.25	20.00
Stock price – low ($)	—	—	—	—	10.00	11.50	7.25
Stock price – close ($)	(17.6%)	—	—	—	13.25	17.75	9.00
P/E – high	—	—	—	—	35	40	36
P/E – low	—	—	—	—	25	21	13
Dividends per share ($)	—	—	—	—	0.00	0.00	0.00
Book value per share ($)	48.4%	—	—	—	3.38	6.84	7.43
Employees	54.8%	—	—	—	1,940	2,900	4,650

1994 Year-end:
Debt ratio: 10.1%
Return on equity: 7.9%
Cash (mil.): $7.3
Current ratio: 1.14
Long-term debt (mil.): $11.8
No. of shares (mil.): 15.6
Dividends
   Yield: —
   Payout: —
Market value (mil.): $140.1
R&D as % of sales: —
Advertising as % of sales: —

TRACOR, INC.

OVERVIEW

No dummy itself, Tracor is the #1 provider of remote-controlled drones (dummy airplanes) used as targets by the US armed forces. The Austin, Texas–based defense electronics contractor is also a leader in 3 other areas: providing aircraft countermeasure systems that release flares to decoy heat-seeking missiles, supplying software and system engineering to the US Navy, and selling avionics automatic test equipment to the US Air Force. About 89% of its revenues is generated by products, systems, and services sold to government agencies in America.

Despite the shrinking defense budget, the company is well positioned to grow. Tracor's sophisticated electronics and systems upgrading capacities make it a prime resource for the Department of Defense, which has earmarked 1/3 ($80 billion) of its 10-year defense budget for operational upgrading and maintenance.

The company was founded in 1955 as Associated Consultants and Engineers by Richard Lane and 3 of his associates in defense research at the University of Texas. In 1962 the company merged with Textran (an Austin-based defense contractor focusing on electronic countermeasures) to become Tracor. The company tried unsuccessfully to enter the computer hardware business in the 1970s. Tracor was acquired by Westmark Systems in a 1987 LBO, but falling defense budgets and heavy debt forced Westmark into bankruptcy in 1991. Tracor emerged as a restructured company later that year under the leadership of turnaround specialist James Skaggs. Expanding its core businesses, Tracor bought Vitro (systems and software engineering) in 1993 for $92 million and GDE Systems (automatic testing) in 1994 for $100 million.

In 1995 the company won a $27 million contract to provide the US Air Force with 400 of its AN/ALE-47 Countermeasures Dispenser Systems (equipped with advanced flare decoys).

WHO

Chairman, President, and CEO: James B. Skaggs, age 57, $893,571 pay
VP; President, GDE Systems: Terry A. Straeter, age 52, $470,769 pay
VP and CFO: Robert K. Floyd, age 59, $301,950 pay
VP; President, Vitro Corp.: Barry G. Campbell, age 53, $278,740 pay
VP, Secretary, and General Counsel: Russell E. Painton, age 54, $270,466 pay
VP Human Resources: Murray Shaw, age 63
Auditors: Ernst & Young LLP

WHERE

HQ: 6500 Tracor Lane, Austin, TX 78725-2000
Phone: 512-926-2800   **Fax:** 512-929-2262

WHAT

	1994 Sales	
	$ mil.	% of total
US government defense	563.0	81
International	63.7	9
US government nondefense	47.6	7
Commercial	15.8	2
State & local government	3.9	1
Total	**694.0**	**100**

Selected Products
Anti-aircraft countermeasures
Automatic test systems
Communications systems
Imagery and information systems
Intelligence systems
Mission planning systems
Weapons/combat systems integration and support
Weapons testing support

Selected Subsidiaries
GDE Systems (automatic testing systems)
Vitro (systems and software engineering)

KEY COMPETITORS

CTA	Northrop	Rockwell
Hughes Electronics	Grumman	Symetrics
ITT Industries	Quantum	Thomson SA
Litton Industries	Research	Whittaker
Loral	Raytheon	

HOW MUCH

Nasdaq symbol: TTRR FY ends: December 31	Annual Growth	1989	1990	1991	1992	1993	1994
Sales ($ mil.)	12.7%	381.2	267.6	253.6	261.8	407.5	694.0
Net income ($ mil.)	—	(0.1)	(0.3)	(39.8)	4.5	9.3	18.5
Income as % of sales	—	—	—	—	1.7%	2.3%	2.7%
Earnings per share ($)	70.5%	—	—	—	0.32	0.54	0.93
Stock price – high ($)	—	—	—	—	—	9.25	12.63
Stock price – low ($)	—	—	—	—	—	2.75	6.88
Stock price – close ($)	34.7%	—	—	—	—	9.00	12.13
P/E – high	—	—	—	—	—	17	14
P/E – low	—	—	—	—	—	5	7
Dividends per share ($)	—	—	—	—	—	0.00	0.00
Book value per share ($)	18.5%	—	—	—	—	6.56	7.77
Employees	68.9%	—	—	—	3,400	8,900	9,700

1994 Year-end:
Debt ratio: 69.4%
Return on equity: 24.1%
Cash (mil.): $24.2
Current ratio: 1.98
Long-term debt (mil.): $195.0
No. of shares (mil.): 11.7
Dividends
 Yield: —
 Payout: —
Market value (mil.): $141.3
R&D as % of sales: 15.8%
Advertising as % of sales: —

TUESDAY MORNING CORPORATION

OVERVIEW

It may be called Tuesday Morning, but it's not open every Tuesday morning. The Dallas-based discount chain, which features top-quality, name-brand gift items at 50–80% below prices at prestigious department or specialty stores, operates only about 6 months each year. Tuesday Morning capitalizes on peak shopping seasons with 4 yearly "sales events" lasting 4–10 weeks each: winter holidays, Mother's Day/Memorial Day, back-to-school, and Presidents' Day. The upscale retailer also keeps expenses low by selling from low-rent strip malls or warehouses and using seasonal help (only about 18% of its employees are full-time). The company operates more than 240 stores in 32 states, selling fine china, tableware, linens, home accessories, toys, seasonal gifts, and gourmet cookware.

Chairman and CEO Lloyd Ross started Tuesday Morning in 1974. Ross, who owns 32.7% of the stock, considered Tuesday the "most positive day of the week" and named the company accordingly. In 1991 the company began soliciting sales through catalogs (discontinued in 1993). Tuesday Morning expanded rapidly, opening 45 stores across the US in 1993 alone. In Virginia, the company tested a new furniture store, Sofas by Design...Fast, which was sold in 1993 after one year of break-even sales.

Aggressive discounting by department stores, stiff competition from large-scale discounters, and the expense of rapid growth caused a $1.6 million loss in 1993. Ross restructured the company, changed its product mix, and scaled back new store openings (11 opened in 1994). In addition, to streamline its distribution process (which is complicated because of the company's reliance on closeout merchandise), the company installed a state-of-the-art computer system.

The company planned to open 10 stores in 1995.

WHO

Chairman and CEO: Lloyd L. Ross, age 60, $325,000 pay
President and COO: Jerry M. Smith, age 58, $227,500 pay
SVP and CFO: Mark E. Jarvis, age 43, $152,500 pay
SVP Store Operations: William D. Flandermeyer, age 50, $130,000 pay
VP Finance: Duane A. Huesers, age 39, $115,000 pay
Director Human Resources: Deborah H. Steenrod
Auditors: KPMG Peat Marwick LLP

WHERE

HQ: 14621 Inwood Rd., Dallas, TX 75244
Phone: 214-387-3562   **Fax:** 214-387-2344

	1994 Stores
	No.
Texas	45
California	29
Florida	17
Illinois	14
Georgia	12
Ohio	12
Colorado	10
Minnesota	10
Virginia	10
Maryland	9
Louisiana	7
North Carolina	7
Other states	64
Total	**246**

WHAT

Selected Merchandise

Bed and bath accessories	Fine jewelry	Silk plants
Books	Gourmet housewares	Silver serving pieces
Christmas trim	Luggage	Sporting goods
Dinnerware	Luxury linen	Stationery
		Toys

KEY COMPETITORS

Ames	Kmart	Solo Serv
Best Products	Lands' End	Spiegel
Damark	Lechter's	Wal-Mart
Dayton Hudson	Pier 1	Williams-Sonoma
Euromarket Designs	Service Merchandise	

HOW MUCH

Nasdaq symbol: TUES FY ends: December 31	5-Year Growth	1989	1990	1991	1992	1993	1994	1994 Year-end: Debt ratio: 14.7%
Sales ($ mil.)	14.5%	96.8	107.4	123.4	160.1	175.8	190.1	Return on equity: 4.6%
Net income ($ mil.)	(9.5%)	4.4	4.2	5.4	6.6	(1.6)	2.7	Cash (mil.): $4.5
Income as % of sales	—	4.5%	4.0%	4.4%	4.1%	—	1.4%	Current ratio: 2.55
Earnings per share ($)	(8.1%)	0.52	0.54	0.67	0.72	(0.19)	0.34	Long-term debt (mil.): $6.8
Stock price – high ($)	—	7.75	7.00	15.50	18.75	14.75	7.25	No. of shares (mil.): 7.8
Stock price – low ($)	—	3.38	3.06	4.25	9.25	4.50	3.50	Dividends
Stock price – close ($)	(2.6%)	6.71	5.13	15.00	10.38	5.50	5.88	Yield: —
P/E – high	—	15	13	23	26	—	21	Payout: —
P/E – low	—	6	6	6	13	—	10	Market value (mil.): $45.8
Dividends per share ($)	—	0.00	0.00	0.00	0.00	0.00	0.00	R&D as % of sales: —
Book value per share ($)	12.2%	4.23	4.83	6.46	7.47	7.21	7.52	Advertising as % of sales: 7.2%
Employees	19.6%	1,410	1,535	1,725	2,877	2,895	3,450	

UNITED INSURANCE COMPANIES, INC.

If you go to school, work for yourself, or have a little trouble getting a credit card, you might want to look into United Insurance Companies (UICI). It sells life and health insurance in niche markets: schools and the self-employed. It also offers supplementary insurance and credit cards in the nonstandard market. Other units offer association management, telemarketing, and long distance phone services.

UICI was founded in 1983 by Ronald Jensen, who had sold Life Investors (Cedar Rapids, Iowa) for nearly $200 million to Dutch insurer Aegon. Jensen then bought United Group Association, which offered insurance to self-employed Texans and Oklahomans, and turned the unprofitable operation around. A 1986 IPO allowed the company to buy more companies, including ones specializing in student accident and health insurance, which is an important niche. Jensen still controls 22% of the company's stock.

In 1988 it bought Orange State Life Insurance, a Florida-based supplemental health insurance company. UICI bought 2 companies that offered credit cards in connection with insurance products in 1992, but this business has performed poorly.

UICI is primarily an insurance marketing organization, finding leads and doing the paperwork. Its more than 4,000 agents are paid on a straight commission basis. It coinsures all its business through other companies. The company's strategy is to buy a company, make it grow, and find new but related business areas (usually some support function) to move into, creating new profit centers. For example, it expanded the in-house printing operations of one of its subsidiaries into a commercial printing business.

In 1995 UICI acquired IPN Network, which provides business office and electronic clearinghouse services to health care facilities.

WHO

Chairman: Ronald L. Jensen, age 64, $1 pay
President and CEO: W. Brian Harrigan, age 40
VP and COO, Student Division: Billy E. McKenzie, age 63, $929,988 pay
EVP; COO, Specialty Health Division: Richard J. Estell, age 49, $335,838 pay
VP and COO, Life Division: Charles T. Prater, age 43, $215,794 pay
VP and Treasurer: Vernon Woelke, age 46, $95,000 pay
VP, Secretary, and General Counsel: Robert B. Vlach, age 54
Manager Human Resources: Linda Flowers
Auditors: Ernst & Young LLP

WHERE

HQ: 4001 McEwen Dr., Ste. 200, Dallas, TX 75244
Phone: 214-960-8497   **Fax:** 214-851-9097

WHAT

	1994 Assets	
	$ mil.	% of total
Cash & equivalents	168.7	16
Bonds	563.0	55
Credit card loans	51.8	5
Policy loans	25.0	2
Deferred acquisition costs	57.5	6
Reinsurance receivables	83.0	8
Other	82.7	8
Total	**1,031.3**	**100**

	1994 Sales	
	$ mil.	% of total
Accident & health premiums	415.3	79
Investment income	48.0	9
Life premiums	37.0	7
Other	28.6	5
Total	**528.9**	**100**

KEY COMPETITORS

Aetna
Aon
Atlantic American
Capitol American Financial
Chubb
CIGNA
Prudential

HOW MUCH

Nasdaq symbol: UICI FY ends: December 31	5-Year Growth	1989	1990	1991	1992	1993	1994
Assets ($ mil.)	33.4%	244.6	283.1	466.7	577.7	814.4	1,031.3
Net income ($ mil.)	48.6%	5.0	11.0	16.9	27.5	32.8	36.2
Income as % of assets	—	2.0%	3.9%	3.6%	4.8%	4.0%	3.5%
Earnings per share ($)	41.0%	0.69	1.37	2.01	3.15	3.50	3.85
Stock price – high ($)	—	8.00	9.13	13.75	21.00	29.25	34.75
Stock price – low ($)	—	4.13	6.75	8.50	12.50	19.75	24.75
Stock price – close ($)	34.4%	7.75	9.00	13.06	19.75	25.50	34.00
P/E – high	—	12	7	7	7	8	9
P/E – low	—	6	5	4	4	6	6
Dividends per share ($)	—	0.00	0.00	0.00	0.00	0.00	0.00
Book value per share ($)	33.9%	4.23	5.88	8.84	12.79	16.57	18.23
Employees	20.7%	300	345	450	—	620	770

1994 Year-end:
Equity as % of assets:16.6%
Return on equity: 22.2%
Return on assets: 3.5%
Long-term debt (mil.): $36.1
No. of shares (mil.): 9.4
Dividends
  Yield: —
  Payout: —
Market value (mil.): $318.0
R&D as % of sales: —
Advertising as % of sales: —
Sales (mil.): $538.9

U.S. HOME CORPORATION

OVERVIEW

Home economics isn't that simple anymore. U.S. Home, which has been shaken by recent housing crashes, a foray into Chapter 11 bankruptcy, and spiking interest rates, can attest to that. Though it's one of the US's largest single-family home builders, it has less than 1% of the market. Besides standard developments (which it sells under the names U.S. Home, Orrin Thompson Homes, and Rutenberg Homes), the company also builds age-restricted retirement communities, primarily in the Sunbelt, but also in New Jersey and Maryland. U.S. Home hopes to build up this line to 30% of its business. Other operations include land acquisition and home financing.

U.S. Home was founded in 1954 as a single-family home builder. It expanded into multi-family and mobile home construction (which it jettisoned in 1986) and into other regions. By 1984 U.S. Home was the largest home builder in the US. It was also in trouble, with many unsold houses, unprofitable operations in some markets, and Texas heading into the oil slump. The situation worsened in 1986, when oil crashed. With nearly 30% of its holdings in Houston, U.S. Home faced disaster. It cut operations, laid off workers, and underwent a management shakeup that brought company lawyers Robert Strudler and Isaac Heimbinder into power. Results improved, but the debt load on its undeveloped land brought another crisis in 1991 and tipped the company into bankruptcy. In 1993 it emerged, recapitalized by bonds, to enjoy the fruits of low interest rates — and suffer from rising rates in 1994.

U.S. Home is noted for its emphasis on employee and management training and for hiring from within. In 1995 the company began another retirement community, Heritage Highlands, in Tucson, Arizona.

WHO

Chairman and CEO: Robert J. Strudler, age 52, $730,000 pay
President and COO: Isaac Heimbinder, age 51, $712,500 pay
VP, Controller, and Chief Accounting Officer: Chester P. Sadowski, age 48, $243,875 pay
VP Planning and Secretary: Richard G. Slaughter, age 50, $243,875 pay
VP Community Development: Craig M. Johnson, age 41, $236,875 pay
VP Finance and CFO: Thomas A. Napoli, age 53
Director Human Resources: Frank Matthews
Auditors: Arthur Andersen & Co, SC

WHERE

HQ: 1800 West Loop South, Houston, TX 77027
Phone: 713-877-2311 **Fax:** 713-877-2452

	1994 Houses Delivered
	No.
Florida	1,948
Arizona	970
Colorado	898
Texas	648
California	643
Other	1,280
Total	**6,387**

WHAT

	1994 Sales	
	$ mil.	% of total
Single-family homes	964.8	97
Land and other	17.6	2
Finance	12.9	1
Total	**995.3**	**100**

KEY COMPETITORS

Centex	Kaufman	UDC Homes
Continental Homes	& Broad	Village Homes
Del Webb	Oriole Homes	Weekley
D. R. Horton	Pulte	Homes
Engle Homes	Rayco	William Lyon

HOW MUCH

NYSE symbol: UH FY ends: December 31	5-Year Growth	1989	1990	1991	1992	1993	1994	1994 Year-end: Debt ratio: 52.6%
Sales ($ mil.)	8.1%	675.6	633.2	495.1	689.9	812.1	995.3	Return on equity: 13.5%
Net income ($ mil.)	89.6%	1.3	(101.6)	(8.8)	(21.4)	71.7	32.8	Cash (mil.): $6.7
Income as % of sales	—	0.2%	—	—	—	8.8%	3.3%	Current ratio: —
Earnings per share ($)	83.5%	0.12	(9.01)	(0.78)	(1.89)	5.93	2.50	Long-term debt (mil.): $293.7
Stock price – high ($)	—	29.25	21.13	13.00	26.00	30.88	29.50	No. of shares (mil.): 10.9
Stock price – low ($)	—	13.00	2.84	3.25	4.47	8.94	14.00	Dividends
Stock price – close ($)	(3.7%)	19.50	5.28	4.06	9.75	26.63	16.13	Yield: —
P/E – high	—	—	—	—	—	5	12	Payout: —
P/E – low	—	—	—	—	—	2	6	Market value (mil.): $175.9
Dividends per share ($)	—	0.00	0.00	0.00	0.00	0.00	0.00	R&D as % of sales: —
Book value per share ($)	43.5%	4.19	1.86	1.66	1.19	22.17	25.53	Advertising as % of sales: —
Employees	5.4%	1,040	886	840	970	1,152	1,353	

U.S. LONG DISTANCE CORP.

San Antonio–based U.S. Long Distance Corp. (USLD) is built on 3 pillars: operator services for the hospitality and private pay-phone industries (its biggest earner, accounting for 37% of revenues); the US's largest billing clearinghouse service (the company's Zero Plus Dialing subsidiary has approximately half of the market serving operator services and direct-dial long-distance carriers); and direct-dial long-distance services (California, Louisiana, New Mexico, Oklahoma, Oregon, Texas, and Washington) provided by its U.S. Long Distance, Inc., subsidiary.

In 1985 USLD entered the telecommunications business under the name International Telepool by acquiring a small pay-phone company. The following year Butch Holmes became CEO, and the company changed its name to US Pay-Tel of Texas. Learning that hotels needed operator services, the company sold the pay-phone operation and adopted its present name in 1987. In 1990 the company's stock began trading through the Nasdaq network. The following year USLD acquired National Telephone Exchange, Valu-Line of Wichita Falls, Texas, and Central Texas Long Distance, collectively known as the NTX companies.

Offering operator-services prices that are up to 25% below those of rivals AT&T, MCI, and Sprint, USLD has targeted small and midsize businesses as its customer base. USLD has also built a strong market niche in operator services to hotels and hospitals. By late 1994 it was providing services to 122,000 hotel, motel, hospital, and dormitory rooms.

In 1994 USLD acquired L.D. Network, a direct-dial long-distance telephone company headquartered in Los Angeles, with 400 long-distance customers. In 1995 USLD acquired the long-distance commercial customer base of TelWest Communications, Inc., and National Telephone Network Management, both based in California.

WHO

Chairman and CEO: Parris H. "Butch" Holmes Jr., age 51, $271,113 pay
President and COO: Larry M. James, age 47, $189,231 pay
SVP Legal and Regulatory Affairs, General Counsel, and Secretary: W. Audie Long, age 50, $172,398 pay
EVP Operations, Billing and Information Management: Alan W. Saltzman, age 47, $146,790 pay
SVP and Chief Information Officer: Robert C. Ingram III, age 36, $126,154 pay
SVP and CFO: Michael E. Higgins, age 45
VP Operations, Long Distance Services: Walter J. Rusak, age 46
VP Human Resources: David S. Horne
Auditors: Arthur Andersen & Co, SC

WHERE

HQ: 9311 San Pedro Ave., Ste. 300, San Antonio, TX 78216
Phone: 210-525-9009   **Fax:** 210-525-0389

WHAT

	1994 Sales	
	$ mil.	% of total
Operator services	67.9	37
Direct-dial long-distance services	61.4	34
Billing services	52.4	29
Total	**181.7**	**100**

Subsidiaries
U.S. Long Distance, Inc. (operator-assisted and direct-dial long-distance services)
Zero Plus Dialing, Inc. (3rd-party billing services)

KEY COMPETITORS

ACC	EDS	SBC
ALC	GTE	Communications
Communications	Impact	Sprint
Ameritech	Telecom.	Telephone Express
AT&T	MCI	Total-Tel
Bell Atlantic	NYNEX	U S WEST
BellSouth	Pacific Telesis	WorldCom
Cable & Wireless		

HOW MUCH

Nasdaq symbol: USLD FY ends: September 30	Annual Growth	1989	1990	1991	1992	1993	1994	1994 Year-end: Debt ratio: 29.9%
Sales ($ mil.)	83.7%	8.7	19.3	36.7	85.1	134.1	181.7	Return on equity: 14.0%
Net income ($ mil.)	—	(0.8)	(0.5)	0.7	2.4	5.2	6.1	Cash (mil.): $16.8
Income as % of sales	—	—	—	1.9%	2.8%	3.9%	3.4%	Current ratio: 1.13
Earnings per share ($)	—	(0.18)	(0.09)	0.06	0.21	0.43	0.43	Long-term debt (mil.): $14.5
Stock price – high ($)	—	—	3.94	9.75	19.75	22.13	14.63	No. of shares (mil.): 12.8
Stock price – low ($)	—	—	1.59	1.69	7.00	9.38	8.63	Dividends
Stock price – close ($)	48.9%	—	2.44	7.25	17.38	14.25	12.00	Yield: —
P/E – high	—	—	—	163	94	52	34	Payout: —
P/E – low	—	—	—	28	33	22	20	Market value (mil.): $153.0
Dividends per share ($)	—	—	0.00	0.00	0.00	0.00	0.00	R&D as % of sales: —
Book value per share ($)	75.2%	—	0.41	0.62	1.13	3.21	3.86	Advertising as % of sales: —
Employees	70.0%	72	150	249	654	904	1,023	

USA WASTE SERVICES, INC.

OVERVIEW

What do you call a merger agreement between waste disposal companies? A trash compact. In 1995 USA Waste consolidated its position as a major player in the waste disposal industry by merging with Chambers Development Corporation. The transaction was prompted by USA Waste's desire to expand through acquisition and Chambers's need for capital to pay debt and to pay the settlement of a shareholder suit. Both companies had pickup and hauling operations in several states, and the Chambers acquisition expanded USA Waste's territory into some states where the 2 businesses did not overlap. Chambers is a leading landfill builder and operator, which will provide the company with more disposal capacity. Chambers also owns and operates a medical waste disposal facility in Hampton, South Carolina.

Founded in 1987, USA Waste ran disposal and collection operations in central Oklahoma. The company went public in 1988, and in 1990 Don Moorehead, a founder and former CEO of Mid-American Waste Systems, bought a controlling interest in the company (he now owns 4%). He embarked on an expansion program, making 12 acquisitions between 1990 and 1994, including 1994's Envirofil merger, which contributed to a more than doubling of sales.

Chambers Development was founded in 1971 to haul waste (including industrial wastes) for utilities and government entities. It branched out into the design and operation of landfills. In 1992 the company lowered its financial results for several previous years. This led to a drop in its stock price and a shareholder class-action suit (which Chambers settled just before the merger).

In August 1995 USA Waste announced it was buying 9 more companies. The Rangos family, which had run Chambers, owns 23.2% of USA Waste, now one of the US's 5 largest waste disposal companies.

WHO

Chairman and CEO: John E. Drury, age 51, $290,217 pay
VC: Donald F. Moorehead Jr., age 44, $370,000 pay
VC: John G. Rangos Sr., age 65
President and COO: David Sutherland-Yoest, age 38, $376,597 pay
EVP, CFO, Secretary, and Treasurer: Earl E. DeFrates, age 51, $225,000 pay
EVP Landfill Development: Alexander W. Rangos, age 35
VP, General Counsel, and Secretary: Gregory T. Sangalis, age 39
VP Human Resources: Steve Shomette
Auditors: Coopers & Lybrand L.L.P.

WHERE

HQ: 5000 Quorum Dr., Ste. 300, Dallas, TX 75240
Phone: 214-383-7900   **Fax:** 214-383-7911

USA Waste operates in California, Florida, Georgia, Illinois, Indiana, Maryland, Mississippi, Missouri, New Jersey, North Carolina, North Dakota, Ohio, Oklahoma, Pennsylvania, South Carolina, Tennessee, Texas, Virginia, Washington, and West Virginia.

WHAT

Operations
Engineering and construction of landfills
Landfill management
Medical waste disposal
Recycling
Soil remediation
Transfer
Trash collection and hauling

KEY COMPETITORS

Allied Waste	North American Recycling
American Waste	Sanifill
Browning-Ferris	United Waste
Integrated Waste Services	Vector Engineering
Laidlaw	Western Waste
Mid-American Waste	WMX Technologies

HOW MUCH

NYSE symbol: UW FY ends: December 31	5-Year Growth	1989	1990	1991	1992	1993	1994
Sales ($ mil.)	132.4%	2.6	3.7	18.3	52.2	78.1	176.2
Net income ($ mil.)	167.9%	0.1	0.2	3.0	7.3	9.6	13.8
Income as % of sales	—	3.8%	5.4%	16.4%	14.0%	12.3%	7.8%
Earnings per share ($)	82.7%	0.03	0.08	0.32	0.65	0.80	0.61
Stock price – high ($)	—	3.13	6.00	18.00	18.50	15.00	15.13
Stock price – low ($)	—	1.56	1.38	5.38	10.50	9.75	10.38
Stock price – close ($)	48.8%	1.56	5.75	17.50	14.50	11.38	11.38
P/E – high	—	104	75	56	29	19	25
P/E – low	—	52	17	17	16	12	17
Dividends per share ($)	—	0.00	0.00	0.00	0.00	0.00	0.00
Book value per share ($)	20.4%	1.89	2.50	3.10	3.80	3.98	4.78
Employees	92.0%	46	65	406	400	650	1,200

1994 Year-end:
Debt ratio: 59.0%
Return on equity: 14.9%
Cash (mil.): $6.6
Current ratio: 1.30
Long-term debt (mil.): $153.9
No. of shares (mil.): 22.6
Dividends
  Yield: —
  Payout: —
Market value (mil.): $257.0
R&D as % of sales: —
Advertising as % of sales: —

VTEL CORPORATION

OVERVIEW

VTEL's vital signs are excellent. The Austin, Texas–based company makes teleconferencing systems that integrate traditional audio- and videoconferencing with other options, including high-resolution images and facsimiles. Its products include desktop conferencing systems and systems customized for both large and small groups. VTEL launched its 2nd generation multimedia, multipoint control unit (MCU) in 1994. The $80,990 product (which allows simultaneous multimedia conferencing at multiple locations) was a hit, and within one year VTEL had installed 150 systems worldwide. VTEL's investments in marketing, distribution, and development in 1992 and 1993 paid off with a return to profitability in 1994.

The company was founded in 1985 in San Antonio by Joe Duran and 2 other engineers. It then moved to Austin, where it was incorporated as Video Telecom in 1986. In 1989, after the company struggled to get off the ground, SRB Associates, a venture capital firm, invested heavily in it. That same year Dick Moeller (a 12-year veteran with Texas Instruments) came on board as CEO. Video Telecom grew rapidly in the early 1990s, and Moeller took it public in 1992.

The company (renamed VTEL in 1993) entered into a cross-licensing and product development agreement with Intel (current holder of 19.3% of VTEL) that year. As part of the deal, Intel advanced VTEL $3 million for R&D.

About 88% of VTEL's 1994 sales were generated by its reseller network, half of which was generated by Ameritech, ATS, GTE, SBC Communications, and Sprint. VTEL has a global service agreement with major client Olivetti.

In 1995 VTEL formed a joint product development, manufacturing, and marketing alliance with Accord Video Telecommunications, an Israel-based telecommunications concern, to help sell its MCUs on a worldwide basis. VTEL holds 12% of Accord.

WHO

Chairman and CEO: F. H. "Dick" Moeller, age 49, $368,187 pay
President and COO: Glenn A. Pierce Jr., age 52, $357,536 pay
SVP Product Development: J. Michael O'Dell, age 46, $266,312 pay
SVP Sales: Clayton A. Reed, age 52, $253,840 pay
VP Finance, CFO, Treasurer, and Secretary: Rodney S. Bond, age 50, $204,246 pay
Chief Technical Officer: Charlie Sauer
Director Human Resources: Carson Brown
Auditors: Price Waterhouse LLP

WHERE

HQ: 108 Wild Basin Rd., Austin, TX 78746
Phone: 512-314-2700 **Fax:** 512-314-2792

	1994 Sales	
	$ mil.	% of total
US	50.5	93
Europe	3.7	7
Total	**54.2**	**100**

WHAT

	1994 Sales
	% of total
Commercial	52
Education	20
Government	17
Health care	11
Total	**100**

Selected Products
Desktop conferencing systems
Large and small group conferencing systems
Multipoint control units (allows simultaneous video-and media conferencing at multiple locations)

KEY COMPETITORS

Alpha Systems Lab	Fujitsu	NEC
AT&T	GEC	PictureTel
BT	Hitachi	Shure Brothers
Compression Labs	IBM	Sony
ConferTech	Matsushita	Target Tech.
Datapoint	Mitsubishi	Zenith

HOW MUCH

Nasdaq symbol: VTEL FY ends: December 31	Annual Growth	1989	1990	1991	1992	1993	1994	1994 Year-end: Debt ratio: 0.0%
Sales ($ mil.)	78.6%	0.0	5.3	11.0	26.1	31.5	54.2	Return on equity: 0.2%
Net income ($ mil.)	—	(2.8)	(2.9)	(2.4)	1.5	(9.3)	0.1	Cash (mil.): $21.4
Income as % of sales	—	—	—	—	5.7%	—	0.2%	Current ratio: 4.43
Earnings per share ($)	—	(0.86)	(0.62)	(0.46)	0.18	(1.05)	0.01	Long-term debt (mil.): $0.0
Stock price – high ($)	—	—	—	—	14.25	10.75	9.00	No. of shares (mil.): 10.0
Stock price – low ($)	—	—	—	—	6.50	3.50	4.00	Dividends
Stock price – close ($)	(10.1%)	—	—	—	10.75	6.50	8.69	Yield: —
P/E – high	—	—	—	—	79	—	—	Payout: —
P/E – low	—	—	—	—	36	—	—	Market value (mil.): $87.0
Dividends per share ($)	—	—	—	—	0.00	0.00	0.00	R&D as % of sales: 16.0%
Book value per share ($)	0.1%	—	—	—	3.71	3.83	3.72	Advertising as % of sales: —
Employees	40.5%	—	70	101	164	262	273	

WESTCOTT COMMUNICATIONS, INC.

OVERVIEW

Westcott Communications doesn't want to teach the world to sing, but it wouldn't mind teaching the world to repair disc brakes, load a gun one-handed, or navigate the latest tax laws. Based in Carrollton, the company is a leading provider of satellite television training and education services. In addition to satellite programming, Westcott Communications offers videotape subscriptions and videotape sales. It produces video training materials and delivers them to more than 2.5 million viewers, including auto dealers, law-enforcement officials, firefighters and emergency medical technicians, accountants, and health care workers. Through its TI-IN Network, it provides 8 to 10 hours of in-class educational programming a day for elementary through high school students. Founder and CEO Carl Westcott owns 11.6% of the company.

A former Ford dealer, Westcott founded the company in 1986 to provide training services to auto dealerships through the Automotive Satellite Television Network. He expanded his operations into police training with the launch of the Law Enforcement Television Network in 1989, the same year the company went public.

The company grew by acquiring other training networks and videotape services, including American Heat Video Productions (firefighting and EMS, 1990) and Health & Sciences Network (1992). It has targeted industries such as health care and accounting, where workers need to learn updated information or methods. It moved into the primary and secondary education market in 1993 with the acquisition of the TI-IN Network.

Westcott Communications continues to look for new niches for its training services. In 1995 it announced plans to launch the Executive Education Network, an interactive satellite network for management training.

WHO

Chairman and CEO: Carl Westcott, age 55, $240,000 pay
President and COO: Jack T. Smith, age 42, $222,000 pay
EVP, CFO, and Secretary: Phyllis Farragut, age 48, $133,125 pay
Director Human Resources: Ellen Hillis
Auditors: Ernst & Young LLP

WHERE

HQ: 1303 Marsh Ln., Carrollton, TX 75006
Phone: 214-417-4100 **Fax:** 214-417-4933

WHAT

Programming	1994 Sales % of total
Corporate & professional	24
Health care	22
Government & public services	20
Automotive	12
Education	10
Financial services	6
Other	6
Total	**100**

Selected Programming

Corporate and Professional
Accounting training
Private security training
Safety and technical training

Health Care
Continuing education for doctors and nurses
Management

Government and Public Service
Fire and emergency medical services training
Law enforcement training

Automotive
Continuing education
Industry news
Management and financial planning

Education
Languages
Literature
Science

Financial Services
Commercial lending
Regulatory compliance
Sales training

KEY COMPETITORS

DeVRY
Industrial Training
ITT Educational
Lambert Communications
National Education
Sandy
Times Mirror

HOW MUCH

Nasdaq symbol: WCTV FY ends: December 31	5-Year Growth	1989	1990	1991	1992	1993	1994
Sales ($ mil.)	41.5%	15.8	22.6	28.7	45.4	69.3	89.7
Net income ($ mil.)	—	(0.8)	1.6	1.9	5.1	9.0	11.8
Income as % of sales	—	—	7.1%	6.6%	11.2%	13.0%	13.2%
Earnings per share ($)	—	(0.06)	0.11	0.12	0.31	0.47	0.61
Stock price – high ($)	—	8.00	6.50	5.13	12.44	22.13	24.75
Stock price – low ($)	—	4.38	1.88	2.13	3.88	10.75	6.75
Stock price – close ($)	20.6%	5.00	2.38	4.00	10.88	18.25	12.75
P/E – high	—	—	59	43	40	47	41
P/E – low	—	—	17	18	13	23	11
Dividends per share ($)	—	0.00	0.00	0.00	0.00	0.00	0.00
Book value per share ($)	28.4%	1.24	1.35	1.46	1.94	3.52	4.32
Employees	23.0%	219	231	294	406	593	616

1994 Year-end:
Debt ratio: 0.0%
Return on equity: 15.6%
Cash (mil.): $5.8
Current ratio: 1.68
Long-term debt (mil.): $0.0
No. of shares (mil.): 19.5
Dividends
 Yield: —
 Payout: —
Market value (mil.): $248.8
R&D as % of sales: —
Advertising as % of sales: —

WHOLE FOODS MARKET, INC.

OVERVIEW

Whole Foods Market is bringing its healthy way of shopping to the whole nation. The company is the #1 natural foods supermarket in the US and the only one with stores in several regions. CEO John Mackey carved out a slice of the $6.5 billion natural foods industry (which still consists mainly of mom-and-pop operators) with his decentralized management style. The company is managed by 6 regional presidents, and store employees are organized into teams with the power to set store policy. Compensation for any team member may not exceed 8 times the average full-time pay for that team. Whole Foods's expansion strategy focuses on urban neighborhoods, and the company plans to open stores in Manhattan, San Francisco, Hillcrest (San Diego), and Mission Viejo (Orange County, CA) in 1996.

Whole Foods began operation in 1978 in Austin, Texas, as Safeway Natural Foods. Two years later Safeway merged with Clarksville Natural Grocery, and Whole Foods was born. Led by founder and ex-hippie Mackey, Whole Foods soon opened a full-sized, one-stop store in Austin. During the 1980s the company opened about 10 stores, primarily in Texas and Northern California. It went public in 1992 and has since accelerated its expansion into other regions. Also in 1992 Whole Foods bought Bread & Circus, the #3 natural foods store chain (Massachusetts and Rhode Island), and Wellspring Grocery (North Carolina), increasing the number of stores to 19. Whole Foods acquired Mrs. Gooch's, a 7-store chain of natural foods stores in Los Angeles, in 1993 and opened 5 stores in 1994 in various locations around the country.

In 1995 the company opened a new store in Plano, Texas, and consolidated its 3 stores in Austin into 2 larger, more modern units. It also purchased Bread of Life, a 2-store chain in Northern California, and Unicorn Village, a natural foods store in Florida.

WHO

Chairman and CEO: John Mackey, age 41, $154,000 pay
President and COO: Peter Roy, age 38, $134,000 pay
President, Southern California Region: John R. Moorman, age 48, $206,000 pay
President, Northeast Region: Chris Hitt, age 44, $180,000 pay
President, Southeast Region: Don Moffitt, age 38, $143,115 pay
President, Midwest Region: Mary Kay Hagen, age 41
President, Southwest Region: Rich Cundiff, age 37
President, Northern California Region: Walter Robb, age 40
VP and CFO: Glenda Flanagan, age 40
Communications Coordinator (HR): Cathy Blackwood
Auditors: KPMG Peat Marwick LLP

WHERE

HQ: 601 N. Lamar Blvd., Ste. 300, Austin, TX 78703
Phone: 512-477-4455   **Fax:** 512-477-1069

Whole Foods Market operates 14 stores in California, 10 in Texas, 6 in Massachusetts, 3 in North Carolina, 2 in Illinois, and one each in Florida, Louisiana, Michigan, Rhode Island, and Wisconsin.

WHAT

	1994 Stores (Open and in Development)
	No.
Whole Foods	23
Bread & Circus	12
Mrs. Gooch's	10
Wellspring Grocery	3
Bread of Life	2
Unicorn Village	1
Total	**51**

KEY COMPETITORS

Albertson's	H. E. Butt	Raley's
American Stores	Herbalife	Randalls
Fiesta Mart	Ingles Markets	Safeway
Food Lion	Kroger	Stop & Shop
Fred Meyer	Meijer	Vons
Fresh Fields	Nature's Sunshine	Winn-Dixie
GNC	Publix	Yucaipa

HOW MUCH

Nasdaq symbol: WFMI FY ends: Last Sun. in Sept.	Annual Growth	1989	1990	1991	1992	1993	1994	1994 Year-end: Debt ratio: 7.9%
Sales ($ mil.)	45.0%	62.6	74.7	92.5	119.9	322.3	401.7	Return on equity: 10.0%
Net income ($ mil.)	—	(0.3)	0.7	1.6	3.1	3.8	8.6	Cash (mil.): $4.3
Income as % of sales	—	—	0.9%	1.7%	2.6%	1.2%	2.2%	Current ratio: 1.20
Earnings per share ($)	—	(0.14)	0.21	0.38	0.44	0.29	0.61	Long-term debt (mil.): $7.2
Stock price – high ($)	—	—	—	—	17.00	23.38	25.38	No. of shares (mil.): 13.8
Stock price – low ($)	—	—	—	—	7.25	13.50	9.50	Dividends
Stock price – close ($)	(16.3%)	—	—	—	14.63	22.50	10.25	Yield: —
P/E – high	—	—	—	—	39	81	42	Payout: —
P/E – low	—	—	—	—	17	47	16	Market value (mil.): $141.1
Dividends per share ($)	—	—	—	—	0.00	0.00	0.00	R&D as % of sales: —
Book value per share ($)	19.3%	—	—	—	4.98	5.87	7.09	Advertising as % of sales: —
Employees	30.1%	1,420	1,615	1,300	2,350	4,150	5,300	

ZAPATA CORPORATION

Zapata is rebelling against its roots. A former integrated oil and gas company and a pioneer in the construction of offshore oil platforms, the Houston-based company has announced plans to exit the oil and gas business. In 1995 Zapata agreed to buy 31% of Envirodyne Industries, an Illinois-based company (with annual sales of $600 million) that manufactures food packaging. Zapata bought Florida financier Malcolm Glazer's stake in Envirodyne. Glazer, a director of Envirodyne and chairman of Zapata, owns about 35% of Zapata.

Zapata was formed through the 1953 merger between former President George Bush's Bush-Overby oil company and another independent oil firm run by Hugh and Bill Liedtke. The company was named after the movie *Viva Zapata!* Shortly after it was formed, Zapata struck it rich with a 100-well oil find in the Jameson Field near Abilene. Bush and the Liedtkes split up the company, with Bush taking over Zapata Off-Shore Company, which he moved to Houston in 1959. He served as president until 1964 and as chairman for the next 2 years before he sold his interest in Zapata to Texas businessman D. Doyle Mize and entered national politics. Zapata struggled through the oil slump of the 1980s and was forced to sell off many of its assets (including its offshore drilling-rig fleet in 1991) to avoid bankruptcy.

In 1993 Zapata began to focus on natural gas, acquiring Cimarron Gas, Stellar Energy, Energy Industries, and 3 other natural gas companies. Glazer became a director of the company in 1993 and became chairman in 1994.

In 1995 the company sold its marine protein business and announced plans to sell its natural gas compression business to Enterra for $130 million. Also in 1995 Glazer's son, Avram, became president and CEO.

Chairman: Malcolm I. Glazer, age 66, $29,800 pay
President and CEO: Avram A. Glazer, age 34
Chairman and President, Zapata Protein, Inc.: Ronald C. Lassiter, age 62, $361,779 pay
President and CEO, Cimarron Gas: Robert W. Jackson, age 51, $200,000 pay
VP, CFO, and Treasurer: Lamar C. McIntyre, age 56
VP General Counsel and Secretary: Joseph L. von Rosenberg III
Auditors: Coopers & Lybrand L.L.P.

HQ: PO Box 4240, Houston, TX 77210-4240
Phone: 713-940-6100   **Fax:** 713-940-6111

	1994 Sales	
	$ mil.	% of total
Natural gas services (gathering, processing & marketing)	156.1	65
Natural gas services (compression)	72.5	30
Oil & gas	12.6	5
Total	**241.2**	**100**

Selected Subsidiaries
Cimarron Gas Holding Company (NGL marketing and trading)
Envirodyne (food packaging, 31%)
Stellar Energy Corporation (natural gas gathering and processing)
Zapata Exploration Company ("Zapex," oil and gas exploration and production in Bolivia and the US)

British Gas
Dolco Packaging
Enron Corp.
Indiana Energy
Interline
Jupiter Industries
KCS Energy
NGC
Panhandle Eastern

Ropak
Sealed Air
Sealright
Seda Specialty Packaging
Tenneco
TransTexas Gas
Unit Corp.
U. S. Gas Transportation

NYSE symbol: ZOS FY ends: September 30	5-Year Growth	1989	1990	1991	1992	1993	1994
Sales ($ mil.)	14.0%	125.2	91.8	93.4	106.4	265.0	241.2
Net income ($ mil.)	—	(58.3)	(105.6)	1.7	2.0	9.0	(8.7)
Income as % of sales	—	—	—	1.8%	1.9%	3.4%	—
Earnings per share ($)	—	(9.10)	(16.55)	0.05	0.10	0.35	(0.28)
Stock price – high ($)	—	21.25	18.13	7.50	7.50	9.69	8.75
Stock price – low ($)	—	10.00	1.56	2.50	2.50	3.75	3.25
Stock price – close ($)	(27.0%)	17.50	2.50	2.50	4.38	6.25	3.63
P/E – high	—	—	—	150	75	28	—
P/E – low	—	—	—	50	25	11	—
Dividends per share ($)	—	0.00	0.00	0.00	0.00	0.00	0.04
Book value per share ($)	—	(11.52)	(28.01)	4.66	4.74	4.90	4.80
Employees	(7.8%)	2,400	2,200	2,200	1,200	1,200	1,600

1994 Year-end:
Debt ratio: 29.0%
Return on equity: —
Cash (mil.): $15.2
Current ratio: 3.96
Long-term debt (mil.): $59.9
No. of shares (mil.): 31.7
Dividends
  Yield: 1.1%
  Payout: —
Market value (mil.): $115.0
R&D as % of sales: —
Advertising as % of sales: —

Key Texas Companies

7TH LEVEL, INC.

1110 E. Collins Blvd., Ste. 122	CEO: George D. Grayson	1994 Sales: $4.1 million
Richardson, TX 75081	CFO: David R. Henkel	1-Yr. Sales Change: 412.5%
Phone: 214-498-8100	HR: Sherry Denning	Exchange: Nasdaq
Fax: 214-437-2717	Employees: 79	Symbol: SEVL

Computers - interactive software (TuneLand), screen savers (Take Your Best Shot) & games (Battle Beast)

50-OFF STORES, INC.

8750 Tesoro Dr.	CEO: Charles M. Siegel	1995 Sales: $201.5 million
San Antonio, TX 78217-0555	CFO: Joseph Lehrman	1-Yr. Sales Change: 1.0%
Phone: 210-805-9300	HR: Roy E. Springer	Exchange: Nasdaq
Fax: 210-804-4952	Employees: 2,742	Symbol: FOFF

Retail - discount & variety regional chain of 109 off-price outlets in 14 states throughout the southern & southwestern United States

ABATIX ENVIRONMENTAL CORP.

8311 Eastpoint Dr., Ste. 400	CEO: Terry W. Shaver	1994 Sales: $26 million
Dallas, TX 75227	CFO: Frank J. Cinati IV	1-Yr. Sales Change: 36.1%
Phone: 214-381-1146	HR: Gary Cox	Exchange: Nasdaq (SC)
Fax: 214-381-9513	Employees: 64	Symbol: ABIX

Protection - safety equipment & supplies for the industrial safety & hazardous materials industries

ABRAXAS PETROLEUM CORPORATION

909 NE Loop 410, PO Box 17485	CEO: Robert L.G. Watson	1994 Sales: $11.3 million
San Antonio, TX 78217	CFO: Rick Porzig	1-Yr. Sales Change: 50.7%
Phone: 210-828-5354	HR: Phil Burch	Exchange: Nasdaq
Fax: 210-828-3611	Employees: 41	Symbol: AXAS

Oil & gas - exploration & production of crude oil & natural gas primarily along the Texas Gulf Coast & the Permian Basin of West Texas

ACADEMY CORPORATION

1800 N. Mason Rd.	CEO: Arthur Gochman	1994 Sales: $268 million
Katy, TX 77449	CFO: James Pierce	1-Yr. Sales Change: —
Phone: 713-579-1555	HR: Sylvia Barrera	Ownership: Privately Held
Fax: 713-492-5204	Employees: 1,700	

Retail - sporting goods & apparel

ACE CASH EXPRESS, INC.

1231 Greenway Dr., Ste. 800	CEO: Donald H. Neustadt	1995 Sales: $47.8 million
Irving, TX 75038-7594	CFO: Thomas E. Larson	1-Yr. Sales Change: 19.8%
Phone: 214-550-5000	HR: Sherry Detwiler	Exchange: Nasdaq
Fax: 214-550-5150	Employees: 867	Symbol: AACE

Financial - check cashing services

ACR GROUP, INC.

3200 Wilcrest Dr., Ste. 440	CEO: Alex Trevino Jr.	1995 Sales: $41.3 million
Houston, TX 77042-6019	CFO: Anthony R. Maresca	1-Yr. Sales Change: 32.8%
Phone: 713-780-8532	HR: Carol Russell	Exchange: Nasdaq (SC)
Fax: 713-780-4067	Employees: 120	Symbol: ACRG

Building products - wholesale heating, ventilating, air conditioning & refrigeration equipment & supplies

ACS COMMUNICATIONS, INC. ✓

1826 Kramer Ln., Ste. M	CEO: Robby Sawyer	1994 Sales: $21.5 million
Austin, TX 78758	CFO: Don Amicucci	1-Yr. Sales Change: 7.5%
Phone: 512-837-4400	HR: Sharon Johnson	Ownership: Privately Held
Fax: 512-837-6767	Employees: 198	

Telecommunications services - cabling for data & voice systems (d/b/a ACS Dataline)

ADAMS RESOURCES & ENERGY, INC.

6910 Fannin St.	CEO: K. S. "Bud" Adams Jr.	1994 Sales: $635 million
Houston, TX 77030	CFO: Richard B. Abshire	1-Yr. Sales Change: -8.7%
Phone: 713-797-9966	HR: Jay Grimes	Exchange: AMEX
Fax: 713-795-4495	Employees: 377	Symbol: AE

Oil & gas - production & pipeline, tank truck transportation of petroleum products & liquid chemicals

 See page 166 for a full profile of this company.

ADMINISTAFF INC.

19001 Crescent Springs Dr.	CEO: Paul Sarvadi	1994 Sales: $564 million
Kingwood, TX 77339	CFO: Richard Rawson	1-Yr. Sales Change: 13.5%
Phone: 713-358-8986	HR: Jim Wilkes	Ownership: Privately Held
Fax: 713-358-3354	Employees: 16,000	

Personnel - staff leasing services

AECTRA REFINING & MARKETING INC.

3 Riverway, Ste. 800
Houston, TX 77056
Phone: 713-629-7563
Fax: 713-629-4643

Oil distribution & marketing

CEO: Mois Mottale
CFO: Anthony J. Voigt
HR: Pat Kinney
Employees: 40

1994 Est. Sales: $700 mil.
1-Yr. Sales Change: —
Ownership: Privately Held

AFFILIATED COMPUTER SERVICES, INC.

2828 N. Haskell Ave.
Dallas, TX 75204
Phone: 214-841-6111
Fax: 214-821-8315

CEO: Darwin Deason
CFO: Mark A. King
HR: Pam McMahan
Employees: 2,200

1995 Sales: $313.2 million
1-Yr. Sales Change: 15.5%
Exchange: Nasdaq
Symbol: ACSA

Computers - data processing outsourcing; ATM network (MoneyMaker); information management systems

AFFILIATED FOODS INCORPORATED

6700 S. Washington
Amarillo, TX 79118
Phone: 806-372-3851
Fax: 806-372-1404

CEO: Benny R. Cooper
CFO: —
HR: Don Barclay
Employees: 850

1994 Sales: $530 million
1-Yr. Sales Change: 6.0%
Ownership: Privately Held

Food - wholesale groceries, drugs, toiletries & sundries

A. H. BELO CORPORATION

400 S. Record St.
Dallas, TX 75202
Phone: 214-977-6606
Fax: 214-977-6603

CEO: Robert W. Decherd
CFO: Michael D. Perry
HR: Jeff Lamb
Employees: 3,469

1994 Sales: $628.1 million
1-Yr. Sales Change: 15.3%
Exchange: NYSE
Symbol: BLC

Broadcasting - radio & TV; newspapers (*Dallas Morning News*)

AKIN, GUMP, STRAUSS, HAUER & FELD

1700 Pacific Ave., Ste. 4100
Dallas, TX 75201
Phone: 214-969-2800
Fax: 214-969-4343

CEO: Alan Feld
CFO: Eva Rowe
HR: Kathy Little
Employees: 1,235

1994 Est. Sales: $125 mil.
1-Yr. Sales Change: -8.4%
Ownership: Privately Held

Law firm

ALAMO GROUP, INC.

1502 E. Walnut
Seguin, TX 78155
Phone: 210-379-1480
Fax: 210-379-0864

CEO: Donald J. Douglass
CFO: Oran F. Logan
HR: Gabrielle Garcia
Employees: 1,012

1994 Sales: $119.6 million
1-Yr. Sales Change: 35.1%
Exchange: NYSE
Symbol: ALG

Machinery - tractor-mounted farm equipment

ALAN YOUNG BUICK-GMC TRUCK, INC.

7724 N.E. Loop 820 North
Richland Hills, TX 76180
Phone: 817-589-3300
Fax: 817-589-3318

CEO: Alan Young
CFO: Judi Standley
HR: —
Employees: 78

1994 Sales: $218.3 million
1-Yr. Sales Change: —
Ownership: Privately Held

Retail - new & used cars

ALBARA CORPORATION

610 S. Frazier
Conroe, TX 77301
Phone: 409-539-2992
Fax: 409-539-4141

CEO: Real Provencher
CFO: Real Provencher
HR: —
Employees: 19

1994 Sales: $2.2 million
1-Yr. Sales Change: -77.6%
Exchange: Nasdaq (SC)
Symbol: ALAB

Computers - Macintosh laser printer accessories & software sales

ALLRIGHT CORPORATION

1111 Fannin St.
Houston, TX 77002
Phone: 713-222-2505
Fax: 713-222-6833

CEO: Bernard M. Meyer
CFO: Terry Chen
HR: Gary Hoffpauir
Employees: 3,000

1994 Est. Sales: $160 mil.
1-Yr. Sales Change: —
Ownership: Privately Held

Business services - parking lot management

ALLWASTE, INC.

5151 San Felipe, Ste. 1600
Houston, TX 77056
Phone: 713-623-8777
Fax: 713-625-7087

CEO: Robert M. Chiste
CFO: Fred M. Ferreira
HR: James E. Reif
Employees: 4,037

1994 Sales: $350.5 million
1-Yr. Sales Change: 15.8%
Exchange: NYSE
Symbol: ALW

Pollution control equipment & services - industrial remediation services

ALTAI, INC.

624 Six Flags Dr.	CEO: James P. Williams	1994 Sales: $14.8 million
Arlington, TX 76011	CFO: Gary E. Leslie	1-Yr. Sales Change: 23.3%
Phone: 817-640-8911	HR: Steve Knisley	Exchange: Nasdaq
Fax: 817-633-4449	Employees: 116	Symbol: ALTI

Computers - automated scheduling system, restart system, & speech recognition system software

AMBER'S STORES, INC.

3737 Gus Thomasson Rd.	CEO: Lance P. Wimmer	1995 Sales: $65.7 million
Mesquite, TX 75150	CFO: J. Lamar Roberts	1-Yr. Sales Change: 6.0%
Phone: 214-682-9993	HR: Larry Burton	Exchange: OTC
Fax: 214-682-1401	Employees: 1,153	Symbol: ABRS

Retail - arts & crafts & picture framing

AMERICAN BINGO & GAMING CORP.

515 Congress Ave., Ste. 1200	CEO: Greg Wilson	1994 Sales: $2 million
Austin, TX 78701	CFO: John Orton	1-Yr. Sales Change: 11.1%
Phone: 512-472-2041	HR: Kip Hix	Exchange: Nasdaq (SC)
Fax: 512-472-4307	Employees: 10	Symbol: BNGO

Leisure & recreational services - bingo centers for charity in Texas & Alabama

AMERICAN BIOMED, INC.

2408 D-5 Timberloch Place	CEO: Steve Rash	1994 Sales: $0.7 million
The Woodlands, TX 77380	CFO: Herbert L. Kalman	1-Yr. Sales Change: -12.5%
Phone: 713-367-3895	HR: —	Exchange: Pink Sheets
Fax: 713-367-3212	Employees: 29	Symbol: ABMI

Medical products - minimally invasive medical, surgical & diagnostic devices

AMERICAN EAGLE GROUP, INC.

12801 N. Central Expwy., Ste. 800	CEO: M. Philip Guthrie	1994 Sales: $87.7 million
Dallas, TX 75243	CFO: Richard M. Kurz	1-Yr. Sales Change: 24.9%
Phone: 214-448-1400	HR: Janiece Biggs	Exchange: NYSE
Fax: 214-448-1417	Employees: 280	Symbol: FLI

Insurance - property & casualty to the aviation, trucking, car dealer & artisan contractor industries

AMERICAN ECOLOGY CORPORATION

5333 Westheimer, Ste. 1000
Houston, TX 77056-5407
Phone: 713-624-1900
Fax: 713-624-1915

CEO: Jack K. Lemley
CFO: C. Clifford Wright Jr.
HR: Cliff Wright
Employees: 491

1994 Sales: $71.9 million
1-Yr. Sales Change: 19.2%
Exchange: Nasdaq
Symbol: ECOL

Pollution control equipment & services - hazardous waste disposal

AMERICAN EXPLORATION COMPANY

1331 Lamar, Ste. 900
Houston, TX 77010
Phone: 713-756-6000
Fax: 713-659-5620

CEO: Mark Andrews
CFO: John M. Hogan
HR: David Broussard
Employees: 202

1994 Sales: $51.4 million
1-Yr. Sales Change: -11.7%
Exchange: AMEX
Symbol: AX

Oil & gas - US exploration & production

AMERICAN GENERAL CORPORATION

2929 Allen Pkwy.
Houston, TX 77019-2155
Phone: 713-522-1111
Fax: 713-831-3028

CEO: Harold S. Hook
CFO: Austin P. Young
HR: Joann Griffith
Employees: 12,900

1994 Sales: $4,841 million
1-Yr. Sales Change: 0.2%
Exchange: NYSE
Symbol: AGC

Insurance - life

 See pages 54–55 for a full profile of this company.

AMERICAN GENERAL HOSPITALITY INC.

3860 W. Northwest Hwy.
Dallas, TX 75220
Phone: 214-352-3330
Fax: 214-351-0568

CEO: Steven Jorns
CFO: Elizabeth Williams
HR: Dorothy Wood
Employees: 5,600

1994 Est. Sales: $300 mil.
1-Yr. Sales Change: —
Ownership: Privately Held

Hotels (franchisee of Best Western, Comfort Inn, Days Inn, Holiday Inn, Hilton, Courtyard Marriott & Ramada)

AMERICAN HOMESTAR CORPORATION

812 E. NASA Rd. One
Webster, TX 77598
Phone: 713-333-5601
Fax: 713-333-9040

CEO: Finis F. Teeter
CFO: Craig A. Reynolds
HR: Susan Wilburn
Employees: 1,212

1995 Sales: $187.7 million
1-Yr. Sales Change: 57.3%
Exchange: Nasdaq
Symbol: HSTR

Building - manufactured homes in the Southwest

AMERICAN INDEMNITY FINANCIAL CORPORATION

One American Indemnity Plaza	CEO: J. Fellman Seinsheimer III	1994 Sales: $70.7 million
Galveston, TX 77550	CFO: Phillip E. Apgar	1-Yr. Sales Change: -0.8%
Phone: 409-766-4600	HR: Lori Termini	Exchange: Nasdaq
Fax: 409-766-5531	Employees: 246	Symbol: AIFC

Insurance - property & casualty

AMERICAN INDUSTRIAL PROPERTIES REIT

6220 N. Beltline, Ste. 205	CEO: Charles W. Wolcott	1994 Sales: $11.2 million
Irving, TX 75063	CFO: Marc A. Simpson	1-Yr. Sales Change: 5.7%
Phone: 214-550-6053	HR: —	Exchange: NYSE
Fax: 214-550-6037	Employees: 6	Symbol: IND

Real estate investment trust - industrial & retail real estate

AMERICAN MEDICAL ELECTRONICS, INC.

250 E. Arapahoe Rd.	CEO: John F. Clifford	1994 Sales: $38.3 million
Richardson, TX 75081	CFO: Wesley E. Johnson Jr.	1-Yr. Sales Change: -2.5%
Phone: 214-918-8300	HR: LaVonne M. Chimbel	Exchange: Nasdaq
Fax: 214-918-8480	Employees: 255	Symbol: AMEI

Medical instruments for spinal fusions & recalcitrant bone fractures

AMERICAN MEDICAL TECHNOLOGIES, INC.

5847 San Felipe, Ste. 900	CEO: James T. Rash	1994 Sales: $13.3 million
Houston, TX 77057	CFO: Leonard A. Bedell	1-Yr. Sales Change: 5.6%
Phone: 713-783-8200	HR: Sue Weatherley	Exchange: Nasdaq (SC)
Fax: 713-783-6003	Employees: 75	Symbol: AMTI

Pollution control - environmental monitoring systems

AMERICAN NATIONAL INSURANCE COMPANY

One Moody Plaza	CEO: Orson C. Clay	1994 Sales: $1,395.4 million
Galveston, TX 77550	CFO: Vincent E. Soler Jr.	1-Yr. Sales Change: 5.0%
Phone: 409-763-4661	HR: Glenn C. Langley	Exchange: Nasdaq
Fax: 409-766-6589	Employees: 1,300	Symbol: ANAT

Insurance - life, health, annuities; personal lines property & casualty & credit insurance

AMERICAN ONCOLOGY RESOURCES, INC.

17001 Northchase Dr., Ste. 330	CEO: R. Dale Ross	1994 Sales: $20.4 million
Houston, TX 77060	CFO: L. Fred Pounds	1-Yr. Sales Change: 183.3%
Phone: 713-873-2674	HR: Allen Pittman	Exchange: Nasdaq
Fax: 800-965-5679	Employees: 613	Symbol: AORI

Medical services - oncology practice management services

AMERICAN PHYSICIANS SERVICE GROUP, INC. ✓

1301 Capital of Texas Hwy.	CEO: Kenneth S. Shifrin	1994 Sales: $17.7 million
Austin, TX 78746	CFO: William H. Hayes	1-Yr. Sales Change: 0.0%
Phone: 512-328-0888	HR: William H. Hayes	Exchange: Nasdaq
Fax: 512-314-4398	Employees: 138	Symbol: AMPH

Financial services - management services to medical & legal malpractice insurance companies; brokerage & investment services

AMERICAN REALTY TRUST, INC.

10670 N. Central Expwy., Ste. 300	CEO: Karl L. Blaha	1994 Sales: $20.5 million
Dallas, TX 75231	CFO: Thomas A. Holland	1-Yr. Sales Change: 118.1%
Phone: 214-692-4700	HR: Lyn Kruger	Exchange: NYSE
Fax: 214-373-0740	Employees: —	Symbol: ARB

Real estate investment trust - apartments & single-family homes

AMERICAN RICE, INC.

16825 Northchase, Ste. 1600	CEO: Douglas D. Murphy	1995 Sales: $373.1 million
Houston, TX 77060	CFO: Richard N. McCombs	1-Yr. Sales Change: 31.1%
Phone: 713-873-8800	HR: Marsha Donaght	Exchange: Nasdaq (SC)
Fax: 713-873-2823	Employees: 1,146	Symbol: RICE

Food - branded rice products processing (#1 in US)

AMERICREDIT CORP.

200 Bailey Ave.	CEO: Clifton H. Morris Jr.	1994 Sales: $15.9 million
Fort Worth, TX 76107	CFO: Daniel E. Berce	1-Yr. Sales Change: -36.1%
Phone: 817-332-7000	HR: Trish Jones	Exchange: NYSE
Fax: 817-336-9519	Employees: 183	Symbol: ACF

Financial - funding source for franchised & independent dealers to finance their customers' purchases of used cars

AMERISERV FOOD CO.

13355 Noel Rd., Ste. 2225	CEO: William R. Burgess	1994 Sales: $875 million
Dallas, TX 75240	CFO: A. Scott Letier	1-Yr. Sales Change: 5.0%
Phone: 214-385-8595	HR: —	Ownership: Privately Held
Fax: 214-702-7391	Employees: 1,250	

Food - wholesale to restaurants

AMR CORPORATION

4333 Amon Carter Blvd.	CEO: Robert L. Crandall	1994 Sales: $16,137 million
Fort Worth, TX 76155	CFO: Gerard J. Arpey	1-Yr. Sales Change: 2.0%
Phone: 817-963-1234	HR: Thomas J. Kiernan	Exchange: NYSE
Fax: 817-967-9641	Employees: 109,800	Symbol: AMR

Transportation - airline (American Airlines)

 See pages 56–57 for a full profile of this company.

AMRE, INC.

8585 N. Stemmons Fwy., Ste. 102	CEO: Robert M. Swartz	1994 Sales: $285.9 million
Dallas, TX 75247	CFO: John S. Vanecko	1-Yr. Sales Change: 9.7%
Phone: 214-658-6300	HR: Patrick J. Aulson	Exchange: NYSE
Fax: 214-658-6100	Employees: 3,385	Symbol: AMM

Building products - siding & related home-improvement products sales & installation

AMRESCO, INC.

1845 Woodall Rodgers Fwy.	CEO: Robert H. Lutz Jr.	1994 Sales: $157.2 million
Dallas, TX 75201	CFO: Barry L. Edwards	1-Yr. Sales Change: -10.9%
Phone: 214-953-7700	HR: W. Ronald Castleman	Exchange: Nasdaq
Fax: 214-969-5478	Employees: 700	Symbol: AMMB

Consulting - management consulting; apartment building operations

AMTECH CORPORATION

17304 Preston Rd., Ste. E100	CEO: G. Russell Mortenson	1994 Sales: $61.5 million
Dallas, TX 75252	CFO: Steve M. York	1-Yr. Sales Change: 3.5%
Phone: 214-733-6600	HR: Joe Crumpton	Exchange: Nasdaq
Fax: 214-733-6699	Employees: 354	Symbol: AMTC

Telecommunications equipment - wireless electronic identification systems, primarily for the transportation & toll road industries

ANADARKO PETROLEUM CORPORATION

17001 Northchase Dr., PO Box 1330
Houston, TX 77251-1330
Phone: 713-875-1101
Fax: 713-874-3385

CEO: Robert J. Allison Jr.
CFO: Michael E. Rose
HR: Randy Rogers
Employees: 1,085

1994 Sales: $482.5 million
1-Yr. Sales Change: 0.1%
Exchange: NYSE
Symbol: APC

Oil & gas - US exploration & production of natural gas, crude oil, condensate & natural gas liquids
domestically & internationally

ANCIRA ENTERPRISES INC.

6111 Bandera Rd.
San Antonio, TX 78238
Phone: 210-681-4900
Fax: 210-681-5541

CEO: Ernesto Ancira Jr.
CFO: Gregory M. Spence
HR: Carol Kopplin
Employees: 434

1994 Sales: $261 million
1-Yr. Sales Change: 44.1%
Ownership: Privately Held

Retail - new & used cars

ANDERSON GRAIN CORPORATION

PO Box 1117
Levelland, TX 79336
Phone: 806-894-4982
Fax: 806-894-1962

CEO: Buck Anderson
CFO: Dick Holland
HR: Bill Fitzherbert
Employees: 325

1994 Sales: $134 million
1-Yr. Sales Change: 21.8%
Ownership: Privately Held

Wholesale distribution - grain, fertilizer & farming supplies

ANDREWS & KURTH L.L.P.

600 Travis St., Ste. 4200
Houston, TX 77002
Phone: 713-220-4200
Fax: 713-220-4285

CEO: Rush Moody
CFO: Kevin Miller
HR: Deborah Ganjevi
Employees: 600

1994 Est. Sales: $85 mil.
1-Yr. Sales Change: -8.1%
Ownership: Privately Held

Law firm

ANGELO STATE UNIVERSITY

2601 West Ave. North
San Angelo, TX 76909
Phone: 915-942-2041
Fax: 915-942-2038

CEO: Michael P. Ryan
CFO: Robert L. Krupala
HR: James Ocker
Employees: 870

1994 Sales: $44.6 million
1-Yr. Sales Change: 3.7%
Ownership: Privately Held

University - offering more than 40 undergraduate & 20 graduate degree programs

APACHE CORPORATION

2000 Post Oak Blvd., Ste. 100	CEO: Raymond Plank	1994 Sales: $545.6 million
Houston, TX 77056-4400	CFO: Mark A. Jackson	1-Yr. Sales Change: 16.9%
Phone: 713-296-6000	HR: Roger B. Rice	Exchange: NYSE
Fax: 303-837-5688	Employees: 1,182	Symbol: APA

Oil & gas - US exploration & production

APROGENEX, INC.

8000 El Rio St.	CEO: Joel Bresser	1994 Sales: $0 million
Houston, TX 77054	CFO: J. D. Payne	1-Yr. Sales Change: —
Phone: 713-748-5114	HR: Beth Racey	Exchange: AMEX
Fax: 713-748-6012	Employees: 33	Symbol: APG

Biomedical & genetic products - diagnostic test systems based on proprietary DNA probe technology

APS HOLDING CORPORATION

15710 John F. Kennedy Blvd.	CEO: Mark S. Hoffman	1995 Sales: $523.5 million
Houston, TX 77032-2347	CFO: William Delaney	1-Yr. Sales Change: 18.0%
Phone: 713-507-1100	HR: Douglas G. Beckstett	Exchange: Nasdaq
Fax: 713-507-1320	Employees: 4,200	Symbol: APSI

Auto parts - replacement parts (Big A brand & other brand names) distribution

AQUILA GAS PIPELINE CORPORATION

100 NE Loop 410, Ste. 1000	CEO: Charles K. Dempster	1994 Sales: $328.7 million
San Antonio, TX 78216-4754	CFO: Damon C. Button	1-Yr. Sales Change: -10.3%
Phone: 210-342-0685	HR: Cindy Downs	Exchange: NYSE
Fax: 210-340-6341	Employees: 256	Symbol: AQP

Oil & gas - production & pipeline

ARABIAN SHIELD DEVELOPMENT COMPANY

10830 N. Central Expwy., Ste. 175	CEO: Hatem El-Khalidi	1994 Sales: $17.8 million
Dallas, TX 75231	CFO: Drew Wilson	1-Yr. Sales Change: 17.1%
Phone: 214-692-7872	HR: —	Exchange: Nasdaq
Fax: 214-692-7874	Employees: 31	Symbol: ARSD

Oil & gas - international specialty

ARAMCO SERVICES CO.

PO Box 4534
Houston, TX 77210
Phone: 713-432-4000
Fax: 713-432-5663

Oil & gas - production

CEO: Muscsa Jalali
CFO: K. Cambridge
HR: —
Employees: 700

1994 Est. Sales: $380 mil.
1-Yr. Sales Change: —
Ownership: Privately Held

ARCH PETROLEUM INC.

777 Taylor St., Ste. II
Fort Worth, TX 76102
Phone: 817-332-9209
Fax: 817-332-9249

Oil & gas - US exploration & production

CEO: Larry Kalas
CFO: Fred Cantu
HR: —
Employees: 45

1994 Sales: $82.7 million
1-Yr. Sales Change: 87.5%
Exchange: Nasdaq
Symbol: ARCH

ARGUS PHARMACEUTICALS, INC.

3400 Research Forest Dr.
The Woodlands, TX 77831
Phone: 713-367-1666
Fax: 713-367-1676

Drugs - treatment of cancer & life-threatening infections

CEO: David M. Leech
CFO: Terance A. Murnane
HR: Connie Stourt
Employees: 41

1994 Sales: $0.7 million
1-Yr. Sales Change: 250.0%
Exchange: Nasdaq
Symbol: ARGS

ARMY & AIR FORCE EXCHANGE SERVICE

3911 S. Walton Walker Blvd.
Dallas, TX 75236
Phone: 214-312-2011
Fax: 214-312-3000

Retail - post & base exchanges at military bases

CEO: Allen D. Bunger
CFO: Kenneth C. Weever
HR: Tom Harmon
Employees: 60,000

1994 Est. Sales: $7,100 mil.
1-Yr. Sales Change: -2.2%
Ownership: Privately Held

 See pages 58–59 for a full profile of this company.

ARRHYTHMIA RESEARCH TECHNOLOGY, INC.

5910 Courtyard Dr., Ste. 300
Austin, TX 78731
Phone: 512-343-6912
Fax: 512-343-7312

Medical instruments - heart condition diagnostic & treatment equipment; electrocardiograph & electro-physiology products

CEO: E. P. "Lou" Marinos
CFO: E. P. "Lou" Marinos
HR: William C. Cooper
Employees: 47

1994 Sales: $17.5 million
1-Yr. Sales Change: -1.7%
Exchange: AMEX
Symbol: HRT

ASSOCIATED MATERIALS INCORPORATED

2200 Ross Ave., Ste. 4100 East
Dallas, TX 75201-6711
Phone: 214-220-4600
Fax: 214-220-4607

CEO: William W. Winspear
CFO: Robert L. Winspear
HR: —
Employees: 2,310

1994 Sales: $352.6 million
1-Yr. Sales Change: 12.7%
Ownership: Privately Held

Building products - vinyl siding products & vinyl replacement windows

ASSOCIATED MILK PRODUCERS, INC.

6609 Blanco Rd., PO Box 790287
San Antonio, TX 78279-0287
Phone: 210-340-9100
Fax: 210-340-9158

CEO: Irvin J. Elkin
CFO: Terry Krueger
HR: Charlie Warren
Employees: 4,500

1994 Sales: $2,628.7 million
1-Yr. Sales Change: -2.4%
Ownership: Privately Held

Food - dairy products

 See pages 60–61 for a full profile of this company.

ASTRAEA AVIATION SERVICES, INC.

7701 Lemmon Ave.
Dallas, TX 75209
Phone: 214-358-6019
Fax: 214-902-0938

CEO: Bruce Leadbetter
CFO: Mathew Fajack
HR: Dominick Pescatore
Employees: 900

1994 Est. Sales: $100 mil.
1-Yr. Sales Change: —
Ownership: Privately Held

Transportation - aircraft maintenance (Dalfort Aviation)

ATMOS ENERGY CORPORATION

5430 LBJ Fwy., Ste. 1800
Dallas, TX 75240
Phone: 214-934-9227
Fax: 214-991-5235

CEO: Robert F. Stephens
CFO: James F. Purser
HR: Wynn D. McGregor
Employees: 1,709

1994 Sales: $500.3 million
1-Yr. Sales Change: 28.8%
Exchange: NYSE
Symbol: ATO

Utility - gas distribution to residential, commerical, industrial & agricultural customers

ATWOOD OCEANICS, INC.

15835 Park Ten Place Dr.
Houston, TX 77218
Phone: 713-492-2929
Fax: 713-492-0345

CEO: John R. Irwin
CFO: James M. Holland
HR: Bill Sullens
Employees: 650

1994 Sales: $68.8 million
1-Yr. Sales Change: 26.9%
Exchange: Nasdaq
Symbol: ATWD

Oil & gas - offshore drilling

AUSTIN INDUSTRIES INC.

PO Box 1590
Dallas, TX 75221
Phone: 214-443-5500
Fax: 214-443-5581

CEO: William T. Solomon
CFO: Paul Hill
HR: Rob Brewer
Employees: 5,000

1994 Est. Sales: $613 mil.
1-Yr. Sales Change: 20.4%
Ownership: Privately Held

Building - commercial & industrial

AUSTIN VENTURES

1300 Norwood Tower, 114 W. 7th St.
Austin, TX 78701
Phone: 512-479-0055
Fax: 512-476-3952

CEO: Jeffery C. Garvey
CFO: John E. Nicholson
HR: —
Employees: 7

1994 Sales: N/A
1-Yr. Sales Change: —
Ownership: Privately Held

Financial - venture capital investment firm specializing in high-tech & communications companies

AVIALL INC.

9311 Reeves St.
Dallas, TX 75235
Phone: 214-956-5000
Fax: 214-956-3383

CEO: Marshall B. Taylor
CFO: Mina Brown
HR: Charlie Kiezel
Employees: 2,900

1994 Sales: $863.3 million
1-Yr. Sales Change: -3.5%
Exchange: NYSE
Symbol: AVL

Aerospace - turbine engine overhaul, accessories & components; aircraft parts & supplies distribution

AZTEC MANUFACTURING CO., INC.

400 N. Tarrant
Crowley, TX 76036
Phone: 817-297-4361
Fax: 817-297-4621

CEO: L. C. Martin
CFO: Dana Perry
HR: Bill Arnold
Employees: 374

1995 Sales: $44.6 million
1-Yr. Sales Change: 9.3%
Exchange: Nasdaq
Symbol: AZTC

Building products - industrial lighting for power generation plants; galvanizing services for makers of fabricated metal products

AZTX CATTLE CO.

PO Box 390
Hereford, TX 79045
Phone: 806-364-8871
Fax: 806-364-3842

CEO: Bob Josserand
CFO: Odess Lovin Jr.
HR: Odess Lovin Jr.
Employees: 151

1994 Est. Sales: $100 mil.
1-Yr. Sales Change: —
Ownership: Privately Held

Agricultural operations - cattle feedlots

BAKER & BOTTS L.L.P.

910 Louisiana St., Ste. 3000
Houston, TX 77002
Phone: 713-229-1234
Fax: 713-229-1522

Law firm

CEO: E. William Barnett
CFO: Lydia Joachim
HR: Sue Robinson
Employees: 1,200

1994 Est. Sales: $175 mil.
1-Yr. Sales Change: 5.4%
Ownership: Privately Held

BAKER HUGHES INCORPORATED

3900 Essex Ln.
Houston, TX 77027-5177
Phone: 713-439-8600
Fax: 713-439-8699

Oil field machinery & equipment

CEO: James D. Woods
CFO: Eric L. Mattson
HR: Phillip A. Rice
Employees: 14,700

1994 Sales: $2,505 million
1-Yr. Sales Change: -7.3%
Exchange: NYSE
Symbol: BHI

 See pages 62–63 for a full profile of this company.

BALTIC INTERNATIONAL USA, INC.

1990 Post Oak Blvd., Ste. 163
Houston, TX 77056
Phone: 713-961-9299
Fax: 713-961-9298

CEO: Robert L. Knauss
CFO: James Goodchild
HR: —
Employees: 15

1994 Sales: $0.1 million
1-Yr. Sales Change: -66.7%
Exchange: Nasdaq (SC)
Symbol: BISA

Transportation - airline (owns 49% of Baltic International Airlines) based at Riga International Airport, serving London, Frankfurt & Amsterdam

BANCTEC, INC.

4435 Spring Valley Rd.
Dallas, TX 75244
Phone: 214-450-7700
Fax: 214-450-7867

CEO: Grahame N. Clark Jr.
CFO: Raghavan Rajaji
HR: Jim Wimberley
Employees: 2,274

1995 Sales: $297.5 million
1-Yr. Sales Change: 20.2%
Exchange: Nasdaq
Symbol: BTEC

Optical character recognition - computerized systems for processing financial transaction documents (ImageFirst)

BANK UNITED OF TEXAS FSB

3200 Southwest Fwy., Ste. 1600
Houston, TX 77027
Phone: 713-963-7900
Fax: 713-963-7915

Financial - savings & loans

CEO: Barry C. Burkholder
CFO: Anthony J. Nocella
HR: Karen Hartnett
Employees: 2,936

1994 Sales: $613.6 million
1-Yr. Sales Change: -2.5%
Exchange: NYSE
Symbol: BKUA

BAPTIST MEMORIAL HOSPITAL SYSTEM

660 N. Main St.
San Antonio, TX 78205
Phone: 210-222-8431
Fax: 210-302-3164

CEO: Callie Smith
CFO: Ferd Gaenzel
HR: William McAtee
Employees: 5,500

1994 Sales: $274.6 million
1-Yr. Sales Change: 19.3%
Ownership: Privately Held

Hospitals - not-for-profit system

BARRETT-CROFOOT, LLP

4 Rd. and J Rd.
Hereford, TX 79045
Phone: 806-364-6081
Fax: 806-357-2384

CEO: E. C. Barrett
CFO: James P. McDowell
HR: Bryan Watts
Employees: 100

1994 Est. Sales: $100 mil.
1-Yr. Sales Change: 2.0%
Ownership: Privately Held

Agricultural operations - cattle feedlot

BASS ENTERPRISES PRODUCTION CO.

201 Main St., Ste. 300
Fort Worth, TX 76102-3107
Phone: 817-390-8400
Fax: 817-390-8751

CEO: Sid R. Bass
CFO: Robert Cotham
HR: Keith Bullard
Employees: 700

1994 Est. Sales: $175 mil.
1-Yr. Sales Change: —
Ownership: Privately Held

Oil & gas - exploration & production

BATTLE MOUNTAIN GOLD COMPANY

333 Clay St., 42nd Fl.
Houston, TX 77002
Phone: 713-650-6400
Fax: 713-650-3636

CEO: Karl E. Elers
CFO: R. Dennis O'Connell
HR: Kenneth T. Row
Employees: 1,407

1994 Sales: $229.7 million
1-Yr. Sales Change: 18.8%
Exchange: NYSE
Symbol: BMG

Gold mining & processing & silver & copper ore in the US, Bolivia, Chile & Australia

BAYLOR HEALTH CARE SYSTEM

3500 Gaston Ave.
Dallas, TX 75246
Phone: 214-820-0111
Fax: 214-824-7499

CEO: Boone Powell Jr.
CFO: John L. Hess
HR: Beverly Bradshaw
Employees: 7,000

1994 Sales: $875.2 million
1-Yr. Sales Change: 7.2%
Ownership: Privately Held

Hospitals - not-for-profit system (including Baylor University Medical Center) serving the Dallas area

BAYLOR UNIVERSITY

PO Box 97056	CEO: Robert B. Sloan Jr.	1994 Sales: $149.2 million
Waco, TX 76798-7056	CFO: James Netherton	1-Yr. Sales Change: 5.2%
Phone: 817-755-1011	HR: Cliff Williams	Ownership: Privately Held
Fax: 817-755-1490	Employees: 1,600	

University - offering 146 undergraduate & 91 graduate degree programs

BEAUTICONTROL COSMETICS, INC.

2121 Midway Rd., PO Box 819076	CEO: Richard W. Heath	1994 Sales: $70.6 million
Carrollton, TX 75006	CFO: M. Douglas Tucker	1-Yr. Sales Change: 10.5%
Phone: 214-458-0601	HR: Sandra L. England	Exchange: Nasdaq
Fax: 214-960-7923	Employees: 477	Symbol: BUTI

Cosmetics & toiletries - skin & nail care; skin condition, color & image analysis

BELLWETHER EXPLORATION COMPANY

1221 Lamar St., Ste. 1600	CEO: Doug Foshee	1995 Sales: $19.3 million
Houston, TX 77010-3039	CFO: James M. Vanderhider	1-Yr. Sales Change: 80.4%
Phone: 713-650-1025	HR: Carolyn Driesbach	Exchange: Nasdaq
Fax: 713-652-2916	Employees: 20	Symbol: BELW

Oil & gas - US exploration & production

BEN E. KEITH CO.

601 E. 7th St.	CEO: Robert Hallam	1994 Sales: $513 million
Fort Worth, TX 76102	CFO: Mel Cockrell	1-Yr. Sales Change: 1.0%
Phone: 817-332-9171	HR: —	Ownership: Privately Held
Fax: 817-332-3471	Employees: 1,446	

Food - wholesale to restaurants

BENCHMARK ELECTRONICS, INC.

3000 Technology Dr.	CEO: Donald E. Nigbor	1994 Sales: $98.2 million
Angleton, TX 77515	CFO: Cary T. Fu	1-Yr. Sales Change: 29.4%
Phone: 409-849-6550	HR: Gwyn Holden	Exchange: AMEX
Fax: 409-848-5269	Employees: 439	Symbol: BHE

Electrical components - contract manufacturer

 See page 167 for a full profile of this company.

BENSON FINANCIAL CORPORATION

40 NE Loop 410
San Antonio, TX 78216
Phone: 210-340-5000
Fax: 210-524-9539

CEO: R. Tom Roddy
CFO: Shirley R. Yoakum
HR: Ellen Marriott
Employees: 301

1994 Sales: $37.2 million
1-Yr. Sales Change: -1.8%
Exchange: Nasdaq
Symbol: BFCX

Banks - Southwest (Groos Bank, Kelly Field National Bank)

BETTIS CORPORATION

18703 GH Circle, PO Box 508
Waller, TX 77484
Phone: 713-463-5100
Fax: 713-463-5189

CEO: W. Todd Bratton
CFO: Wilfred M. Krenek
HR: Gloria Hammons
Employees: 414

1994 Sales: $52 million
1-Yr. Sales Change: -1.3%
Exchange: Nasdaq
Symbol: BETT

Instruments - valve actuators & controls for quarter-turn or linear valves

BJ SERVICES COMPANY

5500 NW Central Dr., PO Box 4442
Houston, TX 77210-4442
Phone: 713-462-4239
Fax: 713-895-5851

CEO: J. W. Stewart
CFO: Michael McShane
HR: Stephen A. Wright
Employees: 2,780

1994 Sales: $434.5 million
1-Yr. Sales Change: 10.2%
Exchange: NYSE
Symbol: BJS

Oil & gas - pressure pumping services

BLOCK DISTRIBUTING COMPANY INC.

827 Coliseum Rd.
San Antonio, TX 78219
Phone: 210-224-7531
Fax: 210-227-7810

CEO: E. L. Block
CFO: Raleigh Lair
HR: —
Employees: 350

1994 Sales: $127 million
1-Yr. Sales Change: 7.6%
Ownership: Privately Held

Wholesale distribution - liquor, wine & wine coolers

BLUE BELL CREAMERIES L.P.

Loop 577
Brenham, TX 77833
Phone: 409-836-7977
Fax: 409-830-2198

CEO: Howard Kruse
CFO: William J. Rankin
HR: Darrell Winkelmann
Employees: 1,600

1994 Est. Sales: $200 mil.
1-Yr. Sales Change: —
Ownership: Privately Held

Food - dairy products & ice cream production (Blue Bell)

BLUE CROSS AND BLUE SHIELD OF TEXAS INC.

901 S. Central Expwy.
Richardson, TX 75080
Phone: 214-766-6900
Fax: 214-766-6234

CEO: Rogers K. Coleman
CFO: Vernon Walker
HR: Mike Jarvis
Employees: 4,500

1994 Sales: $1,504.9 million
1-Yr. Sales Change: 0.8%
Ownership: Privately Held

Insurance - health, hospital & medical service plans

BLUE DOLPHIN ENERGY COMPANY

11 Greenway Plaza, Ste. 1606
Houston, TX 77046
Phone: 713-621-3993
Fax: 713-621-4687

CEO: Michael J. Jacobson
CFO: Brian Lloyd
HR: —
Employees: 14

1994 Sales: $6.8 million
1-Yr. Sales Change: 23.6%
Exchange: Nasdaq (SC)
Symbol: BDCO

Oil & gas - exploration & production

BMC SOFTWARE, INC.

2101 CityWest Blvd.
Houston, TX 77042-2827
Phone: 713-918-8800
Fax: 713-918-1307

CEO: Max P. Watson Jr.
CFO: Steve B. Solcher
HR: Johnnie Horn
Employees: 1,185

1995 Sales: $345 million
1-Yr. Sales Change: 19.6%
Exchange: Nasdaq
Symbol: BMCS

Computers - mainframe database software

 See page 168 for a full profile of this company.

BOLLINGER INDUSTRIES INC.

222 W. Airport Fwy.
Irving, TX 75062
Phone: 214-445-0386
Fax: 214-438-8471

CEO: Glenn D. Bollinger
CFO: Stephen Richman
HR: Janice Holden
Employees: 440

1994 Sales: $45.2 million
1-Yr. Sales Change: 37.8%
Exchange: Pink Sheets
Symbol: BOLLE

Leisure & recreational products - weightlifting & fitness equipment (#1 in US: UltraArm UnderArm Firmer, Bunfirmer, Super-Tummy Trimmer)

THE BOMBAY COMPANY, INC.

550 Bailey Ave., Ste. 700
Fort Worth, TX 76107
Phone: 817-347-8200
Fax: 817-332-7066

CEO: Robert E. M. Nourse
CFO: James E. Herlihy
HR: William S. Goodlatte
Employees: 4,000

1995 Sales: $241.5 million
1-Yr. Sales Change: -23.9%
Exchange: NYSE
Symbol: BBA

Retail - traditionally styled furniture, prints & accessories

 See page 169 for a full profile of this company.

BOUNTY GROUP, INC.

2500 Tanglewilde, Ste. 250	CEO: Oivind Risberg	1994 Sales: $0.7 million
Houston, TX 77063	CFO: Dianne L. Metcalf	1-Yr. Sales Change: -41.7%
Phone: 713-975-1900	HR: —	Exchange: OTC
Fax: 713-975-0221	Employees: 3	Symbol: BNTY

Oil & gas - US exploration & development

BOX ENERGY CORPORATION

8201 Preston Rd., Ste. 600	CEO: Thomas D. Box	1994 Sales: $59.2 million
Dallas, TX 75225-6211	CFO: Jill M. Killam	1-Yr. Sales Change: 59.6%
Phone: 214-890-8000	HR: —	Exchange: Nasdaq
Fax: 214-890-8025	Employees: 54	Symbol: BOXXB

Oil & gas - US exploration & production in Louisiana, Texas & New Mexico

BRACEWELL AND PATTERSON L.L.P.

2900 S. Tower	CEO: Kelly Frels	1994 Est. Sales: $100 mil.
Houston, TX 77002	CFO: Mary Ann Jay	1-Yr. Sales Change: —
Phone: 713-223-2900	HR: Helen Lilienstren	Ownership: Privately Held
Fax: 703-221-1212	Employees: 500	

Law firm

BRAZOS ELECTRIC POWER COOPERATIVE INC.

2404 La Salle	CEO: Richard E. McCaskill	1994 Sales: $217 million
Waco, TX 76706	CFO: Clarence Carpenter	1-Yr. Sales Change: -1.4%
Phone: 817-750-6500	HR: Tom Yows	Ownership: Privately Held
Fax: 817-750-6290	Employees: 300	

Utility - electric power cooperative

BRENHAM WHOLESALE GROCERY CO.

602 W. First St.	CEO: Luther Utesch	1994 Est. Sales: $125 mil.
Brenham, TX 77833	CFO: Don Huebner	1-Yr. Sales Change: —
Phone: 409-836-7925	HR: Russell Engeling	Ownership: Privately Held
Fax: 409-836-6178	Employees: 210	

Food - wholesale groceries

BRINKER INTERNATIONAL, INC.

6820 LBJ Fwy.	CEO: Ronald A. McDougall	1995 Sales: $1,042.2 million
Dallas, TX 75240	CFO: Debra Smithart-Weitzman	1-Yr. Sales Change: 18.6%
Phone: 214-980-9917	HR: John Roberts	Exchange: NYSE
Fax: 214-770-9593	Employees: 38,000	Symbol: EAT

Retail - restaurants (Chili's, Grady's, Romano's Macaroni Grill, Spageddies, Cozymel's, On the Border)

 See page 170 for a full profile of this company.

BRISTOL HOTEL COMPANY

14285 Midway Rd., Ste. 340	CEO: J. Peter Kline	1994 Est. Sales: $75 million
Dallas, TX 75244	CFO: John Bailey	1-Yr. Sales Change: —
Phone: 214-788-0001	HR: Olivia Mongaras	Ownership: Privately Held
Fax: 214-687-0350	Employees: 4,000	

Hotels - over 10,000 rooms in Texas, Georgia, Mississippi, Arizona, California & Colorado (Harvey Hotels, Bristol Suites, Harvey Suites; franchisee of Holiday Inns, Hampton Inns, Ramada Inns & Howard Johnsons)

BROOKSHIRE BROTHERS INCORPORATED

1201 Ellen Trout Dr.	CEO: R. H. Brookshire	1994 Est. Sales: $650 mil.
Lufkin, TX 75901	CFO: Gene H. Nerren	1-Yr. Sales Change: —
Phone: 409-634-8155	HR: Tim Hale	Ownership: Privately Held
Fax: 409-634-8646	Employees: 5,000	

Retail - supermarkets (Budget Chopper, Brookshire Brothers Inc.)

BROOKSHIRE GROCERY COMPANY

1600 SW Loop 323	CEO: James G. Hardin	1994 Est. Sales: $811 mil.
Tyler, TX 75701	CFO: Marvin Massey	1-Yr. Sales Change: 15.9%
Phone: 903-534-3000	HR: Tim Brookshire	Ownership: Privately Held
Fax: 903-534-3352	Employees: 8,000	

Retail - supermarkets (Brookshire Grocery Co., Super 1 Food Stores)

THE BROWN FOUNDATION, INC.

2217 Welch Ave., PO Box 130646	CEO: Louisa S. Sarofim	1994 Sales: $24 million
Houston, TX 77219-0646	CFO: Katherine B. Dobelman	1-Yr. Sales Change: -13.7%
Phone: 713-523-6867	HR: Katherine B. Dobelman	Ownership: Privately Held
Fax: 713-523-2917	Employees: 6	

Charitable foundation providing educational & arts & humanities grants, primarily within the city of Houston

BROWNING-FERRIS INDUSTRIES, INC.

757 N. Eldridge, PO Box 3151	CEO: Bruce E. Ranck	1994 Sales: $4,314.5 million
Houston, TX 77253	CFO: Jeffrey E. Curtiss	1-Yr. Sales Change: 23.4%
Phone: 713-870-8100	HR: Susan J. Piller	Exchange: NYSE
Fax: 713-870-7844	Employees: 37,000	Symbol: BFI

Pollution control equipment & services - waste disposal

 See pages 64–65 for a full profile of this company.

BUFFTON CORPORATION

226 Bailey Ave., Ste. 101	CEO: Robert H. McLean	1994 Sales: $42.5 million
Fort Worth, TX 76107	CFO: Robert Korman	1-Yr. Sales Change: -7.0%
Phone: 817-332-4761	HR: —	Exchange: AMEX
Fax: 817-877-0420	Employees: 320	Symbol: BFX

Computers - electronic filter/surge suppression products, power supply/power conversion products & power distribution systems (Current Technology); PVC fittings; restaurants

BURLINGTON NORTHERN SANTA FE CORPORATION

3800 Continental Plaza, 777 Main St.	CEO: Gerald Grinstein	1994 Sales: $4,995 million
Fort Worth, TX 76102-5384	CFO: Denis E. Springer	1-Yr. Sales Change: 6.3%
Phone: 817-333-2000	HR: James B. Dagnon	Exchange: NYSE
Fax: 817-878-2377	Employees: 30,711	Symbol: BNI

Transportation - rail

 See pages 66–67 for a full profile of this company.

BURLINGTON RESOURCES COAL SEAM GAS ROYALTY TRUST

901 Main St., Ste. 1200	CEO: Ron E. Hooper	1994 Sales: $17.2 million
Dallas, TX 75283-0650	CFO: Ron E. Hooper	1-Yr. Sales Change: 149.3%
Phone: 214-508-2304	HR: —	Exchange: NYSE
Fax: 214-508-2431	Employees: 1,846	Symbol: BRU

Oil & gas - US royalty trust

BURLINGTON RESOURCES INC.

5051 Westheimer, Ste. 1400	CEO: Thomas H. O'Leary	1994 Sales: $1,054.8 million
Houston, TX 77056	CFO: John E. Hagale	1-Yr. Sales Change: 1.1%
Phone: 713-624-9500	HR: Harold E. Haunschild	Exchange: NYSE
Fax: 713-624-9635	Employees: 1,850	Symbol: BR

Oil & gas - US exploration & production

BUSINESS RECORDS CORPORATION HOLDING COMPANY

1111 W. Mockingbird, Ste. 1400	CEO: Perry E. Esping	1994 Sales: $144.2 million
Dallas, TX 75247	CFO: Thomas E. Kiraly	1-Yr. Sales Change: 38.4%
Phone: 214-905-2590	HR: Laura Stelter	Exchange: Nasdaq
Fax: 214-905-2303	Employees: 1,275	Symbol: BRCP

Information management, data processing products & services to local governments & health care institutions

THE C.D. HARTNETT COMPANY

300 N. Main St.	CEO: Charles C. Milliken	1994 Sales: $130 million
Weatherford, TX 76086	CFO: Steve Milliken	1-Yr. Sales Change: 19.3%
Phone: 817-594-3813	HR: Diann Destiguer	Ownership: Privately Held
Fax: 817-594-9714	Employees: 250	

Food - wholesale groceries

CABLEMAXX, INC.

8650 Austin Center Blvd., Ste. 320	CEO: Tommy L. Gleason Jr.	1995 Sales: $13.5 million
Austin, TX 78731	CFO: Ralph G. Kelly	1-Yr. Sales Change: 75.3%
Phone: 512-345-1001	HR: Donna Boyer	Exchange: Nasdaq
Fax: 512-345-2557	Employees: 189	Symbol: CMAX

Cable TV - wireless cable TV via microwave technology in central Texas

CABOT OIL & GAS CORPORATION

15375 Memorial Dr.	CEO: Charles P. Siess Jr.	1994 Sales: $237.1 million
Houston, TX 77079	CFO: Ray R. Seegmiller	1-Yr. Sales Change: 44.3%
Phone: 713-589-4600	HR: Abraham Garza	Exchange: NYSE
Fax: 713-589-4653	Employees: 495	Symbol: COG

Oil & gas - US exploration & production

CACTUS FEEDERS INC.

2209 W. 7th St.	CEO: Paul F. Engler	1994 Sales: $285 million
Amarillo, TX 79106	CFO: Terry K. Manz	1-Yr. Sales Change: -12.3%
Phone: 806-373-2333	HR: Kevin Hazelwood	Ownership: Privately Held
Fax: 806-371-4767	Employees: 355	

Agricultural operations - cattle feedlots & ranching

CAIRN ENERGY USA, INC.

8235 Douglas Ave., Ste. 1221
Dallas, TX 75225
Phone: 214-369-0316
Fax: 214-369-2864

CEO: Michael R. Gilbert
CFO: J. Munro M. Sutherland
HR: Debra Hibbs
Employees: 14

1994 Sales: $9.7 million
1-Yr. Sales Change: -28.1%
Exchange: Nasdaq
Symbol: CEUS

Oil & gas - US exploration & production

CALLOWAY'S NURSERY, INC.

4800 Blue Mound Rd.
Fort Worth, TX 76106
Phone: 817-624-8222
Fax: 817-498-4504

CEO: James C. Estill
CFO: Dan Reynolds
HR: Jack Phenix
Employees: 147

1994 Sales: $30.6 million
1-Yr. Sales Change: 8.5%
Exchange: Nasdaq
Symbol: CLWY

Retail - garden centers offering bedding plants, nursery stock & interior house plants

CALTEX PETROLEUM CORPORATION

125 E. John Carpenter Fwy.
Irving, TX 75602
Phone: 214-830-1000
Fax: 214-830-1156

CEO: David Law-Smith
CFO: Malcolm J. McAuley
HR: E. M. Schmidt
Employees: 8,000

1994 Sales: $14,751 million
1-Yr. Sales Change: -4.3%
Ownership: Subsidiary

Oil & gas - refining & marketing

See pages 68–69 for a full profile of this company.

CAMCO INTERNATIONAL INC.

7030 Ardmore, PO Box 14484
Houston, TX 77221
Phone: 713-747-4000
Fax: 713-747-6751

CEO: Gary D. Nicholson
CFO: Herbert S. Yates
HR: Thomas W. Everitt
Employees: 4,264

1994 Sales: $590.1 million
1-Yr. Sales Change: 0.6%
Exchange: NYSE
Symbol: CAM

Oil & gas - oilfield equipment, tubing & nitrogen services, wireline services & well maintenance

CAMDEN PROPERTY TRUST

3200 Southwest Fwy., Ste. 1500
Houston, TX 77027
Phone: 713-964-3555
Fax: 713-964-3599

CEO: Richard J. Campo
CFO: G. Steven Dawson
HR: John Shaften
Employees: 564

1994 Sales: $75.4 million
1-Yr. Sales Change: 34.4%
Exchange: NYSE
Symbol: CPT

Real estate investment trust - multifamily residential properties

CAMELOT CORP.

17770 Preston Rd.	CEO: Dan Wettreich	1995 Sales: $1.2 million
Dallas, TX 75252	CFO: —	1-Yr. Sales Change: -53.8%
Phone: 214-733-3005	HR: —	Exchange: Nasdaq (SC)
Fax: 214-733-4308	Employees: 38	Symbol: CAML

Computers - CD-ROM distribution (Maxmedia Distributing); retail sales (Mr. CD-ROM); Internet telephone software (Digiphone)

CAMERON ASHLEY INC.

11100 Plano Rd.	CEO: Ronald R. Ross	1994 Sales: $296.3 million
Dallas, TX 75238	CFO: Dixon McElwee	1-Yr. Sales Change: 32.3%
Phone: 214-340-1996	HR: Thomas R. Miller	Exchange: Nasdaq
Fax: 214-342-6177	Employees: 1,151	Symbol: CMSH

Building products - distribution

 See page 171 for a full profile of this company.

CANMAX INC.

150 W. Carpenter Fwy.	CEO: Roger D. Bryant	1994 Sales: $9.7 million
Irving, TX 75039	CFO: Philip M. Parsons	1-Yr. Sales Change: 106.4%
Phone: 214-541-1600	HR: Linda Leckey	Exchange: Nasdaq (SC)
Fax: 214-541-1155	Employees: 135	Symbol: CNMX

Computers - software systems, hardware & licensing of third-party software to convenience store & gas station operators for accounting & inventory

CAP ROCK ELECTRIC COOPERATIVE

Hwy. 80 West	CEO: David W. Pruitt	1994 Est. Sales: $35 mil.
Stanton, TX 79782	CFO: John Parker	1-Yr. Sales Change: —
Phone: 915-756-3381	HR: Jimmy Chandler	Ownership: Privately Held
Fax: 915-756-2866	Employees: 106	

Utility - electric power

CAPITAL SOUTHWEST CORPORATION

12900 Preston Rd., Ste. 700	CEO: William R. Thomas	1995 Sales: $5.1 million
Dallas, TX 75230	CFO: Tim Smith	1-Yr. Sales Change: -7.3%
Phone: 214-233-8242	HR: —	Exchange: Nasdaq
Fax: 214-233-7362	Employees: 8	Symbol: CSWC

Financial - venture capital investment firm

CAPSTEAD MORTGAGE CORPORATION

2711 N. Haskell	CEO: Ronn K. Lytle	1994 Sales: $604.1 million
Dallas, TX 75204	CFO: Andrew F. Jacobs	1-Yr. Sales Change: -5.7%
Phone: 214-874-2323	HR: Donna D. Howard	Exchange: NYSE
Fax: 214-874-2398	Employees: 183	Symbol: CMO

Real estate investment trust - single-family residential properties

CARRINGTON LABORATORIES, INC.

2001 Walnut Hill Ln.	CEO: Carlton Turner	1994 Sales: $25.4 million
Irving, TX 75038	CFO: Christopher S. Record	1-Yr. Sales Change: 19.8%
Phone: 214-518-1300	HR: Carol Kitchell	Exchange: Nasdaq
Fax: 214-518-1020	Employees: 297	Symbol: CARN

Biomedical & genetic product research involving carbohydrate-based therapeutic treatment of major illnesses & wounds

CASH AMERICA INTERNATIONAL, INC.

1600 W. 7th St.	CEO: Jack R. Daugherty	1994 Sales: $262.1 million
Fort Worth, TX 76102-2599	CFO: Thomas A. Bessant Jr.	1-Yr. Sales Change: 16.6%
Phone: 817-335-1100	HR: Robert Brockman	Exchange: NYSE
Fax: 817-335-1119	Employees: 2,475	Symbol: PWN

Financial - pawn shops

 See page 172 for a full profile of this company.

CELEBRITY, INC.

4520 Old Troup Rd., PO Box 6666	CEO: Robert H. Patterson Jr.	1995 Sales: $118.8 million
Tyler, TX 75711	CFO: James R. Thompson	1-Yr. Sales Change: 30.7%
Phone: 903-561-3981	HR: Roger Craft	Exchange: Nasdaq
Fax: 903-581-2887	Employees: 489	Symbol: FLWR

Wholesale distributor - artificial flowers, bushes & foliage for craft stores & wholesale florists

CELLSTAR CORPORATION

1730 Briercroft Dr.	CEO: Alan H. Goldfield	1994 Sales: $518.4 million
Carrollton, TX 75006-7426	CFO: Kenneth W. Sanders	1-Yr. Sales Change: 88.2%
Phone: 214-323-0600	HR: Barbara O'Neal	Exchange: Nasdaq
Fax: 214-994-1516	Employees: 1,250	Symbol: CLST

Retail - cellular telephones & auto security systems

 See page 173 for a full profile of this company.

CENTEX CONSTRUCTION PRODUCTS, INC.

3710 Rawlins, PO Box 19000	CEO: O. G. Dagnan	1995 Sales: $194.3 million
Dallas, TX 75219	CFO: Arthur R. Zunker Jr.	1-Yr. Sales Change: 16.5%
Phone: 214-559-6500	HR: —	Exchange: NYSE
Fax: 214-523-2812	Employees: 990	Symbol: CXP

Building products - cement, aggregates, readymix concrete & gypsum wallboard (spinoff of Centex Corporation)

CENTEX CORPORATION

3333 Lee Pkwy., PO Box 19000	CEO: Laurence E. Hirsch	1995 Sales: $3,277.5 million
Dallas, TX 75219	CFO: David W. Quinn	1-Yr. Sales Change: 2.0%
Phone: 214-559-6500	HR: Mike Albright	Exchange: NYSE
Fax: 214-559-6750	Employees: 6,395	Symbol: CTX

Building - residential & commercial

 See pages 70–71 for a full profile of this company.

CENTRAL AND SOUTH WEST CORPORATION

1616 Woodall Rodgers Fwy.	CEO: E.R. Brooks	1994 Sales: $3,623 million
Dallas, TX 75266	CFO: Glenn D. Rosilier	1-Yr. Sales Change: -1.7%
Phone: 214-777-1000	HR: Venita McCellon-Allen	Exchange: NYSE
Fax: 214-777-1033	Employees: 8,055	Symbol: CSR

Utility - electric power

 See pages 72–73 for a full profile of this company.

CHAMPION HEALTH CARE CORPORATION

14340 Torrey Chase, Ste. 320	CEO: Charles R. Miller	1994 Sales: $154.1 million
Houston, TX 77014	CFO: James G. VanDevender	1-Yr. Sales Change: 0.7%
Phone: 713-583-5491	HR: Randy Stone	Exchange: AMEX
Fax: 713-583-5495	Employees: 1,500	Symbol: CHC

Hospitals - full-service medical care including mental health & rehabilitation programs, skilled nursing units, subacute care, chronic pain & cardiac services

CHAPARRAL STEEL COMPANY

300 Ward Rd.	CEO: Gordon E. Forward	1995 Sales: $531.8 million
Midlothian, TX 76065	CFO: Richard M. Fowler	1-Yr. Sales Change: 15.0%
Phone: 214-775-8241	HR: Dennis Beach	Exchange: NYSE
Fax: 214-775-1930	Employees: 943	Symbol: CSM

Steel - structural steel bars made from recycled scrap steel

CHARLIE THOMAS AUTO WORLD

PO Box 266407
Houston, TX 77207
Phone: 713-944-8181
Fax: 713-948-5703

Retail - new & used cars

CEO: Charles F. Thomas
CFO: Jeff Heath
HR: Laura Trudeau
Employees: 1,250

1994 Sales: $510 million
1-Yr. Sales Change: -0.6%
Ownership: Privately Held

CHARTER BANCSHARES, INC.

2600 Citadel Plaza Dr., PO Box 4525
Houston, TX 77210-4525
Phone: 713-692-6121
Fax: 713-691-7566

Banks - Southwest (Charter National Bank-Houston, Charter National Bank-Colonial, University National Bank-Galveston)

CEO: Jerry E. Finger
CFO: William S. Shropshire Jr.
HR: Jeri Sonnier
Employees: 517

1994 Sales: $58.2 million
1-Yr. Sales Change: 21.5%
Exchange: Nasdaq (SC)
Symbol: SAIL

CHEMICAL LIME COMPANY

PO Box 121874
Fort Worth, TX 76121
Phone: 817-732-8164
Fax: 817-732-3048

Chemicals - lime & lime products

CEO: Tom Chambers
CFO: Joe Payne
HR: Tom Stokes
Employees: 826

1994 Sales: $168 million
1-Yr. Sales Change: 2.4%
Ownership: Privately Held

CHIEF AUTO PARTS INCORPORATED

15303 Dallas Pkwy.
Dallas, TX 75248
Phone: 214-404-1114
Fax: 214-991-9259

Auto parts - retail

CEO: David H. Eisenberg
CFO: Tom Hough
HR: Lynn Ashly
Employees: 5,500

1994 Sales: $400 million
1-Yr. Sales Change: 3.9%
Ownership: Privately Held

CINEMARK USA INC.

7502 Greenville Ave., Ste. 800
Dallas, TX 75231
Phone: 214-696-1644
Fax: 214-696-3946

Motion pictures - movie theaters

CEO: Lee Roy Mitchell
CFO: Jeff Stedman
HR: —
Employees: 5,500

1994 Sales: $283.1 million
1-Yr. Sales Change: 18.0%
Ownership: Privately Held

CITIZENS, INC.

400 E. Anderson Ln., PO Box 149151	CEO: Randall H. Riley	1994 Sales: $49.2 million
Austin, TX 78714-9151	CFO: Mark A. Oliver	1-Yr. Sales Change: 15.2%
Phone: 512-837-7100	HR: Rosanne Canada	Exchange: AMEX
Fax: 512-836-9334	Employees: 71	Symbol: CIA
Insurance - life		

CJC HOLDINGS INC.

7211 Circle S Rd., PO Box 149056	CEO: J.T. Waugh	1994 Est. Sales: $110 mil.
Austin, TX 78714	CFO: Jeff Brennan	1-Yr. Sales Change: —
Phone: 512-444-0571	HR: Suzie Adams	Ownership: Privately Held
Fax: 512-444-7618	Employees: 1,200	
Precious metals & jewelry - manufacturing		

CLAYTON WILLIAMS ENERGY, INC.

6 Desta Dr., Ste. 3000	CEO: Clayton W. Williams Jr.	1994 Sales: $49.5 million
Midland, TX 79705-5510	CFO: Mel G. Riggs	1-Yr. Sales Change: -16.9%
Phone: 915-682-6324	HR: Valerie Coss	Exchange: Nasdaq
Fax: 915-682-1452	Employees: 121	Symbol: CWEI
Oil & gas - US exploration & production		

CLEAR CHANNEL COMMUNICATIONS, INC.

200 Concord Plaza, Ste. 600	CEO: L. Lowry Mays	1994 Sales: $173.1 million
San Antonio, TX 78216	CFO: Herbert W. Hill Jr.	1-Yr. Sales Change: 27.6%
Phone: 210-822-2828	HR: Herbert W. Hill Jr.	Exchange: NYSE
Fax: 210-822-2299	Employees: 1,549	Symbol: CCU
Broadcasting - radio & TV		

 See page 174 for a full profile of this company.

CLIFFS DRILLING COMPANY

1200 Smith St., Ste. 300	CEO: Douglas E. Swanson	1994 Sales: $83.7 million
Houston, TX 77002	CFO: Edward A. Guthrie	1-Yr. Sales Change: 27.8%
Phone: 713-651-9426	HR: Ed O. Davis	Exchange: Nasdaq
Fax: 713-951-0649	Employees: 477	Symbol: CLDR
Oil & gas - offshore drilling		

CLUB CORPORATION INTERNATIONAL

3030 LBJ Fwy., Ste 700
Dallas, TX 75234
Phone: 214-888-7308
Fax: 214-432-0264

CEO: Robert H. Dedman
CFO: R. Michael Carroll
HR: Albert Shew
Employees: 19,200

1994 Sales: $773 million
1-Yr. Sales Change: -35.6%
Ownership: Privately Held

Leisure & recreational services - private club & golf course operations (#1 worldwide) & resorts; bank (Franklin Federal)

CLUCKCORP INTERNATIONAL

1250 N.E. Loop 410, Ste. 335
San Antonio, TX 78209
Phone: 210-824-2496
Fax: 210-824-6725

CEO: D. W. Gibbs
CFO: Sam B. S. Rosser
HR: —
Employees: 16

1994 Sales: $0.2 million
1-Yr. Sales Change: —
Ownership: Privately Held

Retail - rotisserie chicken restaurants (franchisee of Clucker's Wood Roasted Chicken, Harvest Rotisserie; IPO in registration)

CO ENERGY, INC.

4600 Post Oak Place, Ste. 309
Houston, TX 77027
Phone: 713-623-0801
Fax: 713-623-0982

CEO: W. Russell Scheirman
CFO: W. Russell Scheirman
HR: Gayla Cutrer
Employees: 75

1994 Sales: $9.5 million
1-Yr. Sales Change: -44.1%
Exchange: Nasdaq (SC)
Symbol: VEIX

Oil & gas - international specialty with exploration & production in the Philippines, India, Belize & domestically in Goliad, TX

COASTAL BANCORP, INC.

8 Greenway Plaza, Ste. 1500
Houston, TX 77046
Phone: 713-623-2600
Fax: 713-960-9864

CEO: Manuel J. Mehos
CFO: Catherine N. Wylie
HR: Teri Graves
Employees: 298

1994 Sales: $137.6 million
1-Yr. Sales Change: 42.6%
Exchange: Nasdaq
Symbol: CBSA

Financial - savings & loans (Coastal Banc)

THE COASTAL CORPORATION

Coastal Tower, 9 Greenway Plaza
Houston, TX 77046-0995
Phone: 713-877-1400
Fax: 713-877-6754

CEO: David A. Arledge
CFO: Donald H. Gullquist
HR: E. C. Simpson
Employees: 16,300

1994 Sales: $10,215.3 million
1-Yr. Sales Change: 0.8%
Exchange: NYSE
Symbol: CGP

Oil & gas - production & pipeline

See pages 74–75 for a full profile of this company.

COASTWIDE ENERGY SERVICES, INC.

11111 Wilcrest Green Dr., Ste 300	CEO: Stephen A. Wells	1994 Sales: $41.2 million
Houston, TX 77042	CFO: P. Blake Dupuis	1-Yr. Sales Change: 19.8%
Phone: 713-917-4100	HR: Linda Hertenberger	Exchange: Nasdaq (SC)
Fax: 713-917-4112	Employees: 200	Symbol: CNRG

Oil & gas - shore bases & distribution center serving offshore oil exploration in the Gulf of Mexico

COCA-COLA BOTTLING GROUP-SOUTHWEST

1999 Bryan, Ste. 300	CEO: Robert Hoffman	1994 Est. Sales: $470 mil.
Dallas, TX 75201	CFO: Chuck Stephenson	1-Yr. Sales Change: —
Phone: 214-969-1910	HR: —	Ownership: Privately Held
Fax: 214-969-5947	Employees: 1,000	

Beverages - soft drink bottling

CO-COUNSEL, INC.

3 Riverway, Ste. 1140	CEO: Joseph A. Turano	1994 Sales: $6.1 million
Houston, TX 77056	CFO: Joseph McDevitt	1-Yr. Sales Change: 64.9%
Phone: 713-961-5552	HR: Gerra Copenhaver	Exchange: Nasdaq (SC)
Fax: 713-961-9133	Employees: 40	Symbol: LEGL

Personnel - temporary attorneys & paralegals primarily in Houston, Dallas & Chicago

CODA ENERGY, INC.

5735 Pineland Dr., Ste. 300	CEO: Douglas H. Miller	1994 Sales: $71.6 million
Dallas, TX 75231	CFO: Grant W. Henderson	1-Yr. Sales Change: 78.6%
Phone: 214-692-1800	HR: Gary Scoggins	Exchange: Nasdaq
Fax: 214-692-7171	Employees: 150	Symbol: CODA

Oil & gas - US exploration & production

COHO ENERGY, INC.

14785 Preston Rd., Ste. 860	CEO: Jeffrey Clarke	1994 Sales: $34.4 million
Dallas, TX 75240	CFO: Eddie M. LeBlanc III	1-Yr. Sales Change: 21.6%
Phone: 214-991-9493	HR: Lyn Guillory	Exchange: Nasdaq
Fax: 214-991-8514	Employees: 169	Symbol: COHO

Oil & gas - exploration, develpment & production of crude oil & natural gas reserves

COLEMAN WOOD PRODUCTS, INC.

2800 Surveyor Blvd.
Carrollton, TX 75006
Phone: 214-418-0336
Fax: 214-416-8198

CEO: Russell D. Coleman
CFO: Russell D. Coleman
HR: —
Employees: 42

1994 Sales: $3.9 million
1-Yr. Sales Change: 39.3%
Exchange: OTC
Symbol: CWD

Building products - customized kitchen & bathroom cabinets & wood specialty fixtures including mantles, stair banisters, corner pieces & customized panels

COLOR TILE INC.

515 Houston St.
Fort Worth, TX 76102
Phone: 817-870-9400
Fax: 817-870-9589

CEO: Bart A. BrownJr.
CFO: Dan Gilmartin
HR: Dick Andrews
Employees: 3,900

1994 Sales: $675 million
1-Yr. Sales Change: —
Ownership: Privately Held

Retail - tile & floor covering products

COLUMBUS REALTY TRUST

15851 Dallas Pkwy., Ste. 855
Dallas, TX 75248
Phone: 214-387-1492
Fax: 214-770-5109

CEO: Robert L. Shaw
CFO: Richard R. Reupke
HR: Holly McNeely
Employees: 180

1994 Sales: $30.8 million
1-Yr. Sales Change: 161.0%
Exchange: NYSE
Symbol: CLB

Real estate investment trust - multifamily residential development

COMMERCIAL METALS COMPANY

7800 Stemmons Fwy.
Dallas, TX 75247
Phone: 214-689-4300
Fax: 214-689-4320

CEO: Stanley A. Rabin
CFO: Lawrence A. Engels
HR: Bert Romberg
Employees: 4,314

1994 Sales: $1,666.2 million
1-Yr. Sales Change: 6.2%
Exchange: NYSE
Symbol: CMC

Metal processing & fabrication

COMPAQ COMPUTER CORPORATION

20555 SH 249
Houston, TX 77070
Phone: 713-370-0670
Fax: 713-374-1740

CEO: Eckhard Pfeiffer
CFO: Daryl J. White
HR: Hans W. Gutsch
Employees: 14,372

1994 Sales: $10,866 million
1-Yr. Sales Change: 51.1%
Exchange: NYSE
Symbol: CPQ

Computers - PCs (#1 worldwide); peripherals & software (TabWorks)

 See pages 76–77 for a full profile of this company.

COMPROTEK SERVICES, INC.

10435 Burnet Rd., Ste. 114	CEO: Dene Jacobson	1994 Est. Sales: $8 mil.
Austin, TX 78758	CFO: David Gillett	1-Yr. Sales Change: —
Phone: 512-832-9151	HR: Marie Keys	Ownership: Privately Held
Fax: 512-832-9321	Employees: 100	

Computers - dot-matrix print-head refurbishing, monitor & laser fuser repair & parts sales

COMPUADD COMPUTER CORPORATION

12317 Technology Blvd.	CEO: Rick W. Krause	1994 Sales: $120 million
Austin, TX 78727	CFO: Walter Kluchki	1-Yr. Sales Change: -48.5%
Phone: 512-250-1489	HR: Jeanne Nelson	Ownership: Privately Held
Fax: 512-331-2776	Employees: 250	

Computers - microcomputers & equipment

See page 175 for a full profile of this company.

COMPUCOM SYSTEMS, INC.

10100 N. Central Expwy.	CEO: Edward R. Anderson	1994 Sales: $1,255.8 million
Dallas, TX 75231-1800	CFO: Robert J. Boutin	1-Yr. Sales Change: 23.7%
Phone: 214-265-3600	HR: Mark S. Esselman	Exchange: Nasdaq
Fax: 214-265-5220	Employees: 1,800	Symbol: CMPC

Computers - PC reseller to large corporate customers; LAN & WAN installation & other services

 See pages 78–79 for a full profile of this company.

COMPUSA INC.

14951 N. Dallas Pkwy.	CEO: James F. Halpin	1995 Sales: $2,813.1 million
Dallas, TX 75240	CFO: James Skinner	1-Yr. Sales Change: 31.1%
Phone: 214-383-4000	HR: Mel McCall	Exchange: NYSE
Fax: 214-383-4276	Employees: 7,819	Symbol: CPU

Computers - superstore chain (#1 US computer retailer)

 See pages 80–81 for a full profile of this company.

COMPUTER LANGUAGE RESEARCH, INC.

2395 Midway Rd.	CEO: Stephen T. Winn	1994 Sales: $108.5 million
Carrollton, TX 75006	CFO: M. Brian Healy	1-Yr. Sales Change: -0.5%
Phone: 214-250-7000	HR: J.D. Hatch	Exchange: Nasdaq
Fax: 214-250-8181	Employees: 937	Symbol: CLRI

Business services - tax processing services & software to businesses (Fast-Tax)

COMPUTRAC, INC.

222 Municipal Dr.
Richardson, TX 75080-3583
Phone: 214-234-4241
Fax: 214-234-6280

CEO: Harry W. Margolis
CFO: Cheri L. White
HR: Lynda K. Thomas
Employees: 58

1995 Sales: $6.8 million
1-Yr. Sales Change: -29.9%
Exchange: AMEX
Symbol: LLB

Computers - software for law offices

COMSTOCK RESOURCES, INC.

5005 LBJ Fwy., Ste. 1000
Dallas, TX 75244
Phone: 214-701-2000
Fax: 214-701-2111

CEO: M. Jay Allison
CFO: Roland O. Burns
HR: —
Employees: 33

1994 Sales: $32.7 million
1-Yr. Sales Change: 45.3%
Exchange: Nasdaq
Symbol: CMRE

Oil & gas - US exploration & production

CONSOLIDATED GRAPHICS, INC.

2210 W. Dallas St.
Houston, TX 77019
Phone: 713-529-4200
Fax: 713-525-4305

CEO: Joe R. Davis
CFO: Mary K. Collins
HR: Janet Swikard
Employees: 702

1995 Sales: $57.2 million
1-Yr. Sales Change: 17.7%
Exchange: Nasdaq
Symbol: COGI

Printing - general commercial services specializing in promotional, marketing & investor materials for corporate clients

 See page 176 for a full profile of this company.

THE CONTAINER STORE

13405 N. Stemmons Fwy.
Dallas, TX 75234
Phone: 214-247-3768
Fax: 214-243-4161

CEO: Garrett Boone
CFO: Keath Hance
HR: Nancy Donley
Employees: 700

1994 Sales: $75 million
1-Yr. Sales Change: —
Ownership: Privately Held

Retail - household storage & organizational products stores

CONTINENTAL AIRLINES, INC.

2929 Allen Pkwy., Ste. 2010
Houston, TX 77019-2156
Phone: 713-834-5000
Fax: 713-834-2087

CEO: Gordon M. Bethune
CFO: Lawrence W. Kellner
HR: David A. Loeser
Employees: 37,800

1994 Sales: $5,670.1 million
1-Yr. Sales Change: -1.8%
Exchange: NYSE
Symbol: CAIB

Transportation - airline

See pages 82–83 for a full profile of this company.

CONTINENTAL MORTGAGE AND EQUITY TRUST

10670 N. Central Expwy., Ste. 300
Dallas, TX 75231
Phone: 214-692-4800
Fax: 214-373-0740

CEO: Randall M. Paulson
CFO: Thomas A. Holland
HR: Lyn Kruger
Employees: —

1994 Sales: $29.3 million
1-Yr. Sales Change: 23.6%
Exchange: Nasdaq
Symbol: CMETS

Real estate investment trust - development & construction mortgage loans

THE CONTINUUM COMPANY, INC.

9500 Arboretum Blvd.
Austin, TX 78759-6399
Phone: 512-345-5700
Fax: 512-338-7041

CEO: W. Michael Long
CFO: John L. Westermann III
HR: Deborah Stafford
Employees: 3,000

1995 Sales: $323.5 million
1-Yr. Sales Change: 33.2%
Exchange: NYSE
Symbol: CNU

Computers - insurance industry software & data processing services

 See page 177 for a full profile of this company.

CONTRAN CORPORATION

5430 LBJ Fwy., Ste. 1700
Dallas, TX 75240
Phone: 214-233-1700
Fax: 214-385-0586

CEO: Harold C. Simmons
CFO: William C. Timm
HR: Keith A. Johnson
Employees: 14,500

1994 Sales: $1,213 million
1-Yr. Sales Change: 5.8%
Ownership: Privately Held

Diversified operations - refined sugar (Valhi); food & restaurants (Arby's franchisee); chemicals; building products; steel rods, wire & wire products

CONVEST ENERGY CORPORATION

2401 Fountain View Dr., Ste. 700
Houston, TX 77057-4862
Phone: 713-780-1952
Fax: 713-780-8146

CEO: Richard T. Howell
CFO: Gary L. Pittman
HR: Penny Elkhapib
Employees: 35

1994 Sales: $16.9 million
1-Yr. Sales Change: -23.2%
Exchange: AMEX
Symbol: COV

Oil & gas - US exploration & production

CONVEX COMPUTER CORPORATION

3000 Waterview Pkwy.
Richardson, TX 75080
Phone: 214-497-4000
Fax: 214-497-4441

CEO: Robert J. Paluck
CFO: David W. Craig
HR: Larry Ercoline
Employees: 857

1994 Sales: $144.2 million
1-Yr. Sales Change: -25.3%
Exchange: NYSE
Symbol: CNX

Computers - network-oriented parallel processing server (Exemplar) & engineering & scientific software

COOPER CAMERON CORPORATION

515 Post Oak Blvd., Ste. 1200
Houston, TX 77027
Phone: 713-513-3300
Fax: 713-513-3355

CEO: Sheldon R. Erikson
CFO: Thomas R. Hix
HR: Jane Crowder
Employees: 8,000

1994 Sales: $1,110.1 million
1-Yr. Sales Change: -17.2%
Exchange: NYSE
Symbol: RON

Oil field machinery & equipment - valves, wellheads, gas turbines, compressors & turbochargers

COOPER INDUSTRIES, INC.

1001 Fannin St., Ste. 4000
Houston, TX 77002
Phone: 713-739-5400
Fax: 713-739-5555

CEO: H. John Riley Jr.
CFO: D. Bradley McWilliams
HR: Carl J. Plesnicher Jr.
Employees: 40,800

1994 Sales: $4,588 million
1-Yr. Sales Change: -26.9%
Exchange: NYSE
Symbol: CBE

Diversified operations - electrical products; electrical power equipment, tools & hardware; automotive products; petroleum & industrial equipment

 See pages 84-85 for a full profile of this company.

CORNERSTONE NATURAL GAS, INC.

8080 N. Central Expwy., Ste. 1200
Dallas, TX 75206
Phone: 214-691-5536
Fax: 214-739-8251

CEO: Ray C. Davis
CFO: Robert L. Cavnar
HR: Debra Braner
Employees: 88

1994 Sales: $106.4 million
1-Yr. Sales Change: -50.6%
Exchange: AMEX
Symbol: CGA

Oil & gas - production & pipeline

CORPUS CHRISTI BANCSHARES INC.

2402 Leopard St.
Corpus Christi, TX 78408
Phone: 512-887-3000
Fax: 512-887-5991

CEO: R. Jay Phillips
CFO: Jimmy M. Knioun
HR: Hilda Simpson
Employees: 131

1994 Sales: $13.1 million
1-Yr. Sales Change: 8.3%
Exchange: AMEX
Symbol: CTZ

Banks - Southwest (Citizens State Bank of Corpus Christi)

COUNTY SEAT STORES INC.

17950 Preston Rd., Ste. 1000
Dallas, TX 75252
Phone: 214-248-5100
Fax: 214-248-5214

CEO: Barry J. C. Parker
CFO: Barry J. C. Parker
HR: Tom Grissom
Employees: 7,600

1995 Sales: $588 million
1-Yr. Sales Change: 16.9%
Ownership: Privately Held

Retail - specialty apparel

CRAFTMADE INTERNATIONAL, INC.

2700 112th St.
Grand Prairie, TX 75050
Phone: 214-647-8099
Fax: 214-647-4871

CEO: James R. Ridings
CFO: Kenneth Cancienne
HR: Jamie Smith
Employees: 105

1995 Sales: $34.4 million
1-Yr. Sales Change: 7.2%
Exchange: Nasdaq
Symbol: CRFT

Housewares - ceiling fans & lights

CRESCENT REAL ESTATE EQUITIES, INC.

777 Main St., Ste. 2700
Fort Worth, TX 76102
Phone: 817-877-0477
Fax: 817-878-0460

CEO: John C. Goff
CFO: Dallas E. Lucas
HR: Sara L. Carillo
Employees: 180

1994 Sales: $71.5 million
1-Yr. Sales Change: 25.0%
Exchange: NYSE
Symbol: CEI

Real estate investment trust - office & retail properties in 8 metropolitan submarkets in 3 states (Mira Vista Development Corp., Houston Area Development Corp.)

CRINCO INVESTMENTS INC.

PO Box 26808
El Paso, TX 79926
Phone: 915-779-4711
Fax: 915-772-5485

CEO: James Cardwell Sr.
CFO: Rick Porzig
HR: Phil Burch
Employees: 3,000

1994 Est. Sales: $330 mil.
1-Yr. Sales Change: —
Ownership: Privately Held

Retail - truckstops & gas service stations

CROSS TIMBERS OIL COMPANY

810 Houston St., Ste. 2000
Fort Worth, TX 76102
Phone: 817-870-2800
Fax: 817-870-1671

CEO: Bob R. Simpson
CFO: Louis G. Baldwin
HR: Diana Owens
Employees: 225

1994 Sales: $96.3 million
1-Yr. Sales Change: 23.1%
Exchange: NYSE
Symbol: XTO

Oil & gas - US exploration & production

CROSS TIMBERS ROYALTY TRUST

500 W. 7th St., PO Box 1317
Fort Worth, TX 76101-1317
Phone: 817-390-6592
Fax: 817-870-1671

CEO: Joe B. Grissom
CFO: Louis G. Baldwin
HR: —
Employees: 156

1994 Sales: $6.9 million
1-Yr. Sales Change: -12.7%
Exchange: NYSE
Symbol: CRT

Oil & gas - US royalty trust

CROWN CASINO CORPORATION

2415 W. NW Hwy., Ste 103
Dallas, TX 75220-4446
Phone: 214-352-7561
Fax: 214-357-1974

CEO: Edward R. McMurphy
CFO: Mark D. Slusser
HR: Mike Cloud
Employees: 22

1995 Sales: $0 million
1-Yr. Sales Change: —
Exchange: Nasdaq (SC)
Symbol: DICE

Riverboat gaming casino near New Orleans

CROWN STERLING SUITES

3131 Turtle Creek Blvd.
Dallas, TX 75219
Phone: 214-443-1300
Fax: 214-443-1398

CEO: Robert Wooley
CFO: —
HR: Sandy Dudley
Employees: 6,000

1994 Est. Sales: $320 mil.
1-Yr. Sales Change: —
Ownership: Privately Held

Hotel chain operator

CULLEN/FROST BANKERS, INC.

100 W. Houston St.
San Antonio, TX 78205
Phone: 210-220-4011
Fax: 210-220-5557

CEO: Robert S. McClane
CFO: Phillip D. Green
HR: Jim Eckeo
Employees: 1,862

1994 Sales: $282.3 million
1-Yr. Sales Change: 6.2%
Exchange: Nasdaq
Symbol: CFBI

Banks - Southwest (Frost National Bank, United States National Bank of Galveston, Main Plaza
Corporation, Daltex General Agency, Inc.)

CURTIS C. GUNN, INC.

7744 Broadway, Ste. 100
San Antonio, TX 78209
Phone: 210-824-3208
Fax: 210-829-8226

CEO: Robert Bomer
CFO: Kelly Collins
HR: Cindy Rowley
Employees: 800

1994 Sales: $365 million
1-Yr. Sales Change: 32.2%
Ownership: Privately Held

Retail - new & used cars

CURTIS MATHES HOLDING CORPORATION

10911 Petal St.
Dallas, TX 75238
Phone: 214-233-0900
Fax: 214-503-8585

CEO: Patrick A. Custer
CFO: Thomas L. Wilkerson
HR: Neal J. Katz
Employees: 92

1994 Sales: $15 million
1-Yr. Sales Change: —
Exchange: Nasdaq (SC)
Symbol: CRTM

Consumer electronics products, including TVs, VCRs & camcorders

CYBERONICS, INC.

17448 Hwy. 3, Ste. 100
Webster, TX 77598-4135
Phone: 713-332-1375
Fax: 713-332-3615

CEO: Robert P. Cummings
CFO: John K. Bakewell
HR: John K. Bakewell
Employees: 51

1994 Sales: $0.4 million
1-Yr. Sales Change: 300.0%
Exchange: Nasdaq
Symbol: CYBX

Medical instruments - nerve stimulation

CYRIX CORPORATION

2703 N. Central Expwy.
Richardson, TX 75080-2010
Phone: 214-968-8387
Fax: 214-699-9857

CEO: Gerald Jerry D. Rogers
CFO: Timothy W. Kinnear
HR: Margaret Quinn
Employees: 309

1994 Sales: $246.1 million
1-Yr. Sales Change: 96.7%
Exchange: Nasdaq
Symbol: CYRX

Electrical components - math coprocessor & 486-clone microprocessors

 See page 178 for a full profile of this company.

DAISYTEK INTERNATIONAL CORPORATION

500 North Central Expwy.
Plano, TX 75074
Phone: 214-881-4700
Fax: 214-881-0145

CEO: David A. Heap
CFO: Mark C. Layton
HR: Deborah D'Artra
Employees: 261

1995 Sales: $353 million
1-Yr. Sales Change: 27.6%
Exchange: Nasdaq
Symbol: DZTK

Office equipment & supplies - wholesale nonpaper computer supplies, including laser toner, ink-jet cartridges, printer ribbons & diskettes

DALLAS AUTO AUCTION INC.

5333 W. Keist Blvd.
Dallas, TX 75236
Phone: 214-330-1800
Fax: 214-339-3845

CEO: Wayne Stroud
CFO: Stuart Overstreet
HR: Jan Marrs
Employees: 300

1994 Sales: $300 million
1-Yr. Sales Change: —
Ownership: Privately Held

Business services - auctioning of cars, trucks & trailers

DALLAS COWBOYS FOOTBALL CLUB, LTD.

One Cowboys Pkwy.
Irving, TX 75063
Phone: 214-556-9900
Fax: 214-556-9970

CEO: Jerry Jones
CFO: Robert Nunez
HR: Debbie Ross
Employees: 175

1994 Sales: $98.2 million
1-Yr. Sales Change: 5.7%
Ownership: Privately Held

Professional football team; stadium ownership & management (Texas Stadium)

DALLAS MAVERICKS

Reunion Arena, 777 Sports St.
Dallas, TX 75207
Phone: 214-988-0117
Fax: 214-748-0510

Professional basketball team

CEO: Norm Sonju
CFO: Jim Livington
HR: —
Employees: 55

1994 Sales: $35 million
1-Yr. Sales Change: 20.7%
Ownership: Privately Held

DALLAS SEMICONDUCTOR CORPORATION

4401 S. Beltwood Pkwy.
Dallas, TX 75244-3292
Phone: 214-450-0400
Fax: 214-450-3748

CEO: C. V. Prothro
CFO: Alan P. Hale
HR: Gay Vencill
Employees: 821

1994 Sales: $181.4 million
1-Yr. Sales Change: 13.5%
Exchange: NYSE
Symbol: DS

Electrical components - integrated circuits & semiconductor-based subsystems

 See page 179 for a full profile of this company.

DALLAS STARS HOCKEY CLUB INC.

211 Cowboys Pkwy.
Irving, TX 75063-
Phone: 214-868-2890
Fax: 214-868-2860

Professional hockey team

CEO: James Lites
CFO: Richard McLaughin
HR: —
Employees: 70

1994 Sales: $31.1 million
1-Yr. Sales Change: —
Ownership: Privately Held

DAL-TILE INTERNATIONAL INC.

7834 Hawn Fwy., PO Box 17130
Dallas, TX 75217
Phone: 214-398-1411
Fax: 214-944-4390

CEO: Howard I. Bull
CFO: Carlos E. Sala
HR: Steve L. Blake
Employees: 6,300

1994 Sales: $506.3 million
1-Yr. Sales Change: 14.9%
Ownership: Privately Held

Building products - glazed & unglazed tile (#1 in North America), ceramic wall & floor tile

 See page 180 for a full profile of this company.

DANIEL INDUSTRIES, INC.

9753 Pine Lake Dr.
Houston, TX 77055
Phone: 713-467-6000
Fax: 713-827-3889

CEO: W.A. Griffin III
CFO: Henry G. Schopfer III
HR: Jim McCoy
Employees: 1,450

1994 Sales: $203.8 million
1-Yr. Sales Change: 13.1%
Exchange: NYSE
Symbol: DAN

Oil field machinery & equipment - fluid measurement products, pipeline valves, fasteners & gaskets

DARLING INTERNATIONAL INC.

251 O'Connor Ridge Blvd., Ste. 300	CEO: Dennis Longmire	1994 Sales: $354.3 million
Irving, TX 75038	CFO: —	1-Yr. Sales Change: 6.5%
Phone: 214-717-0300	HR: Gilbert L. Gutierrez	Exchange: Nasdaq
Fax: 214-717-1588	Employees: 1,500	Symbol: DARL

Agricultural operations - animal byproducts, including animal & marine fats & oils

DARR EQUIPMENT COMPANY

2000 E. Airport Fwy.	CEO: Randall R. Engstrom	1994 Est. Sales: $250 mil.
Irving, TX 75062	CFO: George Spencer	1-Yr. Sales Change: —
Phone: 214-721-2000	HR: Mike Shropshire	Ownership: Privately Held
Fax: 214-438-2481	Employees: 1,000	

Machinery - construction

DATA RACE, INC.

11550 IH-10 West, Ste. 395	CEO: Herbert T. Hensley ·	1995 Sales: $30.4 million
San Antonio, TX 78230	CFO: Gregory T. Skalla	1-Yr. Sales Change: 31.6%
Phone: 210-558-1900	HR: Greg Williamson	Exchange: Nasdaq
Fax: 210-558-1929	Employees: 160	Symbol: RACE

Computers - intergral notebook modems; telecommunication servers (MACH TS), bridges (MACHnet) & multiplexers

 See page 181 for a full profile of this company.

DATAPOINT CORPORATION

8400 Datapoint Dr.	CEO: Asher B. Edelman	1994 Sales: $172.9 million
San Antonio, TX 78229-8500	CFO: Phillip P. Krumb	1-Yr. Sales Change: -17.0%
Phone: 210-593-7000	HR: Angela Cooper	Exchange: NYSE
Fax: 210-593-7946	Employees: 1,444	Symbol: DPT

Computers - networking, telephone & video communications hardware & software

DAVE & BUSTER'S, INC.

2751 Electronic Ln.	CEO: David O. Corriveau	1995 Sales: $49.4 million
Dallas, TX 75220	CFO: Chas Miichel	1-Yr. Sales Change: 50.2%
Phone: 214-357-9588	HR: —	Exchange: Nasdaq
Fax: 214-350-0941	Employees: 1,250	Symbol: DANB

Multiple attraction restaurant & entertainment facilities, video games, virtual reality systems, pocket billiards & interactive simulators

DAVIS FOOD CITY INC.

PO Box 8748
Houston, TX 77249
Phone: 713-695-2826
Fax: 713-695-4057

Retail - supermarkets

CEO: Neva Davis
CFO: Anne Gray
HR: Gloria Thomas
Employees: 650

1994 Est. Sales: $100 mil.
1-Yr. Sales Change: —
Ownership: Privately Held

DAWSON GEOPHYSICAL COMPANY

208 S. Marienfeld St.
Midland, TX 79701
Phone: 915-682-7356
Fax: 915-683-4298

Oil & gas - 3-D seismic data services

CEO: L. Decker Dawson
CFO: L. Decker Dawson
HR: Paula Henry
Employees: 225

1994 Sales: $23 million
1-Yr. Sales Change: 35.3%
Exchange: Nasdaq
Symbol: DWSN

DAYDOTS LABEL COMPANY, INC.

2501 Ludelle St.
Fort Worth, TX 76105-1036
Phone: 817-534-9950
Fax: 817-534-1771

Office equipment & supplies - self-adhesive labels

CEO: James M. Milliorn
CFO: Mark Smith
HR: Barbara Milliorn
Employees: 50

1994 Est. Sales: $5 mil.
1-Yr. Sales Change: 8.7%
Ownership: Privately Held

DEEPTECH INTERNATIONAL INC.

600 Travis St.
Houston, TX 77002
Phone: 713-224-7400
Fax: 713-224-7574

Oil & gas - US integrated

CEO: Thomas P. Tatham
CFO: Donald V. Weir
HR: Donald V. Weir
Employees: 57

1995 Sales: $25.4 million
1-Yr. Sales Change: -18.3%
Exchange: Nasdaq
Symbol: DEEP

DELL COMPUTER CORPORATION

9505 Arboretum Blvd.
Austin, TX 78759-7299
Phone: 512-338-4400
Fax: 512-728-3653

CEO: Michael S. Dell
CFO: Thomas J. Meredith
HR: Julie A. Sackett
Employees: 6,400

1995 Sales: $3,475.3 million
1-Yr. Sales Change: 21.0%
Exchange: Nasdaq
Symbol: DELL

Manufacture & mail-order sales of microcomputers, notebooks (Latitude) & servers (PowerEdge SP)

 See pages 86–87 for a full profile of this company.

DESTEC ENERGY, INC.

2500 CityWest Blvd., PO Box 4411	CEO: Charles F. Goff	1994 Sales: $726.7 million
Houston, TX 77210-4411	CFO: Enrique M. Larroucau	1-Yr. Sales Change: 7.9%
Phone: 713-735-4000	HR: Gerald Crone	Exchange: NYSE
Fax: 713-735-4201	Employees: 603	Symbol: ENG

Energy - cogeneration & coal gasification

See page 182 for a full profile of this company.

DF&R RESTAURANTS, INC.

2350 Airport Fwy., Ste. 505	CEO: David P. Frazier	1995 Sales: $91.6 million
Bedford, TX 76022	CFO: Lawrence M. Folk	1-Yr. Sales Change: 45.9%
Phone: 817-571-6682	HR: Liz Starkey	Exchange: Nasdaq
Fax: 817-354-9640	Employees: 3,223	Symbol: DFNR

Retail - restaurants (Don Pablo's, Harrigan's)

DI INDUSTRIES, INC.

450 Gears Rd., Ste. 625	CEO: Max M. Dillard	1994 Sales: $52.7 million
Houston, TX 77067	CFO: Thomas L. Easley	1-Yr. Sales Change: -25.1%
Phone: 713-874-0202	HR: —	Exchange: AMEX
Fax: 713-874-0195	Employees: 900	Symbol: DRL

Oil & gas - field services

DIAGNOSTIC HEALTH SERVICES, INC.

2777 Stemmons Fwy., Ste. 1525	CEO: Max W. Batzer	1994 Sales: $10.2 million
Dallas, TX 75207	CFO: Don Caughron	1-Yr. Sales Change: 37.8%
Phone: 214-634-0403	HR: Marilyn Tortoriello	Exchange: Nasdaq (SC)
Fax: 214-631-8537	Employees: 125	Symbol: DHSM

Medical services - diagnostic ultrasound & nuclear imaging

DIAMOND OFFSHORE DRILLING

15415 Katy Fwy.	CEO: Robert E. Rose	1994 Sales: $307.9 million
Houston, TX 77094	CFO: Lawrence R. Dickerson	1-Yr. Sales Change: 6.9%
Phone: 713-492-5300	HR: Gary Lee	Ownership: Privately Held
Fax: 713-492-5317	Employees: 2,750	

Oil & gas - contract drilling of offshore oil & gas wells in the Gulf of Mexico, the North Sea, the Black Sea, South America, Australia & Southeast Asia; (#1 worldwide semisubmersible rigs)

DIAMOND SHAMROCK, INC.

9830 Colonnade Blvd.
San Antonio, TX 78230
Phone: 210-641-6800
Fax: 210-641-8687

CEO: Roger R. Hemminghaus
CFO: Robert C. Becker
HR: Penelope R. Viteo
Employees: 6,400

1994 Sales: $2,606.3 million
1-Yr. Sales Change: 2.0%
Exchange: NYSE
Symbol: DRM

Oil refining & marketing

See pages 88–89 for a full profile of this company.

DIGICON, INC.

3701 Kirby Dr., Ste. 112
Houston, TX 77098
Phone: 713-526-5611
Fax: 713-630-4456

CEO: Stephen J. Ludlow
CFO: Richard W. McNairy
HR: Gayle Irwin
Employees: 1,362

1994 Sales: $118 million
1-Yr. Sales Change: 0.3%
Exchange: AMEX
Symbol: DGC

Oil & gas - seismic data acquisition & processing services

DOCUCON, INCORPORATED

7461 Callaghan Rd.
San Antonio, TX 78229
Phone: 210-525-9221
Fax: 210-525-9484

CEO: Edward P. Gistaro
CFO: Lori A. Turner
HR: Alice Hopkins
Employees: 375

1994 Sales: $8.6 million
1-Yr. Sales Change: -17.3%
Exchange: Nasdaq (SC)
Symbol: DOCU

Business services - document conversion to computer-accessible formats

DOMINION RESOURCES BLACK WARRIOR TRUST

901 Main St., 12th Fl.
Dallas, TX 75202
Phone: 214-508-2400
Fax: 214-508-2431

CEO: Ron E. Hooper
CFO: —
HR: —
Employees: —

1994 Sales: $7.6 million
1-Yr. Sales Change: —
Exchange: NYSE
Symbol: DOM

Oil & gas - US royalty trust

DORCHESTER HUGOTON, LTD.

9696 Skillman St.
Dallas, TX 75243-8200
Phone: 214-340-3443
Fax: 214-341-4053

CEO: Preston A. Peak
CFO: James E. Raley
HR: —
Employees: 16

1994 Sales: $11.6 million
1-Yr. Sales Change: -20.0%
Exchange: Nasdaq
Symbol: DHULZ

Oil & gas - US exploration

D.R. HORTON, INC.

1901 Ascension Blvd., Ste. 100	CEO: Donald R. Horton	1994 Sales: $393.3 million
Arlington, TX 76006	CFO: David J. Keller	1-Yr. Sales Change: 106.9%
Phone: 817-856-8200	HR: Mary Ledbetter	Exchange: Nasdaq
Fax: 817-856-8249	Employees: 461	Symbol: DRHI

Building - single-family homes

 See page 183 for a full profile of this company.

DR PEPPER BOTTLING COMPANY OF TEXAS

2304 Century Center Blvd.	CEO: Jim L. Turner	1994 Sales: $532 million
Irving, TX 75062	CFO: C. Marvin Montgomery	1-Yr. Sales Change: 11.9%
Phone: 214-721-8104	HR: Thomas J. Taszarek	Ownership: Privately Held
Fax: 214-721-8147	Employees: 1,400	

Beverages - soft drink bottling

DR PEPPER/SEVEN-UP COMPANIES, INC.

8144 Walnut Hill Ln.	CEO: John R. Albers	1994 Sales: $769 million
Dallas, TX 75231-4372	CFO: Ira M. Rosenstein	1-Yr. Sales Change: 8.7%
Phone: 214-360-7000	HR: John L. Quigley Jr.	Ownership: Subsidiary
Fax: 214-360-7981	Employees: 952	

Beverages - soft drinks (Dr Pepper, 7-Up, I.B.C.); subsidiary of Cadbury Schweppes

DRCA MEDICAL CORPORATION

3 Riverway, Ste. 1430	CEO: Jose E. Kauachi	1994 Sales: $13.4 million
Houston, TX 77056	CFO: Jefferson R. Casey	1-Yr. Sales Change: 11.7%
Phone: 713-439-7511	HR: Carolyn Kuchera	Exchange: AMEX
Fax: 713-439-0826	Employees: 144	Symbol: DRC

Medical services - fixed & mobile outpatient, diagnostic & rehabilitation centers

DRESSER INDUSTRIES, INC.

2001 Ross Ave.	CEO: John J. Murphy	1994 Sales: $5,330.7 million
Dallas, TX 75201	CFO: Bill D. St. John	1-Yr. Sales Change: 26.4%
Phone: 214-740-6000	HR: Paul M. Bryant	Exchange: NYSE
Fax: 214-740-6584	Employees: 29,200	Symbol: DI

Oil field machinery & equipment

 See pages 90–91 for a full profile of this company.

DREW PEARSON COS.

15006 Beltway Dr.
Addison, TX 75244
Phone: 214-702-8055
Fax: 214-702-0143

CEO: Drew Pearson
CFO: Dave Briskie
HR: Deb Johnson
Employees: 107

1994 Sales: $65 million
1-Yr. Sales Change: -16.1%
Ownership: Privately Held

Apparel - sports licensing & sportswear

DRYPERS CORPORATION

1415 W. Loop North
Houston, TX 77055
Phone: 713-682-6848
Fax: 713-682-3104

CEO: Walter V. Klemp
CFO: T. Jack Gainer
HR: Joan Cunningham
Employees: 762

1994 Sales: $173.6 million
1-Yr. Sales Change: 11.2%
Exchange: Nasdaq
Symbol: DYPR

Paper & paper products - disposable diapers (Drypers, Comfees) & disposable training pants (Drypers Big Boy, Drypers Big Girl)

 See page 184 for a full profile of this company.

DSC COMMUNICATIONS CORPORATION

1000 Coit Rd.
Plano, TX 75075-5813
Phone: 214-519-3000
Fax: 214-519-4122

CEO: James L. Donald
CFO: Gerald F. Montry
HR: John O'Laughlin
Employees: 5,414

1994 Sales: $1,003.1 million
1-Yr. Sales Change: 37.3%
Exchange: Nasdaq
Symbol: DIGI

Telecommunications equipment - digital switching, transmission, access & private network system products

 See page 185 for a full profile of this company.

DSI INDUSTRIES, INC.

5211 Brownfield Hwy., Ste. 230
Lubbock, TX 79407
Phone: 806-785-8400
Fax: 806-785-8420

CEO: Sherman H. Norton Jr.
CFO: David Ridley
HR: Gene Helstrom
Employees: 475

1994 Sales: $21.1 million
1-Yr. Sales Change: -28.2%
Exchange: Nasdaq (SC)
Symbol: DSIC

Oil & gas - drilling rigs & contract drilling services

DUAL DRILLING COMPANY

5956 Sherry Ln., Ste. 1500
Dallas, TX 75225-9004
Phone: 214-373-6200
Fax: 214-373-0558

CEO: L. H. Robertson
CFO: W. Allen Parks
HR: —
Employees: 900

1994 Sales: $104.3 million
1-Yr. Sales Change: -10.2%
Exchange: Nasdaq
Symbol: DUAL

Oil & gas - offshore drilling

DUNLAP CO.

200 Greenleaf St.	CEO: Tom Hoskins	1994 Est. Sales: $200 mil.
Fort Worth, TX 76107	CFO: Gerald Stallard	1-Yr. Sales Change: —
Phone: 817-336-4985	HR: Rick Martin	Ownership: Privately Held
Fax: 817-877-1302	Employees: 3,500	

Retail - department stores (M.M. Cohn, Mark's, Marcom's, Porteous)

DUPEY MANAGEMENT CORP.

9015 Sterling St.	CEO: Michael Dupey	1994 Sales: $200 million
Irving, TX 75063	CFO: Andy Jones	1-Yr. Sales Change: —
Phone: 214-929-1719	HR: Deborah Vfee	Ownership: Privately Held
Fax: 214-929-8283	Employees: 4,100	

Retail - 37 art supply stores in Texas & on the East Coast (MJ Design)

THE DWYER GROUP, INC.

1010 N. University Parks Dr.	CEO: Robert Tunmire	1994 Sales: $13.5 million
Waco, TX 76707	CFO: Stephen E. Beatty	1-Yr. Sales Change: 36.4%
Phone: 817-756-2122	HR: Ron Holland	Exchange: Nasdaq
Fax: 817-752-0661	Employees: 152	Symbol: DWYR

Business services - franchise business operations (Rainbow International, Mr. Rooter, General Business Services, Aire-Serv, Mr. Electric)

E Z MART STORES INCORPORATED

602 Falvey Ave.	CEO: Jim Yates	1994 Est. Sales: $300 mil.
Texarkana, TX 75501	CFO: Sonja Hubbard	1-Yr. Sales Change: —
Phone: 903-832-6502	HR: —	Ownership: Privately Held
Fax: 903-832-7903	Employees: 2,500	

Retail - convenience stores & gas stations

EAST TEXAS DISTRIBUTING INC.

7171 Grand Blvd.	CEO: Ron Eisenberg	1994 Est. Sales: $525 mil.
Houston, TX 77054	CFO: David Streusand	1-Yr. Sales Change: —
Phone: 713-748-2520	HR: Carol Terrando	Ownership: Privately Held
Fax: 713-747-5897	Employees: 800	

Wholesale distribution - magazines & books; videos

EAST TEXAS FINANCIAL SERVICES, INC.

1200 South Beckham Ave., PO Box 1700	CEO: Gerald W. Free	1994 Sales: $7.1 million
Tyler, TX 75701-3319	CFO: Derrell W. Chapman	1-Yr. Sales Change: -6.6%
Phone: 903-593-1767	HR: Derrell W. Chapman	Exchange: Nasdaq
Fax: 903-593-1094	Employees: 25	Symbol: ETFS

Financial - savings & loan (First Federal Savings & Loan Association)

EAST TEXAS MEDICAL CENTER REGIONAL HEALTH CARE SYSEM

PO Box 6400	CEO: Robert Evans	1994 Sales: $201.2 million
Tyler, TX 75701	CFO: Tony Wahl	1-Yr. Sales Change: 12.5%
Phone: 903-597-0351	HR: Mike Gray	Ownership: Privately Held
Fax: 903-535-6158	Employees: 2,000	

Hospitals

EL CHICO RESTAURANTS, INC.

12200 Stemmons, Ste. 100	CEO: Wallace A. Jones	1994 Sales: $97.8 million
Dallas, TX 75234	CFO: Lawrence E. White	1-Yr. Sales Change: 10.5%
Phone: 214-241-5500	HR: Alice M. Kain	Exchange: Nasdaq
Fax: 214-888-8198	Employees: 4,100	Symbol: ELCH

Retail - Mexican-style food restaurants

EL PASO ELECTRIC COMPANY

303 N. Oregon St.	CEO: David H. Wiggs Jr.	1994 Sales: $536.7 million
El Paso, TX 79901	CFO: John E. Droubay	1-Yr. Sales Change: -1.3%
Phone: 915-543-5711	HR: Frank Bates	Exchange: OTC
Fax: 915-542-3905	Employees: 1,100	Symbol: ELPA

Utility - electric power

EL PASO NATURAL GAS COMPANY

One Paul Kayser Center, 304 Texas Ave.	CEO: William A. Wise	1994 Sales: $869.9 million
El Paso, TX 79901	CFO: H. Brent Austin	1-Yr. Sales Change: -4.3%
Phone: 915-541-2600	HR: Bruce Duffy	Exchange: NYSE
Fax: 915-541-3488	Employees: 2,403	Symbol: EPG

Utility - gas distribution

ELCOR CORPORATION

14643 Dallas Pkwy., Ste. 1000
Dallas, TX 75240-8871
Phone: 214-851-0500
Fax: 214-851-0543

CEO: Roy E. Campbell
CFO: Richard J. Rosebery
HR: James J. Waibel
Employees: 623

1995 Sales: $159.1 million
1-Yr. Sales Change: 1.3%
Exchange: NYSE
Symbol: ELK

Building products - roofing materials

ELECTRIC & GAS TECHNOLOGY, INC.

13636 Neutron Rd.
Dallas, TX 75244-4410
Phone: 214-934-8797
Fax: 214-991-3265

CEO: S. Mort Zimmerman
CFO: Edmund W. Bailey
HR: Marie Pazol
Employees: 573

1994 Sales: $46.4 million
1-Yr. Sales Change: 8.4%
Exchange: Nasdaq
Symbol: ELGT

Electric switching devices; metal fabrication; flow control instruments; plastic seat bases, windshields & other accessories for the pleasure boat industry;

ELECTRONIC DATA SYSTEMS CORPORATION

5400 Legacy Dr.
Plano, TX 75024-3199
Phone: 214-604-6000
Fax: 214-645-6798

CEO: Lester M. Alberthal Jr.
CFO: Joseph M. Grant
HR: G. Stuart Reeves
Employees: 70,000

1994 Sales: $10,052.4 mil.
1-Yr. Sales Change: 17.4%
Exchange: NYSE
Symbol: GME

Computers - outsourcing, consulting & system design services

 See pages 92–93 for a full profile of this company.

ELECTROSOURCE, INC.

3800B Drossett Dr.
Austin, TX 78744-1131
Phone: 512-445-6606
Fax: 512-445-6819

CEO: Michael G. Semmens
CFO: Michael Rosen
HR: Glenda Massey
Employees: 40

1994 Sales: $4.6 million
1-Yr. Sales Change: 39.4%
Exchange: Nasdaq (SC)
Symbol: ELSI

Lead-acid rechargeable storage batteries for electric vehicles

ELJER INDUSTRIES, INC.

17120 Dallas Pkwy.
Dallas, TX 75248
Phone: 214-407-2600
Fax: 214-407-2789

CEO: Scott G. Arbuckle
CFO: Brooks Sherman
HR: Nancy Duricic
Employees: 4,200

1994 Sales: $406.1 million
1-Yr. Sales Change: 4.8%
Exchange: NYSE
Symbol: ELJ

Building products - plumbing & heating, ventilating & air conditioning products in the US & heating & air conditioning products in Europe

EMBREE CONSTRUCTION GROUP, INC.

8050 Airport Rd.
Georgetown, TX 78628
Phone: 512-869-2626
Fax: 512-863-6357

CEO: Jim Embree
CFO: Rocky Krenek
HR: Frank Krenek
Employees: 85

1994 Sales: $33 million
1-Yr. Sales Change: —
Ownership: Privately Held

Building - retail & health care development, construction & design

EMCARE HOLDINGS INC.

1717 Main St., Ste. 5200
Dallas, TX 75201
Phone: 214-712-2000
Fax: 214-712-2002

CEO: Leonard M. Riggs Jr.
CFO: Gary W. Cage
HR: Michael Lane
Employees: 130

1994 Sales: $118.3 million
1-Yr. Sales Change: 23.5%
Exchange: Nasdaq
Symbol: EMCR

Medical services - physician services management in hospital emergency departments & related care centers

ENCORE WIRE CORPORATION

1410 Millwood Rd.
McKinney, TX 75069
Phone: 214-562-9473
Fax: 214-542-4744

CEO: Donald M. Spurgin
CFO: Scott D. Weaver
HR: Gina Vogt
Employees: 167

1994 Sales: $122.7 million
1-Yr. Sales Change: 65.8%
Exchange: Nasdaq
Symbol: WIRE

Wire & cable products - copper electrical building wire & cable

 See page 186 for a full profile of this company.

ENERGY BIOSYSTEMS CORPORATION

4200 Research Forest Dr.
The Woodlands, TX 77381-4235
Phone: 713-364-6100
Fax: 713-364-6110

CEO: John H. Webb
CFO: Paul D. Brown III
HR: Marsha A. Nelson
Employees: 61

1994 Sales: $1.7 million
1-Yr. Sales Change: 6.3%
Exchange: Nasdaq
Symbol: ENBC

Energy - alternate sources

ENERGY VENTURES, INC.

5 Post Oak Park, Ste. 1760
Houston, TX 77027-3415
Phone: 713-297-8400
Fax: 713-963-9785

CEO: Bernard J. Duroc-Danner
CFO: James G. Kiley
HR: Diana Lambert
Employees: 2,300

1994 Sales: $248.5 million
1-Yr. Sales Change: 1.0%
Exchange: NYSE
Symbol: EVI

Oil & gas - field services

ENEX RESOURCES CORPORATION

800 Rockmead Dr., Ste. 200	CEO: Gerald B. Eckley	1994 Sales: $6.7 million
Kingwood, TX 77339	CFO: Robert E. Densford	1-Yr. Sales Change: 8.1%
Phone: 713-358-8401	HR: Robert E. Densford	Exchange: Nasdaq
Fax: 713-358-7895	Employees: 26	Symbol: ENEX

Oil & gas - US exploration & production

ENNIS BUSINESS FORMS, INC.

107 N. Sherman St.	CEO: Kenneth A. McCrady	1995 Sales: $140.1 million
Ennis, TX 75119	CFO: Harvey Cathey	1-Yr. Sales Change: 5.4%
Phone: 214-875-6581	HR: Richard Maresh	Exchange: NYSE
Fax: 214-875-4915	Employees: 1,340	Symbol: EBF

Paper - business forms

ENRON CORP.

1400 Smith St.	CEO: Kenneth L. Lay	1994 Sales: $8,983.7 million
Houston, TX 77002-7369	CFO: Kurt S. Huneke	1-Yr. Sales Change: 12.5%
Phone: 713-853-6161	HR: Philip J. Bazelides	Exchange: NYSE
Fax: 713-853-3129	Employees: 6,978	Symbol: ENE

Oil & gas - production & pipeline

See pages 94–95 for a full profile of this company.

ENRON GLOBAL POWER & PIPELINES L.L.C.

3 Allen Center, 333 Clay St.	CEO: Rodney L. Gray	1994 Sales: $8.1 million
Houston, TX 77002	CFO: James M. Alexander	1-Yr. Sales Change: 9.5%
Phone: 713-853-5266	HR: —	Exchange: NYSE
Fax: 713-853-3919	Employees: 30	Symbol: EPP

Utility - power plants & pipelines in Central & South America

ENRON LIQUIDS PIPELINE LP

1400 Smith St.	CEO: Kenneth Lay	1994 Sales: $54 million
Houston, TX 77002	CFO: Kurt Huneke	1-Yr. Sales Change: 6.9%
Phone: 713-853-6161	HR: Theo Vazelides	Exchange: NYSE
Fax: 713-646-3750	Employees: —	Symbol: ENP

Petroleum & natural gas pipelines

ENRON OIL & GAS CO.

1400 Smith St.	CEO: Forrest E. Hoglund	1994 Sales: $571.8 million
Houston, TX 77002-7369	CFO: Walter C. Wilson	1-Yr. Sales Change: 0.7%
Phone: 713-853-6161	HR: —	Exchange: NYSE
Fax: 713-853-3129	Employees: 740	Symbol: EOG

Oil & gas - US exploration & production

ENSCO INTERNATIONAL, INC.

1445 Ross Ave., Ste. 2700	CEO: Carl F. Thorne	1994 Sales: $262 million
Dallas, TX 75202-2792	CFO: C. Christopher Gaut	1-Yr. Sales Change: 6.4%
Phone: 214-922-1500	HR: Michael Wiley	Exchange: AMEX
Fax: 214-855-0080	Employees: 2,300	Symbol: ESV

Oil & gas - offshore drilling

ENSERCH CORPORATION

300 S. St. Paul St.	CEO: David W. Biegler	1994 Sales: $1,857.4 million
Dallas, TX 75201-5598	CFO: Michael E. Rescoe	1-Yr. Sales Change: 7.2%
Phone: 214-651-8700	HR: Dennis Long	Exchange: NYSE
Fax: 214-670-2520	Employees: 4,200	Symbol: ENS

Oil & gas - production & pipeline

ENSERCH EXPLORATION, INC.

4849 Greenville Ave., Ste. 1500	CEO: Joseph T. Williams	1994 Sales: $175.1 million
Dallas, TX 75206-4186	CFO: J. P. McCormick	1-Yr. Sales Change: -5.4%
Phone: 214-987-7878	HR: Gary Junco	Exchange: NYSE
Fax: 214-573-3848	Employees: 373	Symbol: EEX

Oil & gas - US exploration & production

ENTERPRISE PRODUCTS COMPANY

PO Box 4324	CEO: Dan L. Duncan	1994 Est. Sales: $630 mil.
Houston, TX 77210	CFO: Michael J. Knesek	1-Yr. Sales Change: 0.0%
Phone: 713-880-6500	HR: John Tomerlin	Ownership: Privately Held
Fax: 713-880-6573	Employees: 950	

Wholesale distribution - petroleum products

ENTERRA CORPORATION

13100 Northwest Fwy., Ste. 600
Houston, TX 77040-6310
Phone: 713-462-7300
Fax: 713-462-7816
Oil & gas - field services & products

CEO: D. Dale Wood
CFO: Steven W. Krablin
HR: Don Guedry
Employees: 3,500

1994 Sales: $302.2 million
1-Yr. Sales Change: 83.0%
Exchange: NYSE
Symbol: EN

EOTT ENERGY PARTNERS, L.P.

1330 Post Oak Blvd., PO Box 1188
Houston, TX 77251-1188
Phone: 713-993-5200
Fax: 713-993-5873
Oil & gas - independent gatherer & marketer of crude oil in North America

CEO: Phillip J. Hawk
CFO: Walter Z. Berger
HR: Mary Ellen Coombe
Employees: 900

1994 Sales: $5,921.3 million
1-Yr. Sales Change: -6.9%
Exchange: NYSE
Symbol: EOT

 See pages 96–97 for a full profile of this company.

EQUALNET HOLDING CORP.

1250 Wood Branch Park Dr.
Houston, TX 77079
Phone: 713-556-4600
Fax: 713-556-4696
Telecommunications - long distance services competing as a reseller

CEO: Zane D. Russell
CFO: Michael L. Hlinak
HR: Kathleen Smalley
Employees: 137

1995 Sales: $67.9 million
1-Yr. Sales Change: 91.8%
Exchange: Nasdaq
Symbol: ENET

EQUITY CORPORATION INTERNATIONAL

415 S. First St., Ste. 210
Lufkin, TX 75901
Phone: 409-634-1033
Fax: 409-634-1041
Funeral services & related - funeral homes & cemeteries

CEO: James P. Hunter III
CFO: Daryl A. Hays
HR: Carl Burch
Employees: 715

1994 Sales: $49.3 million
1-Yr. Sales Change: 121.1%
Exchange: Nasdaq
Symbol: ECII

E.R. FANT, INC.

5800 Westview Dr.
Houston, TX 77055
Phone: 713-686-9631
Fax: 713-686-5358
Metal products - flat-rolled carbon steel

CEO: Eugene R. Fant
CFO: Phil O. Kelley
HR: Jim Kollaja
Employees: 240

1994 Sales: $252 million
1-Yr. Sales Change: 29.9%
Ownership: Privately Held

ERC INDUSTRIES, INC.

2906 Holmes Rd.
Houston, TX 77051
Phone: 713-733-9301
Fax: 713-731-1183

CEO: Richard H. Rau
CFO: Carl R. Caldwell
HR: —
Employees: 293

1994 Sales: $32.9 million
1-Yr. Sales Change: 65.3%
Exchange: Nasdaq (SC)
Symbol: ERCI

Oil & gas - oilfield wellhead equipment

EVANS SYSTEMS, INC.

720 Avenue F North, PO Box 2480
Bay City, TX 77404-2480
Phone: 409-245-2424
Fax: 409-244-5070

CEO: Jarriel L. Evans Sr.
CFO: Charles N. Way
HR: Darlene Jones
Employees: 402

1994 Sales: $109.9 million
1-Yr. Sales Change: 4.4%
Exchange: Nasdaq
Symbol: EVSI

Oil & gas - wholesale & retail distribution of refined oil products; environmental remediation; automotive after-market chemical products

EVERGREEN MEDIA CORPORATION

433 E. Las Colinas Blvd., Ste. 1130
Irving, TX 75039
Phone: 214-869-9020
Fax: 214-869-3671

CEO: Scott K. Ginsburg
CFO: Matthew E. Devine
HR: Matthew E. Devine
Employees: 585

1994 Sales: $125.5 million
1-Yr. Sales Change: 17.5%
Exchange: Nasdaq
Symbol: EVGM

Broadcasting - radio

THE EXPLORATION COMPANY

500 N. Loop 1604 E., Ste. 250
San Antonio, TX 78232
Phone: 210-496-5300
Fax: 210-496-3232

CEO: James E. Sigmon
CFO: James E. Sigmon
HR: —
Employees: 24

1994 Sales: $1.1 million
1-Yr. Sales Change: 1,000%
Exchange: Nasdaq (SC)
Symbol: TXCO

Oil & gas - natural gas exploration

EXPRESS ONE INTERNATIONAL, INC.

3890 W. Northwest Hwy., Ste. 700
Dallas, TX 75220
Phone: 214-902-2501
Fax: 214-350-1399

CEO: Alinda H. Wikert
CFO: Chris Chorley
HR: Carol Garland
Employees: 810

1994 Sales: $161 million
1-Yr. Sales Change: —
Ownership: Privately Held

Transportation - charter airline

EXXON CORPORATION

225 E. John W. Carpenter Fwy.
Irving, TX 75062-2298
Phone: 214-444-1000
Fax: 214-444-1505

Oil & gas - international integrated

CEO: Lee R. Raymond
CFO: Edgar A. Robinson
HR: Daniel S. Sanders
Employees: 86,000

1994 Sales: $113,904 million
1-Yr. Sales Change: 2.4%
Exchange: NYSE
Symbol: XON

 See pages 98–99 for a full profile of this company.

E-Z SERVE CORPORATION

2550 N. Loop West, Ste. 600
Houston, TX 77092
Phone: 713-684-4300
Fax: 713-684-4367

Retail - convenience stores; retail motor fuels

CEO: Neil H. McLaurin
CFO: John T. Miller
HR: Robert L. Howell
Employees: 2,940

1994 Sales: $563.2 million
1-Yr. Sales Change: -7.0%
Exchange: AMEX
Symbol: EZS

EZCORP, INC.

1901 Capital Pkwy.
Austin, TX 78746-7617
Phone: 512-314-3400
Fax: 512-314-3404

Financial - pawn shops (EZ Pawn)

CEO: Vincent A. Lambiase
CFO: Dan N. Tonissen
HR: John Woodward
Employees: 1,572

1994 Sales: $167.9 million
1-Yr. Sales Change: 54.6%
Exchange: Nasdaq
Symbol: EZPW

 See page 187 for a full profile of this company.

FALCON DRILLING COMPANY, INC.

1900 W. Loop South, Ste. 1910
Houston, TX 77027
Phone: 713-623-8984
Fax: 713-623-8103

Oil & gas - domestic & international contract drilling & workover services

CEO: Steven A. Webster
CFO: Robert F. Fulton
HR: Rick Melancon
Employees: 1,509

1994 Sales: $138.4 million
1-Yr. Sales Change: 135.0%
Exchange: Nasdaq
Symbol: FLCN

FALCON OIL & GAS CO., INC.

4801 Woodway, Ste. 330W
Houston, TX 77056
Phone: 713-623-0853
Fax: 713-622-8125

Oil & gas - US exploration & production

CEO: Spencer M. Murchison
CFO: Spencer M. Murchison
HR: —
Employees: 3

1994 Sales: $2.9 million
1-Yr. Sales Change: -34.1%
Exchange: OTC
Symbol: FLOG

FARAH INCORPORATED

8889 Gateway West
El Paso, TX 79925-6584
Phone: 915-593-4444
Fax: 915-593-4203

Apparel - men & boys

CEO: Richard C. Allender
CFO: James C. Swaim
HR: David Gallardo
Employees: 6,000

1994 Sales: $242.8 million
1-Yr. Sales Change: 34.8%
Exchange: NYSE
Symbol: FRA

 See page 188 for a full profile of this company.

FELCOR SUITE HOTELS, INC.

5215 N. O'Connor Blvd., Ste. 330
Irving, TX 75039
Phone: 214-869-8180
Fax: 214-869-8182

CEO: Thomas J. Corcoran Jr.
CFO: Nicholas R. Peterson
HR: Hervey Feldman
Employees: 8

1994 Sales: $6.3 million
1-Yr. Sales Change: -47.1%
Exchange: Nasdaq
Symbol: FLCO

Real estate investment trust - hotel properties

FFP PARTNERS, L.P.

2801 Glenda Ave.
Fort Worth, TX 76117-4391
Phone: 817-838-4700
Fax: 817-838-4799

CEO: John H. Harvison
CFO: Steven B. Hawkins
HR: —
Employees: 1,274

1994 Sales: $355.5 million
1-Yr. Sales Change: 8.8%
Exchange: AMEX
Symbol: FFP

Retail - convenience stores, truck stops & self-service gas stations (Kwik-Pantry, Nu-Way, Economy)

FIESTA MART INC.

5235 Katy Fwy.
Houston, TX 77007
Phone: 713-869-5060
Fax: 713-869-8210

CEO: Donald L. Bonham
CFO: Robert Z. Walker
HR: Juanita Elizando
Employees: 6,500

1994 Sales: $675 million
1-Yr. Sales Change: 3.8%
Ownership: Privately Held

Retail - supermarkets

FINA, INC.

FINA Plaza, 8350 N. Central Expwy.
Dallas, TX 75206
Phone: 214-750-2400
Fax: 214-750-2508

CEO: Ronald W. Haddock
CFO: Yves Bercy
HR: Bill Bonnett
Employees: 2,770

1994 Sales: $3,421.1 million
1-Yr. Sales Change: -2.2%
Exchange: AMEX
Symbol: FI

Oil & gas - integrated; publicly traded U.S. subsidiary of Petrofina S.A.

 See pages 100–101 for a full profile of this company.

FINANCIAL INDUSTRIES CORPORATION

701 Brazos, Ste. 1400
Austin, TX 78701
Phone: 512-404-5050
Fax: 512-404-5132

CEO: Roy F. Mitte
CFO: James M. Grace
HR: Cindy Gunderson
Employees: 350

1994 Sales: $68.5 million
1-Yr. Sales Change: -7.4%
Exchange: Nasdaq (SC)
Symbol: FNIN

Insurance - mortagage protection & life insurance (Family Life Insurance)

FIRST BANK AMERICA, INC.

PO Box 802527
Dallas, TX 75380-2527
Phone: 214-701-4700
Fax: 214-701-4674

CEO: James F. Dierberg
CFO: D. Kert Moore
HR: Kathryn Aderman
Employees: 164

1994 Sales: $25.1 million
1-Yr. Sales Change: 0.4%
Exchange: NYSE
Symbol: FBA

Banks - Southwest (BankTEXAS)

FIRST CASH, INC.

690 E. Lamar Blvd., Ste. 150
Arlington, TX 76011
Phone: 817-460-3947
Fax: 817-461-7019

CEO: Phillip E. Powell
CFO: Rick L. Wessel
HR: Scott Williamson
Employees: 290

1995 Sales: $32.2 million
1-Yr. Sales Change: 56.3%
Exchange: Nasdaq
Symbol: PAWN

Financial - pawn shops

FIRST FINANCIAL BANKSHARES, INC.

400 Pine St.
Abilene, TX 79601
Phone: 915-675-7155
Fax: 915-675-7393

CEO: Kenneth T. Murphy
CFO: Curtis R. Harvey
HR: Pam Mann
Employees: 515

1994 Sales: $73 million
1-Yr. Sales Change: 2.1%
Exchange: Nasdaq
Symbol: FFIN

Banks - Southwest

FIRST USA, INC.

1601 Elm St.
Dallas, TX 75201
Phone: 214-849-2000
Fax: 214-746-8556

CEO: John C. Tolleson
CFO: Jack M. Antonini
HR: Daniel C. Barr
Employees: 2,600

1995 Sales: $1,082.4 million
1-Yr. Sales Change: 49.0%
Exchange: NYSE
Symbol: FUS

Financial - credit card issuance

FIRST VICTORIA NATIONAL BANKSHARES

101 S. Main St.
Victoria, TX 77901
Phone: 512-573-6321
Fax: 512-574-8429

CEO: David M. Gaddis
CFO: Ivan A. Green
HR: Allen Jones
Employees: 244

1994 Sales: $32.3 million
1-Yr. Sales Change: -0.6%
Exchange: Nasdaq
Symbol: FVNB

Banks - Southwest (First Victoria National Bank)

FISH ENGINEERING & CONSTRUCTION PARTNERS LTD.

1990 Post Oak Blvd.
Houston, TX 77056
Phone: 713-621-8300
Fax: 713-850-7682

CEO: G.L. Turner
CFO: Honey Ashworth
HR: Marsha Padel
Employees: 300

1994 Est. Sales: $150 mil.
1-Yr. Sales Change: —
Ownership: Privately Held

Building - petrochemical plant construction

FITZ AND FLOYD, SILVESTRI CORPORATION

13111 N. Central Expwy.
Dallas, TX 75243
Phone: 214-918-0098
Fax: 214-484-208

CEO: Kenneth R. Marvel
CFO: John Walker
HR: Mignon Cabera
Employees: 535

1994 Sales: $80 million
1-Yr. Sales Change: —
Ownership: Privately Held

Housewares - china & ceramic giftware

FOJTASEK COMPANIES INC.

PO Box 226957
Dallas, TX 75222
Phone: 214-438-4787
Fax: 214-438-8117

CEO: Randall Fojtasek
CFO: Joseph Beigal
HR: Ramon Otero
Employees: 1,200

1994 Est. Sales: $110 mil.
1-Yr. Sales Change: —
Ownership: Privately Held

Building products - aluminum & wooden windows & patio doors

FORT BEND HOLDING CORP.

3400 Avenue H, PO Box 951
Rosenberg, TX 77471-3808
Phone: 713-342-5571
Fax: 713-341-9447

CEO: Lane Ward
CFO: David D. Rinehart
HR: Mariellen Wenzel
Employees: 78

1995 Sales: $16.1 million
1-Yr. Sales Change: 2.5%
Exchange: Nasdaq (SC)
Symbol: FBHC

Financial - savings & loans

FORUM FINANCIAL GROUP

1475 Richardson Dr., Ste. 270	CEO: John Caulfield	1994 Sales: $12.8 million
Richardson, TX 75080	CFO: Tim O'Connor	1-Yr. Sales Change: 29.3%
Phone: 214-690-9444	HR: John Caufield	Ownership: Privately Held
Fax: 214-690-9464	Employees: 10	

Leasing - computers; reconditioned mainframe hardware distribution

FOSSIL, INC.

2280 N. Greenville Ave.	CEO: Tom Kartsotis	1994 Sales: $161.9 million
Richardson, TX 75082	CFO: Randy S. Kercho	1-Yr. Sales Change: 54.0%
Phone: 214-234-2525	HR: Shane Winkles	Exchange: Nasdaq
Fax: 214-348-1366	Employees: 555	Symbol: FOSL

Precious metals & jewelry - fashion watches (FOSSIL, RELIC), leather goods & accessories

 See page 189 for a full profile of this company.

FOUNTAIN OIL, INC.

1400 Broadfield, Ste. 200	CEO: Oistein Nyberg	1994 Sales: $0 million
Houston, TX 77084	CFO: Arnfin Haavik	1-Yr. Sales Change: —
Phone: 713-492-6992	HR: Susan Palmer	Exchange: Nasdaq
Fax: 713-492-6673	Employees: 20	Symbol: GUSH

Oil & gas - viscosity reduction services

FOXMEYER HEALTH CORPORATION

1220 Senlac Dr.	CEO: Melvyn J. Estrin	1995 Sales: $5,177.1 million
Carrollton, TX 75006	CFO: Peter B. McKee	1-Yr. Sales Change: -4.3%
Phone: 214-446-4800	HR: Sandra K. Stevens	Exchange: NYSE
Fax: 214-446-4499	Employees: 4,804	Symbol: FOX

Diversified operations - pharmaceuticals; health & beauty aids; crude oil

 See pages 102–103 for a full profile of this company.

FOXWORTH-GALBRAITH LUMBER COMPANY

17111 Waterview Pkwy.	CEO: Walter Foxworth	1994 Sales: $350 million
Dallas, TX 75252	CFO: Jack Foxworth	1-Yr. Sales Change: 40.0%
Phone: 214-437-6100	HR: Jo Ann Kelly	Ownership: Privately Held
Fax: 214-437-4236	Employees: 1,800	

Wholesale & retail lumber & building materials

FRANK PARRA AUTOPLEX

1000 E. Airport Fwy.
Irving, TX 75062
Phone: 214-721-4300
Fax: 214-579-0712

Retail - new & used cars

CEO: Tim Parra
CFO: Mike Parra
HR: Thomas Quintina
Employees: 365

1994 Sales: $185.5 million
1-Yr. Sales Change: —
Ownership: Privately Held

FREEPORT-MCMORAN OIL AND GAS ROYALTY TRUST

712 Main St.
Houston, TX 77002
Phone: 713-216-5447
Fax: 713-216-5476

Oil & gas - US royalty trust

CEO: Richard L. Melton
CFO: Richard L. Melton
HR: —
Employees: —

1994 Sales: $2.6 million
1-Yr. Sales Change: -61.8%
Exchange: NYSE
Symbol: FMR

FRESH AMERICA CORP.

12450 Cutten Rd.
Houston, TX 77066
Phone: 713-444-8596
Fax: 713-444-7039

Food - wholesale fruit & vegetables to Sam's Wholesale Club

CEO: David I. Sheinfeld
CFO: Marc K. Rieke
HR: Kevin Aden
Employees: 732

1994 Sales: $115.9 million
1-Yr. Sales Change: 29.6%
Exchange: Nasdaq
Symbol: FRES

FRIEDMAN INDUSTRIES, INCORPORATED

4001 Homestead Rd., PO Box 21147
Houston, TX 77226
Phone: 713-672-9433
Fax: 713-672-7043

Steel - coil processing (steel sheet & plate) & tubular products

CEO: Jack Friedman
CFO: Harold Friedman
HR: —
Employees: 106

1995 Sales: $98 million
1-Yr. Sales Change: 38.2%
Exchange: AMEX
Symbol: FRD

FRIENDLY CHEVROLET

5601 Lemmon Ave.
Dallas, TX 75209
Phone: 214-526-8811
Fax: 214-523-1095

Retail - new & used cars; nonresidential building operation

CEO: Mark A. Eddins
CFO: Mitch Vuckovich
HR: Sarah Anthony
Employees: 73

1994 Est. Sales: $150 mil.
1-Yr. Sales Change: —
Ownership: Privately Held

FRIONA INDUSTRIES LP

400 S. Taylor
Amarillo, TX 79101
Phone: 806-374-1811
Fax: 806-374-1324

CEO: James Herring
CFO: Dal Reid
HR: Jim Small
Employees: 400

1994 Est. Sales: $175 mil.
1-Yr. Sales Change: —
Ownership: Privately Held

Agricultural operations - cattle & cattle feedlots

FROZEN FOOD EXPRESS INDUSTRIES, INC.

1145 Empire Central Place
Dallas, TX 75247-4309
Phone: 214-630-8090
Fax: 214-819-5625

CEO: Stoney M. "Mit" Stubbs Jr.
CFO: Burl G. Cott
HR: Bart Bartholomew
Employees: 2,300

1994 Sales: $274.6 million
1-Yr. Sales Change: 20.8%
Exchange: Nasdaq
Symbol: FFEX

Transportation - refrigerated carrier of perishable goods

FULBRIGHT & JAWORSKI L.L.P.

1301 McKinney St., Ste. 5100
Houston, TX 77010
Phone: 713-651-5151
Fax: 713-651-5246

CEO: A. T. Blackshear Jr.
CFO: Scott J. Farrell
HR: Jane Williams
Employees: 1,527

1994 Sales: $226 million
1-Yr. Sales Change: 1.6%
Ownership: Privately Held

International full-service law firm

FURR'S/BISHOP'S, INCORPORATED

6901 Quaker Ave.
Lubbock, TX 79413
Phone: 806-792-7151
Fax: 806-788-2300

CEO: Kevin E. Lewis
CFO: —
HR: Carlene Stewart
Employees: 7,300

1994 Sales: $225.3 million
1-Yr. Sales Change: -11.2%
Exchange: NYSE
Symbol: CHI

Retail - family-style cafeteria restaurants

GADZOOKS, INC.

4801 Spring Valley Rd., Ste. 108B
Dallas, TX 75244
Phone: 214-991-5500
Fax: 214-980-4562

CEO: Gerald R. Szczepanski
CFO: Monty R. Standifer
HR: Sherri Watts
Employees: 1,388

1995 Sales: $56.5 million
1-Yr. Sales Change: 47.9%
Ownership: Privately Held

Retail - casual apparel & related accessories, primarily for teens, with 111 stores in 20 states (IPO in registration)

GAINSCO, INC.

500 Commerce St.
Fort Worth, TX 76102
Phone: 817-336-2500
Fax: 817-335-1230

Insurance - property & casualty

CEO: Joseph D. Macchia
CFO: Daniel J. Coots
HR: Brigitte Doyle
Employees: 158

1994 Sales: $93.5 million
1-Yr. Sales Change: 10.8%
Exchange: AMEX
Symbol: GNA

GAL-TEX HOTEL CORPORATION

Moody National Bank Bldg.
Galveston, TX 77550
Phone: 409-763-8536
Fax: 409-763-5304

CEO: Eugene Lucas
CFO: Dan Dick
HR: —
Employees: 1,800

1994 Sales: $34 million
1-Yr. Sales Change: 6.3%
Ownership: Privately Held

Hotel management, including Holiday Inn North & Holiday Inn Southwest in Houston

GALVESTON-HOUSTON COMPANY

4900 Woodway, Ste. 1200
Houston, TX 77056
Phone: 713-966-2500
Fax: 713-966-2575

CEO: Nathan M. Avery
CFO: W. L. Medford
HR: Dennis G. Berryhill
Employees: 742

1994 Sales: $70.8 million
1-Yr. Sales Change: 12.7%
Ownership: Privately Held

Oil field machinery & equipment - custom steel castings & flow measurement products & systems

THE GAMBRINUS COMPANY

1480 San Pedro Ave.
San Antonio, TX 78232
Phone: 210-490-9128
Fax: 210-490-9984

CEO: Carlos Alvarez
CFO: Jim Bolz
HR: Jim Bolz
Employees: 100

1994 Est. Sales: $75 mil.
1-Yr. Sales Change: —
Ownership: Privately Held

Beverages - beer brewing (Shiner Premium, Shiner Bock) & importing (Corona); beverage distribution

GAMMA BIOLOGICALS, INC.

3700 Mangum Rd.
Houston, TX 77092
Phone: 713-681-8481
Fax: 713-956-3333

CEO: David E. Hatcher
CFO: Margaret J. O'Bannion
HR: Margaret J. O'Bannion
Employees: 122

1995 Sales: $18.3 million
1-Yr. Sales Change: 6.4%
Exchange: AMEX
Symbol: GBL

Biomedical & genetic testing products for the immunohematology market

GARDEN RIDGE CORPORATION

19411 Atrium Place, Ste. 170
Houston, TX 77084
Phone: 713-579-7901
Fax: 713-578-5379

CEO: Armand Shapiro
CFO: Jane L. Arbuthnot
HR: Phyllis C. Hink
Employees: 1,240

1995 Sales: $100 million
1-Yr. Sales Change: 56.3%
Exchange: Nasdaq
Symbol: GRDG

Retail - decorative home accessories, seasonal products & crafts

GARNET RESOURCES CORPORATION

333 Clay St., Ste. 4500
Houston, TX 77002
Phone: 713-759-1692
Fax: 713-759-9122

CEO: George E. Nevers
CFO: W. Kirk Bosche
HR: —
Employees: 9

1994 Sales: $4.4 million
1-Yr. Sales Change: -4.3%
Exchange: Nasdaq
Symbol: GARN

Oil & gas - international specialty

GENEMEDICINE, INC.

8301 New Trails Dr.
The Woodlands, TX 77381-4248
Phone: 713-364-1150
Fax: 713-364-0858

CEO: Eric Tomlinson
CFO: Richard "Rick" Waldron
HR: Kathryn N. Stankis
Employees: 71

1994 Sales: $0.8 million
1-Yr. Sales Change: 700.0%
Exchange: Nasdaq
Symbol: GMED

Biomedical & genetic products - pharmaceuticals that incorporate genes

GERLAND'S FOOD FAIR INC.

3131 Pawnee
Houston, TX 77054
Phone: 713-746-3600
Fax: 713-746-3621

CEO: J. W. Morris
CFO: Jeff Reeder
HR: Dennis Chaivre
Employees: 2,003

1994 Est. Sales: $200 mil.
1-Yr. Sales Change: —
Ownership: Privately Held

Retail - supermarkets

GILLMAN COMPANIES

7611 Bellaire Blvd.
Houston, TX 77036
Phone: 713-776-7000
Fax: 713-776-7085

CEO: Ramsay H. Gillman
CFO: Robert Kennedy
HR: Jody Grubbs
Employees: 750

1994 Sales: $320 million
1-Yr. Sales Change: —
Ownership: Privately Held

Retail - new & used car dealerships in Austin, Houston, Rosenberg & San Antonio

GLAZER'S WHOLESALE DRUG COMPANY INC.

14860 Landmark Blvd.
Dallas, TX 75240
Phone: 214-702-0900
Fax: 214-702-8508

CEO: Robert S. Glazer
CFO: Cary Rossel
HR: Rusty Harmount
Employees: 1,000

1994 Sales: $520 million
1-Yr. Sales Change: 10.6%
Ownership: Privately Held

Wholesale distribution - wine, beer, liquor & bottled water

GLOBAL CASINOS, INC.

5646 Milton, Ste. 228
Dallas, TX 75206
Phone: 214-361-1680
Fax: 214-361-1698

CEO: Nathan Katz
CFO: Nathan Katz
HR: —
Employees: 119

1994 Sales: $1.9 million
1-Yr. Sales Change: —
Exchange: Nasdaq (SC)
Symbol: GBCS

Gambling resorts & casinos in Colorado, South Dakota, Russia, Kyrgyzstan & Aruba

GLOBAL MARINE, INC.

777 N. Eldridge Rd.
Houston, TX 77079
Phone: 713-596-5100
Fax: 713-531-1260

CEO: C. Russell Luigs
CFO: Jerry C. Martin
HR: Don Hansen
Employees: 1,700

1994 Sales: $359 million
1-Yr. Sales Change: 33.5%
Exchange: NYSE
Symbol: GLM

Oil & gas - offshore drilling

GLOBAL NATURAL RESOURCES INC.

5300 Memorial Dr., Ste. 800
Houston, TX 77007
Phone: 713-880-5464
Fax: 713-880-2106

CEO: Robert F. Vagt
CFO: Eric L. Hill
HR: Marsha Kistler
Employees: 92

1994 Sales: $50.8 million
1-Yr. Sales Change: -27.9%
Exchange: NYSE
Symbol: GNR

Oil & gas - US exploration & production

THE GNI GROUP, INC.

2525 Battleground Rd.
Deer Park, TX 77536
Phone: 713-930-0350
Fax: 713-930-0355

CEO: Carl V. Rush Jr.
CFO: Titus H. Harris III
HR: Michelle Houtchens
Employees: 180

1995 Sales: $34.4 million
1-Yr. Sales Change: 66.2%
Exchange: Nasdaq
Symbol: GNUC

Pollution control equipment & services - hazardous waste disposal

GOLD LINE REFINING LTD.

7324 Southwest Fwy.
Houston, TX 77074-2012
Phone: 713-271-3550
Fax: 713-271-3501

Oil refining & marketing

CEO: Earl Thomas
CFO: Clifton Franklin
HR: Mike Thomas
Employees: 53

1994 Est. Sales: $100 mil.
1-Yr. Sales Change: -7.5%
Ownership: Privately Held

GOLDEN EAGLE GROUP, INC.

120 Standifer Dr.
Humble, TX 77338
Phone: 713-446-2656
Fax: 713-446-6165

CEO: Patrick H. Weston
CFO: Donald A. Nordorft
HR: —
Employees: 150

1994 Sales: $41.3 million
1-Yr. Sales Change: 24.4%
Exchange: Nasdaq (SC)
Symbol: GEGP

Shipping - international air & ocean freight forwarding, packing, crating & warehousing

GOLDEN OIL CO.

550 Post Oak Blvd., Ste. 550
Houston, TX 77027
Phone: 713-622-8492
Fax: 713-963-8751

Oil & gas - exploration & production

CEO: Ralph McElvenny
CFO: Jeff Houston
HR: —
Employees: 11

1994 Sales: $1.6 million
1-Yr. Sales Change: -27.3%
Exchange: Nasdaq (SC)
Symbol: GOCO

GOLDEN TRIANGLE ROYALTY & OIL, INC.

1301 Ave. M, PO Box 1629
Cisco, TX 76437-1629
Phone: 817-442-2665
Fax: 817-442-3843

Oil & gas - US royalty trust

CEO: Robert Kamon
CFO: Ivan Webb
HR: —
Employees: 9

1994 Sales: $2.5 million
1-Yr. Sales Change: 400.0%
Exchange: Nasdaq (SC)
Symbol: GTRO

GOLF ENTERPRISES, INC.

1603 LBJ Fwy., Ste. 810
Dallas, TX 75234
Phone: 214-247-1199
Fax: 214-247-3806

CEO: Robert H. Williams
CFO: John H. Berndsen
HR: Fran Adams
Employees: 1,735

1994 Sales: $48.7 million
1-Yr. Sales Change: 26.8%
Exchange: Nasdaq
Symbol: GLFE

Real estate operations - public, resort & country club golf course operations

GOODMAN MANUFACTURING CORPORATION

1501 Seamist Dr.
Houston, TX 77008
Phone: 713-861-2500
Fax: 713-861-5428

CEO: Harold V. Goodman
CFO: Thomas O. Burkett
HR: Cliff Reily
Employees: 1,700

1994 Sales: $425 million
1-Yr. Sales Change: —
Ownership: Privately Held

Building products - refrigeration & heating equipment

GOODRICH PETROLEUM CORPORATION

5847 San Felipe, Ste. 700
Houston, TX 77057
Phone: 713-780-9494
Fax: 713-780-9254

CEO: Walter G. "Gil" Goodrich
CFO: Roland Frautschi
HR: —
Employees: 15

1994 Sales: $19 million
1-Yr. Sales Change: 16.6%
Exchange: NYSE
Symbol: GDP

Oil & gas - US exploration & production

GRANT GEOPHYSICAL, INC.

10615 Shadow Wood Dr.
Houston, TX 77043
Phone: 713-398-9503
Fax: 713-932-4475

CEO: George W. Tilley
CFO: William B. Cleveland
HR: Sue Woelfel
Employees: 1,679

1994 Sales: $73.7 million
1-Yr. Sales Change: 6.3%
Exchange: Nasdaq
Symbol: GRNT

Oil & gas - field services

GREAT PINES WATER COMPANY, INC.

600 N. Shepherd, Ste. 303
Houston, TX 77007
Phone: 713-864-6688
Fax: 713-869-6204

CEO: Robert A. Hammond Jr.
CFO: Nick A. Baki
HR: Laura Rutz
Employees: 107

1994 Sales: $6 million
1-Yr. Sales Change: 66.7%
Exchange: Nasdaq (SC)
Symbol: GPWC

Beverages - bottled water

THE GREAT TRAIN STORE COMPANY

14180 Dallas Parkway, Ste. 618
Dallas, TX 75240
Phone: 214-392-1599
Fax: 214-392-1698

CEO: Stanley R. Herndon
CFO: Stanley R. Herndon
HR: Cheryl Taylor
Employees: 219

1994 Sales: $9 million
1-Yr. Sales Change: 40.6%
Exchange: Nasdaq (SC)
Symbol: GTRN

Retail - hobby stores specializing in model trains & related products

GREINER ENGINEERING, INC.

909 E. Las Colinas Blvd., Ste. 1900
Irving, TX 75039
Phone: 214-869-1001
Fax: 214-869-3111

CEO: Robert L. Costello
CFO: Patrick J. McColpin
HR: Carole A. Chaney
Employees: 1,550

1994 Sales: $151.9 million
1-Yr. Sales Change: 8.0%
Exchange: NYSE
Symbol: GII

Engineering, architectural design & surveying services

GREYHOUND LINES, INC.

15110 N. Dallas Pkwy., Ste. 600
Dallas, TX 75248
Phone: 214-789-7000
Fax: 214-387-1874

CEO: Craig R. Lentzsch
CFO: Steven L. Korby
HR: Daniel R. Weston
Employees: 10,100

1994 Sales: $616.3 million
1-Yr. Sales Change: -7.5%
Exchange: AMEX
Symbol: BUS

Transportation - interstate bus line (#1 in US)

GROCERS SUPPLY CO. INC.

3131 E. Holcombe Blvd.
Houston, TX 77021
Phone: 713-747-5000
Fax: 713-746-5797

CEO: Milton Levit
CFO: Gerald A. Levit
HR: Greg Belsheim
Employees: 1,200

1994 Est. Sales: $1,450 mil.
1-Yr. Sales Change: 3.6%
Ownership: Privately Held

Food - wholesale confectioneries, frozen foods & groceries

GSC ENTERPRISES, INC.

130 Hillcrest Dr.
Sulphur Springs, TX 75482
Phone: 903-885-7621
Fax: 903-885-6928

CEO: Michael K. McKenzie
CFO: Ronald L. Folwell Sr.
HR: Theresa Patterson
Employees: 1,600

1994 Sales: $788.6 million
1-Yr. Sales Change: 4.2%
Ownership: Privately Held

Wholesale distribution of groceries & sundries to grocers in 12 states (Grocery Supply Co., Wagner
Candy Co.); money orders to convenience stores (Fidelity Express)

GULF STATES TOYOTA, INC.

7701 Wilshire Place Dr.
Houston, TX 77240
Phone: 713-744-3300
Fax: 713-744-4639

CEO: Jerry H. Pyle
CFO: F. R. Mason
HR: J. Brooks O'Hara
Employees: 1,500

1994 Est. Sales: $1,743 mil.
1-Yr. Sales Change: 13.6%
Ownership: Privately Held

Retail - new & used cars

GULFMARK INTERNATIONAL, INC.

5 Post Oak Park, Ste. 1170
Houston, TX 77027
Phone: 713-963-9522
Fax: 713-963-9796

CEO: David J. Butters
CFO: Frank R. Pierce
HR: Elizabeth Brumley
Employees: 316

1994 Sales: $34.4 million
1-Yr. Sales Change: 23.3%
Exchange: Nasdaq
Symbol: GMRK

Oil & gas - field services

GUNDLE SLT ENVIRONMENTAL, INC.

19103 Gundle Rd.
Houston, TX 77073
Phone: 713-443-8564
Fax: 713-875-6010

CEO: Thomas L. Caltrider
CFO: Roger J. Klatt
HR: Bill Weatherall
Employees: 534

1995 Sales: $133.1 million
1-Yr. Sales Change: 12.0%
Exchange: AMEX
Symbol: GUN

Pollution control equipment & services - hazardous waste disposal

H & H MEAT PRODUCTS CO., INC.

E. Expwy. 83
Mercedes, TX 78570
Phone: 210-565-6363
Fax: 210-565-4108

CEO: Liborio E. Hinojosa
CFO: Rey Jaquez
HR: Erlinda Cavazos
Employees: 310

1994 Sales: $51.8 million
1-Yr. Sales Change: —
Ownership: Privately Held

Food - meat packing & distribution (d/b/a H & H Foods)

HAGGAR CORPORATION

6113 Lemmon Ave.
Dallas, TX 75209-5715
Phone: 214-352-8481
Fax: 214-956-4367

CEO: J. M. Haggar III
CFO: Ralph A. Beattie
HR: George Greer
Employees: 6,400

1994 Sales: $491.2 million
1-Yr. Sales Change: 24.6%
Exchange: Nasdaq
Symbol: HGGR

Apparel - men's trousers, suits & separates

 See page 190 for a full profile of this company.

HALLIBURTON COMPANY

3600 Lincoln Plaza
Dallas, TX 75201
Phone: 214-978-2600
Fax: 214-978-2611

CEO: Thomas H. Cruikshank
CFO: Jerry H. Blurton
HR: Karen S. Stuart
Employees: 57,200

1994 Sales: $5,740.5 million
1-Yr. Sales Change: -9.6%
Exchange: NYSE
Symbol: HAL

Diversified operations - heavy construction (Brown & Root); oil & gas field services; insurance

 See pages 104–105 for a full profile of this company.

THE HALLWOOD GROUP INCORPORATED

3710 Rawlins St., Ste. 1500
Dallas, TX 75219-4236
Phone: 214-528-5588
Fax: 214-522-9254

Financial - business services

CEO: Anthony J. Gumbiner
CFO: Melvin J. Melle
HR: Donna Henton
Employees: 1,152

1994 Sales: $107.1 million
1-Yr. Sales Change: -2.7%
Exchange: NYSE
Symbol: HWG

HALLWOOD REALTY PARTNERS, L.P.

3710 Rawlins St., Ste. 1500
Dallas, TX 75219-4298
Phone: 214-528-5588
Fax: 214-528-8855

Real estate investment trust - commercial office & industrial properties

CEO: Anthony J. Gumbiner
CFO: Jeffrey D. Gent
HR: Donna Heaton
Employees: —

1994 Sales: $48.6 million
1-Yr. Sales Change: 1.0%
Exchange: AMEX
Symbol: HRY

HARCOR ENERGY, INC.

4400 Post Oak Pkwy., Ste. 2220
Houston, TX 77027-3413
Phone: 713-961-1804
Fax: 713-961-9773

Oil & gas- production & pipeline

CEO: Mark G. Harrington
CFO: Gary S. Peck
HR: Fran Reeder
Employees: 10

1994 Sales: $13.2 million
1-Yr. Sales Change: 97.0%
Exchange: Nasdaq (SC)
Symbol: HARC

HARKEN ENERGY CORPORATION

5605 N. MacArthur Blvd., Ste. 400
Irving, TX 75038
Phone: 214-753-6900
Fax: 214-753-6926

Oil & gas - domestic & international exploration, development & production

CEO: Mikel D. Faulkner
CFO: Bruce N. Huff
HR: —
Employees: 40

1994 Sales: $4.9 million
1-Yr. Sales Change: -25.8%
Exchange: AMEX
Symbol: HEC

HARRIS COUNTY HOSPITAL DISTRICT

PO Box 66769
Houston, TX 77266
Phone: 713-793-2000
Fax: 713-746-6796

Hospitals - system serving Harris County (Ben Taub General Hospital, Lyndon B. Johnson General Hospital)

CEO: Lois J. Moore
CFO: Robert P. Barbier
HR: Jenni Carmoucat
Employees: 5,000

1994 Sales: $329.6 million
1-Yr. Sales Change: -16.5%
Ownership: Privately Held

HARRIS METHODIST HEALTH SYSTEM

1325 Pennsylvania Ave.	CEO: Ron Smith	1994 Sales: $680.8 million
Fort Worth, TX 76104	CFO: Ron Bourland	1-Yr. Sales Change: 12.7%
Phone: 817-462-7788	HR: William Witman	Ownership: Privately Held
Fax: 817-462-6135	Employees: 5,000	

Hospitals - not-for-profit system & HMO (Harris Methodist Health Plan), primarily serving Tarrant County

HART GRAPHICS, INC.

8000 Shoal Creek Blvd.	CEO: W. L. Hart	1994 Est. Sales: $85 mil.
Austin, TX 78757	CFO: Britt Kauffman	1-Yr. Sales Change: -22.7%
Phone: 512-454-4761	HR: Brian Oetzel	Ownership: Privately Held
Fax: 512-467-4583	Employees: 800	

Printing - books

HARTE-HANKS COMMUNICATIONS, INC.

200 Concord Plaza Dr., Ste. 800	CEO: Larry Franklin	1994 Sales: $513.6 million
San Antonio, TX 78216	CFO: Richard L. Ritchie	1-Yr. Sales Change: 10.8%
Phone: 210-829-9000	HR: —	Exchange: NYSE
Fax: 210-829-9403	Employees: 6,225	Symbol: HHS

Diversified operations - newspaper publishing; television broadcasting; direct mail

 See page 191 for a full profile of this company.

HASTINGS BOOKS, MUSIC & VIDEO, INC.

3601 Plains Blvd., Ste. One	CEO: John H. Marmaduke	1994 Sales: $217 million
Amarillo, TX 79120-5350	CFO: Bill Millikin	1-Yr. Sales Change: —
Phone: 806-376-6251	HR: Dan Crunk	Ownership: Privately Held
Fax: 806-374-0093	Employees: 3,500	

Retail - prerecorded music & book stores; video rental

HAT BRANDS INC.

601 Marion Dr.	CEO: Robert S. Stec	1994 Sales: $154 million
Garland, TX 75042	CFO: David Tehle	1-Yr. Sales Change: -23.0%
Phone: 214-494-0511	HR: Vickie Minden	Ownership: Privately Held
Fax: 214-494-2369	Employees: 2,100	

Apparel - western & golf hats (#1 in US)

H. B. ZACHRY COMPANY

527 W. Harding Blvd.
San Antonio, TX 78221
Phone: 210-922-1213
Fax: 210-927-8060

Building - general contracting

CEO: Henry B. Zachry Jr.
CFO: J. J. Lozano
HR: Steve Hoech
Employees: 10,000

1994 Est. Sales: $750 mil.
1-Yr. Sales Change: -5.2%
Ownership: Privately Held

HCB CONTRACTORS

1700 Pacific Ave., Ste. 3800
Dallas, TX 75201
Phone: 214-965-1100
Fax: 214-965-1300

Building - general contracting & management

CEO: Lawrence A. Wilson
CFO: James F. Russell
HR: Gerald D. Cooper
Employees: 500

1994 Sales: $236 million
1-Yr. Sales Change: —
Ownership: Privately Held

HCC INSURANCE HOLDINGS, INC.

13403 Northwest Fwy.
Houston, TX 77040-6094
Phone: 713-690-7300
Fax: 713-462-2401

Insurance - commercial property & casualty for the marine, offshore energy & aviation industries

CEO: Stephen L. Way
CFO: Frank J. Bramanti
HR: Debbie Riffe
Employees: 103

1994 Sales: $59.9 million
1-Yr. Sales Change: 45.7%
Exchange: NYSE
Symbol: HCC

H. D. VEST, INC.

433 E. Las Colinas Blvd., Third Fl.
Irving, TX 75039
Phone: 214-556-1651
Fax: 214-556-1724

Financial - investment & management services

CEO: Herb D. Vest
CFO: Wesley T. Sinclair
HR: Laura Mills
Employees: 139

1994 Sales: $50.3 million
1-Yr. Sales Change: 9.3%
Exchange: Nasdaq
Symbol: HDVS

H. E. BUTT GROCERY COMPANY

646 S. Main Ave.
San Antonio, TX 78204
Phone: 210-246-8000
Fax: 210-246-8169

Retail - supermarkets

CEO: Charles C. Butt
CFO: Jack Brouillard
HR: Louis M. Laguardia
Employees: 25,000

1994 Sales: $4,850 million
1-Yr. Sales Change: 7.8%
Ownership: Privately Held

 See pages 106–107 for a full profile of this company.

HEALTHCARE AMERICA, INC.

912 Capital of Texas Hwy. South
Austin, TX 78746
Phone: 512-329-8821
Fax: 512-314-5254

CEO: Kevin P. Sheehan
CFO: J. Mack Nunn
HR: Jay Gemperle
Employees: 3,371

1994 Sales: $149.9 million
1-Yr. Sales Change: 147.8%
Exchange: Pink Sheets
Symbol: HAMM

Hospitals - health care facilities in 6 states, including 9 psychiatric hospitals (Laurel Ridge, San Antonio; The Oaks, Austin; San Marcos Treatment Center), 2 rehabilitation hospitals, 2 acute care hospitals & 8 community living facilities

HEARTLAND WIRELESS COMMUNICATIONS, INC.

903 North Bowser, Ste. 140
Richardson, TX 75081
Phone: 214-479-9244
Fax: 214-479-1023

CEO: David E. Webb
CFO: John R. Bailey
HR: John R. Bailey
Employees: 370

1994 Sales: $2.2 million
1-Yr. Sales Change: 144.4%
Exchange: Nasdaq
Symbol: HART

Wireless cable TV systems in 35 small to midsize markets, primarily in the southwestern US

HELEN OF TROY LIMITED

6827 Market Ave.
El Paso, TX 79915
Phone: 915-779-6363
Fax: 915-774-4793

CEO: Gerald J. Rubin
CFO: Sam L. Henry
HR: Sivi Martinez
Employees: 274

1995 Sales: $138.1 million
1-Yr. Sales Change: 12.1%
Exchange: Nasdaq
Symbol: HELE

Cosmetics & toiletries - hair-care appliances & accessories (Vidal Sassoon, Revlon, Helen of Troy)

HERITAGE MEDIA CORPORATION

13355 Noel Rd., Ste. 1500
Dallas, TX 75240
Phone: 214-702-7380
Fax: 214-702-7382

CEO: David N. Walthall
CFO: Douglas N. Woodrum
HR: Amy Kruckemeyer
Employees: 24,500

1994 Sales: $317.6 million
1-Yr. Sales Change: 9.1%
Exchange: AMEX
Symbol: HTG

Business services - marketing (Actmedia, Actradio); broadcasting (5 TV network affiliates & 15 radio stations)

 See page 192 for a full profile of this company.

HERNANDEZ ENGINEERING INC.

17625 El Camino Real, Ste. 200
Houston, TX 77058
Phone: 713-280-5159
Fax: 713-480-7525

CEO: Miquel A. Hernandez
CFO: Tery Hernandez
HR: Bettianne Rigano
Employees: 564

1994 Sales: $28.9 million
1-Yr. Sales Change: —
Ownership: Privately Held

Engineering - training, technical & R&D services

HICKS, MUSE, TATE & FURST INC.

200 Crescent Ct., Ste. 1600	CEO: Thomas O. Hicks	1994 Sales: $0 million
Dallas, TX 75201	CFO: Michael Salem	1-Yr. Sales Change: —
Phone: 214-740-7300	HR: —	Ownership: Privately Held
Fax: 214-740-7313	Employees: 23	

Financial - investment banking (Berg Electronics, Hat Brands, Healthco, G. Heilemann Brewing, The Morningstar Group, Spectradyne, Trident NGL)

HIGHWAYMASTER COMMUNICATIONS, INC.

16479 Dallas Pkwy., Ste. 710	CEO: William C. Saunders	1994 Sales: $13.5 million
Dallas, TX 75248	CFO: Steven C. Whitehead	1-Yr. Sales Change: 694.1%
Phone: 214-732-2500	HR: Carolyn Locke	Exchange: Nasdaq
Fax: 214-650-0182	Employees: 195	Symbol: HWYM

Telecommunications services - wireless enhanced services network

HILITE INDUSTRIES INC.

1671 S. Broadway	CEO: Daniel W. Brady	1995 Sales: $45 million
Carrollton, TX 75006	CFO: Roy Wiegmann	1-Yr. Sales Change: 22.0%
Phone: 214-466-0475	HR: George Del Rio	Exchange: Nasdaq
Fax: 214-242-2902	Employees: 343	Symbol: HILI

Automotive & trucking - brake proportioning valves & electromagnetic clutches

HI-LO AUTOMOTIVE, INC.

2575 W. Bellfort	CEO: T. Michael Young	1994 Sales: $235.4 million
Houston, TX 77054	CFO: Gary D. Walther	1-Yr. Sales Change: 14.7%
Phone: 713-663-6700	HR: Ed Fabritiis	Exchange: NYSE
Fax: 713-663-9296	Employees: 3,246	Symbol: HLO

Auto parts - retail & wholesale

HINES INTERESTS L.P.

2800 Post Oak Blvd.	CEO: Jeff Hines	1994 Est. Sales: $600 mil.
Houston, TX 77056	CFO: Hasty Johnson	1-Yr. Sales Change: —
Phone: 713-621-8000	HR: David LeVrier	Ownership: Privately Held
Fax: 713-966-2053	Employees: 1,300	

Commercial real estate development & management

HITOX CORPORATION OF AMERICA

418 Peoples St., PO Box 2544
Corpus Christi, TX 78403-2544
Phone: 512-882-5175
Fax: 512-882-6948

CEO: Thomas A. Landshof
CFO: Craig A. Schkade
HR: Russsell C. Rahn
Employees: 47

1994 Sales: $11.6 million
1-Yr. Sales Change: -17.7%
Exchange: Nasdaq (SC)
Symbol: HTXA

Chemicals - mineral products for use as pigments & pigment extenders used in the manufacture of paints, industrial coatings & plastics

HOGAN SYSTEMS, INC.

5080 Spectrum Dr., Ste. 400E
Dallas, TX 75248
Phone: 214-386-0020
Fax: 214-386-0315

CEO: Michael H. Anderson
CFO: David R. Bankhead
HR: Dan Johnson
Employees: 721

1995 Sales: $92.6 million
1-Yr. Sales Change: 29.3%
Exchange: Nasdaq
Symbol: HOGN

Computers - banking software

HOLLY CORPORATION

100 Crescent Ct., Ste. 1600
Dallas, TX 75201-6927
Phone: 214-871-3555
Fax: 214-871-3566

CEO: Lamar Norsworthy
CFO: Henry A. Teichholz
HR: Ron Loyd
Employees: 531

1995 Sales: $614.8 million
1-Yr. Sales Change: 11.2%
Exchange: AMEX
Symbol: HOC

Oil refining & marketing

HOLLYWOOD CASINO CORPORATION

13455 Noel Rd., Ste. 2200, LB 48
Dallas, TX 75240
Phone: 214-392-7777
Fax: 214-386-7411

CEO: Jack E. Pratt
CFO: Albert J. Cohen
HR: Steve Byars
Employees: 6,275

1994 Sales: $463.9 million
1-Yr. Sales Change: 35.4%
Exchange: Nasdaq
Symbol: HWCC

Gambling resorts & casinos - riverboat & dockside gaming facilities in Aurora, IL & Tunica, MS; 80% ownership of Pratt Hotel Corporation (Sands Hotel & Casino in Atlantic City, NJ & San Juan, PR)

HOLLYWOOD MARINE INC.

55 Waugh Dr., Ste. 1000
Houston, TX 77007
Phone: 713-868-1661
Fax: 713-868-6476

CEO: Charles B. Lawrence
CFO: Jill Cloud
HR: Jane Kerr
Employees: 650

1994 Est. Sales: $125 mil.
1-Yr. Sales Change: —
Ownership: Privately Held

Transportation - canal barge shipping

HOME INTERIORS & GIFTS, INC.

4550 Spring Valley Dr.	CEO: Donald J. Carter	1994 Sales: $534 million
Dallas, TX 75244-3705	CFO: Leonard Shipley	1-Yr. Sales Change: 6.8%
Phone: 214-386-1000	HR: Bob McComas	Ownership: Privately Held
Fax: 214-233-8825	Employees: 1,400	

Retail - direct sales of decorative accessories through in-home parties

HORIZON MENTAL HEALTH MANAGEMENT, INC.

2220 San Jacinto Blvd., Ste. 320	CEO: James K. Newman	1994 Sales: $34.6 million
Denton, TX 76205	CFO: James W. McAtee	1-Yr. Sales Change: 20.6%
Phone: 817-387-4775	HR: Dan Perkins	Exchange: AMEX
Fax: 817-387-3593	Employees: 556	Symbol: HMH

Medical services - contract manager of mental health programs offered by general acute care hospitals

HORNBECK OFFSHORE SERVICES, INC.

7707 Harborside Dr.	CEO: Larry D. Hornbeck	1994 Sales: $45.8 million
Galveston, TX 77554	CFO: Robert W. Hampton	1-Yr. Sales Change: -3.2%
Phone: 409-744-9500	HR: Tim Zeringue	Exchange: Nasdaq
Fax: 409-744-0201	Employees: 500	Symbol: HOSS

Oil & gas - offshore drilling

HOUSTON ASTROS BASEBALL CLUB

8400 Kirby Dr.	CEO: Drayton McLain	1994 Sales: $34.3 million
Houston, TX 77054	CFO: Bob McLaren	1-Yr. Sales Change: -43.3%
Phone: 713-799-9500	HR: Marcos Torres	Ownership: Privately Held
Fax: 713-799-9562	Employees: 50	

Professional baseball team

HOUSTON BIOTECHNOLOGY INC.

3608 Research Forest Dr.	CEO: J. Russell Denson	1994 Sales: $0.3 million
The Woodlands, TX 77381	CFO: Audrie Mallory	1-Yr. Sales Change: -40.0%
Phone: 713-363-0999	HR: —	Exchange: AMEX
Fax: 713-363-3715	Employees: 27	Symbol: HBI

Drugs

HOUSTON ENDOWMENT, INC.

600 Travis, Ste. 6400
Houston, TX 77002-3007
Phone: 713-238-8100
Fax: 713-238-8101

CEO: H. Joe Nelson III
CFO: Sheryl L. Johns
HR: Sheryl L. Johns
Employees: 18

1994 Est. Sales: $37 mil.
1-Yr. Sales Change: -5.6%
Ownership: Privately Held

Charitable foundation providing grants for building & scholarship funds, special projects, fellowships, professorships & renovation projects

HOUSTON INDUSTRIES INCORPORATED

5 Post Oak Park, 4400 Post Oak Pkwy.
Houston, TX 77027
Phone: 713-629-3000
Fax: 713-629-3129

CEO: Don D. Jordan
CFO: Mary P. Ricciardello
HR: Susan D. Fabre
Employees: 11,498

1994 Sales: $4,001.9 million
1-Yr. Sales Change: -7.4%
Exchange: NYSE
Symbol: HOU

Utility - electric power

 See pages 108–109 for a full profile of this company.

HOUSTON MCLANE COMPANY, INC.

Loop 610 and Kirby
Houston, TX 77021
Phone: 713-799-9629
Fax: 713-799-9718

CEO: Drayton McLane Jr.
CFO: Teresa Pelenne
HR: Mike Anders
Employees: 1,300

1994 Est. Sales: $100 mil.
1-Yr. Sales Change: 7.5%
Ownership: Privately Held

Leisure and recreational services - professional baseball team (Houston Astros); stadium operation (Houston Astrodome)

HOUSTON OILERS INC.

6910 Fannin St.
Houston, TX 77046
Phone: 713-797-9111
Fax: 713-797-6631

CEO: K.S. "Bud" Adams
CFO: Scott Thompson
HR: Norma Russell
Employees: 77

1994 Sales: $58.1 million
1-Yr. Sales Change: -6.3%
Ownership: Privately Held

Professional football team

HOUSTON ROCKETS

10 Greenway Plaza East
Houston, TX 77046
Phone: 713-627-0600
Fax: 713-627-8159

CEO: Leslie Alexander
CFO: Marcus Jolibois
HR: —
Employees: 60

1994 Sales: $44.7 million
1-Yr. Sales Change: 38.0%
Ownership: Privately Held

Professional basketball team

HOWARD B. WOLF, INC.

3809 Parry Ave.	CEO: Robert D. Wolf	1995 Sales: $14.4 million
Dallas, TX 75226-1753	CFO: Eugene K. Friesen	1-Yr. Sales Change: -3.4%
Phone: 214-823-9941	HR: Eugene K. Friesen	Exchange: AMEX
Fax: 214-828-0631	Employees: 92	Symbol: HBW

Apparel - women's sportwear (Howard Wolf, Ernestow, Pret-A-Porte)

HOWELL CORPORATION

1111 Fanin St., Ste. 1500	CEO: Paul N. Howell	1994 Sales: $449 million
Houston, TX 77002-6923	CFO: Allyn R. Skelton II	1-Yr. Sales Change: 9.1%
Phone: 713-658-4000	HR: —	Exchange: NYSE
Fax: 713-658-4007	Employees: 329	Symbol: HWL

Oil & gas - US integrated

HUMAN CODE, INC.

1411 West Ave., Ste. 100	CEO: Chipp Walters	1995 Sales: $2.5 million
Austin, TX 78701	CFO: Chipp Walters	1-Yr. Sales Change: —
Phone: 512-477-5455	HR: Bettye Nowlin	Ownership: Privately Held
Fax: 512-477-5456	Employees: 35	

Computers - interactive multimedia products for business professionals, software publishers & content owners

HUNT BUILDING CORPORATION

4401 N. Mesa, Ste. 201	CEO: W. L. Hunt	1994 Est. Sales: $100 mil.
El Paso, TX 79902	CFO: William Sanders	1-Yr. Sales Change: —
Phone: 915-533-1122	HR: Patricia Minor	Ownership: Privately Held
Fax: 915-545-2631	Employees: 200	

Building - multifamily residential & commercial buildings

HUNT CONSOLIDATED INC.

1445 Ross at Field	CEO: Ray L. Hunt	1994 Sales: $1,000 million
Dallas, TX 75202	CFO: Don F. Robillard	1-Yr. Sales Change: 0.0%
Phone: 214-978-8000	HR: Chuck Mills	Ownership: Privately Held
Fax: 214-978-8888	Employees: 2,600	

Oil & gas - petroleum & natural gas extraction

HYDRIL CO.

3300 N. Belt East
Houston, TX 77032
Phone: 713-449-2000
Fax: 713-985-3457

Oil field machinery & equipment

CEO: Chris Seaver
CFO: Jim Tidwell
HR: Wayne Williams
Employees: 2,000

1994 Est. Sales: $110 mil.
1-Yr. Sales Change: —
Ownership: Privately Held

ICO, INC.

100 Glenborough Dr., Ste. 250
Houston, TX 77067
Phone: 713-872-4994
Fax: 713-872-9610

Oil field machinery & equipment

CEO: Sylvia A. Pacholder
CFO: Asher O. Pacholder
HR: John Cook
Employees: 1,000

1994 Sales: $76 million
1-Yr. Sales Change: 26.2%
Exchange: Nasdaq
Symbol: ICOC

ID SOFTWARE, INC.

18601 LBJ Fwy., Ste. 615
Mesquite, TX 75150
Phone: 214-613-3589
Fax: 214-686-9288

Computer - game software (Commander Keen, Doom, Heretic, Spear of Destiny, Wolfenstein 3-D)

CEO: Jay Wilbur
CFO: Jay Wilbur
HR: —
Employees: 10

1994 Sales: $13 million
1-Yr. Sales Change: 333.3%
Ownership: Privately Held

 See page 193 for a full profile of this company.

IGLOO HOLDINGS INC.

1001 W. Sam Houston Pkwy. North
Houston, TX 77043
Phone: 713-465-2571
Fax: 713-935-7701

Leisure & recreational products - ice chests & water coolers

CEO: Jonathan H. Godshall
CFO: Sam E. Davis Jr.
HR: Mary Alice Eureste
Employees: 1,200

1994 Est. Sales: $125 mil.
1-Yr. Sales Change: —
Ownership: Privately Held

IMCO RECYCLING INC.

5215 N. O'Connor Blvd., Ste. 940
Irving, TX 75039
Phone: 214-869-6575
Fax: 214-869-6556

Metal processing & fabrication - aluminum recycling

CEO: Frank H. Romanelli
CFO: Paul V. Dufour
HR: James B. Walburg
Employees: 740

1994 Sales: $101.1 million
1-Yr. Sales Change: 36.3%
Exchange: NYSE
Symbol: IMR

IMPERIAL HOLLY CORPORATION

8016 Hwy 90-A, Ste. 200, PO Box 9
Sugar Land, TX 77487
Phone: 713-491-9181
Fax: 713-491-9198

Food - sugar & refining

CEO: James C. Kempner
CFO: James C. Kempner
HR: William M. Krocak
Employees: 1,500

1995 Sales: $586.9 million
1-Yr. Sales Change: -10.5%
Exchange: AMEX
Symbol: IHK

INCOME OPPORTUNITY REALTY TRUST

10670 N. Central Expwy., Ste. 300
Dallas, TX 75231
Phone: 214-692-4800
Fax: 214-750-6280

Real estate investment trust - office buildings & shopping centers

CEO: Randall M. Paulson
CFO: Thomas A. Holland
HR: Lyn Kruger
Employees: —

1994 Sales: $6.9 million
1-Yr. Sales Change: -5.5%
Exchange: AMEX
Symbol: IOT

INDEPENDENT BANKSHARES, INC.

547 Chestnut St.
Abilene, TX 79602
Phone: 915-677-5550
Fax: 915-677-5943

Banks - Southwest

CEO: Bryan W. Stephenson
CFO: Randal N. Crosswhite
HR: —
Employees: 93

1994 Sales: $11.6 million
1-Yr. Sales Change: 4.5%
Exchange: AMEX
Symbol: IBK

INDEPENDENT GROCERS INC.

4109 Vine St.
Abilene, TX 79602
Phone: 915-692-1440
Fax: 915-692-0848

Food - wholesale groceries

CEO: Mark Brown
CFO: Bob Liboon
HR: —
Employees: 125

1994 Est. Sales: $100 mil.
1-Yr. Sales Change: —
Ownership: Privately Held

INDRESCO INC.

2121 San Jacinto St., Ste. 2500
Dallas, TX 75201
Phone: 214-953-4500
Fax: 214-953-4596

Machinery - mining equipment & specialized air tools

CEO: J. L. Jackson
CFO: Gary G. Garrison
HR: Roberta F. Marshall
Employees: 4,508

1994 Sales: $440.8 million
1-Yr. Sales Change: -18.4%
Exchange: NYSE
Symbol: ID

INDUSTRIAL HOLDINGS, INC.

7135 Ardmore
Houston, TX 77054
Phone: 713-747-1025
Fax: 713-749-9642

Machinery - general industrial

CEO: Robert E. Cone
CFO: Christine A. Smith
HR: —
Employees: 207

1994 Sales: $34.7 million
1-Yr. Sales Change: -1.1%
Exchange: Nasdaq
Symbol: IHII

INFOMART

1950 Stemmons Fwy.
Dallas, TX 75207-3199
Phone: 214-746-3500
Fax: 214-746-3501

Computers - industry market center for computer companies

CEO: Tom Jones
CFO: Joe Bentley
HR: Susan Lauderdale
Employees: 150

1994 Est. Sales: $40 mil.
1-Yr. Sales Change: —
Ownership: Privately Held

INOTEK TECHNOLOGIES CORPORATION

11212 Indian Tr.
Dallas, TX 75229
Phone: 214-243-7000
Fax: 214-243-2924

Instruments - wholesale process control

CEO: David L. White
CFO: R. Lee Simpson
HR: Cynthia Tooley
Employees: 119

1995 Sales: $24.9 million
1-Yr. Sales Change: -15.6%
Exchange: Nasdaq (SC)
Symbol: INTK

INPUT/OUTPUT, INC.

12300 Parc Crest Dr.
Stafford, TX 77477-2416
Phone: 713-933-3339
Fax: 713-240-2419

Oil & gas - seismic data technology services

CEO: Gary D. Owens
CFO: Robert P. Brindley
HR: Lacy Rice
Employees: 449

1995 Sales: $134.7 million
1-Yr. Sales Change: 37.7%
Exchange: NYSE
Symbol: IO

INTEGRATED FLOOR SOURCES INC.

520 N. Wildwood Dr.
Irving, TX 75061
Phone: 214-579-3500
Fax: 214-579-3637

Wholesale distribution - floor coverings

CEO: Lavonne Ezell
CFO: Jack Wultz
HR: Virginia Hade
Employees: 1,250

1994 Est. Sales: $320 mil.
1-Yr. Sales Change: —
Ownership: Privately Held

INTEGRATED SECURITY SYSTEMS, INC.

8200 Springwood Dr., Ste. 230	CEO: Gerald K. Beckmann	1994 Sales: $10.4 million
Irving, TX 75063	CFO: James W. Casey	1-Yr. Sales Change: 40.5%
Phone: 214-444-8280	HR: Dianne Boysen	Exchange: Nasdaq (SC)
Fax: 214-401-2500	Employees: 100	Symbol: IZZI

Protection - crash barriers, lane changers, navigational & airport lighting & electronically controlled security gates

INTELLICALL, INC.

2155 Chenault Dr., Ste. 410	CEO: William O. Hunt	1994 Sales: $84.1 million
Carrollton, TX 75006-5023	CFO: Michael H. Barnes	1-Yr. Sales Change: -3.6%
Phone: 214-416-0022	HR: Joni Ortega	Exchange: NYSE
Fax: 214-416-7213	Employees: 245	Symbol: ICL

Telecommunications equipment - pay telephones

INTERCONTINENTAL LIFE CORP.

Austin Centre, 701 Brazos, Ste. 1200	CEO: Roy F. Mitte	1994 Sales: $114.8 million
Austin, TX 78701	CFO: James M. Grace	1-Yr. Sales Change: -2.5%
Phone: 512-404-5000	HR: Cindy Gunderson	Exchange: Nasdaq (SC)
Fax: 512-404-5210	Employees: 350	Symbol: ILCO

Insurance - individual & group life, disability & annuity products

INTERNATIONAL BANCSHARES CORPORATION

1200 San Bernardo Ave.	CEO: Dennis E. Nixon	1994 Sales: $181.7 million
Laredo, TX 78040	CFO: Imelda Navarro	1-Yr. Sales Change: 13.2%
Phone: 210-722-7611	HR: Rosie Ramirez	Ownership: Privately Held
Fax: 210-726-6647	Employees: 850	

Banks - Southwest

INTERNATIONAL TESTING SERVICES, INC.

363 N. Sam Houston Pkwy. East	CEO: Aurelio Madrazo	1994 Sales: $15.5 million
Houston, TX 77060	CFO: John B. Connally III	1-Yr. Sales Change: -40.6%
Phone: 713-591-8880	HR: Sandy Evenson	Exchange: Pink Sheets
Fax: 713-591-6312	Employees: 296	Symbol: ITST

Oil & gas - field services

INTERPHASE CORPORATION

13800 Senlac	CEO: R. Stephen Polley	1994 Sales: $40.6 million
Dallas, TX 75234	CFO: Robert L. Drury	1-Yr. Sales Change: 4.1%
Phone: 214-919-9000	HR: Paula Jandura	Exchange: Nasdaq
Fax: 214-919-9200	Employees: 188	Symbol: INPH

Computers - disk drive controller subsystems

INTERSYSTEMS, INC.

8790 Wallisville Rd.	CEO: Fred S. Zeidman	1994 Sales: $15 million
Houston, TX 77029-0769	CFO: Daniel T. Murphy	1-Yr. Sales Change: 22.0%
Phone: 713-675-0307	HR: Karen Roe	Exchange: AMEX
Fax: 713-672-0923	Employees: 151	Symbol: II

Machinery - material handling equipment

INTERVOICE, INC.

17811 Waterview Pkwy.	CEO: Daniel D. Hammond	1995 Sales: $76.3 million
Dallas, TX 75252	CFO: Rob-Roy J. Graham	1-Yr. Sales Change: 25.3%
Phone: 214-454-8862	HR: H. Don Brown	Exchange: Nasdaq
Fax: 214-454-8905	Employees: 634	Symbol: INTV

Telecommunications equipment - phone-call automation equipment

IRATA, INC.

6150 Richmond Ave., Ste. 116	CEO: Robert A. Searles Jr.	1994 Sales: $1.3 million
Houston, TX 77057	CFO: Merlon G. Morgan	1-Yr. Sales Change: 225.0%
Phone: 713-785-4433	HR: Katie Kirby	Exchange: Nasdaq (SC)
Fax: 713-785-1966	Employees: 12	Symbol: IRATA

Computerized self-service photo booths

JACKSON AND WALKER LLP

901 Main St.	CEO: Mike Wilson	1994 Est. Sales: $100 mil.
Dallas, TX 75202	CFO: Rick Herlan	1-Yr. Sales Change: 0.0%
Phone: 214-953-6000	HR: Gail Horne	Ownership: Privately Held
Fax: 214-953-5822	Employees: 400	

Law firm

JACKSONVILLE SAVINGS AND LOAN ASSOCIATION

Commerce and Neches Sts.	CEO: Charles Broadway	1994 Sales: $13.9 million
Jacksonville, TX 75766	CFO: Bill W. Taylor	1-Yr. Sales Change: -10.3%
Phone: 903-586-9861	HR: —	Exchange: Nasdaq (SC)
Fax: 903-586-5044	Employees: 66	Symbol: JXVL
Financial - savings & loan		

JAGEE CORP

3228 Camp Bowie Rd.	CEO: Richard F. Garvey	1995 Sales: $200 million
Fort Worth, TX 76107	CFO: Bedford Bursher	1-Yr. Sales Change: —
Phone: 817-335-5881	HR: Richard Garvey	Ownership: Privately Held
Fax: 817-335-1905	Employees: 255	

Agricultural operations - grains wholesaler

JAYARK CORPORATION

PO Box 741528	CEO: David L. Koffman	1995 Sales: $48.4 million
Houston, TX 77027	CFO: Clayton Whitehead	1-Yr. Sales Change: -3.8%
Phone: 713-783-9184	HR: —	Exchange: Nasdaq (SC)
Fax: 713-783-7850	Employees: 101	Symbol: JAYA

Wholesale distribution - furniture, brass & jewelry cases; audio & video equipment leasing

JAYHAWK ACCEPTANCE CORPORATION

13455 Noel Rd. Ste. 1800	CEO: Michael I. Smartt	1994 Sales: $5.8 million
Dallas, TX 75240	CFO: Jerry W. Bayless	1-Yr. Sales Change: —
Phone: 214-663-1000	HR: Cameron Chandler	Exchange: Nasdaq
Fax: 214-663-1355	Employees: 200	Symbol: JACC

Financial - used car & accounts receivable financing

J. C. PENNEY COMPANY, INC.

6501 Legacy Dr.	CEO: James E. Oesterreicher	1995 Sales: $20,380 million
Plano, TX 75024-3698	CFO: Robert E. Northam	1-Yr. Sales Change: 7.4%
Phone: 214-431-1000	HR: Gale Duff-Bloom	Exchange: NYSE
Fax: 214-431-1977	Employees: 202,000	Symbol: JCP

Retail - major department stores, catalog stores & drugstores

 See pages 110–111 for a full profile of this company.

JRL SYSTEMS INC.

8305 Hwy. 71 West
Austin, TX 78735
Phone: 512-288-6750
Fax: 512-288-7676

CEO: Fred Klingensmith
CFO: Larry Hall
HR: Jan Johnson
Employees: 25

1994 Sales: $8 million
1-Yr. Sales Change: —
Ownership: Privately Held

Computers - high resolution printers & plotters

JUSTIN INDUSTRIES, INC.

2821 W. 7th St.
Fort Worth, TX 76107
Phone: 817-336-5125
Fax: 817-390-2477

CEO: John Justin
CFO: Richard J. Savitz
HR: John Bennett
Employees: 5,007

1994 Sales: $483 million
1-Yr. Sales Change: 1.7%
Exchange: Nasdaq
Symbol: JSTN

Diversified operations - boots (Tony Lama); building materials (Acme Brick); evaporative coolers; publishing (Northland)

KAISER ALUMINUM CORPORATION

5847 San Felipe, Ste. 2600
Houston, TX 77057-3010
Phone: 713-267-3777
Fax: 713-267-3710

CEO: George T. Haymaker Jr.
CFO: John T. La Duc
HR: James P. McKnight
Employees: 9,744

1994 Sales: $1,781.5 million
1-Yr. Sales Change: 3.6%
Exchange: NYSE
Symbol: KLU

Metals - aluminum

KANEB PIPE LINE PARTNERS, L.P.

2435 N. Central Expwy.
Richardson, TX 75080
Phone: 214-699-4000
Fax: 214-699-4025

CEO: Leon E. Hutchens
CFO: Howard C. Wadsworth
HR: William Kettler
Employees: 144

1994 Sales: $78.7 million
1-Yr. Sales Change: 13.7%
Exchange: NYSE
Symbol: KPP

Oil & gas - production & pipeline

KANEB SERVICES, INC.

2435 N. Central Expwy.
Richardson, TX 75080
Phone: 214-699-4000
Fax: 214-699-4025

CEO: John R. Barnes
CFO: Tony M. Regan
HR: William Kettler
Employees: 2,134

1994 Sales: $208.7 million
1-Yr. Sales Change: 5.1%
Exchange: NYSE
Symbol: KAB

Oil & gas - petroleum pipeline & storage facilities; industrial services such as leak sealing, machining, bolting, valve testing & repair

 **See page 194 for a full profile of this company.**

KBK CAPITAL CORPORATION

301 Commerce St., Ste. 2200	CEO: Robert J. McGee	1994 Sales: $6.9 million
Fort Worth, TX 77251-1642	CFO: Michael D. Magill	1-Yr. Sales Change: 9.5%
Phone: 817-335-7557	HR: Deborah S. Cain	Exchange: Nasdaq
Fax: 817-335-9339	Employees: 55	Symbol: KBKC

Financial - accounts-receivable financing

KELLEY OIL & GAS CORPORATION

601 Jefferson St., Ste. 1100	CEO: David L. Kelley	1994 Sales: $59.8 million
Houston, TX 77002	CFO: W. Matt Ralls	1-Yr. Sales Change: -20.5%
Phone: 713-652-5200	HR: Jerri Weller	Exchange: Nasdaq
Fax: 713-652-5235	Employees: 98	Symbol: KOGC

Oil & gas - US exploration & production

KENT ELECTRONICS CORPORATION

7433 Harwin Dr.	CEO: Morrie K. Abramson	1995 Sales: $253.5 million
Houston, TX 77036-2015	CFO: Stephen J. Chapko	1-Yr. Sales Change: 31.4%
Phone: 713-780-7770	HR: Pam Huffman	Exchange: NYSE
Fax: 713-978-5892	Employees: 957	Symbol: KNT

Electrical components - custom contract manufacturer & distributor of wire, cable & electronic connectors & components

 See page 195 for a full profile of this company.

KEYSTONE CONSOLIDATED INDUSTRIES, INC.

5430 LBJ Fwy., Ste. 1740	CEO: Glenn R. Simmons	1994 Sales: $364.5 million
Dallas, TX 75240	CFO: Harold M. Curdy	1-Yr. Sales Change: 5.4%
Phone: 214-458-0028	HR: Kathy Brownlee	Exchange: NYSE
Fax: 214-458-8108	Employees: 2,000	Symbol: KES

Carbon steel rods, wires & fabricated wire products

KEYSTONE INTERNATIONAL, INC.

9600 W. Gulf Bank Dr., PO Box 40010	CEO: Nishan Teshoian	1994 Sales: $535.1 million
Houston, TX 77240	CFO: Mark E. Baldwin	1-Yr. Sales Change: 3.7%
Phone: 713-466-1176	HR: Kathy Ruf	Exchange: NYSE
Fax: 713-937-5453	Employees: 4,200	Symbol: KII

Instruments - valves & actuators to regulate the movement of liquids, gases & solid materials in industries such as food processing, paper production, power generation & chemical processing

 See page 196 for a full profile of this company.

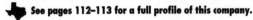

KIMBERLY-CLARK CORPORATION

DFW Airport Station, PO Box 619100	CEO: Wayne R. Sanders	1994 Sales: $7,364.2 million
Dallas, TX 75261-9100	CFO: John W. Donehower	1-Yr. Sales Change: 5.6%
Phone: 214-830-1200	HR: Bruce J. Olson	Exchange: NYSE
Fax: 214-830-1490	Employees: 42,707	Symbol: KMB

Paper & paper products - facial tissues (Kleenex), diapers (Huggies), tampons (Kotex), towels & napkins

 See pages 112–113 for a full profile of this company.

KINETIC CONCEPTS, INC.

8023 Vantage Dr.	CEO: Raymond R. Hannigan	1994 Sales: $269.6 million
San Antonio, TX 78230-	CFO: Bianca A. Rhodes	1-Yr. Sales Change: 0.3%
Phone: 210-524-9000	HR: Larry Baker	Exchange: Nasdaq
Fax: 210-554-1727	Employees: 1,938	Symbol: KNCI

Medical products - therapeutic beds & equipment (RotoRest, FirstStep, HomeKair, NuTech, TriaDyne, BariKare) for victims of serious burns, cancer, severe arthritis & other acute illnesses

KING RANCH, INC.

10055 Grogan's Mill Rd., Ste. 100	CEO: Jack Hunt	1994 Est. Sales: $250 mil.
The Woodlands, TX 77380	CFO: Mark Kent	1-Yr. Sales Change: 0.0%
Phone: 713-367-7300	HR: Rickey Blackman	Ownership: Privately Held
Fax: 713-367-7332	Employees: 700	

Agricultural operations - cattle & horse ranching, cotton, sugar cane, corn, wheat, sorghum, sod, wild-flowers; real estate; oil & gas exploration

 See pages 114–115 for a full profile of this company.

KINSEL MOTORS INC.

415 S. 11th St.	CEO: Joe B. KinselJr.	1994 Est. Sales: $90 mil.
Beaumont, TX 77702	CFO: Steven Odle	1-Yr. Sales Change: -2.2%
Phone: 409-838-6611	HR: Steven Odle	Ownership: Privately Held
Fax: 409-838-0663	Employees: 300	

Retail - automobiles

KIRBY CORPORATION

1775 St. James Place, Ste. 300	CEO: J. H. Pyne	1994 Sales: $433.1 million
Houston, TX 77056-3453	CFO: Brian K. Harrington	1-Yr. Sales Change: 14.5%
Phone: 713-629-9370	HR: Jack M. Sims	Exchange: AMEX
Fax: 713-964-2200	Employees: 2,300	Symbol: KEX

Diversified operations - petrochemical transport; diesel repair; insurance

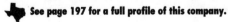 **See page 197 for a full profile of this company.**

KITTY HAWK, INC.

1515 W. 20th St.	CEO: M. Tom Christopher	1994 Sales: $107.7 million
Dallas, TX 75261	CFO: Richard R. Wadsworth	1-Yr. Sales Change: 63.7%
Phone: 214-456-2200	HR: Lena Knowlton	Ownership: Privately Held
Fax: 214-456-2210	Employees: 204	

Transportation - air-charter management & cargo services

 See page 198 for a full profile of this company.

K.S.A. INDUSTRIES INC.

6910 Fannin St.	CEO: Kenneth S. Adams Jr.	1994 Est. Sales: $110 mil.
Houston, TX 77030	CFO: Scott Thompson	1-Yr. Sales Change: —
Phone: 713-797-1500	HR: Norma Russell	Ownership: Privately Held
Fax: 713-797-6631	Employees: 165	

Diversified - professional football team (Houston Oilers); oil & gas; farms & ranches; new & used cars

LA QUINTA INNS, INC.

112 E. Pecan St., PO Box 2636	CEO: Gary L. Mead	1994 Sales: $362.2 million
San Antonio, TX 78299-2636	CFO: Michael A. Depatie	1-Yr. Sales Change: 33.2%
Phone: 210-302-6000	HR: Robert T. Foley	Exchange: NYSE
Fax: 210-302-6191	Employees: 5,800	Symbol: LQI

Hotels & motels - accomodations primarily in Texas & other sunbelt states for the budget-minded business traveler

 See page 199 for a full profile of this company.

LAMAR UNIVERSITY

4600 MLK Pkwy.	CEO: James Cottle	1994 Sales: $114.6 million
Beaumont, TX 77710	CFO: Sue Tellier	1-Yr. Sales Change: 2.4%
Phone: 409-880-7011	HR: Joann Birkner	Ownership: Privately Held
Fax: 409-880-8409	Employees: 1,050	

University - offering 62 undergraduate & 30 graduate degree programs

LANCER CORPORATION

235 W. Turbo	CEO: George F. Schroeder	1994 Sales: $70.9 million
San Antonio, TX 78216	CFO: Dennis D. Stout	1-Yr. Sales Change: 25.0%
Phone: 210-344-3071	HR: Irene Garza	Exchange: AMEX
Fax: 210-344-8174	Employees: 1,172	Symbol: LAN

Machinery - fountain soft drink & citrus beverage dispensing systems & other equipment for use in the food service & beverage industry

L&H PACKING COMPANY INC.

647 Steves
San Antonio, TX 78210
Phone: 210-532-3241
Fax: 210-532-3399

CEO: Kenneth Leonard
CFO: Terry Black
HR: Fred Pokrant
Employees: 500

1994 Est. Sales: $130 mil.
1-Yr. Sales Change: —
Ownership: Privately Held

Food - wholesale meats & meat products

LANDMARK GRAPHICS CORPORATION

15150 Memorial Dr.
Houston, TX 77079-4304
Phone: 713-560-1000
Fax: 713-560-1410

CEO: Robert P. Peebler
CFO: William H. Seippel
HR: Daniel Casaccia
Employees: 900

1995 Sales: $171.2 million
1-Yr. Sales Change: 29.4%
Exchange: Nasdaq
Symbol: LMRK

Computers - geoscientific exploration software (CAEX) & systems for the oil & gas industry

 See page 200 for a full profile of this company.

LANDRY'S SEAFOOD RESTAURANTS, INC.

1400 Post Oak Blvd., Ste. 1010
Houston, TX 77056
Phone: 713-850-1010
Fax: 713-623-4702

CEO: Tilman J. Fertitta
CFO: Paul S. West
HR: Rex E. Lee
Employees: 2,500

1994 Sales: $62.5 million
1-Yr. Sales Change: 82.7%
Exchange: Nasdaq
Symbol: LDRY

Retail - seafood restaurants in Texas & Louisiana

 See page 201 for a full profile of this company.

LAWRENCE MARSHALL CHEVROLET-OLDS, INC.

905 Austin
Hempstead, TX 77445
Phone: 409-826-2411
Fax: 409-826-2411

CEO: Lawrence Marshall
CFO: Kenneth Siber
HR: Elizabeth Moore
Employees: 250

1994 Est. Sales: $150 mil.
1-Yr. Sales Change: —
Ownership: Privately Held

Retail - new & used cars

THE LEATHER FACTORY, INC.

3847 E. Loop 820 South
Fort Worth, TX 76119
Phone: 817-496-4414
Fax: 817-496-9806

CEO: Wray Thompson
CFO: John R. Tittle Jr.
HR: Robin Morgan
Employees: 325

1994 Sales: $28.1 million
1-Yr. Sales Change: 15.2%
Exchange: AMEX
Symbol: TLF

Leather & related products - leather, leatherworking tools, buckles & other belt supplies, shoe care & repair supplies, hat trims, leather dyes & finishes, saddle & tack hardware & do-it-yourself kits

LEE LEWIS CONSTRUCTION, INC.

7810 Orlando Ave.	CEO: Lee Lewis	1994 Est. Sales: $60 mil.
Lubbock, TX 79423	CFO: Jim Hester	1-Yr. Sales Change: —
Phone: 806-797-8400	HR: —	Ownership: Privately Held
Fax: 806-797-8492	Employees: 150	

Building - commercial & industrial buildings

LENNOX INTERNATIONAL INC.

2100 Lake Park Blvd.	CEO: John W. Norris Jr.	1994 Sales: $1,000 million
Richardson, TX 75080	CFO: Clyde Wyant	1-Yr. Sales Change: -4.8%
Phone: 214-497-5017	HR: Harry Ashenhurst	Ownership: Privately Held
Fax: 214-497-5299	Employees: 11,000	

Building products - air conditioning & heating

LEVIATHAN GAS PIPELINE PARTNERS, L.P.

600 Travis St.	CEO: Grant E. Sims	1994 Sales: $34.1 million
Houston, TX 77002	CFO: Keith B. Forman	1-Yr. Sales Change: 21.8%
Phone: 713-224-7400	HR: John Gray	Exchange: NYSE
Fax: 713-224-7574	Employees: 25	Symbol: LEV

Utility - gas distribution

LIFE INSURANCE COMPANY OF THE SOUTHWEST

1300 W. Mockingbird	CEO: Wade Mayo	1994 Sales: $159 million
Dallas, TX 75247	CFO: Michael F. Goni	1-Yr. Sales Change: 11.2%
Phone: 214-638-7100	HR: Susan Jennings	Ownership: Privately Held
Fax: 214-638-9170	Employees: 121	

Insurance - annuity sales & life insurance products

LIFECELL CORPORATION

3606 Research Forest Dr.	CEO: Paul M. Frison	1994 Sales: $0.9 million
The Woodlands, TX 77381	CFO: Anthony A. Brown	1-Yr. Sales Change: 50.0%
Phone: 713-367-5368	HR: Judy Colyn	Exchange: Nasdaq (SC)
Fax: 713-363-3360	Employees: 50	Symbol: LIFC

Medical products - universal tissue grafts & preserved blood cells

LIFEQUEST MEDICAL, INC.

9601 McAllister Fwy., Ste. 1120
San Antonio, TX 78216
Phone: 210-366-2100
Fax: 210-349-0500

CEO: Herbert H. Spoon
CFO: Randall K. Boatright
HR: Randall K. Boatright
Employees: 8

1994 Sales: $0.4 million
1-Yr. Sales Change: 0.0%
Exchange: Nasdaq
Symbol: LQMD

Medical products - vascular access devices

LINBECK CONSTRUCTION CORPORATION

3810 W. Alabama
Houston, TX 77027
Phone: 713-621-2350
Fax: 713-840-7525

CEO: Leo Linbeck
CFO: Glen Graff
HR: John Sylvester
Employees: 150

1994 Est. Sales: $110 mil.
1-Yr. Sales Change: —
Ownership: Privately Held

Building - contractors of commercial & health care facilities

LINCOLN PROPERTY COMPANY

500 N. Akard, Ste. 3300
Dallas, TX 75201
Phone: 214-740-3300
Fax: 214-740-3313

CEO: Mack Pogue
CFO: Mark Wallis
HR: Connie Rutledge
Employees: 4,200

1994 Sales: $790 million
1-Yr. Sales Change: -21.0%
Ownership: Privately Held

Real estate development & management

LIVING CENTERS OF AMERICA, INC.

15415 Katy Fwy., Ste. 800
Houston, TX 77094
Phone: 713-578-4600
Fax: 713-578-4735

CEO: Edward L. Kuntz
CFO: C. William Frank
HR: Tom Gillson
Employees: 17,800

1994 Sales: $499 million
1-Yr. Sales Change: 28.3%
Exchange: NYSE
Symbol: LCA

Nursing homes

LL&E ROYALTY TRUST

712 Main St.
Houston, TX 77002
Phone: 713-216-6369
Fax: 713-216-5476

CEO: Michael J. Ulrich
CFO: Mary V.K. Morris
HR: —
Employees: —

1994 Sales: $10.4 million
1-Yr. Sales Change: 14.3%
Exchange: NYSE
Symbol: LRT

Oil & gas - US royalty trust

LOCKE PURNELL RAIN HARRELL

2200 Ross Ave.
Dallas, TX 75201
Phone: 214-740-8000
Fax: 214-740-8800

Law firm

CEO: Robert F. See Jr.
CFO: Richard Woodmansee
HR: Mark Florence
Employees: 400

1994 Est. Sales: $120 mil.
1-Yr. Sales Change: 0.0%
Ownership: Privately Held

LOMAK PETROLEUM, INC.

500 Throckmorton St., Ste. 2104
Fort Worth, TX 76102-3708
Phone: 817-870-2601
Fax: 817-870-2316

Oil & gas - US exploration & production

CEO: John H. Pinkerton
CFO: Thomas W. Stoelk
HR: Sally Hayes
Employees: 220

1994 Sales: $34.8 million
1-Yr. Sales Change: 82.2%
Exchange: Nasdaq
Symbol: LOMK

LOMAS FINANCIAL CORPORATION

1600 Viceroy Dr.
Dallas, TX 75235
Phone: 214-879-4000
Fax: 214-879-5589

Financial - real estate investment management & mortgage banking

CEO: Eric D. Booth
CFO: Gary White
HR: Jim Alleman
Employees: 2,146

1994 Sales: $271 million
1-Yr. Sales Change: -12.0%
Exchange: NYSE
Symbol: LFC

LONE STAR CASINO CORPORATION

One Riverway, Ste. 2550
Houston, TX 77050
Phone: 713-960-9881
Fax: 702-871-4131

Gambling resorts & casinos in Central City, CO (Papone's Palace)

CEO: Paul J. Montle
CFO: Roger Cope
HR: —
Employees: 63

1994 Sales: $2.3 million
1-Yr. Sales Change: 1,050%
Exchange: Nasdaq (SC)
Symbol: LONE

LONE STAR TECHNOLOGIES, INC.

5501 LBJ Fwy., Ste. 1200
Dallas, TX 75240
Phone: 214-386-3981
Fax: 214-770-6471

Steel - production; oil field products

CEO: John P. Harbin
CFO: Judith A. Murrell
HR: —
Employees: 1,592

1994 Sales: $357 million
1-Yr. Sales Change: 7.4%
Exchange: Nasdaq
Symbol: LSST

LUBY'S CAFETERIAS, INC.

2211 NE Loop 410, PO Box 33069
San Antonio, TX 78265-3069
Phone: 210-654-9000
Fax: 210-654-3211

Retail - cafeterias

CEO: Ralph Erben
CFO: John E. Curtis Jr.
HR: —
Employees: 10,100

1994 Sales: $390.7 million
1-Yr. Sales Change: 6.2%
Exchange: NYSE
Symbol: LUB

 See page 202 for a full profile of this company.

LUCKY LADY OIL COMPANY

107 NW 28th St.
Fort Worth, TX 76106
Phone: 817-740-7400
Fax: 817-740-0245

Oil & gas distribution; convenience stores

CEO: Sue Palmer
CFO: Charles Kirk
HR: Karen Mogonye
Employees: 260

1994 Sales: $89.3 million
1-Yr. Sales Change: —
Ownership: Privately Held

LUFKIN INDUSTRIES, INC.

601 S. Raguet, PO Box 849
Lufkin, TX 75902
Phone: 409-634-2211
Fax: 409-637-5474

CEO: Douglas V. Smith
CFO: C. James Haley Jr.
HR: Paul Perez
Employees: 1,950

1994 Sales: $217.3 million
1-Yr. Sales Change: 7.5%
Exchange: Nasdaq
Symbol: LUFK

Power transmission products, oil field pumping units, foundry castings & highway trailers

LYONDELL PETROCHEMICAL COMPANY

1221 McKinney St., Ste. 1600
Houston, TX 77010
Phone: 713-652-7200
Fax: 713-652-7430

CEO: Robert G. Gower
CFO: Russell S. Young
HR: Richard W. Park
Employees: 2,263

1994 Sales: $3,857 million
1-Yr. Sales Change: 0.2%
Exchange: NYSE
Symbol: LYO

Chemicals - ethylene, propylene & other petrochemicals

 See pages 116–117 for a full profile of this company.

MAPLINX CORPORATION

5068 W. Plano Pkwy.
Plano, TX 75093-5099
Phone: 214-231-1400
Fax: 214-248-2690

CEO: William McNeil
CFO: Randy Bradford
HR: Ronna Alexander
Employees: 12

1994 Est. Sales: $1 mil.
1-Yr. Sales Change: —
Ownership: Privately Held

Computers - database mapping utilities (MapLinx 3.0 for Windows & Macintosh)

THE M/A/R/C GROUP

7850 N. Belt Line Rd.	CEO: Sharon M. Munger	1994 Sales: $68.5 million
Irving, TX 75063	CFO: Harold R. Curtis	1-Yr. Sales Change: 10.1%
Phone: 214-506-3400	HR: Jim Farrell	Exchange: Nasdaq
Fax: 214-500-3416	Employees: 1,010	Symbol: MARC

Business services - management consulting, marketing research & database marketing

MARCUS CABLE COMPANY L.P.

2911 Turtle Creek Blvd., Ste. 1300	CEO: Jeffrey A. Marcus	1994 Sales: $65 million
Dallas, TX 75219	CFO: Tom McMillin	1-Yr. Sales Change: —
Phone: 214-521-7898	HR: Cindy Mannes	Ownership: Privately Held
Fax: 214-526-2154	Employees: 1,035	

Cable TV systems

MARINE DRILLING COMPANIES, INC.

One Sugar Creek Center Blvd., Ste. 600	CEO: William O. Keyes	1994 Sales: $70.6 million
Sugar Land, TX 77478-3556	CFO: William H. Flores	1-Yr. Sales Change: -14.9%
Phone: 713-243-3000	HR: Gayle Schmidt	Exchange: Nasdaq
Fax: 713-243-9090	Employees: 670	Symbol: MDCO

Oil & gas - field services

MARINE PETROLEUM TRUST

NationsBank of Texas, PO Box 831402	CEO: Kathy McQuistion	1994 Sales: $3.3 million
Dallas, TX 75283	CFO: R. Ray Bell	1-Yr. Sales Change: 26.9%
Phone: 214-508-1792	HR: —	Exchange: Nasdaq (SC)
Fax: 214-508-3430	Employees: 1	Symbol: MARPS

Oil & gas - US royalty trust

MARTIN GAS CORPORATION

101 E. Sabine	CEO: R. S. Martin Jr.	1994 Est. Sales: $190 mil.
Kilgore, TX 75662	CFO: Robert D. Bondurant	1-Yr. Sales Change: —
Phone: 903-983-1551	HR: Wes Skelton	Ownership: Privately Held
Fax: 903-983-6211	Employees: 600	

Utility - liquefied petroleum gas distribution

MARY KAY COSMETICS INC.

8787 Stemmons Fwy.
Dallas, TX 75247
Phone: 214-630-8787
Fax: 214-905-5699

CEO: John P. Rochon
CFO: Ronald L. Smith
HR: Tim Wentworth
Employees: 2,400

1994 Sales: $850 million
1-Yr. Sales Change: 15.3%
Ownership: Privately Held

Cosmetics & toiletries, including fragrances & bath & body products

 See pages 118–119 for a full profile of this company.

MAVERICK MARKETS INC.

5440 Old Brownsville
Corpus Christi, TX 78469
Phone: 512-289-1585
Fax: 512-289-7824

CEO: Erich Wendl
CFO: Ricardo Elizondo
HR: Joe McGlen
Employees: 600

1994 Est. Sales: $110 mil.
1-Yr. Sales Change: 0.0%
Ownership: Privately Held

Retail - convenience stores

MAXSERV INC.

8317 Cross Park Dr., Ste. 350
Austin, TX 78754
Phone: 512-834-8341
Fax: 512-834-1137

CEO: Neil A. Johnson
CFO: Neil A. Johnson
HR: Steve Knowles
Employees: 660

1994 Sales: $15.7 million
1-Yr. Sales Change: 109.3%
Exchange: Nasdaq (SC)
Symbol: MXSV

Repair of TVs, VCRs, washers, dryers & other electronic appliances

MAXXAM INC.

5847 San Felipe, Ste. 2600
Houston, TX 77257-2887
Phone: 713-975-7600
Fax: 713-267-3701

CEO: Charles E. Hurwitz
CFO: Paul N. Schwartz
HR: Diane M. Dudley
Employees: 13,860

1994 Sales: $2,115.7 million
1-Yr. Sales Change: 4.2%
Exchange: AMEX
Symbol: MXM

Diversified operations - forest products; real estate development; aluminum

 See pages 120–121 for a full profile of this company.

MAXXIM MEDICAL, INC.

104 Industrial Blvd.
Sugar Land, TX 77478
Phone: 713-240-5588
Fax: 713-240-2577

CEO: Kenneth W. Davidson
CFO: Peter M. Graham
HR: Donna Hustis
Employees: 1,626

1994 Sales: $191.4 million
1-Yr. Sales Change: 47.6%
Exchange: NYSE
Symbol: MAM

Medical products - physical therapy & pain management products

 See page 203 for a full profile of this company.

MAYNARD OIL COMPANY

8080 N. Central Expwy., Ste. 660	CEO: James G. Maynard	1994 Sales: $13.4 million
Dallas, TX 75206	CFO: Kenneth W. Hatcher	1-Yr. Sales Change: -10.7%
Phone: 214-891-8880	HR: —	Exchange: Nasdaq
Fax: 214-891-8827	Employees: 32	Symbol: MOIL

Oil & gas - US exploration & production

MCCOY CORPORATION

1200 IH-35 North	CEO: Emmett F. McCoy	1994 Est. Sales: $400 mil.
San Marcos, TX 78667	CFO: Chuck Churchwell	1-Yr. Sales Change: —
Phone: 512-353-5400	HR: Rick Bell	Ownership: Privately Held
Fax: 512-392-2950	Employees: 1,600	

Building products - retail lumber & other building materials; hardware stores; paint, glass & wallpaper stores

THE MEADOWS FOUNDATION, INC.

3003 Swiss Ave.	CEO: Curtis Meadows Jr.	1994 Est. Sales: $37 mil.
Dallas, TX 75204-6090	CFO: Robert E. Wise	1-Yr. Sales Change: —
Phone: 214-826-9431	HR: Robert Weiss	Ownership: Privately Held
Fax: 214-823-1723	Employees: 45	

Charitable foundation providing grants in 5 areas: arts & culture; civic & public affairs; education; health; human services

MEDICAL INNOVATIONS, INC.

One Riverway, Ste. 2300	CEO: Mark H. Fisher	1994 Sales: $59.1 million
Houston, TX 77056	CFO: David C. Horn	1-Yr. Sales Change: 76.4%
Phone: 713-688-6600	HR: Tom Clark	Exchange: Nasdaq (SC)
Fax: 713-888-0371	Employees: 670	Symbol: MIXX

Health care - home nursing services, outpatient services & home intravenous therapies

MEDICAL RESOURCE COMPANIES OF AMERICA

4265 Kellway Circle	CEO: James R. Gilley	1994 Sales: $17 million
Addison, TX 75244-2033	CFO: Gene S. Bertcher	1-Yr. Sales Change: -17.9%
Phone: 214-407-8400	HR: —	Exchange: AMEX
Fax: 214-407-8421	Employees: 11	Symbol: MRA

Health care - residential retirement & mobility assistance services

MEDICALCONTROL, INC.

9649 Webb Chapel Rd., Ste. 500
Dallas, TX 75220
Phone: 214-352-2666
Fax: 214-352-5777

CEO: John W. Hunt
CFO: Abraham J. Rosmarin
HR: Cindy Orie
Employees: 244

1994 Sales: $9.4 million
1-Yr. Sales Change: 51.6%
Exchange: Nasdaq
Symbol: MDCL

Health maintenance organization - insurance costs management for self-insured businesses

MEMOREX TELEX N.V.

545 E. John Carpenter Fwy.
Irving , TX 75062-3931
Phone: 214-444-3500
Fax: 214-444-3501

CEO: Marcelo A. Gumucio
CFO: Rudolph G. Morin
HR: Rudolph G. Morin
Employees: 4,500

1995 Sales: $909.8 million
1-Yr. Sales Change: -10.4%
Exchange: Nasdaq
Symbol: MEMXY (ADR)

Computers -systems integration, data storage products & service support

 See page 204 for a full profile of this company.

MEMORIAL HEALTHCARE SYSTEM

7737 Southwest Fwy., Ste. 200
Houston, TX 77074
Phone: 713-776-5484
Fax: 713-776-6978

CEO: Dan S. Wilford
CFO: John D. Gay
HR: R. Eugene Ross
Employees: 6,428

1994 Sales: $470.8 million
1-Yr. Sales Change: 5.7%
Ownership: Privately Held

Hospitals - not-for-profit system serving the Houston area, including acute-care hospitals, home health services & retirement centers

THE MEN'S WEARHOUSE, INC.

5803 Glenmont Dr.
Houston, TX 77081
Phone: 713-295-7200
Fax: 713-664-1957

CEO: George Zimmer
CFO: David H. Edwab
HR: Julie Maciag
Employees: 3,190

1995 Sales: $317.1 million
1-Yr. Sales Change: 31.9%
Exchange: Nasdaq
Symbol: SUIT

Retail - men's clothing stores

 See page 205 for a full profile of this company.

MERICHEM CO.

4800 Texas Commerce
Houston, TX 77002
Phone: 713-224-3030
Fax: 713-224-4403

CEO: John T. Files
CFO: O. R. Cable
HR: Steven Trncak
Employees: 300

1994 Est. Sales: $100 mil.
1-Yr. Sales Change: —
Ownership: Privately Held

Chemicals - cresylic acids & soda chemicals

MERIT STUDIOS, INC.

13707 Gamma Rd.	CEO: Jack E. Irons	1994 Sales: $4 million
Dallas, TX 75244	CFO: W. D. Hollon	1-Yr. Sales Change: 60.0%
Phone: 214-385-2353	HR: Linda Herrington	Exchange: OTC
Fax: 214-385-8205	Employees: 55	Symbol: MRIPP

Computers - edutainment software distribution

MESA INC.

5205 N. O'Conner Blvd., Ste. 1400	CEO: T. Boone Pickens	1994 Sales: $228.7 million
Irving, TX 75039-3746	CFO: Stephen K. Gardner	1-Yr. Sales Change: 2.9%
Phone: 214-444-9001	HR: Paul M. Cashion	Exchange: NYSE
Fax: 214-402-7023	Employees: 399	Symbol: MXP

Oil & gas - US exploration & production

 See page 206 for a full profile of this company.

MESA ROYALTY TRUST

712 Main St.	CEO: David Snyder	1994 Sales: $7 million
Houston, TX 77002	CFO: David Snyder	1-Yr. Sales Change: 18.6%
Phone: 713-216-5100	HR: —	Exchange: NYSE
Fax: 713-236-5476	Employees: —	Symbol: MTR

Oil & gas - US royalty trust

METAL RECOVERY TECHNOLOGIES, INC.

9600 Long Pt., Ste. 101	CEO: Michael S. Lucas	1994 Sales: $1 million
Houston, TX 77055	CFO: Roy Pearce	1-Yr. Sales Change: 11.1%
Phone: 713-722-9595	HR: —	Exchange: OTC
Fax: 713-722-9598	Employees: 15	Symbol: MRTI

Protection - automotive antitheft device (Malvy Device)

THE METHODIST HOSPITAL SYSTEM

6565 Fannin St.	CEO: Larry L. Mathis	1994 Sales: $470.2 million
Houston, TX 77030-2707	CFO: Ron Gerado	1-Yr. Sales Change: -8.3%
Phone: 713-790-3311	HR: Bill Fugauzzi	Ownership: Privately Held
Fax: 713-524-6831	Employees: 6,700	

Hospitals - not-for-profit system with 35 affiliated centers serving Houston, Mexico, Guatemala, Italy, Venezuela, Turkey & Peru

MICHAELS STORES, INC.

5931 Campus Circle Dr., PO Box 619566
Irving, TX 75063
Phone: 214-714-7000
Fax: 214-714-7155

CEO: Sam Wyly
CFO: R. Don Morris
HR: Donald C. Toby
Employees: 17,440

1995 Sales: $994.6 million
1-Yr. Sales Change: 60.5%
Exchange: Nasdaq
Symbol: MIKE

Retail - arts & crafts

See page 207 for a full profile of this company.

MICROELECTRONICS & COMPUTER TECHNOLOGY CORPORATION

3500 West Balcones Center Dr.
Austin, TX 78759
Phone: 512-343-0978
Fax: 512-338-3892

CEO: John W. McRary
CFO: Terrence Sullivan
HR: Roger Malek
Employees: 200

1994 Est. Sales: $40 mil.
1-Yr. Sales Change: —
Ownership: Privately Held

Computers - high-technology research consortium

MICROGRAFX, INC.

1303 Arapaho
Richardson, TX 75081
Phone: 214-234-1769
Fax: 214-994-6475

CEO: J. Paul Grayson
CFO: Gregory A. Peters
HR: Katie Rohlman
Employees: 251

1995 Sales: $60.7 million
1-Yr. Sales Change: 0.3%
Exchange: Nasdaq
Symbol: MGXI

Computers - high-powered graphics software for business, professional & home markets

MIDLAND RESOURCES, INC.

16701 Greenspoint Dr., Ste. 200
Houston, TX 77060
Phone: 713-873-4828
Fax: 713-873-5058

CEO: Deas H. Warley III
CFO: Deas H. Warley III
HR: Deas H. Warley III
Employees: 23

1994 Sales: $5.5 million
1-Yr. Sales Change: 17.0%
Exchange: Nasdaq (SC)
Symbol: MRIX

Financial - oil & gas property acquisition

MINYARD FOOD STORES INC.

777 Freeport Pkwy.
Coppell, TX 75019
Phone: 214-393-8700
Fax: 214-462-9407

CEO: J. L. "Sonny" Williams
CFO: Mario J. LaForte
HR: Alan Vaughan
Employees: 6,500

1994 Sales: $810 million
1-Yr. Sales Change: 5.2%
Ownership: Privately Held

Retail - supermarkets (81 units: Minyard, Carnival, Sack 'n Pack) & grocery distribution

MITCHAM INDUSTRIES, INC.

44000 Hwy. 75 South
Huntsville, TX 77340
Phone: 409-291-2277
Fax: 409-295-1922

CEO: Billy F. Mitcham Jr.
CFO: Roberto Rios
HR: Roberto Rios
Employees: 10

1995 Sales: $5.3 million
1-Yr. Sales Change: 17.8%
Exchange: Nasdaq (SC)
Symbol: MIND

Electronics - leasing & sale of seismic equipment to the oil & gas industry

MITCHELL ENERGY & DEVELOPMENT CORP.

2001 Timberloch Place, PO Box 4000
The Woodlands, TX 77387-4000
Phone: 713-377-5500
Fax: 713-377-6910

CEO: George P. Mitchell
CFO: Philip S. Smith
HR: Clyde Black
Employees: 2,900

1995 Sales: $894.6 million
1-Yr. Sales Change: -6.1%
Exchange: NYSE
Symbol: MNDA

Oil & gas - US exploration & production

MMI PRODUCTS INC.

515 W. Greens Rd.
Houston, TX 77067
Phone: 713-876-0080
Fax: 713-876-1648

CEO: Julius Burns
CFO: Bob Tewczar
HR: Vicki Viereck
Employees: 1,000

1994 Est. Sales: $150 mil.
1-Yr. Sales Change: —
Ownership: Privately Held

Wire & cable products - welded wire

MOBLEY ENVIRONMENTAL SERVICES, INC.

3800 Stone Rd.
Kilgore, TX 75663
Phone: 903-984-0270
Fax: 903-983-1227

CEO: Michael M. Stark
CFO: W. Christopher Chisholm
HR: Sammy Culpepper
Employees: 176

1994 Sales: $29.5 million
1-Yr. Sales Change: -17.1%
Exchange: Nasdaq
Symbol: MBLYA

Pollution control equipment & services - waste disposal & oil field services

THE MOODY FOUNDATION

2302 Postoffice St., Ste. 704
Galveston, TX 77550
Phone: 409-763-5333
Fax: 409-763-5564

CEO: Robert E. Baker
CFO: Robert E. Baker
HR: —
Employees: 16

1994 Est. Sales: $33 mil.
1-Yr. Sales Change: —
Ownership: Privately Held

Charitable foundation providing grants for historic restoration projects, arts & humanities organizations, health, science & education programs & religious organizations

MORNINGSTAR GROUP, INC.

5956 Sherry Ln., Ste. 1100
Dallas, TX 75225-6522
Phone: 214-360-4700
Fax: 214-360-9100

Food - specialty dairy products

CEO: C. Dean Metropoulos
CFO: Tracy L. Noll
HR: Mary Burns
Employees: 1,400

1994 Sales: $292.3 million
1-Yr. Sales Change: -26.3%
Exchange: Nasdaq
Symbol: MSTR

MRS. BAIRD'S BAKERIES INC.

7301 South Fwy.
Fort Worth, TX 76134
Phone: 817-293-6230
Fax: 817-568-3691

Food - bread & other baked goods

CEO: Allen Baird
CFO: Bradley Lummis
HR: Richard Haub
Employees: 3,000

1994 Sales: $230 million
1-Yr. Sales Change: —
Ownership: Privately Held

MUNDY COS.

11150 S. Wilcrest Dr.
Houston, TX 77099
Phone: 713-530-8711
Fax: 713-530-8561

Building - petrochemical plant & petroleum refinery repairs

CEO: Joe S. Mundy
CFO: David Hartsell
HR: William Nixon
Employees: 4,500

1994 Est. Sales: $200 mil.
1-Yr. Sales Change: —
Ownership: Privately Held

MUSTANG TRACTOR AND EQUIPMENT CO.

12800 Northwest Fwy.
Houston, TX 77040
Phone: 713-460-2000
Fax: 713-462-4032

Machinery - wholesaler of Caterpillar construction equipment

CEO: F. Louis Tucker Jr.
CFO: Bradford Tucker
HR: Anna Keys
Employees: 700

1994 Est. Sales: $175 mil.
1-Yr. Sales Change: —
Ownership: Privately Held

NAB ASSET CORPORATION

5851 San Felipe, Ste. 300
Houston, TX 77057
Phone: 713-952-6800
Fax: 713-952-6899

Banks - Southwest

CEO: Michael A. Hrebenar
CFO: Richard A. Durham
HR: Scott Kline
Employees: 27

1994 Sales: $3.4 million
1-Yr. Sales Change: 0.0%
Exchange: Nasdaq
Symbol: NABC

NABORS INDUSTRIES, INC.

515 W. Greens Rd., Ste. 1200
Houston, TX 77067
Phone: 713-874-0035
Fax: 713-872-5205

Oil & gas - land drilling services

CEO: Eugene M. Isenberg
CFO: Bruce P. Koch
HR: Daniel McLachlin
Employees: 4,833

1994 Sales: $422.6 million
1-Yr. Sales Change: 20.1%
Exchange: AMEX
Symbol: NBR

 See page 208 for a full profile of this company.

NATIONAL BANCSHARES CORPORATION OF TEXAS

I-35 at Mann Rd.
Laredo, TX 78040
Phone: 210-724-2424
Fax: 210-717-2734

Banks - Southwest

CEO: Jay H. Lustig
CFO: Anne Renfroe
HR: Dwayne Kolly
Employees: 147

1994 Sales: $18.5 million
1-Yr. Sales Change: 6.9%
Exchange: AMEX
Symbol: NBT

NATIONAL CONVENIENCE STORES INCORPORATED

100 Waugh Dr.
Houston, TX 77007
Phone: 713-863-2200
Fax: 713-880-0579

Retail - convenience stores (Stop N Go)

CEO: V. H. Van Horn
CFO: Brian Fontana
HR: —
Employees: 5,300

1994 Sales: $880.5 million
1-Yr. Sales Change: 0.2%
Exchange: Nasdaq (SC)
Symbol: NCSI

NATIONAL ENERGY GROUP, INC.

4925 Greenville Ave., Ste. 1400
Dallas, TX 75206
Phone: 214-692-9211
Fax: 214-692-9310

Oil & gas - production & exploration

CEO: Miles D. Bender
CFO: Robert A. Imel
HR: Melissa Rutledge
Employees: 12

1994 Sales: $3.2 million
1-Yr. Sales Change: 77.8%
Exchange: Nasdaq (SC)
Symbol: NRGIA

NATIONAL INCOME REALTY TRUST

3878 Oaklawn, Ste. 300
Dallas, TX 75219
Phone: 214-522-5172
Fax: 214-522-2241

Real estate investment trust - industrial & commercial properties

CEO: William S. Friedman
CFO: John Doyle
HR: —
Employees: —

1994 Sales: $40.1 million
1-Yr. Sales Change: 10.2%
Exchange: Nasdaq
Symbol: NIRTS

NATIONAL INSTRUMENTS CORPORATION

6504 Bridge Point Pkwy.
Austin, TX 78730
Phone: 512-250-9119
Fax: 512-794-8411

CEO: James J. Truchard
CFO: Joel B. Rollins
HR: Mark Finger
Employees: 892

1994 Sales: $127 million
1-Yr. Sales Change: 20.4%
Exchange: Nasdaq
Symbol: NATI

Computers - computer-based testing & measuring equipment for scientific & engineering applications

NATIONAL REALTY, L.P.

10670 N. Central Expwy., Ste. 300
Dallas, TX 75231
Phone: 214-692-4700
Fax: 214-890-0752

CEO: Gene E. Phillips
CFO: Hamilton P. Schrauff
HR: Lyn Kruger
Employees: 209

1994 Sales: $107.5 million
1-Yr. Sales Change: 4.4%
Exchange: AMEX
Symbol: NLP

Real estate operations

NATIONAL WESTERN LIFE INSURANCE COMPANY

850 E. Anderson Ln.
Austin, TX 78752-1602
Phone: 512-836-1010
Fax: 512-835-2729

CEO: Robert L. Moody
CFO: Robert L. Busby III
HR: Carol Jackson
Employees: 231

1994 Sales: $317 million
1-Yr. Sales Change: -16.0%
Exchange: Nasdaq
Symbol: NWLIA

Insurance - life; bond brokerage (Westcap)

NATIONAL-OILWELL

5555 San Felipe
Houston, TX 77056
Phone: 713-960-5100
Fax: 713-960-5428

CEO: Joel V. Staff
CFO: Diane Molinaro
HR: Gary Hooker
Employees: 3,000

1994 Sales: $562.1 million
1-Yr. Sales Change: -10.4%
Ownership: Privately Held

Production & drilling equipment & supplies for the oil & gas industry; oilfield pipe & related supplies distribution from 120 centers worldwide (Armco-USX joint venture)

NCH CORPORATION

2727 Chemsearch Blvd., PO Box 152170
Irving, TX 75015
Phone: 214-438-0211
Fax: 214-438-0186

CEO: Irvin L. Levy
CFO: Tom Hetzer
HR: Neil Thomas
Employees: 10,569

1995 Sales: $735.1 million
1-Yr. Sales Change: 8.1%
Exchange: NYSE
Symbol: NCH

Wholesale industrial - maintenance, repair & supply products, specialty chemicals, fasteners, welding supplies, plumbing, electronic parts & safety supplies

NCI BUILDING SYSTEMS, INC.

7301 Fairview	CEO: Johnie Schulte Jr.	1994 Sales: $167.8 million
Houston, TX 77041	CFO: Robert J. Medlock	1-Yr. Sales Change: 24.8%
Phone: 713-466-7788	HR: Karen Rosales	Exchange: Nasdaq
Fax: 713-466-3194	Employees: 1,224	Symbol: BLDG

Building products - prefabricated steel kits used to build schools, auto dealerships, shopping centers & restaurants

 See page 209 for a full profile of this company.

NDE ENVIRONMENTAL CORPORATION

8906 Wall St., Ste. 306	CEO: Daniel Sharplin	1994 Sales: $9.4 million
Austin, TX 78754	CFO: Rick Hopkins	1-Yr. Sales Change: 54.1%
Phone: 512-719-4633	HR: Amy Graham	Exchange: Pink Sheets
Fax: 512-719-5517	Employees: 110	Symbol: NDEC

Environmental compliance, information & management services to owners & operators of underground storage tanks

NEOSTAR RETAIL GROUP, INC.

10741 King William Dr.	CEO: James B. McCurry	1995 Sales: $503.7 million
Dallas, TX 75220	CFO: Opal P. Ferraro	1-Yr. Sales Change: 103.9%
Phone: 214-401-9000	HR: Michael A. Ivanich	Exchange: Nasdaq
Fax: 214-401-9002	Employees: 6,150	Symbol: NEOS

Computers - retail personal computer software (Babbage's, Software Etc.)

 See page 210 for a full profile of this company.

NEST ENTERTAINMENT

6100 Colwell Blvd.	CEO: Doug Martin	1994 Sales: $48.1 million
Irving, TX 75039	CFO: Marjean Henderson	1-Yr. Sales Change: -12.7%
Phone: 214-402-7100	HR: Jim Hess	Ownership: Privately Held
Fax: 214-402-7181	Employees: 225	

Toys - educational products for children

NETSOLVE INCORPORATED

9130 Jollyville Rd., Ste. 200	CEO: Craig Tysdal	1995 Sales: $19.5 million
Austin, TX 78759-7475	CFO: Kenneth C. Kieley	1-Yr. Sales Change: —
Phone: 512-795-3000	HR: Jenny Voight	Ownership: Privately Held
Fax: 512-795-3008	Employees: 70	

Computers - wide-area internetworking outsourcing services, including network design, equipment installation & network management

NETWORTH, INC.

8404 Esters Blvd.	CEO: John F. McHale	1995 Sales: $55.5 million
Irving, TX 75063	CFO: Paul S. Zito	1-Yr. Sales Change: 14.2%
Phone: 214-929-1700	HR: Cecelia Gannon	Exchange: Nasdaq
Fax: 214-929-1720	Employees: 196	Symbol: NWTH

Computers - intelligent hubs & switches for networks

 See page 211 for a full profile of this company.

NEW PROCESS STEEL CORP.

5800 Westview Dr.	CEO: E.R. Fant	1994 Est. Sales: $200 mil.
Houston, TX 77055	CFO: Jim Kollaja	1-Yr. Sales Change: —
Phone: 713-686-9631	HR: Jim Kollaja	Ownership: Privately Held
Fax: 713-686-5358	Employees: 250	

Metal products - service centers

NEWELL RECYCLING COMPANY INC.

726 Probandt	CEO: Alton S. Newell	1994 Est. Sales: $75 mil.
San Antonio, TX 78204	CFO: Shirley Canady	1-Yr. Sales Change: —
Phone: 210-227-3141	HR: —	Ownership: Privately Held
Fax: 210-227-8948	Employees: 200	

Metal products - wholesaler of processed scrap metals

NEWFIELD EXPLORATION COMPANY

363 N. Sam Houston Pkwy. East	CEO: Joe B. Foster	1994 Sales: $69.7 million
Houston, TX 77060	CFO: T. W. Rathert	1-Yr. Sales Change: 15.8%
Phone: 713-847-6000	HR: —	Exchange: NYSE
Fax: 713-847-6006	Employees: 51	Symbol: NFX

Oil & gas - US exploration & production in Gulf of Mexico

NGC CORPORATION

13430 Northwest Fwy., Ste. 1200	CEO: C. L. "Chuck" Watson	1994 Sales: $3,237.8 million
Houston, TX 77040	CFO: H. Keith Kaelber	1-Yr. Sales Change: 16.0%
Phone: 713-507-6400	HR: M.B. Barton	Exchange: NYSE
Fax: 713-507-3871	Employees: 1,070	Symbol: NGL

Oil & gas - natural gas marketing & distribution; gas processing plants; 9,400 miles of gas pipeline

 See pages 122–123 for a full profile of this company.

NL INDUSTRIES, INC.

16825 Northchase Dr., Ste. 1200
Houston, TX 77060
Phone: 713-423-3300
Fax: 713-987-5742

Chemicals - specialty

CEO: J. Landis Martin
CFO: Joseph S. Compofelice
HR: Brian Gallagher
Employees: 3,100

1994 Sales: $908.3 million
1-Yr. Sales Change: 9.8%
Exchange: NYSE
Symbol: NL

NOBLE DRILLING CORPORATION

10370 Richmond Ave., Ste. 400
Houston, TX 77042
Phone: 713-974-3131
Fax: 713-974-3181

Oil & gas - field services

CEO: James C. Day
CFO: Byron L. Welliver
HR: Julie Robertson
Employees: 2,673

1994 Sales: $352 million
1-Yr. Sales Change: 80.6%
Exchange: Nasdaq
Symbol: NDCO

NORAM ENERGY CORP.

1600 Smith, 11th Floor, PO Box 2628
Houston, TX 77252-2628
Phone: 713-654-5100
Fax: 713-654-7511

Utility - gas distribution

CEO: T. Milton Honea Jr.
CFO: Michael B. Bracy
HR: Rick L. Spurlock
Employees: 6,840

1994 Sales: $2,801.4 million
1-Yr. Sales Change: -5.0%
Exchange: NYSE
Symbol: NAE

 See pages 124–125 for a full profile of this company.

NORTH AMERICAN TECHNOLOGIES GROUP, INC.

9818 Wilcrest
Houston, TX 77099
Phone: 713-495-3900
Fax: 713-495-3434

CEO: Tim B. Tarrillion
CFO: Judith Knight Shields
HR: —
Employees: 31

1994 Sales: $0 million
1-Yr. Sales Change: —
Exchange: Nasdaq (SC)
Symbol: NATK

Pollution control - environmental remediation technologies for the treatment of contaminated soils & waters

NORTHERN BORDER PARTNERS, L.P.

1400 Smith St., PO Box 1188
Houston, TX 77002-7369
Phone: 713-853-6161
Fax: 713-853-3919

Oil & gas - pipeline

CEO: Larry L. DeRoin
CFO: Jerry L. Peters
HR: —
Employees: 174

1994 Sales: $211.6 million
1-Yr. Sales Change: 3.1%
Exchange: NYSE
Symbol: NBP

NORWOOD PROMOTIONAL PRODUCTS, INC.

817 N. Frio St.
San Antonio, TX 78207-5702
Phone: 210-227-7629
Fax: 210-224-5531

CEO: Frank P. Krasovec
CFO: J. Max Waits
HR: Robert P. Whitesell
Employees: 1,082

1994 Sales: $62.4 million
1-Yr. Sales Change: 26.6%
Exchange: Nasdaq
Symbol: NPPI

Business services - supplier of promotional items imprinted with name or logo of advertiser

NRP INC.

8150 N. Central Expwy., Ste. 795
Dallas, TX 75206
Phone: 214-373-8662
Fax: 214-890-0744

CEO: Michael G. Santry
CFO: Jerry L. Sims Jr.
HR: —
Employees: 1,663

1994 Sales: $37.5 million
1-Yr. Sales Change: 109.5%
Exchange: Nasdaq
Symbol: ATCT

Business services - telecommunications-based marketing & information services

NUEVO ENERGY COMPANY

1221 Lamar, Ste. 1600
Houston, TX 77010
Phone: 713-652-0706
Fax: 713-655-1866

CEO: Michael D. Watford
CFO: James M. Vanderhider
HR: Carolyn Driesbach
Employees: 630

1994 Sales: $119.3 million
1-Yr. Sales Change: 10.7%
Exchange: NYSE
Symbol: NEV

Oil & gas - US exploration & production

NU-KOTE HOLDING, INC.

17950 Preston Rd., Ste. 690
Dallas, TX 75252-5634
Phone: 214-250-2785
Fax: 214-250-4097

CEO: David F. Brigante
CFO: Daniel M. Kerrane
HR: Kathy Fields
Employees: 3,100

1995 Sales: $193.6 million
1-Yr. Sales Change: 28.0%
Exchange: Nasdaq
Symbol: NKOT

Office supplies & home printing services

NUTRITION FOR LIFE INTERNATIONAL, INC.

8801 Jameel, Ste. 100
Houston, TX 77040
Phone: 713-460-1976
Fax: 713-460-9049

CEO: David P. Bertrand
CFO: Barry C. Loder
HR: Barry C. Loder
Employees: 59

1994 Sales: $17.6 million
1-Yr. Sales Change: 27.5%
Exchange: Nasdaq
Symbol: NFLI

Vitamins & nutritional products - nutritional supplements, health foods, weight management products, skin care products & other consumer products

OCCUSYSTEMS INC.

3010 LBJ Fwy., Ste. 400
Dallas, TX 75234
Phone: 214-484-2700
Fax: 214-247-5791

CEO: John K. Carlyle
CFO: James M. Greenwood
HR: Mike Malone
Employees: 1,400

1994 Sales: $59.9 million
1-Yr. Sales Change: 40.0%
Exchange: Nasdaq
Symbol: OSYS

Physician practice management (#1 in US) specializing in occupational health care

OCEANEERING INTERNATIONAL, INC.

16001 Park Ten Place, Ste. 600
Houston, TX 77084
Phone: 713-578-8868
Fax: 713-578-5243

CEO: John R. Huff
CFO: Marvin J. Migura
HR: Sheila Jaynes
Employees: 1,950

1995 Sales: $239.9 million
1-Yr. Sales Change: 4.4%
Exchange: NYSE
Symbol: OII

Oil & gas - field services

O.I. CORPORATION

151 Graham Rd., PO Box 9010
College Station, TX 77842-9010
Phone: 409-690-1711
Fax: 409-690-0440

CEO: William W. Botts
CFO: William W. Botts
HR: Harold Dorsey
Employees: 136

1994 Sales: $18.4 million
1-Yr. Sales Change: 19.5%
Exchange: Nasdaq
Symbol: OICO

Analytical instruments & systems for sample handling, analyzing, detecting & reporting compounds
that contaminate air, water & soil

OLD AMERICA STORES, INC.

811 N. Collins Fwy., Hwy 75 North
Howe, TX 75459
Phone: 903-532-5549
Fax: 903-532-6708

CEO: Richard Tredinnick
CFO: Jim D. Schultz
HR: Roy Morton
Employees: 2,500

1995 Sales: $117.9 million
1-Yr. Sales Change: 22.8%
Exchange: Nasdaq
Symbol: OASI

Retail - arts & crafts stores

OMNI U.S.A., INC.

7502 Mesa Rd.
Houston, TX 77028
Phone: 713-635-6331
Fax: 713-635-9275

CEO: Jeffrey K. Daniel
CFO: Jeffrey K. Daniel
HR: —
Employees: 35

1995 Sales: $10.9 million
1-Yr. Sales Change: 2.8%
Exchange: Nasdaq (SC)
Symbol: OUSAE

Automotive & trucking - power transmissions, enclosed gear drives & gearboxes for agricultural equipment, irrigation systems & heavy-duty construction, industrial & utility equipment

OPTICAL DATA SYSTEMS, INC.

1101 E. Arapaho Rd.
Richardson, TX 75081
Phone: 214-234-6400
Fax: 214-234-1467

CEO: G. Ward Paxton
CFO: Roger H. Hughes
HR: Donna J. Combs
Employees: 297

1994 Sales: $86.6 million
1-Yr. Sales Change: 54.9%
Exchange: Nasdaq
Symbol: ODSI

Computers - networking hubs (Infinity), bridges & routers

ORYX ENERGY COMPANY

13155 Noel Rd.
Dallas, TX 75240-5067
Phone: 214-715-4000
Fax: 214-715-3798

CEO: Robert L. Keiser
CFO: Edward W. Moneypenny
HR: Frances G. Heartwell
Employees: 1,200

1994 Sales: $1,082 million
1-Yr. Sales Change: 2.7%
Exchange: NYSE
Symbol: ORX

Oil & gas - US exploration & production

 See pages 126–127 for a full profile of this company.

OSHMAN'S SPORTING GOODS, INC.

2302 Maxwell Ln.
Houston, TX 77023
Phone: 713-928-3171
Fax: 713-967-8254

CEO: Alvin N. Lubetkin
CFO: William N. Anderson
HR: Mark Groenemon
Employees: 3,300

1995 Sales: $311.4 million
1-Yr. Sales Change: 1.1%
Exchange: AMEX
Symbol: OSH

Retail - sporting goods

OVERHEAD DOOR CORPORATION

6750 LBJ Fwy., Ste. 1200
Dallas, TX 75240
Phone: 214-233-6611
Fax: 214-233-0367

CEO: Brian J. Bolton
CFO: Jim Brum
HR: Cal Brunson
Employees: 4,250

1994 Sales: $524 million
1-Yr. Sales Change: —
Ownership: Privately Held

Building products - overhead doors, automatic entrances & truck doors

OWEN HEALTHCARE, INC.

9800 Centre Pkwy., Ste. 1100
Houston, TX 77036
Phone: 713-777-8173
Fax: 713-777-5417

CEO: Carl E. Isgren
CFO: Stanley H. Florance
HR: Dennis S. Stepanik
Employees: 3,000

1994 Sales: $320.4 million
1-Yr. Sales Change: 10.4%
Exchange: Nasdaq
Symbol: OWEN

Medical services - hospital pharmacy & materials management services

P AND P EQUITY COMPANY LTD.

308 Wall St.
Midland, TX 79701
Phone: 915-683-4768
Fax: 915-571-5087

Oil & gas - production

CEO: Scott D. Scheffield
CFO: Steven L. Beal ·
HR: Larry Paulsen
Employees: 715

1994 Est. Sales: $390 mil.
1-Yr. Sales Change: —
Ownership: Privately Held

PAGEMART, INC.

6688 N. Central Expwy., Ste. 800
Dallas, TX 75206
Phone: 214-750-5809
Fax: 214-750-7687

Telecommunications services - nationwide wireless messaging services

CEO: John D. Beletic
CFO: Clay Meyers
HR: L. Wecslar
Employees: 1,400

1994 Sales: $109 million
1-Yr. Sales Change: —
Ownership: Privately Held

PAGING NETWORK, INC.

4965 Preston Park Blvd.
Plano, TX 75093
Phone: 214-985-4100
Fax: 214-985-6711

Telecommunications services - paging service (#1 in US)

CEO: Terry L. Scott
CFO: Barry A. Fromberg
HR: Levy H. Curry
Employees: 3,997

1994 Sales: $489.7 million
1-Yr. Sales Change: 57.3%
Exchange: Nasdaq
Symbol: PAGE

🔸 **See page 212 for a full profile of this company.**

PALM BEACH TAN, INC.

17400 Dallas Pkwy., Ste. 120
Dallas, TX 75287
Phone: 214-931-6595
Fax: 214-931-6594

Retail - tanning facilities & related supplies

CEO: Parrish Medley
CFO: Bruce A. Rockett
HR: DeAnne Fugitt
Employees: 44

1994 Sales: $1.9 million
1-Yr. Sales Change: 35.7%
Ownership: Privately Held

PALM HARBOR HOMES, INC.

15301 Dallas Pkwy., Ste 800
Dallas, TX 75248
Phone: 214-991-2422
Fax: 214-991-5949

Building - manufactured homes

CEO: Lee Posey
CFO: Kelly Tacke
HR: —
Employees: 2,887

1995 Sales: $330.5 million
1-Yr. Sales Change: 42.6%
Exchange: Nasdaq
Symbol: PHHM

PANCHO'S MEXICAN BUFFET, INC.

3500 Noble Ave., PO Box 7407
Fort Worth, TX 76111-0407
Phone: 817-831-0081
Fax: 817-838-1480

CEO: Hollis Taylor
CFO: William Fagan
HR: David Dixon
Employees: 3,967

1994 Sales: $86.1 million
1-Yr. Sales Change: 13.3%
Exchange: Nasdaq
Symbol: PAMX

Retail - Mexican-style buffet restaurants

PANHANDLE EASTERN CORPORATION

5400 Westheimer Ct., PO Box 1642
Houston, TX 77251-1642
Phone: 713-627-5400
Fax: 713-627-4145

CEO: Paul M. Anderson
CFO: Paul F. Ferguson
HR: Dan R. Hennig
Employees: 5,500

1994 Sales: $4,585.1 million
1-Yr. Sales Change: 116.2%
Exchange: NYSE
Symbol: PEL

Oil & gas - production & pipeline (acquired Associated Natural Gas)

See pages 128–129 for a full profile of this company.

PARAGON GROUP, INC.

7557 Rambler Rd., Ste. 1200
Dallas, TX 75231
Phone: 214-891-2000
Fax: 214-891-2019

CEO: William R. Cooper
CFO: Jerry J. Bonner
HR: Ron Anderson
Employees: 1,200

1994 Sales: $91.6 million
1-Yr. Sales Change: -5.5%
Exchange: NYSE
Symbol: PAO

Real estate investment trust - commercial & multi family residential properties

PARALLEL PETROLEUM CORPORATION

110 N. Marienfeld St., Ste. 465
Midland, TX 79701
Phone: 915-684-3727
Fax: 915-684-3905

CEO: Thomas R. Cambridge
CFO: Larry C. Oldham
HR: Larry C. Oldham
Employees: 5

1994 Sales: $4.7 million
1-Yr. Sales Change: 38.2%
Exchange: Nasdaq
Symbol: PLLL

Oil & gas - exploration & production

PARK PLACE MOTOR CARS

4023 Oak Lawn Ave.
Dallas, TX 75219
Phone: 214-526-8701
Fax: 214-443-8270

CEO: Kenneth Schnitzer Jr.
CFO: Paul Morgan
HR: Lee Ann Bince
Employees: 200

1994 Est. Sales: $115 mil.
1-Yr. Sales Change: —
Ownership: Privately Held

Retail - new & used cars

PARKER & PARSLEY PETROLEUM COMPANY

303 W. Wall, Ste. 101, PO Box 2080	CEO: Scott D. Scheffield	1994 Sales: $479.7 million
Midland, TX 79702-2080	CFO: Steven L. Beal	1-Yr. Sales Change: 52.7%
Phone: 915-683-4768	HR: Larry Paulsen	Exchange: NYSE
Fax: 915-571-5063	Employees: 1,004	Symbol: PDP

Oil & gas - exploration & production

 See page 213 for a full profile of this company.

PATTERSON ENERGY, INC.

4510 Lamesa Hwy., PO Drawer 1416	CEO: Cloyce A. Talbott	1994 Sales: $35.1 million
Snyder, TX 79550	CFO: James C. Brown	1-Yr. Sales Change: 41.5%
Phone: 915-573-1104	HR: Mark Cullifer	Exchange: Nasdaq
Fax: 915-573-0281	Employees: 417	Symbol: PTEN

Oil & gas - US exploration & production

PAY 'N SAVE INC.

1804 Hall Ave.	CEO: R.C. Lowe	1994 Est. Sales: $110 mil.
Littlefield, TX 79339	CFO: D. Arthro	1-Yr. Sales Change: —
Phone: 806-385-3366	HR: Leslie Lowe Harlan	Ownership: Privately Held
Fax: 806-385-5438	Employees: 1,600	

Retail - supermarkets

PC SERVICE SOURCE, INC.

1221 Champion Circle, Ste. 105	CEO: Mark T. Hilz	1994 Sales: $42.3 million
Carrollton, TX 75006	CFO: Brian R. Ervine	1-Yr. Sales Change: 75.5%
Phone: 214-406-8583	HR: Mary Zapata	Exchange: Nasdaq
Fax: 214-406-9081	Employees: 260	Symbol: PCSS

Electronics - repair parts distribution for PCs & related peripherals; inventory management & outsourcing services

PEARCE INDUSTRIES INC.

12312 Main St.	CEO: Gary M. Pearce	1994 Est. Sales: $170 mil.
Houston, TX 77035	CFO: Richard E. Bean	1-Yr. Sales Change: —
Phone: 713-723-1050	HR: John Gutta	Ownership: Privately Held
Fax: 713-551-0427	Employees: 750	

Machinery & equipment - industrial, oil & gas field & general construction

PEDERNALES ELECTRIC COOPERATIVE, INC.

200 Avenue F, PO Box 467
Johnson City, TX 78636-0467
Phone: 210-868-7155
Fax: 210-868-4999

CEO: Bennie Fuelberg
CFO: Nicki Cox
HR: Toni Reyes
Employees: 417

1994 Sales: $127.9 million
1-Yr. Sales Change: 8.8%
Ownership: Privately Held

Utility - electric power cooperative (#1 in Texas) serving 13 counties in central Texas

PEERLESS MANUFACTURING COMPANY

2819 Walnut Hill Ln.
Dallas, TX 75229
Phone: 214-357-6181
Fax: 214-351-0194

CEO: Sherrill Stone
CFO: Kent J. Van Houten
HR: Bobbie Jackson
Employees: 150

1995 Sales: $32.1 million
1-Yr. Sales Change: 25.4%
Exchange: Nasdaq
Symbol: PMFG

Filtration products

PENNZOIL COMPANY

PO Box 2967, Pennzoil Place
Houston, TX 77252-2967
Phone: 713-546-4000
Fax: 713-546-6639

CEO: James L. Pate
CFO: David P. Alderson II
HR: Terry Hemeyer
Employees: 10,501

1994 Sales: $2,562.9 million
1-Yr. Sales Change: -7.9%
Exchange: NYSE
Symbol: PZL

Oil & gas - US integrated; automotive products

 See pages 130–131 for a full profile of this company.

PERIODICAL MANAGEMENT GROUP INC.

1011 N. Frio St.
San Antonio, TX 78207
Phone: 210-226-6820
Fax: 210-226-5716

CEO: Brian Weiner
CFO: Walter Biegler
HR: Steve Parma
Employees: 500

1994 Est. Sales: $100 mil.
1-Yr. Sales Change: —
Ownership: Privately Held

Wholesale distribution - periodicals

PERMIAN BASIN ROYALTY TRUST

500 W. 7th St., Ste. 1300, PO Box 1317
Fort Worth, TX 76101
Phone: 817-390-6905
Fax: 817-390-6777

CEO: Pamela J. Bradley
CFO: Pamela J. Bradley
HR: —
Employees: —

1994 Sales: $16.6 million
1-Yr. Sales Change: -14.4%
Exchange: NYSE
Symbol: PBT

Oil & gas - US royalty trust

PEROT SYSTEMS CORPORATION

12377 Merit Dr., Ste. 1100	CEO: Morton H. Meyerson	1994 Est. Sales: $320 mil.
Dallas, TX 75251	CFO: John Bonesh	1-Yr. Sales Change: 14.3%
Phone: 214-383-5600	HR: Carol Barnett	Ownership: Privately Held
Fax: 214-383-5827	Employees: 2,300	

Computers - systems integration & consulting services & custom software design

 See page 214 for a full profile of this company.

PETRO INC.

6080 Surety Dr.	CEO: James A. Cardwell	1994 Est. Sales: $400 mil.
El Paso, TX 79905	CFO: James A. Cardwell	1-Yr. Sales Change: —
Phone: 915-779-4711	HR: Phil Booch	Ownership: Privately Held
Fax: 915-774-7373	Employees: 2,500	

Retail - truck gas service stations (Petro Stopping Centers)

PETROCORP INCORPORATED

16800 Greenspoint Park Dr., Ste. 300	CEO: Lealon L. Sargent	1994 Sales: $28 million
Houston, TX 77060-2391	CFO: Don A. Turkleson	1-Yr. Sales Change: -14.9%
Phone: 713-875-2500	HR: —	Exchange: Nasdaq
Fax: 713-875-5080	Employees: 87	Symbol: PETR

Oil & gas - US exploration & production

PHYSICIAN RELIANCE NETWORK, INC.

8115 Preston Rd., Ste. 300	CEO: Merrick H. Reese	1994 Sales: $59.2 million
Dallas, TX 75225	CFO: Randall D. Kurtz	1-Yr. Sales Change: 48.4%
Phone: 214-692-3800	HR: Sheila Deason	Exchange: Nasdaq
Fax: 214-826-8109	Employees: 394	Symbol: PHYN

Medical services - cancer-treatment practice management

PHYSICIANS RESOURCE GROUP, INC.

4801 Woodway Dr., Ste. 300 East	CEO: Gregory L. Solomon	1994 Sales: $57.4 million
Houston, TX 77056	CFO: Richard M. Owen	1-Yr. Sales Change: 5.1%
Phone: 713-964-2734	HR: —	Exchange: NYSE
Fax: 713-965-0239	Employees: 605	Symbol: PRG

Medical practice management services

PIER 1 IMPORTS, INC.

301 Commerce St., Ste. 600
Fort Worth, TX 76102
Phone: 817-878-8000
Fax: 817-878-7883

CEO: Clark A. Johnson
CFO: Robert G. Herndon
HR: E. Mitchell Weatherly
Employees: 8,671

1995 Sales: $712 million
1-Yr. Sales Change: 3.9%
Exchange: NYSE
Symbol: PIR

Retail - imported apparel & home furnishings

 See page 215 for a full profile of this company.

PILGRIM'S PRIDE CORPORATION

110 S. Texas St.
Pittsburg, TX 75686-0093
Phone: 903-855-1000
Fax: 903-856-7505

CEO: Lonnie A. Pilgrim
CFO: Clifford E. Butler
HR: Ray Gameson
Employees: 10,300

1994 Sales: $923.3 million
1-Yr. Sales Change: 4.0%
Exchange: NYSE
Symbol: CHX

Food - poultry products

 See page 216 for a full profile of this company.

PILLOWTEX CORPORATION

4111 Mint Way
Dallas, TX 75237-1605
Phone: 214-333-3225
Fax: 214-330-6016

CEO: Charles M. Hansen Jr.
CFO: Jeffrey D. Cordes
HR: Rudy Sanchez
Employees: 3,770

1994 Sales: $351.9 million
1-Yr. Sales Change: 20.4%
Exchange: NYSE
Symbol: PTX

Textiles - pillows, mattress pads, down comforters, blankets, comforter covers & feather beds

PIONEER CHLOR ALKALI INVESTMENTS INC.

700 Louisiana St.
Houston, TX 77002
Phone: 713-225-3831
Fax: 713-225-4426

CEO: Richard C. Kellogg
CFO: George T. Henning
HR: Sara Rasmussen
Employees: 600

1994 Est. Sales: $180 mil.
1-Yr. Sales Change: —
Ownership: Privately Held

Chemicals - industrial

PITTENCRIEFF COMMUNICATIONS, INC.

One Village Dr., Ste. 500, PO Box 6088
Abilene, TX 79608
Phone: 915-690-5800
Fax: 915-690-5885

CEO: Warren D. Harkins
CFO: Thomas R. Modisett
HR: Dan Baldwin
Employees: 420

1994 Sales: $32.6 million
1-Yr. Sales Change: 16.0%
Exchange: Nasdaq
Symbol: PITC

Telecommunications services - specialized mobile radio (SMR) wireless communications services covering Texas, New Mexico, Oklahoma, Arizona, Colorado, North Dakota & South Dakota

PIZZA INN, INC.

5050 Quorum, Ste. 500
Dallas, TX 75240
Phone: 214-701-9955
Fax: 214-702-9507

CEO: C. Jeffrey Rogers
CFO: Ronald W. Parker
HR: Rhena Carr
Employees: 320

1995 Sales: $62 million
1-Yr. Sales Change: 8.0%
Exchange: Nasdaq (SC)
Symbol: PZZI

Business services - restaurant franchising (Pizza Inn)

PLAINS COTTON COOPERATIVE ASSOCIATION

3301-11 E. 50th St.
Lubbock, TX 79404
Phone: 806-763-8011
Fax: 806-762-7333

CEO: Van May
CFO: Billy Morton
HR: Lee Phenix
Employees: 800

1995 Sales: $1,013.9 million
1-Yr. Sales Change: 27.1%
Ownership: Privately Held

Textiles - cotton marketing for over 29,000 farmers; textile mill; cotton warehouses

PLAINS RESOURCES INC.

1600 Smith St., Ste. 1500
Houston, TX 77002-7346
Phone: 713-654-1414
Fax: 713-654-1523

CEO: Greg L. Armstrong
CFO: Phillip D. Kramer
HR: Mary O. Peters
Employees: 217

1994 Sales: $256.7 million
1-Yr. Sales Change: 38.0%
Exchange: AMEX
Symbol: PLX

Oil & gas - US exploration & production

PLANTATION FOODS INC.

2510 E. Lake Shore
Waco, TX 76705
Phone: 817-799-6211
Fax: 817-799-6499

CEO: Joel D. Taylor
CFO: Pete Palasota
HR: Mike Whiteland
Employees: 2,000

1994 Sales: $150 million
1-Yr. Sales Change: —
Ownership: Privately Held

Food - poultry processing

PLAY BY PLAY TOYS & NOVELTIES, INC.

4400 Tejasco
San Antonio, TX 78218
Phone: 210-829-4666
Fax: 210-824-6565

CEO: Arturo G. Torres
CFO: Joe M. Guerra
HR: —
Employees: 172

1994 Sales: $35.4 million
1-Yr. Sales Change: 26.0%
Exchange: Nasdaq
Symbol: PBYP

Stuffed toys & novelty items for the amusement & retail markets

PM REALTY GROUP

1177 W. Loop St.
Houston, TX 77027
Phone: 713-966-3600
Fax: 713-966-3780

CEO: Mike Lutton
CFO: Tom Kennedy
HR: Brenda Johnson
Employees: 3,000

1994 Est. Sales: $430 mil.
1-Yr. Sales Change: —
Ownership: Privately Held

Real estate operations - apartments & commercial properties

PMC COMMERCIAL TRUST

17290 Preston Rd., 3rd Fl.
Dallas, TX 75252
Phone: 214-380-0044
Fax: 214-380-1371

CEO: Lance B. Rosemore
CFO: Barry N. Berlin
HR: Cindy Tucker
Employees: —

1994 Sales: $3.7 million
1-Yr. Sales Change: —
Exchange: AMEX
Symbol: PCC

Real estate investment trust - originates small business loans

POGO PRODUCING COMPANY

5 Greenway Plaza, PO Box 2504
Houston, TX 77252-2504
Phone: 713-297-5000
Fax: 713-297-5100

CEO: Paul G. Van Wagenen
CFO: D. Stephen Slack
HR: John O. McCoy Jr.
Employees: 108

1994 Sales: $173.6 million
1-Yr. Sales Change: 24.4%
Exchange: NYSE
Symbol: PPP

Oil & gas - US exploration & production

POLISH TELEPHONES AND MICROWAVE CORPORATION

1721 W. Plano Pkwy., Ste. 121
Plano, TX 75075
Phone: 214-423-2472
Fax: 214-424-3118

CEO: S. P. Krishna Murthy
CFO: Donald J. Hoff
HR: Donald J. Hoff
Employees: 36

1994 Sales: $1 million
1-Yr. Sales Change: -41.2%
Exchange: Nasdaq (SC)
Symbol: PTMC

Telecommunications equipment, including PBX switches, to Eastern European countries

POLYPHASE CORPORATION

16885 Dallas Pkwy., Ste. 400
Dallas, TX 75248
Phone: 214-732-0010
Fax: 214-732-6430

CEO: Paul A. Tanner
CFO: William E. Shatley
HR: Paul Tanner
Employees: 179

1994 Sales: $25 million
1-Yr. Sales Change: 242.5%
Exchange: AMEX
Symbol: PLY

Industrial & commercial timber & logging equipment distribution, leasing & financing; computer networking services; electronic transformers, inductors & filters

PONDER INDUSTRIES, INC.

511 Commerce Rd., PO Box 2229	CEO: Mack Ponder	1994 Sales: $7.9 million
Alice, TX 78333-2229	CFO: Charles E. Greenwood	1-Yr. Sales Change: -9.2%
Phone: 512-664-5831	HR: Frank J. Wall	Exchange: Nasdaq
Fax: 512-664-8451	Employees: 52	Symbol: PNDR

Oil & gas - tools, equipment & personnel for the clearing of obstructions in oil rig bore holes

POOL ENERGY SERVICES CO.

10375 Richmond Ave.	CEO: James T. Jongebloed	1994 Sales: $234.2 million
Houston, TX 77042	CFO: Ernest J. Spillard	1-Yr. Sales Change: -5.3%
Phone: 713-954-3000	HR: Louis E. Dupre	Exchange: Nasdaq
Fax: 713-954-3319	Employees: 4,449	Symbol: PESC

Oil & gas - well servicing & rig operations

POSITRON CORPORATION

16350 Park Ten Place	CEO: Gary B. Wood	1994 Sales: $6.1 million
Houston, TX 77084	CFO: David O. Rodrigue	1-Yr. Sales Change: 154.2%
Phone: 713-492-7100	HR: —	Exchange: Nasdaq
Fax: 713-492-2961	Employees: 57	Symbol: POSI

Medical instruments - advanced medical imaging devices (POSICAM)

POWELL INDUSTRIES, INC.

8550 Mosley Dr., PO Box 12818	CEO: Thomas W. Powell	1994 Sales: $152 million
Houston, TX 77075-1180	CFO: J. F. Ahart	1-Yr. Sales Change: 10.1%
Phone: 713-944-6900	HR: Robert J. Murphy	Exchange: Nasdaq
Fax: 713-947-4435	Employees: 857	Symbol: POWL

Machinery - electrical

PRATT HOTEL CORPORATION

13455 Noel Rd., Ste. 2200, LB 48	CEO: Jack E. Pratt	1994 Sales: $295.4 million
Dallas, TX 75240	CFO: Albert J. Cohen	1-Yr. Sales Change: 6.8%
Phone: 214-386-9777	HR: —	Exchange: AMEX
Fax: 214-386-7411	Employees: 5,150	Symbol: PHC

Hotels & casino management (Sands Hotel & Casino in Atlantic City, NJ & casino riverboats in Aurora, IL)

PRESBYTERIAN HEALTHCARE SYSTEM

8220 Walnut Hill Ln., Ste. 700
Dallas, TX 75231
Phone: 214-345-8500
Fax: 214-345-4999

CEO: Doug Hawthorne
CFO: William Kraft
HR: Vic Vuzachero
Employees: 5,000

1994 Sales: $320.9 million
1-Yr. Sales Change: 4.4%
Ownership: Privately Held

Hospitals - not-for-profit system

PRIDE COMPANIES, L.P.

1209 N. 4th St., PO Box 3237
Abilene, TX 79604
Phone: 915-674-8000
Fax: 915-676-8792

CEO: Brad Stephens
CFO: George Percival
HR: John E. Pearson
Employees: 545

1994 Sales: $589.9 million
1-Yr. Sales Change: -10.3%
Exchange: NYSE
Symbol: PRF

Oil & gas - refined products & crude oil gathering

PRIDE PETROLEUM SERVICES, INC.

1500 City West Blvd., Ste. 400
Houston, TX 77042
Phone: 713-789-1400
Fax: 713-789-1430

CEO: Ray H. Tolson
CFO: Paul A. Bragg
HR: Robert Randall
Employees: 3,850

1994 Sales: $182.3 million
1-Yr. Sales Change: 43.4%
Exchange: Nasdaq
Symbol: PRDE

Oil & gas - field services, well servicing, workover, completion & plugging & abandonment service for domestic & international oil & gas industry (2nd largest worldwide)

PRIME MEDICAL SERVICES, INC.

1301 Capital of Texas Hwy.
Austin, TX 78746
Phone: 512-328-2892
Fax: 512-328-8510

CEO: Jackie C. Majors
CFO: Cheryl L. McLeod
HR: Dana L. Nau
Employees: 62

1994 Sales: $24.8 million
1-Yr. Sales Change: 20.4%
Exchange: Nasdaq
Symbol: PMSI

Medical services - rehabilitation center management

PRO GROUP HOLDINGS, INC.

520 N. Wildwood Dr.
Irving, TX 75061
Phone: 214-579-3500
Fax: 214-579-3631

CEO: Thomas D. Karol
CFO: Jack Wulz
HR: Virginia Hade
Employees: 1,300

1994 Sales: $285 million
1-Yr. Sales Change: —
Ownership: Privately Held

Building products - flooring (L.D. Brinkman)

PRODUCTION OPERATORS CORP

11302 Tanner Rd., PO Box 40262	CEO: D. John Ogren	1994 Sales: $75.5 million
Houston, TX 77240-0262	CFO: William S. Robinson Jr.	1-Yr. Sales Change: 4.6%
Phone: 713-466-0980	HR: —	Exchange: Nasdaq
Fax: 713-896-2528	Employees: 414	Symbol: PROP

Oil & gas - gas handling & compression services

PROLER INTERNATIONAL CORP.

4265 San Felipe, Ste. 900	CEO: Herman Proler	1995 Sales: $18.6 million
Houston, TX 77027	CFO: Michael F. Loy	1-Yr. Sales Change: -57.4%
Phone: 713-627-3737	HR: Carol Martin	Exchange: NYSE
Fax: 713-675-2737	Employees: 387	Symbol: PS

Metal processing & fabrication - recovery, recycling & processing ferrous & nonferrous scrap metals & industrial waste into high-quality raw materials & energy resources for industrial customers

PRONET INC.

600 Data Dr., Ste. 100	CEO: Jackie R. Kimzey	1994 Sales: $39.7 million
Plano, TX 75075	CFO: Jan E. Gaulding	1-Yr. Sales Change: 86.4%
Phone: 214-964-9500	HR: Martie Chaplin	Exchange: Nasdaq
Fax: 214-964-9570	Employees: 321	Symbol: PNET

Telecommunications services - wireless messaging

PUBLISHERS EQUIPMENT CORPORATION

16660 Dallas Pkwy., Ste. 1100	CEO: Evans Kostas	1994 Sales: $14.7 million
Dallas, TX 75248	CFO: Roger R. Baier	1-Yr. Sales Change: 13.1%
Phone: 214-931-2312	HR: —	Exchange: Nasdaq
Fax: 214-931-2399	Employees: 133	Symbol: PECN

Machinery - printing, including single-width web offset presses for newspapers & semi commercial printers

QUANEX CORPORATION

1900 W. Loop South, Ste. 1500	CEO: Robert C. Snyder	1994 Sales: $704.4 million
Houston, TX 77027	CFO: Wayne M. Rose	1-Yr. Sales Change: 13.4%
Phone: 713-961-4600	HR: Joseph K. Peery	Exchange: NYSE
Fax: 713-877-5333	Employees: 2,652	Symbol: NX

Steel - pipes & tubes

QUEST MEDICAL, INC.

201 Allentown Pkwy.
Allen, TX 75002
Phone: 214-390-9800
Fax: 214-390-2881

CEO: Thomas C. Thompson
CFO: F. Robert Merrill III
HR: Jim Calhoun
Employees: 201

1994 Sales: $14 million
1-Yr. Sales Change: 2.9%
Exchange: Nasdaq
Symbol: QMED

Medical products - surgical refracting tapes & IV systems

QUINTANA PETROLEUM CORPORATION

601 Jefferson, Ste. 3800
Houston, TX 77002
Phone: 713-651-8600
Fax: 713-651-8663

CEO: J. Michael Trotter
CFO: Chris Sisk
HR: Wilburn V. Lunn Jr.
Employees: 240

1994 Sales: $250 million
1-Yr. Sales Change: —
Ownership: Privately Held

Oil & gas - exploration & production

R CORPORATION

1000 IH–10 North
Beaumont, TX 77702
Phone: 409-892-6696
Fax: 409-892-7690

CEO: Kenneth E. Ruddy
CFO: Charles R. King
HR: —
Employees: 350

1994 Est. Sales: $125 mil.
1-Yr. Sales Change: —
Ownership: Privately Held

Retail - new & used cars

RAILTEX, INC.

4040 Broadway, Ste. 200
San Antonio, TX 78209-3745
Phone: 210-841-7600
Fax: 210-841-7629

CEO: Bruce M. Flohr
CFO: Laura D. Davies
HR: Susan Mustacchio
Employees: 652

1994 Sales: $74.5 million
1-Yr. Sales Change: 24.6%
Exchange: Nasdaq
Symbol: RTEX

Transportation - short-line freight railroad

 See page 217 for a full profile of this company.

RANDALL'S FOOD MARKETS, INC.

3663 Briarpark Dr.
Houston, TX 77042
Phone: 713-268-3500
Fax: 713-268-3601

CEO: Robert R. Onstead Jr.
CFO: Bob L. Gowens
HR: Ronnie W. Barclay
Employees: 21,000

1994 Sales: $2,400 million
1-Yr. Sales Change: 0.0%
Ownership: Privately Held

Retail - Texas supermarkets (121 units, primarily in Houston, Dallas and Austin)

 See pages 132–133 for a full profile of this company.

RAWSON-KOENIG, INC.

2301 Central Pkwy.
Houston, TX 77092
Phone: 713-688-4414
Fax: —

CEO: Thomas C. Rawson
CFO: Catherine A. Rawson
HR: Catherine A. Rawson
Employees: 285

1994 Sales: $17.2 million
1-Yr. Sales Change: 18.6%
Exchange: Nasdaq (SC)
Symbol: RAKO

Truck service bodies, tool boxes, winches & truck-mounted cranes

RAYCO LTD.

4800 Fredericksburg
San Antonio, TX 78229
Phone: 210-349-1111
Fax: 210-308-1307

CEO: John H. Willome
CFO: Jack Biagler
HR: Sandra Martinez
Employees: 750

1994 Est. Sales: $250 mil.
1-Yr. Sales Change: —
Ownership: Privately Held

Building - no-frills single-family homes (#1 in San Antonio)

READING & BATES CORPORATION

901 Threadneedle, PO Box 79627
Houston, TX 77279
Phone: 713-496-5000
Fax: 713-496-2298

CEO: Paul B. Loyd Jr.
CFO: Tim W. Nagle
HR: D. L. McIntire
Employees: 1,500

1994 Sales: $169.1 million
1-Yr. Sales Change: -8.0%
Exchange: NYSE
Symbol: RB

Oil & gas - offshore drilling

RECOGNITION INTERNATIONAL INC.

2701 E. Grauwyler Rd.
Irving, TX 75266-0204
Phone: 214-579-6000
Fax: 214-579-6830

CEO: Robert Vanourek
CFO: Thomas E. Hoefert
HR: Wilemia Shaw
Employees: 1,525

1994 Sales: $219.4 million
1-Yr. Sales Change: -4.9%
Exchange: NYSE
Symbol: REC

Optical character recognition - document scanning & imaging processing systems for use in archiving & easy retrieval

REDMAN INDUSTRIES, INC.

2550 Walnut Hill Ln., Ste. 200
Dallas, TX 75229-5672
Phone: 214-353-3600
Fax: 214-350-5927

CEO: Tom Sturgess
CFO: Fergus J. Walker Jr.
HR: Gary Allen
Employees: 3,967

1995 Sales: $558 million
1-Yr. Sales Change: 25.9%
Exchange: Nasdaq
Symbol: RDMN

Building - manufactured homes

THE REFERENCE PRESS, INC.

6448 Hwy. 290 East, Ste. E-104
Austin, TX 78723-1041
Phone: 512-454-7778
Fax: 512-454-9401

CEO: Patrick J. Spain
CFO: Deborah Dunlap
HR: Tammy Fisher
Employees: 21

1995 Sales: $1.6 million
1-Yr. Sales Change: 60.0%
Ownership: Privately Held

Business reference books (Hoover's Handbooks), online services (Hoover's Online) & software (#1 publisher of reasonably priced business reference information in print, disk & CD-ROM formats)

REGAL INTERNATIONAL, INC.

PO Box 1237
Corsicana, TX 75151
Phone: 903-872-3091
Fax: 903-872-3095

CEO: Janak N. Desai
CFO: Gary M. Kohlschmidt
HR: Lavonne Tipping
Employees: 89

1994 Sales: $7.1 million
1-Yr. Sales Change: -19.3%
Exchange: Pink Sheets
Symbol: RGLI

Oil field machinery & equipment

RELIABILITY INC.

16400 Park Row
Houston, TX 77084
Phone: 713-492-0550
Fax: 713-492-0615

CEO: Everett Hanlon
CFO: Max T. Langley
HR: Toni McConkey
Employees: 376

1994 Sales: $23.4 million
1-Yr. Sales Change: -13.3%
Exchange: Nasdaq
Symbol: REAL

Electronics - measuring instruments

RELIABLE CHEVROLET INC.

800 N. Central Expwy.
Richardson, TX 75080
Phone: 214-952-1500
Fax: 214-952-8171

CEO: Darrell McCutcheon
CFO: Dave Anderson
HR: —
Employees: 235

1994 Est. Sales: $125 mil.
1-Yr. Sales Change: —
Ownership: Privately Held

Retail - new & used cars

RENTERS CHOICE, INC.

2720 N. Stemmons Fwy., Ste. 300
Dallas, TX 75207
Phone: 214-638-6633
Fax: 214-638-7711

CEO: J. Ernie Talley
CFO: David M. Glasgow
HR: Robert D. Davis
Employees: 688

1994 Sales: $74.4 million
1-Yr. Sales Change: 39.8%
Exchange: Nasdaq
Symbol: RCII

Leasing - rent-to-own electronics, appliances, furniture & accessories

 See page 218 for a full profile of this company.

REUNION RESOURCES COMPANY

2801 Post Oak Blvd., Ste. 400
Houston, TX 77056
Phone: 713-627-9277
Fax: 713-627-2069

Oil production - crude & natural gas

CEO: Thomas N. Amonett
CFO: W. Kyle Willis
HR: Judy Dugan
Employees: 40

1994 Sales: $7.5 million
1-Yr. Sales Change: -25.0%
Exchange: Nasdaq (SC)
Symbol: RUNR

REXENE CORPORATION

5005 LBJ Fwy.
Dallas, TX 75244
Phone: 214-450-9000
Fax: 214-450-9197

Chemicals - diversified

CEO: Andrew J. Smith
CFO: Kevin W. McAleer
HR: Jonathan R. Wheeler
Employees: 1,310

1994 Sales: $538 million
1-Yr. Sales Change: 25.3%
Exchange: NYSE
Symbol: RXN

RF MONOLITHICS, INC.

4441 Sigma Rd.
Dallas, TX 75244
Phone: 214-233-2903
Fax: 214-387-8148

CEO: Gary A. Anderson
CFO: Sam L. Densmore
HR: Diana S. Handler
Employees: 377

1994 Sales: $24.9 million
1-Yr. Sales Change: 45.6%
Exchange: Nasdaq
Symbol: RFMI

Electrical components - radio frequency components & modules; digital clocks

RICE FOOD MARKETS INC.

5333 Gulfton St.
Houston, TX 77081
Phone: 713-662-7700
Fax: 713-662-7757

Retail - supermarkets

CEO: Alfred L. Friedlander
CFO: James Potter
HR: Kent Milton
Employees: 1,200

1994 Est. Sales: $150 mil.
1-Yr. Sales Change: —
Ownership: Privately Held

RICE UNIVERSITY

6100 Main St.
Houston, TX 77005
Phone: 713-527-8101
Fax: 713-831-4747

CEO: S. Malcolm Gillis
CFO: Dean W. Currie
HR: Caroline Garcia
Employees: 2,000

1994 Sales: $167.5 million
1-Yr. Sales Change: 4.1%
Ownership: Privately Held

University - offering 42 undergraduate degree programs

RICHARDS GROUP INC.

10000 N. Central Expwy.
Dallas, TX 75231
Phone: 214-891-5700
Fax: 214-891-5844

Business services - advertising

CEO: Stan Richards
CFO: Scott Dykema
HR: Teresa Boyce
Employees: 300

1994 Est. Sales: $210 mil.
1-Yr. Sales Change: —
Ownership: Privately Held

RIP GRIFFIN TRUCK/TRAVEL CENTERS INC.

5202 4th St.
Lubbock, TX 79416
Phone: 806-795-8785
Fax: 806-795-6574

Retail - gas stations; restaurants; gift stores; motels

CEO: Rip Griffin
CFO: Don Hayden
HR: Risa Barron
Employees: 1,240

1994 Sales: $210 million
1-Yr. Sales Change: 5.0%
Ownership: Privately Held

RIVIANA FOODS INC.

2777 Allen Pkwy.
Houston, TX 77019
Phone: 713-529-3251
Fax: 713-529-1661

Food - rice milling, canning & baking

CEO: Joseph A. Hafner Jr.
CFO: E. Wayne Ray
HR: Jack Nolingberg
Employees: 2,645

1995 Sales: $427.2 million
1-Yr. Sales Change: -11.4%
Exchange: Nasdaq
Symbol: RVFD

ROWAN COMPANIES, INC.

2800 Post Oak Blvd.
Houston, TX 77056-6196
Phone: 713-621-7800
Fax: 713-960-7660

Oil & gas - international offshore drilling contracting & air charter services; heavy equipiment for the mining, timber & marine rig industries; mini–steel mill

CEO: C. R. Palmer
CFO: E. E. Thiele
HR: Bill S. Person
Employees: 3,484

1994 Sales: $438.2 million
1-Yr. Sales Change: 24.1%
Exchange: NYSE
Symbol: RDC

RSR CORPORATION

2777 Stemmons Fwy.
Dallas, TX 75207
Phone: 214-631-6070
Fax: 214-631-3047

Pollutin control - nonferrous metal recycling, primarily lead

CEO: Albert P. Lospinoso
CFO: Sandra M. Anderson
HR: Sandra Coss
Employees: 690

1994 Sales: $193 million
1-Yr. Sales Change: 17.7%
Ownership: Privately Held

SA HOLDINGS, INC.

1600 Promenade	CEO: Jack W. Matz Jr.	1994 Sales: $9.8 million
Richardson, TX 75074	CFO: J. David Darnell	1-Yr. Sales Change: 237.9%
Phone: 214-516-0662	HR: —	Exchange: Nasdaq (SC)
Fax: 214-881-0656	Employees: 58	Symbol: SAHI

Telecommunications services - international carrier

SABINE ROYALTY TRUST

901 Main St., 12th Fl.	CEO: Ron E. Hooper	1994 Sales: $18.6 million
Dallas, TX 75202	CFO: Ron E. Hooper	1-Yr. Sales Change: -16.2%
Phone: 214-508-2400	HR: —	Exchange: NYSE
Fax: 214-508-2431	Employees: —	Symbol: SBR

Oil & gas - US royalty trust

SAM HOUSTON STATE UNIVERSITY

1700 Sam Houston Ave.	CEO: Lamar G. Urbanovsky	1994 Sales: $76.6 million
Huntsville, TX 77340	CFO: Jack C. Parker	1-Yr. Sales Change: 8.3%
Phone: 409-294-1111	HR: Ted Michael	Ownership: Privately Held
Fax: 409-294-1097	Employees: 1,760	

University - offering 96 undergraduate & 76 graduate degree programs

SAMMONS ENTERPRISES, INC.

300 Crescent Ct., Ste. 700	CEO: Robert W. Korba	1994 Sales: $1,300 million
Dallas, TX 75201	CFO: Joseph A. Ethridge	1-Yr. Sales Change: -0.6%
Phone: 214-855-2800	HR: Pam Fain	Ownership: Privately Held
Fax: 214-855-2899	Employees: 3,300	

Diversified operations - insurance; cable TV; industrial equipment

SAN ANTONIO SPURS

100 Montana	CEO: John Dilliard	1994 Sales: $50.5 million
San Antonio, TX 78203	CFO: Rick Pych	1-Yr. Sales Change: 52.6%
Phone: 210-554-7787	HR: Paula Winslow	Ownership: Privately Held
Fax: 210-554-7701	Employees: 77	

Professional basketball team

SAN JUAN BASIN ROYALTY TRUST

PO Box 2604
Fort Worth, TX 76113
Phone: 817-884-4630
Fax: 817-884-4560

Oil & gas - US royalty trust

CEO: Lee A. Anderson
CFO: Lee A. Anderson
HR: Lee Ann Anderson
Employees: —

1994 Sales: $23.3 million
1-Yr. Sales Change: -37.9%
Exchange: NYSE
Symbol: SJT

SANIFILL, INC.

2777 Allen Pkwy., Ste. 700
Houston, TX 77019
Phone: 713-942-6200
Fax: 713-942-6299

Pollution control equipment & services - solid waste disposal

CEO: Lorne D. Bain
CFO: J. Chris Brewster
HR: Ken Rose
Employees: 1,300

1994 Sales: $172.8 million
1-Yr. Sales Change: 42.5%
Exchange: NYSE
Symbol: FIL

SANTA FE ENERGY RESOURCES, INC.

1616 S. Voss, Ste. 1000
Houston, TX 77057
Phone: 713-507-5000
Fax: 713-268-5341

Oil & gas - US exploration & production

CEO: James L. Payne
CFO: R. Graham Whaling
HR: Charles C. Hain Jr.
Employees: 647

1994 Sales: $391.4 million
1-Yr. Sales Change: -10.4%
Exchange: NYSE
Symbol: SFR

SANTA FE ENERGY TRUST

600 Travis, Ste. 1150
Houston, TX 77002
Phone: 713-216-5100
Fax: 713-216-5476

Oil & gas - US royalty trust

CEO: Richard L. Melton
CFO: —
HR: —
Employees: —

1994 Sales: $10.8 million
1-Yr. Sales Change: -5.3%
Exchange: NYSE
Symbol: SFF

SANTA ROSA HEALTH CARE CORP.

519 W. Houston St.
San Antonio, TX 78207
Phone: 210-704-2114
Fax: 210-704-3632

Hospitals - general medical hospitals

CEO: Robert Nolan
CFO: David A. Poland
HR: Sam Buscetta
Employees: 3,300

1994 Sales: $214.5 million
1-Yr. Sales Change: -4.0%
Ownership: Privately Held

SBC COMMUNICATIONS INC.

175 E. Houston	CEO: Edward E. Whitacre Jr.	1994 Sales: $11,619 million
San Antonio, TX 78205-2233	CFO: Donald E. Kiernan	1-Yr. Sales Change: 8.7%
Phone: 210-821-4105	HR: Cassandra C. Carr	Exchange: NYSE
Fax: 210-351-2071	Employees: 58,750	Symbol: SBC

Utility - telephone service (Southwestern Bell), cellular telephone services, long distance advertising

 See pages 134–135 for a full profile of this company.

SEABOARD OIL CO.

731 W. Wadley, Bldg. O, PO Box 3120	CEO: E. E. Runyan	1995 Sales: $4.4 million
Midland, TX 79702	CFO: Gary B. Gilliam	1-Yr. Sales Change: 15.8%
Phone: 915-684-7005	HR: Mitzi Salinas	Exchange: Nasdaq (SC)
Fax: 915-684-7060	Employees: 12	Symbol: SBRD

Oil & gas - domestic oil & gas exploration, development & production, primarily in the Permian Basin area of TX, secondarily in NM, LA, OK, AR, ND, CO & WY

SEACOR HOLDINGS, INC.

11200 Westheimer Road, Ste. 850	CEO: Charles Fabrikant	1994 Sales: $74.4 million
Houston, TX 77042	CFO: Randall Blank	1-Yr. Sales Change: 0.9%
Phone: 713-782-5990	HR: Rodney Coco	Exchange: Nasdaq
Fax: 504-385-0139	Employees: 492	Symbol: CKOR

Oil & gas - field services

SEAGULL ENERGY CORPORATION

1001 Fannin St., Ste. 1700	CEO: Barry J. Galt	1994 Sales: $408.1 million
Houston, TX 77002-6714	CFO: Robert W. Shower	1-Yr. Sales Change: 8.2%
Phone: 713-951-4700	HR: Jack M. Robertson	Exchange: NYSE
Fax: 713-951-4819	Employees: 764	Symbol: SGO

Oil & gas - production & pipeline

SEARCH CAPITAL GROUP INC.

700 N. Pearl St., Ste. 401	CEO: George C. Evans	1994 Sales: $14.1 million
Dallas, TX 75201-7490	CFO: Robert D. Idzi	1-Yr. Sales Change: 107.4%
Phone: 214-965-6000	HR: Carolyn Malone	Exchange: OTC
Fax: 214-965-6096	Employees: 118	Symbol: SRCG

Financial - used car loan factoring

SECURITY CAPITAL PACIFIC TRUST

7777 Market Center Ave.
El Paso, TX 79912
Phone: 915-877-3900
Fax: 915-877-3301

CEO: C. Ronald Blackenship
CFO: William Kell
HR: Lydia Pie
Employees: —

1994 Sales: $186.1 million
1-Yr. Sales Change: 137.4%
Exchange: NYSE
Symbol: PTR

Real estate investment trust - multifamily residential properties

SEITEL, INC.

50 Briar Hollow Ln., 7th Fl. West
Houston, TX 77027
Phone: 713-627-1990
Fax: 713-627-1114

CEO: Paul A. Frame
CFO: Debra D. Valice
HR: Paul A. Frame
Employees: 90

1994 Sales: $73.8 million
1-Yr. Sales Change: 69.7%
Exchange: NYSE
Symbol: SEI

Oil & gas - seismic data & corollary geophysical services for petroleum exploration

SEMATECH, INC.

2706 Montopolis Dr.
Austin, TX 78741-6499
Phone: 512-356-3500
Fax: 512-356-3083

CEO: Bill Spencer
CFO: Dan Damon
HR: Mike Foster
Employees: 841

1994 Sales: N/A
1-Yr. Sales Change: —
Ownership: Privately Held

Engineering - R&D services, semiconductor technology

 See page 219 for a full profile of this company.

SERVICE CORPORATION INTERNATIONAL

1929 Allen Pkwy.
Houston, TX 77019
Phone: 713-522-5141
Fax: 713-525-5586

CEO: Robert L. Waltrip
CFO: George R. Champagne
HR: Jack L. Stoner
Employees: 18,756

1994 Sales: $1,117.2 million
1-Yr. Sales Change: 24.2%
Exchange: NYSE
Symbol: SRV

Funeral homes & cemeteries

SERV-TECH, INC.

5200 Cedar Crest Blvd.
Houston, TX 77087
Phone: 713-644-9974
Fax: 713-644-0731

CEO: Richard L. Daerr
CFO: David P. Tusa
HR: Joyce Currie
Employees: 1,383

1994 Sales: $181.1 million
1-Yr. Sales Change: 11.8%
Exchange: Nasdaq
Symbol: STEC

Oil & gas - environmental & cleaning services

 See page 220 for a full profile of this company.

SETPOINT, INC.

14701 St. Mary's Ln.	CEO: Douglas C. White	1994 Est. Sales: $40 mil.
Houston, TX 77079-2995	CFO: Mel Hohle	1-Yr. Sales Change: -4.8%
Phone: 713-584-1000	HR: Jan Germen	Ownership: Privately Held
Fax: 713-496-3232	Employees: 350	

Computer automation systems for process control

SHELL OIL COMPANY

One Shell Plaza, PO Box 2463	CEO: Philip J. Carroll	1994 Sales: $21,581 million
Houston, TX 77002	CFO: P. G. Turberville	1-Yr. Sales Change: -8.5%
Phone: 713-241-6161	HR: Bert W. Levan	Exchange: NYSE
Fax: 713-241-4044	Employees: 21,496	Symbol: SC

Oil & gas - international integrated (owned by Royal Dutch/Shell Group, the largest oil company in the world)

 See pages 136–137 for a full profile of this company.

SHOWBIZ PIZZA TIME, INC.

4441 W. Airport Fwy., PO Box 152077	CEO: Richard M. Frank	1994 Sales: $267.8 million
Irving, TX 75015	CFO: Larry G. Page	1-Yr. Sales Change: -1.5%
Phone: 214-258-8507	HR: Catherine Kreston	Exchange: Nasdaq
Fax: 214-258-8545	Employees: 13,500	Symbol: SHBZ

Retail - restaurants (Chuck E. Cheese)

SI DIAMOND TECHNOLOGY, INC.

2435 North Blvd.	CEO: Robert H. Gow	1994 Sales: $1.9 million
Houston, TX 77098	CFO: Lawrence K. King	1-Yr. Sales Change: 35.7%
Phone: 713-529-9040	HR: Marijane Ensminger	Exchange: Nasdaq (SC)
Fax: 713-529-1147	Employees: 71	Symbol: SIDT

Thin-film diamond coatings & related products, including flat-panel displays

SISTERS OF CHARITY OF THE INCARNATE WORD HEALTH CARE SYSTEM

2600 N. Loop West	CEO: Stanley T. Urban	1994 Sales: $2,027 million
Houston, TX 77092	CFO: Willy Kuehn	1-Yr. Sales Change: 5.5%
Phone: 713-681-8877	HR: Kay Saathoff	Ownership: Privately Held
Fax: 713-683-2065	Employees: 19,000	

Hospitals - not-for-profit system with acute-care hospitals & long-term health care centers mainly in the Houston area, but also located in California, Utah, Louisiana, Arkansas & Ireland

SIXX HOLDINGS, INCORPORATED

300 Crescent Ct., Ste. 1630
Dallas, TX 75201
Phone: 214-855-8800
Fax: 214-855-8808

CEO: Jack D. Knox
CFO: Jean S. Baggett
HR: Dorothy Douglas
Employees: 169

1994 Sales: $5.3 million
1-Yr. Sales Change: —
Exchange: Nasdaq (SC)
Symbol: SIXX

Retail - Italian food restaurants (Patrizio)

SMITH ENVIRONMENTAL TECHNOLOGIES CORPORATION

13455 Noel Rd., Ste. 1500
Dallas, TX 75240
Phone: 214-770-1800
Fax: 214-770-0249

CEO: E. Brian Smith
CFO: William T. Campbell
HR: Gail M. Fulwider
Employees: 1,260

1995 Sales: $104.7 million
1-Yr. Sales Change: 76.0%
Exchange: Nasdaq
Symbol: SMTH

Pollution control equipment & services - environmental consulting, engineering & on-site remediation services

SMITH INTERNATIONAL, INC.

16740 Hardy St., PO Box 60068
Houston, TX 77205-0068
Phone: 713-443-3370
Fax: 713-233-5104

CEO: Doug Rock
CFO: Loren K. Carroll
HR: Joe Sizemore
Employees: 4,100

1994 Sales: $653.9 million
1-Yr. Sales Change: 196.3%
Exchange: NYSE
Symbol: SII

Oil field machinery & equipment, drilling fluids, drill bits, drilling & completion products & services

SNYDER OIL CORPORATION

777 Main St.
Fort Worth, TX 76102
Phone: 817-338-4043
Fax: 817-882-5992

CEO: John C. Snyder
CFO: James H. Shonsey
HR: —
Employees: 460

1994 Sales: $262.3 million
1-Yr. Sales Change: 14.1%
Exchange: NYSE
Symbol: SNY

Oil & gas - US exploration & production in the Rocky Mountains & Gulf Coast

 See page 221 for a full profile of this company.

SOFTWARE SPECTRUM, INC.

2140 Merritt Dr.
Garland, TX 75041
Phone: 214-840-6600
Fax: 214-864-7878

CEO: Judy O. Sims
CFO: Deborah A. Nugent
HR: Sue Zurber
Employees: 667

1995 Sales: $352.1 million
1-Yr. Sales Change: 24.4%
Exchange: Nasdaq
Symbol: SSPE

Computers - retails software directly to companies

 See page 222 for a full profile of this company.

SOLO SERVE CORPORATION

1610 Cornerway Blvd.
San Antonio, TX 78219
Phone: 210-662-6262
Fax: 210-662-0938

CEO: Robert J. Grimm
CFO: Timothy L. Grady
HR: Janet Polluck
Employees: 1,600

1995 Sales: $138.9 million
1-Yr. Sales Change: -17.9%
Exchange: Nasdaq
Symbol: SOLOQ

Retail - discount fragrances, apparel & home furnishings

SONAT OFFSHORE DRILLING INC.

4 Greenway Plaza
Houston, TX 77046
Phone: 713-871-7500
Fax: 713-850-3818

CEO: J. Michael Talbert
CFO: Barbara S. Koucouthakis
HR: Marie B. Roberts
Employees: 2,100

1994 Sales: $243 million
1-Yr. Sales Change: -10.4%
Exchange: NYSE
Symbol: RIG

Oil & gas - offshore drilling

SOUTH WEST PROPERTY TRUST INC.

5949 Sherry Ln., Ste. 1400
Dallas, TX 75225-8010
Phone: 214-369-1995
Fax: 214-369-6882

CEO: John S. Schneider
CFO: Diana M. Laing
HR: Colleen Collins
Employees: 360

1994 Sales: $58.9 million
1-Yr. Sales Change: 77.9%
Exchange: NYSE
Symbol: SWP

Real estate investment trust - apartments in Texas, Arizona & New Mexico

SOUTHDOWN, INC.

1200 Smith St., Ste. 2400
Houston, TX 77002-4486
Phone: 713-650-6200
Fax: 713-653-6815

CEO: Clarence C. Comer
CFO: James L. Persky
HR: L. Ross Buckner
Employees: 2,600

1994 Sales: $561.9 million
1-Yr. Sales Change: 10.3%
Exchange: NYSE
Symbol: SDW

Construction - cement & concrete

SOUTHERN FOODS GROUPS INCORPORATED

3114 S. Haskell Ave.
Dallas, TX 75223
Phone: 214-824-8163
Fax: 214-824-0967

CEO: Pete Schenkel
CFO: Jerry Fry
HR: Stuart Bibson
Employees: 1,900

1994 Sales: $395 million
1-Yr. Sales Change: —
Ownership: Privately Held

Food - dairy products

SOUTHERN METHODIST UNIVERSITY

PO Box 750200
Dallas, TX 75275-0200
Phone: 214-768-2000
Fax: 214-768-7663

CEO: R. Gerald Turner
CFO: Elizabeth C. Williams
HR: Bill Detwiler
Employees: 3,800

1994 Sales: $177.7 million
1-Yr. Sales Change: 2.5%
Ownership: Privately Held

University - offering 68 undergraduate & 59 graduate degree programs

SOUTHERN MINERAL CORPORATION

17001 Northchase, Ste. 690
Houston, TX 77060-2138
Phone: 713-872-7621
Fax: 713-872-5232

CEO: Steven H. Mikel
CFO: Donna Ashmun
HR: Margie Ewald
Employees: 4

1994 Sales: $1.9 million
1-Yr. Sales Change: -38.7%
Exchange: Nasdaq
Symbol: SMIN

Oil & gas - US exploration & production

SOUTHERN UNION COMPANY

504 Lavaca St., 8th Fl.
Austin, TX 78701
Phone: 512-477-5981
Fax: 512-370-8215

CEO: George L. Lindemann
CFO: Ronald J. Endres
HR: Nancy Capezzuti
Employees: 1,811

1995 Sales: $480 million
1-Yr. Sales Change: 28.2%
Exchange: NYSE
Symbol: SUG

Utility - distribution of natural gas as a public utility

THE SOUTHLAND CORPORATION

2711 N. Haskell Ave.
Dallas, TX 75204-2906
Phone: 214-828-7011
Fax: 214-822-7848

CEO: Clark J. MatthewsII
CFO: Vernon P. Lotman
HR: David M. Finley
Employees: 30,417

1994 Sales: $6,759.8 million
1-Yr. Sales Change: -0.8%
Exchange: Nasdaq (SC)
Symbol: SLCMC

Retail - convenience stores

 See pages 138–139 for a full profile of this company.

SOUTHWEST AIRLINES CO.

PO Box 36611
Dallas, TX 75235-1611
Phone: 214-904-4000
Fax: 214-904-4200

CEO: Herbert D. Kelleher
CFO: Gary C. Kelly
HR: Elizabeth Pedrick Sartain
Employees: 16,818

1994 Sales: $2,592 million
1-Yr. Sales Change: 12.9%
Exchange: NYSE
Symbol: LUV

Transportation - airline

 See pages 140–141 for a full profile of this company.

SOUTHWEST RESEARCH INSTITUTE INC.

6220 Culebra Rd.	CEO: Martin Goland	1994 Est. Sales: $230 mil.
San Antonio, TX 78228	CFO: Jesse D. Bates	1-Yr. Sales Change: —
Phone: 210-522-2122	HR: Bill Crumlett	Ownership: Privately Held
Fax: 210-522-3496	Employees: 2,600	

Engineering - R&D services, noncommercial

SOUTHWEST SECURITIES GROUP, INC.

1201 Elm St., Ste. 4300	CEO: Raymond E. Wooldridge	1994 Sales: $113.8 million
Dallas, TX 75270	CFO: Stacy Hodges	1-Yr. Sales Change: 24.8%
Phone: 214-651-1800	HR: Lynn Kurtz	Exchange: Nasdaq
Fax: 214-749-0810	Employees: 550	Symbol: SWST

Financial - investment management

SOUTHWEST TEXAS STATE UNIVERSITY

601 University Dr.	CEO: Jerome H. Supple	1994 Sales: $190 million
San Marcos, TX 78666-4603	CFO: William A. Nance	1-Yr. Sales Change: -4.3%
Phone: 512-245-2541	HR: John McBride	Ownership: Privately Held
Fax: 512-245-8153	Employees: 2,300	

University - offering 71 undergraduate degree programs, as well as professional & graduate degree programs

SOUTHWEST TOYOTA, INC.

9400 Southwest Fwy.	CEO: Sterling McCall	1994 Est. Sales: $175 mil.
Houston, TX 77074	CFO: Rebecca Schoenfeldt	1-Yr. Sales Change: —
Phone: 713-270-3900	HR: Donna Jensen	Ownership: Privately Held
Fax: 713-270-3909	Employees: 275	

Retail - new & used cars

SOUTHWESTERN IRRIGATED COTTON GROWERS ASSOCIATION

3500 Doniphan Dr.	CEO: David L. Hand	1994 Sales: $107 million
El Paso, TX 79922	CFO: William G. Jones	1-Yr. Sales Change: 18.9%
Phone: 915-581-5441	HR: William G. Jones	Ownership: Privately Held
Fax: 915-581-4138	Employees: 65	

Wholesale cotton & cottonseed cooperative

SOUTHWESTERN LIFE CORPORATION

500 N. Akard St.	CEO: Glenn H. Gettier Jr.	1994 Sales: $529.5 million
Dallas, TX 75201	CFO: John T. Hull	1-Yr. Sales Change: -51.1%
Phone: 214-954-7111	HR: Hubert Mathis	Exchange: AMEX
Fax: 214-954-7714	Employees: 1,000	Symbol: SLC

Insurance - life

SOUTHWESTERN PUBLIC SERVICE COMPANY

SPS Tower, Tyler & Sixth Sts.	CEO: Bill D. Helton	1994 Sales: $843.4 million
Amarillo, TX 79170	CFO: Bill D. Helton	1-Yr. Sales Change: 4.1%
Phone: 806-378-2121	HR: John L. Anderson	Exchange: NYSE
Fax: 806-378-2995	Employees: 2,000	Symbol: SPS

Utility - electric power

SPACE INDUSTRIES INTERNATIONAL INC.

101 Courageous Dr.	CEO: Joseph Allen	1994 Est. Sales: $340 mil.
League City, TX 77573	CFO: —	1-Yr. Sales Change: —
Phone: 713-538-6000	HR: Mary Seabranch	Ownership: Privately Held
Fax: 713-334-4010	Employees: 2,500	

Space flight & computer peripheral equipment manufacturing, computer integrated systems design & engineering services

SPAGHETTI WAREHOUSE, INC.

402 West I-30	CEO: Phillip Ratner	1995 Sales: $79 million
Garland, TX 75043	CFO: H. G. Carrington Jr.	1-Yr. Sales Change: 0.8%
Phone: 214-226-6000	HR: G. Kenna Davidson	Exchange: NYSE
Fax: 214-203-9594	Employees: 1,310	Symbol: SWH

Retail - restaurants in 17 states & Canada

SPECIALTY RETAILERS INC.

10201 Main St.	CEO: Carl Tooker	1994 Sales: $557 million
Houston, TX 77025	CFO: Jerry Izie	1-Yr. Sales Change: 10.5%
Phone: 713-667-5601	HR: Jack Chipperfield	Ownership: Privately Held
Fax: 713-669-2708	Employees: 8,000	

Retail - apparel stores (Palais Royal, Beall's & Fashion Bar)

SPECTRAVISION, INC.

1501 N. Plano Rd.	CEO: Gary G. Weik	1994 Sales: $143.5 million
Richardson, TX 75083-0775	CFO: Richard M. Gozia	1-Yr. Sales Change: -12.0%
Phone: 214-234-2721	HR: Scott Campbell	Exchange: OTC
Fax: 214-301-9607	Employees: 283	Symbol: SVN

Pay-per-view movies for hotels & motels

SPINNAKER INDUSTRIES, INC.

600 N. Pearl St., Ste. 2160	CEO: Richard J. Boyle	1994 Sales: $33.6 million
Dallas, TX 75201	CFO: James W. Toman	1-Yr. Sales Change: 425.0%
Phone: 214-855-0322	HR: Ned Fleming	Exchange: Nasdaq (SC)
Fax: 214-855-0093	Employees: 389	Symbol: SPNI

Industrial processing equipment, including centrifugal impact milling & scrap reclamation equipment

SPORT SUPPLY GROUP, INC.

1901 Diplomat, PO Box 7726	CEO: Michael J. Blumenfeld	1994 Sales: $88.5 million
Dallas, TX 75209	CFO: William R. Estill	1-Yr. Sales Change: 28.4%
Phone: 214-484-9484	HR: Joe Holt	Exchange: NYSE
Fax: 214-243-0149	Employees: 489	Symbol: GYM

Leisure & recreational products - sports equipment

STANLEY STORES INC.

1400 8th St.	CEO: O. B. Stanley	1994 Est. Sales: $225 mil.
Bay City, TX 77414	CFO: Joe Barlass	1-Yr. Sales Change: —
Phone: 409-245-6355	HR: Esther Gomez	Ownership: Privately Held
Fax: 409-245-1032	Employees: 1,400	

Retail - supermarkets (Stanley Stores, Foods 4 Less, Price-Low Foods)

STAR ENTERPRISE

12700 Northborough Dr.	CEO: Seth L. Sharr	1994 Sales: $6,086 million
Houston, TX 77067	CFO: William J. Mathe	1-Yr. Sales Change: -3.4%
Phone: 713-874-7000	HR: Floyd Chaney	Ownership: Subsidiary
Fax: 713-874-7760	Employees: 4,000	

Oil refining & marketing of Texaco-branded products in 26 eastern & Gulf Coast states & Washington, D.C. (Texaco-Aramco joint venture)

 See pages 142–143 for a full profile of this company.

STB SYSTEMS, INC.

1651 N. Glenville Dr., Ste. 210	CEO: William E. Ogle	1994 Sales: $89.8 million
Richardson, TX 75081	CFO: James L. Hopkins	1-Yr. Sales Change: 129.1%
Phone: 214-234-8750	HR: Sherri Wolf	Exchange: Nasdaq
Fax: 214-234-1306	Employees: 675	Symbol: STBI

Computers - graphics adapters for single- & multimonitor configurations, primarily in IBM-compatible PCs

STECK-VAUGHN PUBLISHING CORPORATION

8701 N. MoPac Expwy., Ste. 200	CEO: Roy E. Mayers	1994 Sales: $53.6 million
Austin, TX 78759-8365	CFO: Floyd D. Rogers	1-Yr. Sales Change: 0.8%
Phone: 512-343-8227	HR: —	Exchange: Nasdaq
Fax: 512-795-3397	Employees: 329	Symbol: STEK

Publishing - books

STEPHEN F. AUSTIN STATE UNIVERSITY

PO Box 9100, SFA Station	CEO: Daniel D. Angel	1994 Sales: $104 million
Nacogdoches, TX 75962-9100	CFO: Roland Smith	1-Yr. Sales Change: 1.9%
Phone: 409-468-2011	HR: Cathy Allen	Ownership: Privately Held
Fax: 409-468-1732	Employees: 3,450	

University - offering 63 undergraduate degree programs, as well as graduate & professional degree programs

STERLING BANCSHARES, INC.

15000 Northwest Fwy.	CEO: George Martinez	1994 Sales: $46.9 million
Houston, TX 77040	CFO: C. Frank Kurtin	1-Yr. Sales Change: 47.9%
Phone: 713-466-8300	HR: Jan Newton	Exchange: Nasdaq
Fax: 713-937-9849	Employees: 295	Symbol: SBIB

Banks - Southwest (Sterling Bank)

STERLING CHEMICALS, INC.

1200 Smith St., Ste. 1900	CEO: J. Virgil Waggoner	1994 Sales: $700.8 million
Houston, TX 77002-4312	CFO: Jim P. Wise	1-Yr. Sales Change: 35.1%
Phone: 713-650-3700	HR: Robert D. McAlister	Exchange: NYSE
Fax: 713-654-9551	Employees: 1,210	Symbol: STX

Chemicals - petrochemicals, including styrene, acrylonitrile, acetic acide, plasticizers & lactic acid; chemicals & large-scale generators for the pulp & paper industry

STERLING ELECTRONICS CORPORATION

4201 Southwest Fwy.
Houston, TX 77027-1229
Phone: 713-627-9800
Fax: 713-629-3938

CEO: Ronald S. Spolane
CFO: Mac McConnell
HR: Sheila Babin
Employees: 554

1995 Sales: $242.3 million
1-Yr. Sales Change: 20.8%
Exchange: AMEX
Symbol: SEC

Electronics - parts distribution

STERLING INFORMATION GROUP

515 Capital of Texas Hwy. South
Austin, TX 78746-4305
Phone: 512-327-0090
Fax: 512-327-0197

CEO: Chip Wolfe
CFO: Michael Haney
HR: Leslie Martinich
Employees: 55

1994 Sales: $3.7 million
1-Yr. Sales Change: 15.6%
Ownership: Privately Held

Computers - software consulting services

 See page 223 for a full profile of this company.

STERLING SOFTWARE, INC.

8080 N. Central Expwy., Ste. 1100
Dallas, TX 75206
Phone: 214-891-8600
Fax: 214-739-0535

CEO: Sterling L. Williams
CFO: George H. Ellis
HR: —
Employees: 3,000

1994 Sales: $473.4 million
1-Yr. Sales Change: 15.0%
Exchange: NYSE
Symbol: SSW

Computers - software & network services; automated program design software (acquired KnowledgeWare, Inc.)

 See page 224 for a full profile of this company.

STEVENS INTERNATIONAL, INC.

5500 Airport Fwy.
Fort Worth, TX 76117
Phone: 817-831-3911
Fax: 817-838-4344

CEO: Paul I. Stevens
CFO: Kenneth W. Reynolds
HR: Claudia Teague
Employees: 820

1994 Sales: $106.7 million
1-Yr. Sales Change: 2.8%
Exchange: AMEX
Symbol: SVGA

Machinery - printing presses

STEVENS TRANSPORT INC.

9757 Military Pkwy.
Dallas, TX 75227
Phone: 214-216-9000
Fax: 214-289-7002

CEO: Steven L. Aaron
CFO: Bob Nelson
HR: —
Employees: 1,100

1994 Sales: $131 million
1-Yr. Sales Change: 9.2%
Ownership: Privately Held

Transportation - refrigerated trucking

STEWART & STEVENSON SERVICES, INC.

2707 N. Loop West
Houston, TX 77008
Phone: 713-868-7700
Fax: 713-868-7692

CEO: Robert L. Hargrave
CFO: Robert L. Hargrave
HR: Bobby Brown
Employees: 4,300

1995 Sales: $1,138.3 million
1-Yr. Sales Change: 15.9%
Exchange: Nasdaq
Symbol: SSSS

Engines - adapts diesel & jet engines for power plants & vehicles

STEWART INFORMATION SERVICES CORPORATION

1980 Post Oak Blvd.
Houston, TX 77056
Phone: 713-871-1100
Fax: 713-629-2330

CEO: Carloss Morris
CFO: Max Crisp
HR: Nita Hanks
Employees: 3,470

1994 Sales: $302.2 million
1-Yr. Sales Change: -13.3%
Exchange: NYSE
Symbol: STC

Financial - title insurance

STRAFCO, INC.

1964 S. Alamo
San Antonio, TX 78204
Phone: 210-226-0101
Fax: 210-271-7495

CEO: David Straus
CFO: Huey J. Rhudy
HR: Murray Betts
Employees: 1,176

1994 Sales: $128 million
1-Yr. Sales Change: 0.8%
Ownership: Privately Held

Auto parts - distribution

SUIZA FOODS CORPORATION

3811 Turtle Creek Blvd., Ste. 1950
Dallas, TX 75219
Phone: 214-528-9922
Fax: 214-528-9929

CEO: Gregg L. Engles
CFO: Tracy L. Noll
HR: —
Employees: 1,740

1994 Est. Sales: $189 mil.
1-Yr. Sales Change: 4.2%
Ownership: Privately Held

Food - fresh milk products, ice cream & refrigerated fruit drinks in Puerto Rico & Florida (Suiza Dairy, Velda Farms) & packaged ice in Florida & the southwestern US (Reddy Ice)

SUMMAGRAPHICS CORPORATION

8500 Cameron Rd.
Austin, TX 78754-3999
Phone: 512-835-0900
Fax: 512-339-1490

CEO: Michael S. Bennett
CFO: David G. Osowski
HR: Kay Secord
Employees: 293

1995 Sales: $78.5 million
1-Yr. Sales Change: 21.3%
Exchange: Nasdaq
Symbol: SUGR

Computers - digitizing tablets & pen plotters

SUMMIT BANCSHARES, INC.

1300 Summit Ave.	CEO: Philip E. Norwood	1994 Sales: $20.5 million
Fort Worth, TX 76102-4414	CFO: Bob G. Scott	1-Yr. Sales Change: 4.1%
Phone: 817-336-6817	HR: Mary Flores	Exchange: Nasdaq
Fax: 817-336-2814	Employees: 125	Symbol: SBIT

Banks - Southwest (Summit National Bank)

SUN COAST INDUSTRIES, INC.

2700 S. Westmoreland Ave.	CEO: R. Carter Pate	1995 Sales: $86 million
Dallas, TX 75233	CFO: Cynthia R. Morris	1-Yr. Sales Change: 17.6%
Phone: 214-330-8671	HR: Karen Carter	Exchange: NYSE
Fax: 214-337-7428	Employees: 624	Symbol: SN

Rubber & plastic products - plastic tops for containers

SUN COAST RESOURCES INC.

14825 Willis	CEO: Kathy Prasnicki	1994 Sales: $200 million
Houston, TX 77039	CFO: —	1-Yr. Sales Change: 19.8%
Phone: 713-449-7274	HR: Lisa Smith	Ownership: Privately Held
Fax: 713-449-7288	Employees: 66	

Wholesale distribution - gasoline & diesel fuel

SUNBELT CORPORATION

5111 Woodway	CEO: Jose Domene	1994 Est. Sales: $125 mil.
Houston, TX 77056	CFO: Jeff Smith	1-Yr. Sales Change: —
Phone: 713-626-2005	HR: Manuel Familiar	Ownership: Privately Held
Fax: 713-960-0275	Employees: 1,000	

Construction - concrete

SUNBELT NURSERY GROUP, INC.

6500 West Fwy., Ste. 600	CEO: Donald W. Davis	1995 Sales: $138.6 million
Fort Worth, TX 76116	CFO: Mark L. Jones	1-Yr. Sales Change: -5.1%
Phone: 817-738-8111	HR: Jim Mason	Exchange: AMEX
Fax: 817-626-6279	Employees: 1,720	Symbol: SBN

Retail - garden centers (Wolfe Nursery)

SUPERTRAVEL

361 Greens Rd.	CEO: Stan St. Pierre	1994 Sales: $173 million
Houston, TX 77060	CFO: Gene McDaniel	1-Yr. Sales Change: -2.8%
Phone: 713-876-2900	HR: Tommy McDaniel	Ownership: Privately Held
Fax: 713-920-7180	Employees: 300	

Business services - travel agency specializing in corporate travel management, cruise/tour discounts & custom group travel

SURETY CAPITAL CORPORATION

1845 Precinct Line Rd., Ste. 100	CEO: Bobby W. Hackler	1994 Sales: $6.5 million
Hurst, TX 76054-3107	CFO: Bobby W. Hackler	1-Yr. Sales Change: 25.0%
Phone: 817-498-8154	HR: Robert Crews	Exchange: AMEX
Fax: 817-498-0647	Employees: 89	Symbol: SRY

Banks - Southwest (Surety Bank)

SWIFT ENERGY COMPANY

16825 Northchase Dr., Ste. 400	CEO: A. Earl Swift	1994 Sales: $25.4 million
Houston, TX 77060-9968	CFO: John R. Alden	1-Yr. Sales Change: 5.4%
Phone: 713-874-2700	HR: Charles Lopez	Exchange: NYSE
Fax: 713-874-2726	Employees: 209	Symbol: SFY

Oil & gas - US exploration & production

SYNAGRO TECHNOLOGIES, INC.

20515 State Hwy 249, Ste. 380	CEO: Don Thone	1994 Sales: $13.2 million
Houston, TX 77070	CFO: Joan M. McKinney	1-Yr. Sales Change: 38.9%
Phone: 713-370-6700	HR: —	Exchange: Nasdaq (SC)
Fax: 713-370-9292	Employees: 168	Symbol: SYGR

Transportation, treatment, site monitoring & documentation services to organic waste generators (Synagro, CDR, Organi-Gro)

SYSCO CORPORATION

1390 Enclave Pkwy.	CEO: Bill M. Lindig	1995 Sales: $12,118 million
Houston, TX 77077-2099	CFO: John K. Stubblefield Jr.	1-Yr. Sales Change: 10.7%
Phone: 713-584-1390	HR: Mike Nichols	Exchange: NYSE
Fax: 713-584-1245	Employees: 26,200	Symbol: SYY

Food - wholesale to restaurants

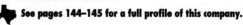 **See pages 144–145 for a full profile of this company.**

TACO CABANA, INC.

262 Losoya St., Ste. 330	CEO: Steve Clark	1994 Sales: $127.3 million
San Antonio, TX 78205	CFO: David G. Lloyd	1-Yr. Sales Change: 31.4%
Phone: 210-231-8226	HR: Linda Wishard	Exchange: Nasdaq
Fax: 210-227-0436	Employees: 4,650	Symbol: TACO

Retail - Taco Cabana restaurants

 See page 225 for a full profile of this company.

TANDY BRANDS, INC.

690 E. Lamar Blvd., Ste. 200	CEO: J. S. B. Jenkins	1994 Sales: $68.4 million
Arlington, TX 76011	CFO: Bruce Cole	1-Yr. Sales Change: 35.7%
Phone: 817-548-0090	HR: Jan Bland	Exchange: Nasdaq
Fax: 817-548-1144	Employees: 550	Symbol: TBAC

Leather & related products

TANDY CORPORATION

1800 One Tandy Center	CEO: John V. Roach	1994 Sales: $4,943.7 million
Fort Worth, TX 76102	CFO: Dwain H. Hughes	1-Yr. Sales Change: 20.5%
Phone: 817-390-3700	HR: George Berger	Exchange: NYSE
Fax: 817-390-3500	Employees: 45,800	Symbol: TAN

Retail - consumer electronics (Radio Shack, Computer City, McDuff, VideoConcepts, The Edge, Incredible Universe)

 See pages 146–147 for a full profile of this company.

TANDYCRAFTS, INC.

1400 Everman Pkwy.	CEO: Jerry L. Roy	1995 Sales: $256.5 million
Fort Worth, TX 76140	CFO: Michael J. Walsh	1-Yr. Sales Change: 19.4%
Phone: 817-551-9600	HR: Michael J. Walsh	Exchange: NYSE
Fax: 817-551-9795	Employees: 3,700	Symbol: TAC

Diversified operations - retail leathercrafts (Tandy Leather), inspirational books & gifts (Joshua's Christian Stores), office supplies (Sav-On Discount Office Supplies) & furniture (Cargo Furniture); manufacturing of frames & framed art, belts & accessories, outerwear & leather products

TANKNOLOGY ENVIRONMENTAL, INC.

5225 Hollister St.	CEO: Donald R. Campbell	1994 Sales: $44.1 million
Houston, TX 77040-6294	CFO: Rick Berry	1-Yr. Sales Change: -2.9%
Phone: 713-690-8265	HR: Beth Martin	Exchange: Nasdaq
Fax: 713-690-2255	Employees: 350	Symbol: TANK

Pollution control equipment & services - storage tank maintenance

TARRANT DISTRIBUTORS INC.

9835 Genard Rd.	CEO: N. B. Strauss	1994 Est. Sales: $200 mil.
Houston, TX 77041	CFO: David L. Ritch	1-Yr. Sales Change: —
Phone: 713-690-8888	HR: Rose Clark	Ownership: Privately Held
Fax: 713-690-1169	Employees: 370	

Wholesale distribution - alcoholic beverages

TATHAM OFFSHORE, INC.

600 Travis St.	CEO: Donald S. Taylor	1995 Sales: $8.1 million
Houston, TX 77002	CFO: Donald V. Weir	1-Yr. Sales Change: -33.1%
Phone: 713-224-7400	HR: Donald V. Weir	Exchange: Nasdaq
Fax: 713-224-7574	Employees: 56	Symbol: TOFF

Oil & gas - independent offshore deep-water drilling in the Gulf of Mexico

TAUBER OIL COMPANY

55 Waugh Dr., Ste. 700	CEO: O. J. Tauber Jr.	1994 Sales: $846 million
Houston, TX 77007	CFO: Stephen E. Hamlin	1-Yr. Sales Change: 13.3%
Phone: 713-869-8700	HR: Nancy Dillard	Ownership: Privately Held
Fax: 713-869-8069	Employees: 56	

Petroleum & petrochemical products marketing

TCA CABLE TV, INC.

3015 SSE Loop 323	CEO: Robert M. Rogers	1994 Sales: $162.3 million
Tyler, TX 75713-0489	CFO: Jimmie F. Taylor	1-Yr. Sales Change: 6.6%
Phone: 903-595-3710	HR: Jerry Yandell	Exchange: Nasdaq
Fax: 903-595-1929	Employees: 991	Symbol: TCAT

Cable TV

TCC INDUSTRIES, INC.

816 Congress Ave.	CEO: Lawrence W. Schumann	1994 Sales: $23.1 million
Austin, TX 78701	CFO: Larry T. Marek	1-Yr. Sales Change: -9.4%
Phone: 512-320-0976	HR: —	Exchange: NYSE
Fax: 512-320-0063	Employees: 181	Symbol: TEL

Machinery - bulk material–conveying equipment & systems; wholesale souvenirs (collectible spoons), gifts & novelty items (whoopee cushions)

TEAM, INC.

1001 Fannin St., Ste. 4656	CEO: William A. Ryan	1995 Sales: $55.7 million
Houston, TX 77002	CFO: Russell G. Donham	1-Yr. Sales Change: -22.2%
Phone: 713-659-3600	HR: Clark Ingram	Exchange: AMEX
Fax: 713-659-3420	Employees: 823	Symbol: TMI

Environmental consulting services

TECH-SYM CORPORATION

10500 Westoffice Dr., Ste. 200	CEO: Wendell W. Gamel	1994 Sales: $197.6 million
Houston, TX 77042-5391	CFO: Ray F. Thompson	1-Yr. Sales Change: 7.2%
Phone: 713-785-7790	HR: Mike Kahn	Exchange: NYSE
Fax: 713-780-3524	Employees: 1,988	Symbol: TSY

Active & passive electronic microwave products & radio frequency energy sources; 3D seismic equipment used to find oil; military flight crew evaluation systems

TECNOL MEDICAL PRODUCTS, INC.

7201 Industrial Park Blvd.	CEO: Vance M. Hubbard	1994 Sales: $120.7 million
Fort Worth, TX 76180	CFO: David Radunsky	1-Yr. Sales Change: 39.2%
Phone: 817-581-6424	HR: Chris Gonser	Exchange: Nasdaq
Fax: 817-577-6599	Employees: 1,787	Symbol: TCNL

Medical products - disposable face masks, ice packs & patient safety restraints

TEJAS GAS CORPORATION

1301 McKinney St., Ste. 700	CEO: Jay A. Precourt	1994 Sales: $1,031.9 million
Houston, TX 77010	CFO: James W. Whalen	1-Yr. Sales Change: 30.6%
Phone: 713-658-0509	HR: Clyde M. Bradford	Exchange: NYSE
Fax: 713-658-9600	Employees: 387	Symbol: TEJ

Oil & gas - production & pipeline

TEJAS POWER CORPORATION

200 WestLake Park Blvd., Ste. 1000	CEO: Larry W. Bickle	1994 Sales: $295.4 million
Houston, TX 77079	CFO: William W. Elting	1-Yr. Sales Change: 14.5%
Phone: 713-597-6200	HR: Marianne Finch	Exchange: AMEX
Fax: 713-597-6500	Employees: 136	Symbol: TPC

Oil & gas - production & pipeline to integrated system of market hubs located in Texas, Louisiana, Mississippi & the northeastern & midwestern US

TEL OFFSHORE TRUST

712 Main St.
Houston, TX 77002
Phone: 713-216-5712
Fax: 713-216-5476

CEO: Debbie Miller
CFO: —
HR: —
Employees: —

1994 Sales: $3.4 million
1-Yr. Sales Change: 47.8%
Exchange: Nasdaq (SC)
Symbol: TELOZ

Oil & gas - US royalty trust

TELESCAN, INC.

10550 Richmond Ave., Ste. 250
Houston, TX 77042
Phone: 713-952-1060
Fax: 713-952-7138

CEO: David L. Brown
CFO: Roderick A. Schultz
HR: Brigette Dewhurst
Employees: 142

1994 Sales: $10.5 million
1-Yr. Sales Change: 50.0%
Exchange: Nasdaq (SC)
Symbol: TSCN

Computers - on-line financial information services

TELETOUCH COMMUNICATIONS, INC.

2121 Old Henderson Hwy.
Tyler, TX 75702
Phone: 903-595-8800
Fax: 903-595-8826

CEO: Robert M. McMurrey
CFO: Robert M. McMurrey
HR: Jane Barton
Employees: 200

1995 Sales: $6.6 million
1-Yr. Sales Change: 100.0%
Exchange: Nasdaq (SC)
Symbol: TELL

Telecommunications services - two-way mobile communications services & telemessaging services

TEMPLE-INLAND INC.

303 S.Temple Dr., Drawer N
Diboll, TX 75941
Phone: 409-829-2211
Fax: 409-829-1366

CEO: Clifford J. Grum
CFO: Kenneth M. Jastrow II
HR: Herb George
Employees: 15,000

1994 Sales: $2,937.5 million
1-Yr. Sales Change: 7.4%
Exchange: NYSE
Symbol: TIN

Containers & containerboard; bleached paperboard; building products

 See pages 148–149 for a full profile of this company.

TEMTEX INDUSTRIES, INC.

3010 LBJ Fwy., Ste. 650
Dallas, TX 75234-2705
Phone: 214-484-1845
Fax: 214-241-1452

CEO: Edwin R. Buford
CFO: Roger N. Stivers
HR: Dan Goode
Employees: 576

1994 Sales: $43.9 million
1-Yr. Sales Change: 28.7%
Exchange: Nasdaq
Symbol: TMTX

Building products - face brick for home & commercial use; bomb fins & other defense hardware

TENNECO INC.

Tenneco Bldg., PO Box 2511
Houston, TX 77252-2511
Phone: 713-757-2131
Fax: 713-757-1410

CEO: Dana G. Mead
CFO: Robert T. Blakely
HR: Barry R. Schuman
Employees: 55,000

1994 Sales: $12,174 million
1-Yr. Sales Change: -8.2%
Exchange: NYSE
Symbol: TEN

Diversified operations - natural gas pipelines; shipbuilding (Newport News Shipbuilding & Drydock); auto parts (Monroe & Walker); chemicals; packaging

 See pages 150–151 for a full profile of this company.

TEPPCO PARTNERS, L.P.

2929 Allen Pkwy., PO Box 2521
Houston, TX 77252-2521
Phone: 713-759-3636
Fax: 713-759-3783

CEO: William L. Thacker Jr.
CFO: Charles H. Leonard
HR: Sharon Stratton
Employees: 499

1994 Sales: $197.3 million
1-Yr. Sales Change: 7.5%
Exchange: NYSE
Symbol: TPP

Oil & gas - pipeline

TESCORP, INC.

327 Congress Ave., Ste. 200
Austin, TX 78701
Phone: 512-476-2995
Fax: 512-474-1610

CEO: Jack R. Crosby
CFO: John Becker
HR: Lesley Carter
Employees: 7

1995 Sales: $1.1 million
1-Yr. Sales Change: 450.0%
Exchange: Nasdaq (SC)
Symbol: TESC

Cable TV & telecommunications services in Latin America

TESORO PETROLEUM CORPORATION

8700 Tesoro Dr.
San Antonio, TX 78217
Phone: 210-828-8484
Fax: 210-828-8600

CEO: Bruce A. Smith
CFO: William T. Van Kleef
HR: Thomas E. Reardon
Employees: 857

1994 Sales: $877.2 million
1-Yr. Sales Change: 5.1%
Exchange: NYSE
Symbol: TSO

Oil refining & marketing

TETCO INC.

1777 NE Loop 410, Ste. 1500
San Antonio, TX 78217
Phone: 210-821-5900
Fax: 210-826-3003

CEO: Tom E. Turner
CFO: Dayton Simms
HR: Bob Gutmueller
Employees: 1,550

1994 Est. Sales: $100 mil.
1-Yr. Sales Change: 6.4%
Ownership: Privately Held

Transportation - nationwide trucking

TETRA TECHNOLOGIES, INC.

25025 I-45 North	CEO: Michael L. Jeane	1994 Sales: $88.5 million
The Woodlands, TX 77380	CFO: Geoffrey M. Hertel	1-Yr. Sales Change: 40.9%
Phone: 713-367-1983	HR: Linden Price	Exchange: Nasdaq
Fax: 713-364-2240	Employees: 433	Symbol: TTRA

Pollution control equipment & services - environmental engineering & consulting

THE TEXAS A&M UNIVERSITY SYSTEM

State Headquarters Building	CEO: Barry P. Thompson	1994 Sales: $1,286.5 million
College Station, TX 77843	CFO: Richard Lindsay	1-Yr. Sales Change: 6.1%
Phone: 409-845-4331	HR: Patti Courer	Ownership: Privately Held
Fax: 409-862-2679	Employees: 19,000	

University - land-grant system comprised of 7 universities & 8 research agencies, offering 100 undergraduate & 218 graduate degree programs

 See pages 152–153 for a full profile of this company.

TEXAS BIOTECHNOLOGY CORPORATION

7000 Fannin St., Ste. 1920	CEO: David B. McWilliams	1994 Sales: $4.7 million
Houston, TX 77030	CFO: Stephen L. Mueller	1-Yr. Sales Change: 4,600%
Phone: 713-796-8822	HR: Debbie Hedgepath	Exchange: AMEX
Fax: 713-796-8232	Employees: 97	Symbol: TXB

Drugs to treat cardiovascular disease

TEXAS CHRISTIAN UNIVERSITY

2800 S. University Dr.	CEO: William E. Tucker	1995 Sales: $119.1 million
Fort Worth, TX 76129	CFO: Larry H. Calloway	1-Yr. Sales Change: —
Phone: 817-921-7000	HR: John Weis	Ownership: Privately Held
Fax: 817-921-7272	Employees: 1,300	

University - offering 74 undergraduate & 33 graduate degree programs

TEXAS INDUSTRIES, INC.

1341 W. Mockingbird Ln.	CEO: Robert D. Rogers	1995 Sales: $830.5 million
Dallas, TX 75247	CFO: Richard M. Fowler	1-Yr. Sales Change: 17.4%
Phone: 214-647-6700	HR: Brooke E. Brewer	Exchange: NYSE
Fax: 214-647-3878	Employees: 2,800	Symbol: TXI

Diversified operations - steel; concrete; cement

TEXAS INSTRUMENTS INCORPORATED

13500 N. Central Expwy.	CEO: Jerry R. Junkins	1994 Sales: $10,315 million
Dallas, TX 75265	CFO: William A. Aylesworth	1-Yr. Sales Change: 21.0%
Phone: 214-995-2551	HR: Charles F. Nielson	Exchange: NYSE
Fax: 214-995-4360	Employees: 56,333	Symbol: TXN

Notebooks (TravelMate 486), RISC & SPARC microprocessors, analog & digital semiconductors & printers; defense systems

 See pages 154–155 for a full profile of this company.

TEXAS MERIDIAN RESOURCES CORPORATION

15995 N. Barkers Landing, Ste. 300	CEO: Joseph A. Reeves Jr.	1994 Sales: $7.9 million
Houston, TX 77079	CFO: Lloyd V. Delano	1-Yr. Sales Change: 58.0%
Phone: 713-558-8080	HR: —	Exchange: AMEX
Fax: 713-558-5595	Employees: 22	Symbol: TMR

Oil & gas - US exploration & production utilizing 3-D seismic & computer-aided exploration technology

TEXAS MICROSYSTEMS, INC.

5959 Corporate Dr.	CEO: Wayne Patterson	1994 Est. Sales: $40 mil.
Houston, TX 77036	CFO: Michael Stewart	1-Yr. Sales Change: 12.0%
Phone: 713-541-8200	HR: Reba Teague	Ownership: Privately Held
Fax: 713-933-1029	Employees: 150	

Computers - industrial microcomputers

TEXAS OLEFINS CO.

8707 Katy Fwy., Ste. 300	CEO: B. W. Waycaster	1994 Est. Sales: $375 mil.
Houston, TX 77024	CFO: C. E. Manning	1-Yr. Sales Change: —
Phone: 713-461-2223	HR: Jimmy Rhodes	Ownership: Privately Held
Fax: 713-461-1029	Employees: 349	

Chemicals - hydrocarbon fluids & industrial organic chemicals

TEXAS RANGERS BASEBALL CLUB

1000 Ballpark Way	CEO: J. Thomas	1994 Sales: $50.1 million
Arlington, TX 76011	CFO: John McMichael	1-Yr. Sales Change: -16.9%
Phone: 817-273-5222	HR: Kim Smith	Ownership: Privately Held
Fax: 817-273-5174	Employees: 150	

Professional baseball team

TEXAS REGIONAL BANCSHARES, INC.

3700 N. 10th, Ste. 301
McAllen, TX 78501
Phone: 210-631-5400
Fax: 210-631-5450

CEO: Glen E. Roney
CFO: George R. Carruthers
HR: Nancy F. Schultz
Employees: 294

1994 Sales: $40.4 million
1-Yr. Sales Change: 16.4%
Exchange: Nasdaq
Symbol: TRBS

Banks - Southwest (Texas State Bank)

TEXAS SOUTHERN UNIVERSITY

3100 Cleburne
Houston, TX 77004
Phone: 713-527-7011
Fax: 713-639-1023

CEO: Joann Horton
CFO: Howard Turnley
HR: Christopher Bowen
Employees: 2,212

1994 Sales: $87.2 million
1-Yr. Sales Change: —
Ownership: Privately Held

University - offering 40 undergraduate & 31 graduate degree programs

TEXAS STAR RESOURCES CORPORATION

2000 S. Dairy Ashford, Ste. 510
Houston, TX 77077
Phone: 713-870-9882
Fax: 713-870-9934

CEO: J. David Edwards
CFO: J. David Edwards
HR: —
Employees: 2

1994 Sales: $0.1 million
1-Yr. Sales Change: —
Exchange: Nasdaq (SC)
Symbol: TEXSF

Diamond exploration & mining in North America & Russia

TEXAS TECH UNIVERSITY

250 West Hall
Lubbock, TX 79409
Phone: 806-742-2011
Fax: 806-742-1615

CEO: Robert W. Lawless
CFO: Don E. Cosby
HR: Jeanette Hodges
Employees: 10,066

1994 Sales: $262.3 million
1-Yr. Sales Change: 4.5%
Ownership: Privately Held

University - system offering 92 undergraduate & 126 graduate degree programs

TEXAS UTILITIES COMPANY

1601 Bryan St.
Dallas, TX 75201-3411
Phone: 214-812-4600
Fax: 214-812-4651

CEO: Erle Nye
CFO: H. Dan Farell
HR: Pitt Pittman
Employees: 10,798

1994 Sales: $5,663.5 million
1-Yr. Sales Change: 4.2%
Exchange: NYSE
Symbol: TXU

Utility - electric power

 See pages 156–157 for a full profile of this company.

TEXOIL, INC.

1600 Smith, Ste. 4000	CEO: Walter L. Williams	1994 Sales: $0.7 million
Houston, TX 77002	CFO: D. Hughes Watler Jr.	1-Yr. Sales Change: 0.0%
Phone: 713-652-5741	HR: Lynn Graves	Exchange: Nasdaq (SC)
Fax: 713-652-9601	Employees: 10	Symbol: TXLI

Oil & gas - exploration & production in South Louisiana

TGC INDUSTRIES, INC.

1304 Summit, Ste. 2	CEO: Allen T. McInnes	1994 Sales: $22.9 million
Plano, TX 75074	CFO: Doug Kirkpatrick	1-Yr. Sales Change: 129.0%
Phone: 214-881-1099	HR: —	Exchange: Nasdaq (SC)
Fax: 214-424-3943	Employees: 634	Symbol: TGCI

Oil & gas - geophysical services, seismic surveys & gravity information; specialty packaging for agricultural industry

T.H. LEHMAN & CO., INC.

4900 Woodway, Ste. 650	CEO: Edmond Nagel	1995 Sales: $1.1 million
Houston, TX 77056	CFO: Shannon C. Gries	1-Yr. Sales Change: -8.3%
Phone: 713-621-8404	HR: Brenda Heartfield	Exchange: OTC
Fax: 713-621-8027	Employees: 22	Symbol: THLM

Financing & collection of accounts receivable generated by doctors

THOMAS GROUP, INC.

5215 N. O'Connor Blvd., Ste. 2500	CEO: Philip R. Thomas	1994 Sales: $52.5 million
Irving, TX 75039-3714	CFO: Lee Grubb	1-Yr. Sales Change: 17.7%
Phone: 214-869-3400	HR: David A. Marconi	Exchange: Nasdaq
Fax: 214-869-6501	Employees: 257	Symbol: TGIS

Consultants - time management

THOMPSON AND KNIGHT PC

3300 First City Center	CEO: B. Berry	1994 Est. Sales: $120 mil.
Dallas, TX 75201	CFO: Mitch Hopwood	1-Yr. Sales Change: 0.0%
Phone: 214-969-1700	HR: Sam Phillips	Ownership: Privately Held
Fax: 214-969-1751	Employees: 500	

Law firm

TIC UNITED CORPORATION

4645 N. Central Expwy.
Dallas, TX 75205
Phone: 214-559-0580
Fax: 214-559-9510

CEO: Stratton J. Georgoulis
CFO: Bryan L. Parker
HR: Harold Hatley
Employees: 2,000

1994 Sales: $275 million
1-Yr. Sales Change: -8.3%
Ownership: Privately Held

Transportation - trucking; steel foundries

TITAN HOLDINGS, INC.

1020 NE Loop 410, Ste. 700
San Antonio, TX 78209
Phone: 210-824-4546
Fax: 210-824-3681

CEO: Mark E. Watson Jr.
CFO: Michael J. Bodayle
HR: Carol Fox
Employees: 184

1994 Sales: $97.8 million
1-Yr. Sales Change: 21.9%
Exchange: NYSE
Symbol: TH

Insurance - multiline

TIVOLI SYSTEMS INC.

9442 Capital of TX Hwy. North, Ste. 500
Austin, TX 78759
Phone: 512-794-9070
Fax: 512-418-4992

CEO: Franklin H. Moss
CFO: James R. Offerdahl
HR: Dale Wylie
Employees: 201

1994 Sales: $26.9 million
1-Yr. Sales Change: 111.8%
Exchange: Nasdaq
Symbol: TIVS

Computers - systems management software for mainframe to client/server systems

TM CENTURY, INC.

2002 Academy
Dallas, TX 75234-9220
Phone: 214-406-6800
Fax: 214-406-6885

CEO: Neil Sargent
CFO: Lynne L. Mabry
HR: Deedee Pruett
Employees: 72

1994 Sales: $8.2 million
1-Yr. Sales Change: -9.9%
Exchange: Nasdaq (SC)
Symbol: TMCI

Broadcasting - compact disc & production libraries, station indentification jingles, radio commercials for TV & computer software for music scheduling

TMBR/SHARP DRILLING, INC.

4607 W. Industrial Blvd.
Midland, TX 79703
Phone: 915-699-5050
Fax: 915-699-5828

CEO: Thomas C. Brown
CFO: Patricia R. Elledge
HR: Jim Singleton
Employees: 235

1995 Sales: $19.4 million
1-Yr. Sales Change: 1.0%
Exchange: Nasdaq (SC)
Symbol: TBDI

Oil & gas - contract well drilling

TNP ENTERPRISES, INC.

4100 International Plaza, PO Box 2934
Fort Worth, TX 76113
Phone: 817-731-0099
Fax: 817-737-1343

Utility - electric power

CEO: Kevern R. Joyce
CFO: Manjit Cheema
HR: Dennis R. Cash
Employees: 893

1994 Sales: $478 million
1-Yr. Sales Change: 0.8%
Exchange: NYSE
Symbol: TNP

TOM BROWN, INC.

508 W. Wall, Ste. 500, PO Box 2608
Midland, TX 79701
Phone: 915-682-9715
Fax: 915-682-9171

Oil & gas - US exploration & production

CEO: Donald L. Evans
CFO: R. Kim Harris
HR: Jack Reed
Employees: 62

1994 Sales: $29.1 million
1-Yr. Sales Change: 1.4%
Exchange: Nasdaq
Symbol: TMBR

TOREADOR ROYALTY CORPORATION

8117 Preston Rd., Ste. 530-LB34
Dallas, TX 75225-6332
Phone: 214-220-2141
Fax: 214-220-3116

Oil & gas - US royalty trust

CEO: Peter R. Vig
CFO: Peter R. Vig
HR: —
Employees: 3

1994 Sales: $1.9 million
1-Yr. Sales Change: -9.5%
Exchange: Nasdaq
Symbol: TRGL

TRACOR, INC.

6500 Tracor Ln.
Austin, TX 78725-2000
Phone: 512-926-2800
Fax: 512-929-2262

CEO: James B. Skaggs
CFO: Robert K. Floyd
HR: Murray Shaw
Employees: 9,700

1994 Sales: $694 million
1-Yr. Sales Change: 70.3%
Exchange: Nasdaq
Symbol: TTRR

Electronics - defense countermeasure systems & software & related management & technical support & services; automatic test systems for the US Air Force (GDE Systems, Inc.)

 See page 226 for a full profile of this company.

TRAMMELL CROW COMPANY

3500 Trammell Crow Center
Dallas, TX 75201
Phone: 214-979-5100
Fax: 214-979-6058

CEO: James D. Carreker
CFO: Mike Decker
HR: Mary Jo Francis
Employees: 2,500

1994 Sales: $175 million
1-Yr. Sales Change: 0.0%
Ownership: Privately Held

Real estate operations - land development & construction management

TRANSAMERICAN WASTE INDUSTRIES, INC.

314 N. Post Oak Ln.
Houston, TX 77024-5904
Phone: 713-956-1212
Fax: 713-956-0262

CEO: Tom J. Fatjo Jr.
CFO: Lance C. Rudd
HR: Barbara Kaiser
Employees: 102

1994 Sales: $14.3 million
1-Yr. Sales Change: 24.3%
Exchange: Nasdaq (SC)
Symbol: WSTE

Pollution control - nonhazardous industrial & municipal solid waste processing, treatment & disposal

TRANSCONTINENTAL REALTY INVESTORS, INC.

10670 N. Central Expwy., Ste. 300
Dallas, TX 75231
Phone: 214-692-4800
Fax: 214-750-6280

CEO: Randall M. Paulson
CFO: Thomas A. Holland
HR: Lyn Krueger
Employees: —

1994 Sales: $37.9 million
1-Yr. Sales Change: 18.4%
Exchange: NYSE
Symbol: TCI

Real estate investment trust - office buildings, industrial properties & shopping centers

TRANSPORT HOLDINGS INC.

714 Main St.
Fort Worth, TX 76102
Phone: 817-390-8000
Fax: 817-390-1056

CEO: Garland M. Lasater Jr.
CFO: A. Foster Nelson
HR: Jack Kocks
Employees: 400

1994 Sales: $270.9 million
1-Yr. Sales Change: -18.2%
Exchange: Nasdaq
Symbol: TLIC

Supplemental health insurance & long-term care insurance underwriting & distribution

TRANSTEXAS GAS CORPORATION

363 N. Sam Houston Pkwy. East
Houston, TX 77060
Phone: 713-447-3111
Fax: 713-447-1050

CEO: John R. Stanley
CFO: Edwin B. Donahue
HR: Gerald Barkley
Employees: 2,100

1994 Sales: $335.9 million
1-Yr. Sales Change: 3.1%
Exchange: Nasdaq
Symbol: TTXG

Oil & gas - natural gas production & pipeline

TRAVELFEST SUPERSTORES, INC.

1214 W. 6th St., Ste. 200
Austin, TX 78703-5230
Phone: 512-479-6131
Fax: 512-479-6380

CEO: Gary E. Hoover
CFO: Glenn R. Astolfi
HR: Marybeth Gavin
Employees: 77

1995 Sales: $2.4 million
1-Yr. Sales Change: —
Ownership: Privately Held

Retail - travel superstores, including personal travel services (tickets & reservations) & travel products (maps, luggage, accessories & travel books), with 2 locations in Austin

TRIANGLE PACIFIC CORP.

16803 Dallas Pkwy., PO Box 660100
Dallas, TX 75266-0100
Phone: 214-931-3000
Fax: 214-931-3284

CEO: Floyd F. Sherman
CFO: Robert J. Symon
HR: Jennifer Wisdom
Employees: 4,001

1994 Sales: $410.2 million
1-Yr. Sales Change: 18.5%
Exchange: Nasdaq
Symbol: TRIP

Building products - cabinets & hardwood floors

TRINITY INDUSTRIES, INC.

2525 Stemmons Fwy., PO Box 568887
Dallas, TX 75356-8887
Phone: 214-631-4420
Fax: 214-689-0501

CEO: W. Ray Wallace
CFO: K. W. Lewis
HR: Jack Cunningham
Employees: 16,500

1995 Sales: $2,314.9 million
1-Yr. Sales Change: 29.7%
Exchange: NYSE
Symbol: TRN

Metal products - railcars, marine products, construction products, pressure & nonpressure containers, fittings & flanges; railcar leasing

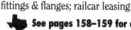 **See pages 158–159 for a full profile of this company.**

TRINITY UNIVERSITY

715 Stadium Dr.
San Antonio, TX 78212
Phone: 210-736-7011
Fax: 210-736-8449

CEO: Ronald K. Calgaard
CFO: Craig McCoy
HR: Linda Freeman-Sendala
Employees: 700

1994 Sales: $62.2 million
1-Yr. Sales Change: 5.4%
Ownership: Privately Held

University - offering 26 undergraduate & 4 graduate degree programs

TRISM, INC.

301 Commerce St., Ste. 1101
Fort Worth, TX 76102
Phone: 817-335-1791
Fax: 817-335-1913

CEO: Michael L. Lawrence
CFO: Daryl W. Deel
HR: Mike May
Employees: 2,629

1994 Sales: $225.2 million
1-Yr. Sales Change: 11.7%
Exchange: Nasdaq
Symbol: TRSM

Transportation - specialty trucking

TRI-STATE WHOLESALE ASSOCIATED GROCERS INC.

1000 Hawkins Blvd.
El Paso, TX 79915
Phone: 915-774-6400
Fax: 915-774-6443

CEO: Stanton L. Irvin
CFO: Maxine H. Hixon
HR: Carey Prather
Employees: 250

1995 Sales: $200.9 million
1-Yr. Sales Change: —
Ownership: Privately Held

Food - wholesale groceries

TRITON ENERGY CORPORATION

6688 N. Central Expwy., Ste. 1400
Dallas, TX 75206
Phone: 214-691-5200
Fax: 214-987-0571

CEO: Thomas G. Finck
CFO: Peter Rugg
HR: Andy Mormon
Employees: 340

1994 Sales: $120.4 million
1-Yr. Sales Change: 9.3%
Exchange: NYSE
Symbol: OIL

Oil & gas - US exploration & production

TST/IMPRESO, INC.

652 Southwestern Blvd.
Coppell, TX 75019
Phone: 214-462-0100
Fax: 214-462-7764

CEO: Marshall D. Sorokwasz
CFO: Susan M. Atkins
HR: Jayni Sellers
Employees: 113

1994 Sales: $25.9 million
1-Yr. Sales Change: -0.8%
Exchange: Nasdaq
Symbol: TSTI

Paper - standard continuous computer stock business forms, thermal fax paper & cut sheet paper for use in copy machines, laser printers, ink-jet printers & plain paper fax machines

TSX CORPORATION

5-D Butterfield Trail
El Paso, TX 79906
Phone: 915-772-4400
Fax: 915-778-9930

CEO: William H. Lambert
CFO: Harold C. Tamburro
HR: Wes Schotten
Employees: 850

1995 Sales: $72.4 million
1-Yr. Sales Change: 92.0%
Exchange: Nasdaq
Symbol: TSXX

Fiber optics - high technology distribution equipment & advertising insertion equipment for worldwide cable TV markets

TTI INC.

2441 Northeast Pkwy.
Fort Worth, TX 76106
Phone: 817-740-9000
Fax: 817-740-1682

CEO: Paul E. Andrews Jr.
CFO: Nick M. Kypreos
HR: Sharon Carrell
Employees: 709

1994 Est. Sales: $175 mil.
1-Yr. Sales Change: —
Ownership: Privately Held

Electronics - distribution of passive electronic components, including resistors & capacitors

TUBOSCOPE VETCO INTERNATIONAL CORPORATION

2835 Holmes Rd.
Houston, TX 77051
Phone: 713-799-5100
Fax: 713-799-1460

CEO: William V. Larkin Jr.
CFO: Ronald L. Koons
HR: Kenneth L. Nibling
Employees: 1,954

1994 Sales: $192.2 million
1-Yr. Sales Change: 4.9%
Exchange: Nasdaq
Symbol: TUBO

Oil & gas - tubular inspection & coating services to the worldwide petroleum industries

TUCKER DRILLING COMPANY, INC.

14 East Beauregard, PO Box 1876
San Angelo, TX 76902-1876
Phone: 915-655-6773
Fax: 915-653-4873

CEO: Larry J. Tucker
CFO: Charles B. Middlekauf
HR: Janet Herode
Employees: 200

1995 Sales: $24 million
1-Yr. Sales Change: 34.1%
Exchange: Nasdaq
Symbol: TUCK

Oil & gas - US exploration & production

TUESDAY MORNING CORPORATION

14621 Inwood Rd.
Dallas, TX 75244
Phone: 214-387-3562
Fax: 214-387-2344

CEO: Lloyd L. Ross
CFO: Mark E. Jarvis
HR: Deborah H. Steenrod
Employees: 3,450

1994 Sales: $190.1 million
1-Yr. Sales Change: 8.1%
Exchange: Nasdaq
Symbol: TUES

Retail - discount & variety

 See page 227 for a full profile of this company.

TYLER CORPORATION

3200 San Jacinto Tower
Dallas, TX 75201
Phone: 214-754-7800
Fax: 214-969-9352

CEO: Joseph F. McKinney
CFO: Linda K. Hill
HR: Sandie Shepherd
Employees: 4,000

1994 Sales: $357.8 million
1-Yr. Sales Change: 26.7%
Exchange: NYSE
Symbol: TYL

Cast iron pipe & fittings for drain, waste & vent applications & fittings for waterworks applications; retail auto parts (Forest City Auto Parts); institutional financing services

UETA INC.

3407 N.E. Pkwy.
San Antonio, TX 78218
Phone: 210-828-8382
Fax: 210-824-9022

CEO: John Edmondson
CFO: Bob Petka
HR: Mary Ince
Employees: 360

1994 Est. Sales: $150 mil.
1-Yr. Sales Change: —
Ownership: Privately Held

Diversified operations - transportation; alcohol storage; distilled liquors distribution

ULTRAK, INC.

1220 Champion Circle, Ste. 100
Carrollton, TX 75006
Phone: 214-280-9675
Fax: 214-280-9674

CEO: George K. Broady
CFO: Tim D. Torno
HR: Patty Cramer
Employees: 148

1994 Sales: $78.8 million
1-Yr. Sales Change: 50.4%
Exchange: Nasdaq
Symbol: ULTK

Video equipment - closed-circuit TV systems

UNIMAR COMPANY

1221 McKinney, Ste. 600	CEO: William M. Krips	1994 Sales: $197.9 million
Houston, TX 77010-2015	CFO: William M. Krips	1-Yr. Sales Change: -1.3%
Phone: 713-654-8550	HR: —	Exchange: AMEX
Fax: 713-654-8569	Employees: 2,130	Symbol: UMR

Oil & gas - exploration in Indonesia

THE UNIMARK GROUP, INC.

UniMark House, PO Box 229	CEO: Jorn Budde	1994 Sales: $25.3 million
Argyle, TX 76226	CFO: Keith Ford	1-Yr. Sales Change: 33.9%
Phone: 817-491-2992	HR: Viki Coffman	Exchange: Nasdaq (SC)
Fax: 817-491-1272	Employees: 1,347	Symbol: UNMG

Food - processed chilled & canned fruits (Sunfresh, Fruits of Four Seasons)

UNION TEXAS PETROLEUM HOLDINGS, INC.

1330 Post Oak Blvd.	CEO: A. Clark Johnson	1994 Sales: $769.6 million
Houston, TX 77056	CFO: Larry D. Kalmbach	1-Yr. Sales Change: 10.5%
Phone: 713-623-6544	HR: —	Exchange: NYSE
Fax: 713-968-2771	Employees: 1,000	Symbol: UTH

Oil & gas - international exploration & production in Indonesia, the UK sector of the North Sea & Pakistan

UNITED HERITAGE CORPORATION

2 N. Caddo St., PO Box 1956	CEO: Walter G. Mize	1995 Sales: $3.5 million
Cleburne, TX 76033-1956	CFO: Harold L. Gilliam	1-Yr. Sales Change: -10.3%
Phone: 817-641-3681	HR: —	Exchange: Nasdaq (SC)
Fax: 817-641-3683	Employees: 7	Symbol: UHCP

Food - beef products distribution (Heritage Lifestyle Lite Beef) to suppliers for retail sale to consumers

UNITED INSURANCE COMPANIES, INC.

4001 McEwen Dr., Ste. 200	CEO: W. Brian Harrigan	1994 Sales: $528.9 million
Dallas, TX 75244	CFO: Vernon R. Woelke	1-Yr. Sales Change: 17.1%
Phone: 214-960-8497	HR: Linda Flowers	Exchange: Nasdaq
Fax: 214-851-9097	Employees: 770	Symbol: UICI

Insurance - accident, life & health

► **See page 228 for a full profile of this company.**

UNITED MERIDIAN CORPORATION

1201 Louisiana, Ste. 1400	CEO: John B. Brock	1994 Sales: $99.1 million
Houston, TX 77002-5603	CFO: Jonathan M. Clarkson	1-Yr. Sales Change: 19.3%
Phone: 713-654-9110	HR: Paul Priest	Exchange: NYSE
Fax: 713-653-5124	Employees: 292	Symbol: UMC

Oil & gas - US exploration & production

UNITED SERVICES ADVISORS, INC.

7900 Callaghan Rd.	CEO: Frank E. Holmes	1994 Sales: $10.9 million
San Antonio, TX 78229	CFO: Bobby D. Duncan	1-Yr. Sales Change: 47.3%
Phone: 210-308-1234	HR: Irene Hernandez	Exchange: Nasdaq (SC)
Fax: 210-308-1279	Employees: 122	Symbol: USVSP

Financial - investment adviser to institutions, transfer agency, record keeping & administrative services for IRAs & other retirement plans

UNITED STATES LIME & MINERALS, INC.

12221 Merit Dr., Ste. 500	CEO: Robert F. Kizer	1994 Sales: $36.9 million
Dallas, TX 75251	CFO: Timothy W. Byrne	1-Yr. Sales Change: 13.9%
Phone: 214-991-8400	HR: Gwen Bays	Exchange: Nasdaq
Fax: 214-385-1430	Employees: 313	Symbol: USLM

Building products - aggregate, pulverized limestone & quicklime for the steel, paper, agriculture & construction industries (Arkansas Lime Co., Corson Lime Co., Texas Lime Co.)

UNITED SUPERMARKETS INCORPORATED

7830 Orlando Ave.	CEO: Robert Snell	1994 Est. Sales: $350 mil.
Lubbock, TX 79423	CFO: Kent Moore	1-Yr. Sales Change: —
Phone: 806-791-0220	HR: Dan Sanders	Ownership: Privately Held
Fax: 806-791-7480	Employees: 2,600	

Retail - supermarkets (42 units in Texas: United Supermarkets)

UNITED SYSTEMS TECHNOLOGY, INC.

3021 Gateway Dr., Ste. 240	CEO: Thomas E. Gibbs	1994 Sales: $2.3 million
Irving, TX 75063	CFO: Randall L. McGee	1-Yr. Sales Change: -23.3%
Phone: 214-518-0728	HR: —	Exchange: Nasdaq (SC)
Fax: 214-580-8280	Employees: 30	Symbol: USTI

Computer - financial, general administration, public works, civil processing & public safety software products for state, county & local governments

UNIVERSAL SEISMIC ASSOCIATES, INC.

16420 Park Ten Place, Ste. 300
Houston, TX 77084
Phone: 713-578-8081
Fax: 713-578-7091

CEO: Michael J. Pawelek
CFO: Ronald L. England
HR: —
Employees: 130

1995 Sales: $22.8 million
1-Yr. Sales Change: 52.0%
Exchange: Nasdaq
Symbol: USAC

Oil & gas - 3D seismic mapping & processing services

UNIVERSITY OF HOUSTON

4800 Calhoun
Houston, TX 77204-2163
Phone: 713-743-1000
Fax: 713-743-8199

CEO: Glenn A. Goerke
CFO: James Hale
HR: Carol Parmer
Employees: 7,197

1994 Sales: $414 million
1-Yr. Sales Change: 3.1%
Ownership: Privately Held

University - offering 102 undergraduate & 65 graduate degree programs

UNIVERSITY OF NORTH TEXAS

PO Box 13767
Denton, TX 76203-6797
Phone: 817-565-2000
Fax: 817-565-2000

CEO: Alfred F. Hurley
CFO: Phillip C. Diebel
HR: Steve Miller
Employees: 5,500

1994 Sales: $199.2 million
1-Yr. Sales Change: 0.1%
Ownership: Privately Held

University - offering 32 undergraduate programs and 52 graduate degree programs

THE UNIVERSITY OF TEXAS SYSTEM

O. Henry Hall
Austin, TX 78701
Phone: 512-471-3434
Fax: 512-499-4215

CEO: William H. Cunningham
CFO: R. D. Burck
HR: Trennis Jones
Employees: 68,996

1994 Sales: $4,030.3 million
1-Yr. Sales Change: 7.6%
Ownership: Privately Held

University - system comprised of 9 general academic universities & 6 health institutions, offering 108 undergraduate & 179 graduate degree programs

 See pages 160–161 for a full profile of this company.

URANIUM RESOURCES, INC.

12750 Merit Dr., Ste. 1210
Dallas, TX 75251
Phone: 214-387-7777
Fax: 214-387-7779

CEO: Paul K. Willmott
CFO: Laura Greig
HR: Laura Greig
Employees: 50

1995 Sales: $17.3 million
1-Yr. Sales Change: 31.1%
Exchange: Nasdaq
Symbol: URIX

Metal ores - uranium mining in South Texas for commercial use as fuel for nuclear-powered reactors

U.S. CONTRACTORS INC.

622 Commerce	CEO: Harold E. Monical	1994 Est. Sales: $130 mil.
Clute, TX 77531	CFO: Lynn D. Monical	1-Yr. Sales Change: —
Phone: 409-265-7451	HR: Floyd E. Scott	Ownership: Privately Held
Fax: 409-265-9281	Employees: 2,900	

Building - general contractor of industrial plants

U.S. DELIVERY SYSTEMS, INC.

11 Greenway Plaza, Ste. 250	CEO: Clayton K. Trier	1994 Sales: $156 million
Houston, TX 77046	CFO: James H. Haddox	1-Yr. Sales Change: 43.6%
Phone: 713-867-5070	HR: Ann R. Wankum	Exchange: NYSE
Fax: 713-867-5004	Employees: 3,732	Symbol: DLV

Transportation - same-day local delivery service

U.S. ENVIRONMENTAL SOLUTIONS, INC.

13700 Veterans Memorial Dr., Ste. 350	CEO: Darvin G. Watson	1994 Sales: $3.3 million
Houston, TX 77014	CFO: Robert G. Patterson	1-Yr. Sales Change: 57.1%
Phone: 713-444-4077	HR: —	Exchange: Nasdaq (SC)
Fax: 713-444-4336	Employees: 105	Symbol: USES

Pollution control equipment & services - integrated waste management, transportation & disposition in selected Gulf Coast US markets

U.S. GAS TRANSPORTATION, INC.

2711 Haskell Ave., Ste. 2050	CEO: Nanci G. Mackenzie	1994 Sales: $130 million
Dallas, TX 75204	CFO: Al Paybon	1-Yr. Sales Change: —
Phone: 214-827-9464	HR: Al Paybon	Ownership: Privately Held
Fax: 214-827-2718	Employees: 20	

Oil refining & marketing - natural gas marketing

U.S. HOME CORPORATION

1800 W. Loop South	CEO: Robert J. Strudler	1994 Sales: $995.3 million
Houston, TX 77027	CFO: Thomas A. Napoli	1-Yr. Sales Change: 22.6%
Phone: 713-877-2311	HR: Frank Matthews	Exchange: NYSE
Fax: 713-877-2452	Employees: 1,353	Symbol: UH

Building - residential & commercial

 See page 229 for a full profile of this company.

U.S. INTEC, INC.

1212 Brai Dr., PO Box 2845
Port Arthur, TX 77643
Phone: 409-724-7024
Fax: 409-724-2348

CEO: Danny J. Adair
CFO: J. Roane Ruddy
HR: Melinda Huber
Employees: 356

1994 Sales: $95.6 million
1-Yr. Sales Change: 14.8%
Exchange: AMEX
Symbol: USI

Building products - roofing materials

U.S. LONG DISTANCE CORP.

9311 San Pedro, Ste. 300
San Antonio, TX 78216-4476
Phone: 210-525-9009
Fax: 210-525-0389

CEO: Parris H. Holmes Jr.
CFO: Michael E. Higgins
HR: David S. Horne
Employees: 1,023

1994 Sales: $181.7 million
1-Yr. Sales Change: 35.5%
Exchange: Nasdaq
Symbol: USLD

Telecommunications services - direct-dial long distance telephone service

 See page 230 for a full profile of this company.

U.S. MEDICAL PRODUCTS, INC.

12201 Technology Blvd., Ste. 100
Austin, TX 78727
Phone: 512-257-8787
Fax: 512-257-8300

CEO: J. Melville Engle
CFO: William Regan
HR: Christi Carlin
Employees: 20

1994 Sales: $0.5 million
1-Yr. Sales Change: —
Exchange: Nasdaq (SC)
Symbol: USMD

Medical & surgical products - prostheses to replace diseased or fractured joints & the specialized surgical instruments used to implant those devices

U.S. PHYSICAL THERAPY, INC.

3040 Post Oak Blvd., Ste. 222
Houston, TX 77056
Phone: 713-297-9050
Fax: 713-297-7090

CEO: Roy Spradlin
CFO: Mark J. Brookner
HR: Kimberly Cox
Employees: 316

1994 Sales: $17.2 million
1-Yr. Sales Change: 104.8%
Exchange: Nasdaq (SC)
Symbol: USPH

Health care - 53 outpatient physical & occupational therapy clinics providing post-operative care & treatment

U.S. TECHNOLOGIES INC.

1402 Industrial Blvd., PO Box 960
Lockhart, TX 78644
Phone: 512-376-1049
Fax: 512-376-1042

CEO: William Meehan
CFO: William Meehan
HR: Valerie Fulps
Employees: 88

1994 Sales: $1.7 million
1-Yr. Sales Change: -74.6%
Exchange: Nasdaq (SC)
Symbol: USXX

Electronic circuit boards for computers, security & communications systems, medical equipment & testing devices

USA WASTE SERVICES, INC.

5000 Quorum Dr., Ste. 300	CEO: John E. Drury	1994 Sales: $176.2 million
Dallas, TX 75240	CFO: Earl E. DeFrates	1-Yr. Sales Change: 87.8%
Phone: 214-383-7900	HR: Steve Shomette	Exchange: NYSE
Fax: 214-383-7911	Employees: 1,200	Symbol: UW

Pollution control equipment & services - solid waste management, including trash disposal services & landfill operations

 See page 231 for a full profile of this company.

USAA

9800 Fredericksburg Rd., USAA Bldg.	CEO: Robert T. Herres	1994 Sales: $6,181 million
San Antonio, TX 78288	CFO: Josue Robles Jr.	1-Yr. Sales Change: 3.2%
Phone: 210-498-2211	HR: William B. Tracy	Ownership: Privately Held
Fax: 210-498-9940	Employees: 15,233	

Multiline insurance for consumers; brokerage services; mutual funds; banking; retirement plans & services

 See pages 162–163 for a full profile of this company.

USDATA CORPORATION

2435 N. Central Expwy.	CEO: William G. Moore Jr.	1994 Sales: $36 million
Richardson, TX 75080-2722	CFO: Michael P. Sullivan	1-Yr. Sales Change: 9.8%
Phone: 214-680-9700	HR: John Pellegrini	Exchange: Nasdaq
Fax: 214-669-9557	Employees: 211	Symbol: USDC

Computers - automation software tools

VALERO ENERGY CORPORATION

530 McCullough Ave., PO Box 500	CEO: William E. Greehey	1994 Sales: $1,837.4 million
San Antonio, TX 78292	CFO: Don M. Heep	1-Yr. Sales Change: 50.3%
Phone: 210-246-2000	HR: Robert R. Taylor	Exchange: NYSE
Fax: 210-246-2646	Employees: 1,658	Symbol: VLO

Oil & gas - production & pipeline

VALHI, INC.

5430 LBJ Fwy., Ste. 1700	CEO: Harold C. Simmons	1994 Sales: $842.4 million
Dallas, TX 75240-2697	CFO: William C. Timm	1-Yr. Sales Change: 6.1%
Phone: 214-233-1700	HR: Kathy Brownlee	Exchange: NYSE
Fax: 214-385-0586	Employees: 11,500	Symbol: VHI

Diversified operations - chemicals; refined sugar; forest products

VALLEN CORPORATION

13333 Northwest Fwy.
Houston, TX 77040-6086
Phone: 713-462-8700
Fax: 713-462-5145

CEO: James W. Thompson
CFO: Leighton J. Stephenson
HR: Kent M. Edwards
Employees: 729

1995 Sales: $203.3 million
1-Yr. Sales Change: 9.4%
Exchange: Nasdaq
Symbol: VALN

Protection - safety equipment & services

VANGUARD ENERGY CORPORATION

1111 N. Loop West
Houston, TX 77008
Phone: 713-880-8750
Fax: 713-880-9311

CEO: Phillip Trotter
CFO: Phillip Trotter
HR: —
Employees: 15

1994 Est. Sales: $300 mil.
1-Yr. Sales Change: —
Ownership: Privately Held

Oil & gas - wholesale petroleum & liquid petroleum gases

VASTAR RESOURCES, INC.

15375 Memorial Dr.
Houston, TX 77079
Phone: 713-584-6000
Fax: 713-584-3232

CEO: Michael E. Wiley
CFO: Steven J. Shapiro
HR: Jeff Bender
Employees: 964

1994 Sales: $816.5 million
1-Yr. Sales Change: -47.2%
Exchange: NYSE
Symbol: VRI

Oil & gas - US exploration & production

VERTEX COMMUNICATIONS CORPORATION

2600 N. Longview St.
Kilgore, TX 75662
Phone: 903-984-0555
Fax: 903-984-1826

CEO: J. Rex Vardeman
CFO: James D. Carter
HR: Wilora Tucker
Employees: 500

1994 Sales: $57.2 million
1-Yr. Sales Change: 5.5%
Exchange: Nasdaq
Symbol: VTEX

Telecommunications equipment - earth station antennas

VICTORIA BANKSHARES, INC.

One O'Connor Plaza
Victoria, TX 77902
Phone: 512-573-9432
Fax: 512-574-5279

CEO: Charles R. Hrdlicka
CFO: Gregory Sprawka
HR: Brenda Wilson
Employees: 1,034

1994 Sales: $127.7 million
1-Yr. Sales Change: 3.2%
Exchange: Nasdaq
Symbol: VICT

Banks - Southwest (Victoria Bank & Trust)

VINLAND PROPERTY TRUST

3878 Oak Lawn, Ste. 300	CEO: William S. Friedman	1994 Sales: $6.8 million
Dallas, TX 75219	CFO: John W. Pritchett	1-Yr. Sales Change: 13.3%
Phone: 214-522-9910	HR: —	Exchange: Nasdaq (SC)
Fax: 214-522-9945	Employees: —	Symbol: VIPTS

Real estate investment trust - apartment & office buildings

VINSON & ELKINS L.L.P.

1001 Fannin St., Ste. 2500	CEO: Harry M. Reasoner	1994 Sales: $211.2 million
Houston, TX 77002	CFO: John Spire	1-Yr. Sales Change: 4.3%
Phone: 713-758-2222	HR: David Hedges	Ownership: Privately Held
Fax: 713-758-2346	Employees: 1,550	

Law firm

VIRGINIA INDONESIA CO.

PO Box 1551	CEO: Charles Reimer	1994 Est. Sales: $665 mil.
Houston, TX 77251	CFO: Fred Buttaccio	1-Yr. Sales Change: —
Phone: 713-654-7404	HR: Paul Dusha	Ownership: Privately Held
Fax: 713-754-6698	Employees: 2,850	

Diversified operations - mining; manufacturing; petroleum production & refining

VISTA OIL CO.

6 1/2 miles north of 10th St.	CEO: Gus E. Clemons Jr.	1994 Est. Sales: $15 mil.
McAllen, TX 78504-	CFO: Gary Clemons	1-Yr. Sales Change: —
Phone: 210-381-0976	HR: —	Ownership: Privately Held
Fax: 210-383-1744	Employees: 22	

Rubber tires distribution; petroleum products

VISUAL NUMERICS INC.

9990 Richmond Ave, Ste. 400	CEO: Richard G. Couch	1994 Est. Sales: $30 mil.
Houston, TX 77042-4548	CFO: Richard G. Couch	1-Yr. Sales Change: -11.8%
Phone: 713-784-3131	HR: Michael Zak	Ownership: Privately Held
Fax: 713-781-9260	Employees: 150	

Math, visualization & statistics software

VOICE CONTROL SYSTEMS, INC.

14140 Midway Rd., Ste. 100
Dallas, TX 75224
Phone: 214-386-0300
Fax: 214-388-5555

CEO: Peter J. Foster
CFO: Kim Terry
HR: Mary Tanner
Employees: 51

1994 Sales: $6.3 million
1-Yr. Sales Change: -11.3%
Exchange: AMEX
Symbol: VPS

Telecommunications equipment - speech recognition systems

VOLUNTARY HOSPITALS OF AMERICA INC.

5215 N. O'Connor Rd.
Irving, TX 75039
Phone: 214-830-0000
Fax: 214-830-0141

CEO: C. Thomas Smith
CFO: Curt Nonomaque
HR: Kim Alleman
Employees: 950

1994 Est. Sales: $110 mil.
1-Yr. Sales Change: 0.0%
Ownership: Privately Held

Medical products - medical supplies, pharmaceuticals & information systems

VTEL CORPORATION

108 Wild Basin Rd.
Austin, TX 78746
Phone: 512-314-2700
Fax: 512-314-2792

CEO: F. H. "Dick" Moeller
CFO: Rodney S. Bond
HR: Carson D. Brown
Employees: 273

1994 Sales: $54.2 million
1-Yr. Sales Change: 72.1%
Exchange: Nasdaq
Symbol: VTEL

Telecommunications equipment - multimedia conferencing systems

 See page 232 for a full profile of this company.

WAGNER AND BROWN, LTD.

Summit Bldg.
Midland, TX 79702
Phone: 915-682-7936
Fax: 915-686-5928

CEO: Paul Morris
CFO: A. J. Brune III
HR: Sherri Rotan
Employees: 200

1994 Est. Sales: $75 mil.
1-Yr. Sales Change: -17.6%
Ownership: Privately Held

Oil and gas - exploration & production

WAINOCO OIL CORPORATION

1200 Smith St., Ste. 2100
Houston, TX 77002-4367
Phone: 713-658-9900
Fax: 713-658-8136

CEO: James R. Gibbs
CFO: Julie H. Edwards
HR: George E. Aldrich
Employees: 400

1994 Sales: $353.7 million
1-Yr. Sales Change: -3.5%
Exchange: NYSE
Symbol: WOL

Oil & gas - US exploration & production

WALDEN RESIDENTIAL PROPERTIES, INC.

5400 LBJ Fwy., LB 45, Ste. 400
Dallas, TX 75240
Phone: 214-788-0510
Fax: —

CEO: Donald R. Daseke
CFO: Mark S. Dillinger
HR: Susan W. Huber
Employees: 411

1994 Sales: $45.4 million
1-Yr. Sales Change: 51.3%
Exchange: NYSE
Symbol: WDN

Real estate investment trust - multifamily residential properties

WALSH-LUMPKIN DRUG CO.

5005 State Line Ave.
Texarkana, TX 75503
Phone: 903-794-5141
Fax: 903-794-3728

CEO: Ron Nelson
CFO: David Harrel
HR: Lou Lynch
Employees: 170

1994 Est. Sales: $150 mil.
1-Yr. Sales Change: —
Ownership: Privately Held

Drugs & sundries - wholesale

WARREN ELECTRIC CO.

2929 McKinney
Houston, TX 77003
Phone: 713-236-0971
Fax: 713-236-2261

CEO: John Peterson
CFO: Rita Hausman
HR: Genice Guice
Employees: 315

1994 Est. Sales: $125 mil.
1-Yr. Sales Change: —
Ownership: Privately Held

Electronics - parts & equipment

WATERMARC FOOD MANAGEMENT

10777 Westheimer, Ste. 1030
Houston, TX 77042
Phone: 713-783-0500
Fax: 713-783-4608

CEO: Ghulam Bombaywala
CFO: Thomas J. Buckley
HR: —
Employees: 1,320

1995 Sales: $37.7 million
1-Yr. Sales Change: 2.7%
Exchange: Nasdaq (SC)
Symbol: WAMA

Retail - casual dining restaurants (Marco's Mexican Restaurants, Longhorn Cafe, Pete's Barbecue)

WEATHERFORD INTERNATIONAL INCORPORATED

1360 Post Oak Blvd., Ste. 1000
Houston, TX 77056
Phone: 713-439-9400
Fax: 713-621-0994

CEO: Philip Burguieres
CFO: Norman W. Nolen
HR: Jon Nicholson
Employees: 3,158

1994 Sales: $372.3 million
1-Yr. Sales Change: 11.8%
Exchange: NYSE
Symbol: WII

Oil & gas - tubular handling services; oilfield equipment rental & other field services

WEEKLEY HOMES INC.

1300 Post Oak Blvd., Ste. 1000	CEO: David Weekley	1994 Est. Sales: $360 mil.
Houston, TX 77056	CFO: Dennis Bailey	1-Yr. Sales Change: —
Phone: 713-963-0500	HR: Marian Wright	Ownership: Privately Held
Fax: 713-963-0322	Employees: 600	

Building - residential single-unit homes

WEINER'S STORES, INC.

6005 Westview	CEO: Leon Weiner	1994 Sales: $300 million
Houston, TX 77055	CFO: Raymond J. Miller	1-Yr. Sales Change: -18.9%
Phone: 713-688-1331	HR: Larry Kleypas	Ownership: Privately Held
Fax: 713-688-6976	Employees: 4,000	

Retail - 158 discount & variety stores in Texas & Louisiana

WEINGARTEN REALTY INVESTORS

2600 Citadel Plaza Dr.	CEO: Stanford Alexander	1994 Sales: $120.7 million
Houston, TX 77292-4133	CFO: Joseph W. Robertson Jr.	1-Yr. Sales Change: 17.0%
Phone: 713-866-6000	HR: Brenda C. Corn	Exchange: NYSE
Fax: 713-866-6049	Employees: 13	Symbol: WRI

Real estate investment trust - shopping centers

WELLTECH INC.

3535 Briarpark, Ste. 200	CEO: Douglas B. Thompson	1994 Est. Sales: $50 mil.
Houston, TX 77042	CFO: —	1-Yr. Sales Change: —
Phone: 713-975-1600	HR: Sandy Richardson	Ownership: Privately Held
Fax: 713-977-7331	Employees: 650	

Oil field machinery & equipment - drill equipment repairs

WESTBRIDGE CAPITAL CORP.

777 Main St.	CEO: Martin E. Kantor	1994 Sales: $106.5 million
Fort Worth, TX 76102	CFO: Patrick J. Mitchell	1-Yr. Sales Change: 41.4%
Phone: 817-878-3300	HR: Maria Jones	Exchange: NYSE
Fax: 817-878-3480	Employees: 248	Symbol: WBC

Insurance - accident & health

WESTCOTT COMMUNICATIONS, INC.

1303 Marsh Ln.	CEO: Carl Westcott	1994 Sales: $89.7 million
Carrollton, TX 75006	CFO: Phyllis Farragut	1-Yr. Sales Change: 29.4%
Phone: 214-417-4100	HR: Ellen Hillis	Exchange: Nasdaq
Fax: 214-417-4933	Employees: 616	Symbol: WCTV

Motion pictures & services - satellite broadcast training films

 See page 233 for a full profile of this company.

WESTERN NATIONAL CORPORATION

5555 San Felipe Rd.	CEO: Michael J. Poulos	1994 Sales: $615.7 million
Houston, TX 77056	CFO: Arthur R. McGimsey	1-Yr. Sales Change: -20.5%
Phone: 713-888-7800	HR: David Green	Exchange: NYSE
Fax: 713-888-7893	Employees: 230	Symbol: WNH

Insurance - annuity products

WHATABURGER SYSTEMS INC.

4600 Parkdale Dr., PO Box 6220	CEO: Thomas Dobson	1994 Est. Sales: $240 mil.
Corpus Christi, TX 78466	CFO: Bruce Able	1-Yr. Sales Change: —
Phone: 512-878-0650	HR: Peter Oppel	Ownership: Privately Held
Fax: 512-878-0314	Employees: 8,500	

Retail - restaurants

WHITEHALL CORPORATION

2659 Nova Dr., PO Box 29709	CEO: George F. Baker	1994 Sales: $32.1 million
Dallas, TX 75229	CFO: E. Forrest Campbell III	1-Yr. Sales Change: 3.9%
Phone: 214-247-8747	HR: Randy Johnson	Exchange: NYSE
Fax: 214-247-2024	Employees: 512	Symbol: WHT

Electronics - military

WHOLE FOODS MARKET, INC.

601 N. Lamar, Ste. 300	CEO: John Mackey	1994 Sales: $401.7 million
Austin, TX 78703	CFO: Glenda Flanagan	1-Yr. Sales Change: 24.6%
Phone: 512-477-4455	HR: Cathy Blackwood	Exchange: Nasdaq
Fax: 512-477-1069	Employees: 5,300	Symbol: WFMI

Retail - grocery stores specializing in natural & health foods

 See page 234 for a full profile of this company.

WHOLESALE ELECTRIC SUPPLY COMPANY OF HOUSTON, INC.

4040 Gulf Fwy.
Houston, TX 77004
Phone: 713-748-6100
Fax: 713-749-8415

CEO: Clyde G. Rutland
CFO: Joe R. Jones Sr.
HR: —
Employees: 235

1994 Est. Sales: $110 mil.
1-Yr. Sales Change: —
Ownership: Privately Held

Electrical products - electric apparatus & equipment distribution

WILLIAMS COAL SEAM GAS ROYALTY TRUST

901 Main St., 17th Floor
Dallas, TX 75202
Phone: 214-508-2364
Fax: 918-588-2296

CEO: K. E. Bailey
CFO: Jack McCarthy
HR: Walter Elcock
Employees: —

1994 Sales: $22.4 million
1-Yr. Sales Change: 14.9%
Exchange: NYSE
Symbol: WTU

Oil & gas - US royalty trust

WILLIAMSON-DICKIE MANUFACTURING CO.

319 Lipscomb
Fort Worth, TX 76104
Phone: 817-336-7201
Fax: 817-336-5183

CEO: Philip C. Williamson
CFO: Craig Mackey
HR: Estelle Lewis
Employees: 6,000

1994 Sales: $450 million
1-Yr. Sales Change: 12.5%
Ownership: Privately Held

Apparel - men's trousers & work clothing

WILSON INDUSTRIES INCORPORATED

1301 Conti
Houston, TX 77002
Phone: 713-237-3700
Fax: 713-237-3300

CEO: Wallace S. Wilson
CFO: Robert E. Brown
HR: Rebecca Snyder
Employees: 950

1994 Est. Sales: $350 mil.
1-Yr. Sales Change: —
Ownership: Privately Held

Oil field machinery & equipment - wholesale

WINGATE PARTNERS LP

750 N. Saint Paul St.
Dallas, TX 75201
Phone: 214-720-1313
Fax: 214-871-8799

CEO: Frederick B. Hegi
CFO: Bud Applebaum
HR: —
Employees: 6,300

1994 Est. Sales: $800 mil.
1-Yr. Sales Change: —
Ownership: Privately Held

Financial - leveraged buyout firm

THE WISER OIL COMPANY

8115 Preston Rd., Ste. 400
Dallas, TX 75225
Phone: 214-265-0080
Fax: 214-373-3610

CEO: Andrew J. Shoup Jr.
CFO: Lawrence J. Finn
HR: Karin O'Connor
Employees: 130

1994 Sales: $65.4 million
1-Yr. Sales Change: 52.4%
Exchange: NYSE
Symbol: WZR

Oil & gas - US exploration & production

W. O. BANKSTON ENTERPRISES INC.

4755 McEwen Rd.
Dallas, TX 75244
Phone: 214-788-5400
Fax: 214-490-6753

CEO: James G. Bankston
CFO: Chris Price
HR: Chris Price
Employees: 600

1994 Est. Sales: $200 mil.
1-Yr. Sales Change: —
Ownership: Privately Held

Retail - new & used cars

WRT ENERGY CORPORATION

4200 Research Forest Dr.
The Woodlands, TX 77381-4257
Phone: 713-363-0030
Fax: 713-363-4097

CEO: Steven S. McGuire
CFO: Ronald E. Hale Jr.
HR: William L. Walter
Employees: 60

1994 Sales: $11 million
1-Yr. Sales Change: 134.0%
Exchange: Nasdaq
Symbol: WRTE

Oil & gas - field services

W.S. BELLOWS CONSTRUCTION CORP.

1906 Afton
Houston, TX 77055
Phone: 713-680-2132
Fax: 713-680-0643

CEO: Thomas F. Bellows
CFO: Paul Oliver
HR: —
Employees: 200

1994 Est. Sales: $65 mil.
1-Yr. Sales Change: —
Ownership: Privately Held

Commercial & heavy plant construction

WYATT CAFETERIAS INC.

10726 Plano Rd.
Dallas, TX 75238
Phone: 214-349-0060
Fax: 214-553-7798

CEO: Joe Colonnetta
CFO: Kenneth Cichocki
HR: Kim Hill
Employees: 2,500

1994 Sales: $90 million
1-Yr. Sales Change: -10.0%
Ownership: Privately Held

Retail - restaurants & food (wholesale groceries)

WYNDHAM HOTEL COMPANY LTD.

2001 Bryan St., Ste. 2300	CEO: James D. Carreker	1994 Est. Sales: $400 mil.
Dallas, TX 75201	CFO: Anne Raymond	1-Yr. Sales Change: —
Phone: 214-978-4500	HR: Susan Bolger	Ownership: Privately Held
Fax: 214-978-4695	Employees: 7,000	

Hotels & motels - administrative management

THE YORK GROUP INC.

9430 Old Katy Rd.	CEO: Eldon Nuss	1994 Est. Sales: $110 mil.
Houston, TX 77055	CFO: Dave Beck	1-Yr. Sales Change: —
Phone: 713-984-5500	HR: Tony Wheeler	Ownership: Privately Held
Fax: 713-984-5569	Employees: 1,100	

Wholesale distribution - funeral caskets

ZALE CORPORATION

901 W. Walnut Hill Ln.	CEO: Robert DiNicola	1995 Sales: $1,036.1 million
Irving, TX 75038-1003	CFO: Thomas E. Whiddon	1-Yr. Sales Change: 14.0%
Phone: 214-580-4000	HR: A. Herschel Kranitz	Exchange: Nasdaq
Fax: 214-580-5336	Employees: 9,500	Symbol: ZALE

Retail - jewelry stores (Zales, Gordon's, Bailey Banks & Biddle)

ZAPATA CORPORATION

One Riverway, PO Box 4240	CEO: Malcolm I. Glazer	1994 Sales: $241.2 million
Houston, TX 77210-4240	CFO: Lamar C. McIntyre	1-Yr. Sales Change: 9.0%
Phone: 713-940-6100	HR: Vivian Schott	Exchange: NYSE
Fax: 713-940-6111	Employees: 1,600	Symbol: ZOS

Oil & gas - natural gas services including gathering, compression, processing & marketing

 See page 235 for a full profile of this company.

ZONAGEN, INC.

2408 Timberloch Place, Ste. B-4	CEO: Joseph S. Podolski	1994 Sales: $1 million
The Woodlands, TX 77380	CFO: Louis Ploth Jr.	1-Yr. Sales Change: 900.0%
Phone: 713-367-5892	HR: Louis Ploth Jr.	Exchange: Nasdaq (SC)
Fax: 713-363-8796	Employees: 49	Symbol: ZONA

Biomedical - human reproductive health care management providing products & services to health care professionals & individual consumers

TEXAS The Indexes

INTRODUCING
HOOVER'S COMPANY
PROFILES ON DEMAND

A new fax delivery service that puts detailed company profiles from the

Hoover's Company Database
at your fingertips

WHY WAIT? Get invaluable information immediately on more than 1,000 public and private companies.

The information is arranged in the same easy-to-use format as the company profiles found in *Hoover's Handbook*s and includes company overviews and histories, up to 10 years of key financial and employment data, lists of products and key competitors, names of key officers, addresses, and phone and fax numbers.

IT'S SIMPLE.

1. Choose any number of companies from the index on the following pages.

2. Then call **415-598-4335**, 24 hours a day, 7 days a week, to receive a detailed profile for **only $2.95*** for each company you choose. Have your fax number and the five-digit company code number ready.

3. A voice-automated system will guide you through your order, and you'll receive your company profiles via fax within minutes.

*American Express, MasterCard, and Visa accepted.

Company	No.	Company	No.	Company	No.
2Market, Inc.	42464	America West Airlines, Inc.	41891	Attachmate Corporation	42453
3Com Corporation	12475	American Brands, Inc.	10075	Audre Recognition Systems Inc.	15978
3D Systems Corporation	15229	American Business Information	15513	Auspex Systems, Inc.	16036
The 3DO Company	16077	American Classic Voyages Co.	15544	Austin Ventures	43266
7th Level, Inc.	42268	American Eagle Outfitters, Inc.	17231	Authentic Fitness Corporation	15727
AAON, Inc.	16562	American Electric Power Company	10084	Autocam Corporation	15442
ABB Asea Brown Boveri Ltd.	40615	American Express Company	10085	Autodesk, Inc.	12689
Abbott Laboratories	10030	American Financial Group, Inc.	11161	Automatic Data Processing, Inc.	10148
ACC Corp.	12483	American Freightways Corporation	12657	Autotote Corporation	15023
Acclaim Entertainment, Inc.	10544	American Greetings Corporation	12591	AutoZone, Inc.	11376
Accor SA	40552	American Healthcorp, Inc.	10387	Avid Technology, Inc.	15999
Ace Hardware Corporation	40005	American Home Products Corp.	10093	Avis, Inc.	40050
Acer Incorporated	42451	American HomePatient, Inc.	13121	Avnet, Inc.	10151
Acordia, Inc.	12336	American International Group, Inc.	10095	Avon Products, Inc.	10152
Action Performance Companies, Inc.	10014	American Management Systems, Inc.	12600	Baby Superstore, Inc.	42110
Active Voice Corporation	16684	American Medical Response, Inc.	15818	Bacardi Imports, Inc.	40051
Activision, Inc.	42465	American Power Conversion Corporation	12609	Baker & McKenzie	40052
Acuson Corporation	10034	American President Companies, Ltd.	10097	Baker & Taylor Inc.	40053
ADAC Laboratories	12486	American Software, Inc.	12614	Ballard Medical Products	12722
Adaptec, Inc.	12515	American Standard Companies, Inc.	40026	Bally Entertainment Corporation	10166
Addison-Wesley Longman/Penguin	43656	American Stock Exchange, Inc.	40590	Banc One Corporation	10169
Adia S.A.	12517	American Stores Company	10102	Bank of Boston Corporation	10175
Adobe Systems Incorporated	12518	Ameridata Technologies, Inc.	16433	Bank of Montreal	42380
Adolph Coors Company	12519	AmeriSource	40016	The Bank of New York Co., Inc.	10177
Advance Publications, Inc.	40006	Ameritech Corporation	10094	BankAmerica Corporation	10178
Advance Ross Corporation	12522	Ames Department Stores, Inc.	42031	Bankers Trust New York Corporation	10179
Advanced Marketing Services, Inc.	12525	Amgen Inc.	12623	Bantam Doubleday Dell Publishing Group Inc.	43807
Advanced Micro Devices, Inc.	10037	Amoco Corporation	10108	Banyan Systems Incorporated	15842
Advanta Corp.	12489	AMP Incorporated	10020	Barclays PLC	41754
ADVO, Inc.	12490	Ampex Incorporated	15804	Bard, Inc., C. R.	10253
The AES Corporation	10667	Amway Corporation	40031	Barefoot, Inc.	15449
Aetna Life and Casualty Company	10039	Anacomp, Inc.	10110	Barnes & Noble, Inc.	16513
AFLAC Incorporated	13111	Analog Devices, Inc.	10112	Barnett Banks, Inc.	10183
AFL-CIO	40565	Anam Group	43398	BASF AG	41755
AGCO Corporation	15593	Andersen Consulting	43516	Bass PLC	41788
Agway Inc.	40013	Andrew Corporation	12640	B.A.T Industries PLC	41762
Airbus Industrie	40566	Anglo American Corporation	41809	Battelle Memorial Institute	40057
Airgas, Inc.	10044	Anheuser-Busch Companies, Inc.	10116	Bausch & Lomb Incorporated	10187
Akzo Nobel N.V.	41855	Apple Computer, Inc.	12644	Baxter International Inc.	10188
Aladdin Knowledge Systems Ltd.	42429	Apple South, Inc.	15463	Bay Networks, Inc.	15419
Alaska Air Group, Inc.	10046	Applebee's International, Inc.	13585	Bayer AG	41808
Albertson's, Inc.	10049	Applied Bioscience International	12645	Bayerische Motoren Werke AG	41758
Alcan Aluminium Limited	42408	Applied Materials, Inc.	12647	BCE Inc.	43059
Alcatel Alsthom	41751	ARAMARK Corporation	40038	The Bear Stearns Companies Inc.	10191
Alco Standard Corporation	10051	Archer-Daniels-Midland Company	10124	Beazer Homes USA, Inc.	16951
Alex. Brown Incorporated	12547	Arctco, Inc.	13346	Bechtel Group, Inc.	40059
All Nippon Airways Co, Ltd.	41752	Argosy Gaming Company	14601	Becton, Dickinson and Company	10195
Allegro New Media, Inc.	43500	Ark Restaurants Corporation	11727	Bed Bath & Beyond Inc.	14933
Allergan, Inc.	10059	Armstrong World Industries, Inc.	10129	BEI Electronics, Inc.	11644
Alliance Semiconductor Corp.	16807	Arrow Electronics, Inc.	10130	Bell Atlantic Corporation	10197
Allianz AG Holding	40572	Arthur Andersen & Co, S.C.	40040	Bell Microproducts Inc.	16410
Allied Domecq PLC	50001	Artisoft, Inc.	15359	Bell Sports Corp.	14323
AlliedSignal Inc.	10062	Asante Technologies, Inc.	16624	BellSouth Corporation	10200
Allou Health & Beauty Care, Inc.	11024	ASARCO Incorporated	10133	Ben & Jerry's Homemade, Inc.	12763
The Allstate Corporation	16182	The ASCII Group Inc.	42489	Benetton Group S.p.A	41756
The Alpine Group, Inc.	11695	Ashland Oil, Inc.	10135	Benson Eyecare Corporation	11905
Alpine Lace Brands, Inc.	13478	Aspect Telecommunications Corporation	14113	Bergen Brunswig Corporation	11761
Altera Corporation	12568	AST Research, Inc.	12500	Berkshire Hathaway Inc.	10206
Alternative Resources Corporation	20015	Asymetrix Corporation	43338	Bertelsmann AG	40661
Aluminum Company of America	10068	AT&T Corporation	10103	Bertucci's Inc.	13144
ALZA Corporation	11677	AT&T Global Information Solutions	43707	Best Buy Co., Inc.	10209
Amdahl Corporation	11697	Atari Corporation	11732	BET Holdings, Inc.	10916
Amerada Hess Corporation	10073	Atlantic Richfield Company	10142	Bethlehem Steel Corporation	10210
America Online, Inc.	15558	Atmel Corporation	14420	Beverly Enterprises, Inc.	10211

Index of Hoover's Company Profiles Available by Fax

CALL TODAY FOR A FREE CATALOG FEATURING OVER 140 BUSINESS SOURCES

The 100 Best Companies to Work for in America	$27.95
1995 American Stock Exchange Fact Book	$14.95
1995 Information Please Business Almanac & Desk Reference	$21.95
1995 Nasdaq Fact Book & Company Directory	$19.95
The 1995 National Directory of Addresses and Telephone Numbers	$94.95
The 1995 What Color Is Your Parachute?	$14.95
The Almanac of American Employers 1994–95	$109.95
The American Forecaster Almanac	$14.95
Association Directories 1995 — 2-volume set	$134.95
The Best Business Schools	$14.95
Bond's Franchise Guide	$29.95
Built to Last	$24.95
The Burwell World Directory of Information Brokers	$99.95
Business Information Sources	$34.95
Competing for the Future	$24.95
The Computer Industry Almanac 1994–1995	$59.95
Cover Letters	$10.95
Customers As Partners	$24.95
Data Sources for Business and Market Analysis	$54.95
The Discipline of Market Leaders	$24.95
The Ernst & Young Almanac and Guide to U.S. Business Cities	$16.95
First Things First	$22.95
The Fitzroy Dearborn Directory of Venture Capital Funds	$64.95
Forbes MediaGuide 500	$19.95
The FORTUNE Encyclopedia of Economics	$49.95
Guide to Information Access	$18.95
Hollywood Financial Directory	$44.95
The Inc. 100 Handbook	$19.95
The Internet Business Book	$22.95

Interviewing	$10.95
Living Logos: How U.S. Corporations Revitalize Their Trademarks	$22.95
Logos of America's Fastest Growing Corporations	$39.95
Logos of America's Largest Corporations	$39.95
Logos of Major World Corporations	$39.95
The National Book of Lists	$19.95
National Directory of Corporate Public Affairs 1995	$89.95
Net Guide	$26.95
Net Money	$18.95
Networking	$10.95
The New Competitor Intelligence	$24.95
The New Rules	$24.95
New York Stock Exchange Fact Book	$9.95
The Official Guide to American Incomes	$69.95
The Official Guide to Household Spending	$69.95
The Official Guide to the American Marketplace	$79.95
The On-line Job Search Companion	$14.95
Plunkett's Health Care Industry Almanac	$124.95
Quantum Companies	$21.95
Reengineering Management	$24.95
Resumes	$10.95
Standard & Poor's 500 Guide 1995	$19.95
Standard & Poor's Midcap 400 Guide 1995	$19.95
Standard & Poor's Smallcap 600 Guide 1995	$24.95
Standard & Poor's Stock and Bond Guide 1995	$19.95
Statistical Abstract of the United States 1994	$24.95
Stop Selling Start Partnering	$21.95
The Universal Almanac 1995	$19.95
U.S. Industrial Outlook 1994	$27.95
Who Knows What	$27.95
Zapp! The Lightning of Empowerment	$19.95

ALSO INCLUDES COMPANY INFORMATION FROM AROUND THE WORLD

THE FOLLOWING IS A SAMPLING OF THE INTERNATIONAL BUSINESS RESOURCES AVAILABLE THROUGH THE *HOOVER'S CATALOG*:

LATIN AMERICA

1995 Trade Directory of Mexico	$89.95
American Companies	$94.95
Argentina Company Handbook 1995/96	$34.95
Brazil Company Handbook 1994/95	$34.95
Cracking Latin America	$44.95
Mexico Business	$24.95
Mexico Company Handbook 1994/95	$34.95
Venezuela Company Handbook 1992/93	$29.95

ASIA/PACIFIC

Access Nippon 1994	$34.95
Asia Pacific Securities Handbook 1994–95	$99.95
Asian and Australasian Companies	$94.95
Australian Company Handbook	$69.95
China Business	$24.95
China Securities Handbook 1995–96	$99.95
Cracking the Pacific Rim	$44.95
Hong Kong Business	$24.95
Japan Business	$24.95
Korea Business	$24.95
Philippines Business	$24.95
Singapore Business	$24.95
Taiwan Business	$24.95
Thailand 1995	$46.95
Vietnam Business Directory 1994–95	$49.95

EUROPE

Company Handbook Spain 1995	$84.95
Cracking Eastern Europe	$44.95
Directory of East European Businesses	$74.95
The European 5000 4-volume set	$359.95
European Companies	$89.95
French Company Handbook 1995	$59.95
Germany's Top 500 1995	$49.95
The Guardian Guide to the UK's Top Companies 1995	$49.95
Nordic Stock Guide 1994	$34.95
The Times 1000 1995	$49.95
Weissmann Travel Planner for Western and Eastern Europe	$49.95

OTHER GLOBAL INFORMATION

The African Business Handbook	$34.95
Canada Company Handbook 1995	$49.95
The Complete American Depository Receipt Directory	$24.95
The Dow Jones Guide to the World Stock Market 1995–1996	$34.95
Emerging Markets Analyst 1995	$49.95
Importers Manual USA 1995–96	$86.95
International Investing with ADRs	$24.95
The McGraw-Hill Handbook of American Depositary Receipts	$59.95
Russia 1994	$64.95
The Statesman's Year-Book 1994–95	$89.95
World Trade Almanac 1995–1996	$86.95
The World's Emerging Stock Markets	$64.95